Fundamentals of Physics

Fundamentals of Physics

Alternate Edition

Robert W. Heath
Robert R. Macnaughton
David G. Martindale

D.C. Heath Canada Ltd.

ISBN 0-669-95010-6

Photographs (on the pages indicated) were supplied by: Air Canada, 389; Argonne National Laboratory, 325; Atomic Energy of Canada, 310, 330, 332; Attic Records Limited, Rock Group TRIUMPH, Photographer – Bruce Cole, 387; Bell Northern Research, 395; Bombadier, 35, 36, 37; Book Haven National Laboratory, 317; Allan Bowering, 490; British Airways, 383; Bushnell Optical of Canada, 487; Centre for History of Physics, 542; C.P. Picture Service, 19, 52, 71, 74, 98, 104, 164, 191; Walt Disney Productions, 256; Eastman Kodak Company, 268-9; Dr. Harold Egerton, M.I.T., 99, 117, 118; Dr. Alistair B. Fraser, 486; French Embassy, English Information Service, 167, 462; Gale Research Company, 59, 176; General Motors of Canada Limited, 516; Government of Canada, Department of National Defense, 49, 51, 261; Energy, Mines and Resources Canada, 261, 262; Industry and Tourism, 50, 126, 422, 436; Lands and Forests, 51; D.C. Heath and Company, Lexington, Mass., 341, 343, 345, 346, 350, 354, 356, 358, 359, 367, 535, colour plate; Dave Martin, colour plate; David G. Martindale, 447, 485; NASA, 22, 54, 74, 77, 91, 93, 112, 213, 543; National Library of Medicine, Bethesda, Maryland, 207, 279; National Portrait Gallery, London, 59; New Massey Hall, 395; New York Academy of Medicine Library, 215, 225, 321, 541; Nikon, 442; Metropolitan Toronto Library Board, 194, 386, 525; Miller Services, 2, 41, 155, 165, 325, 336-7, 373, 428, 431, 450, 461, 462, 463, 484, 487, 503; Robert R. MacNaughton, 3, 55, 60, 61, 72, 95, 96, 139, 143, 144, 167, 174-5, 195, 204, 209, 259, 365, 386, 412, 420, 431, 439, 450, 453, 455, 459, 460, 470, 475, 482, 483, 495, 538, 539, 540; Ontario Hydro, 159, 160, 212, 246; Ontario Place Corp., 390; Ontario Science Centre, 390; Picker Corp., 393; Polaroid, 502; Raytheon Canada Ltd., 544; R.D. Systems of Canada Ltd., 391; Ross Laboratories, 393; Royal Ontario Museum, 255; The Science Museum, London, 215, 270, 273, 277, 283, 312, 313, 384, 432, 488; Courtesy of S.T.E.M. Laboratories, Kansas City, Missouri and Fisher Scientific Company, Chicago, Ill., 443; SCALA, New York, Florence, 63; Stanford Linear Accelerator Centre, 313; Toronto Blue Jays, 49; Maestro Kazuyoshi Akiyama and the Vancouver Symphony Orchestra, 395; Harold Whyte, 444; Xerox of Canada, 227.

Authors' acknowledgements

During the writing of this book, we have benefitted from the skill and insight of many people, in education as well as in publishing. We would like to express our gratitude to the following for their invaluable assistance: to Tom Fairley and Bob Grundy for their editorial excellence and attention to detail; to Steve Mills, Magee Carney, and Susan Crowdy of D. C. Heath Canada Ltd., whose encouragement and technical expertise were always at hand; to Peter Maher and John Murtagh for their unique and fresh approach to design and layout; and, finally, our most sincere appreciation to our families for their patience and encouragement during the many hours away from home, in front of the typewriter, and behind the pencil.

Design/Maher & Murtagh

Illustrations/Frank Zsigo and Acorn Technical Art

Contents

Unit Four — Waves: The Energy of Sound and Light

Appendices

To the student

The boundaries of knowledge are expanding as never before. Every responsible citizen must try to understand the new knowledge and take part in the discussion of what it means for our future on this planet. This book is about some of the fundamental principles of the branch of science that many believe to be the foundation of all the sciences—physics.

We believe that learning thrives on personal experience, and, to let you take part actively, we have woven nearly 60 laboratory investigations into this text. We have noticed also that, for students to grasp a concept in physics, they must be able to solve related numerical problems. The ability to do this gives you a feeling of real competence. If you are like most students, you will find numerical problems worrisome, so we have included sample and practice problems all through the book, as well as extra problems at the end of most chapters. Answers are given for every problem that has a numerical answer.

Unit One will introduce you to the basic skills and techniques of the study of motion, leading you to a grasp of the concept of energy and the reasons for the universal concern about sources of energy. Electricity and magnetism are the subjects of Unit Two. Unit Three goes into recent developments in physics that have changed our way of looking at the atom and put nuclear energy at the service of man. And in Unit Four, you will be looking at wave phenomena, especially in sound and light, and this will lead you to an understanding of the wave nature of light.

We know the joy and satisfaction that come from greater awareness and understanding of the physical world, and we wish you luck as you set out to capture those rewards for yourself.

1

Mechanics: The Energy of Motion

1 Time and Distance

Few things in our universe are at rest. Most are in constant motion, whether it be planets orbiting suns, electrons in atoms, or birds in the sky. Describing these motions mathematically, using the branch of physics known as kinematics, is the first step towards understanding them.

1.1 Time

Time is measured by clocks. Any regular repeated motion can be used as a clock. Early man marked time by the rising and setting of the sun. Grandfather clocks use the to-and-fro motion of a pendulum. Modern cesium atomic clocks use the regular repeated motion inside cesium atoms, measuring time to an accuracy of a few millionths of a second per year.

To describe any regular repeated motion, we use the quantities called period and frequency.

1.2 Period and Frequency

When an object makes repeated motions, one complete motion is called a **cycle**. The time required for one cycle is called the **period**. The number of cycles in one **second** is called the **frequency**.

Sample problem

A pendulum on a clock completes 240 cycles in 60 s.
(**a**) What is its period?
(**b**) What is its frequency?

(**a**) Period

$$T = \frac{60 \text{ s}}{240}$$
$$= 0.25 \text{ s}$$

(b) Frequency

$$f = \frac{240 \text{ c}}{60 \text{ s}}$$
$$= 4.0 \text{ c/s}$$
$$= 4.0 \text{ Hz}$$

In SI (the International System of units), the unit of frequency is called the **hertz** (Hz) and

$$1 \text{ c/s} = 1 \text{ Hz}$$

From this example, you can see that period and frequency are related by a simple equation. They are reciprocals of each other.

$$T = \frac{1}{f} \quad \text{or} \quad f = \frac{1}{T}$$

Practice

1. A guitar string vibrates 750 times in 3.00 s. Calculate its period and frequency.   (0.004 00 s, 250 Hz)
2. If 180 waves wash up on a shore in 1.00 h, what is the time between waves, in seconds?   (20.0 s)
3. Calculate the frequency and period of a car engine that makes 4800 revolutions in 1.00 min.   (80.0 Hz, 0.0125 s)
4. A ticker tape timer makes 360 dots in 6.0 s. How long does it take to make six dots?   (0.10 s)

1.3 Recording Timers

In many of the investigations of motion that follow, you will be using a recording timer as a clock. A photograph of one of these is shown. A moving arm, driven by an electromagnet, strikes a metal block at a high frequency. A long strip of ticker tape, attached at one end to the moving object under study, slides between the moving arm and the metal block. A circular piece of carbon paper, attached so that it can rotate, makes a dot on the ticker tape every time the moving arm strikes it. In this way, a complete record is made of the motion. An analysis of the marks on the paper tape will give information about distance, time, speed, and acceleration.

Examine your timer carefully. Does it work in the same way as the one shown? Follow your teacher's directions and be sure to connect your timer correctly to the power supply. When you turn your timer on, it should make a regular sound.

Investigation: The Period of a Recording Timer

Problem:
What are the period and the frequency of the recording timer?

Materials:
recording timer
power supply
2 m ticker tape
carbon paper disc
stopwatch

Procedure
1. Connect the timer to the power supply.
2. Attach the carbon paper disc to the timer, with the carbon side up.
3. Thread one end of the paper tape into the timer, over the carbon paper disc.
4. Pull the tape through the timer for exactly 3 s. One person pulls the tape while the other uses the stopwatch.

Observations
In a data table, record the time for the run, in seconds, and the number of dots. Calculate and record the frequency and the period of the timer.

Questions
1. Why is it important in this investigation not to pull the tape too quickly?
2. Why is it equally important not to pull the tape too slowly?
3. Does it matter whether the dots are unevenly spaced along the tape? What would that indicate?
4. The period of many recording timers is 1/60 s or 0.017 s. If this is true for your timer (your teacher can tell you whether it is), calculate the **percentage error** in your measurement of the period. (See Appendix C)
5. What are the major sources of error that could affect your measurements and your calculation of the period? How could you allow for each of these sources of error, so as to obtain a more accurate value for the period?

Conclusion
Each investigation must have a conclusion. The conclusion is the best answer you can give to the problem posed at the start of the

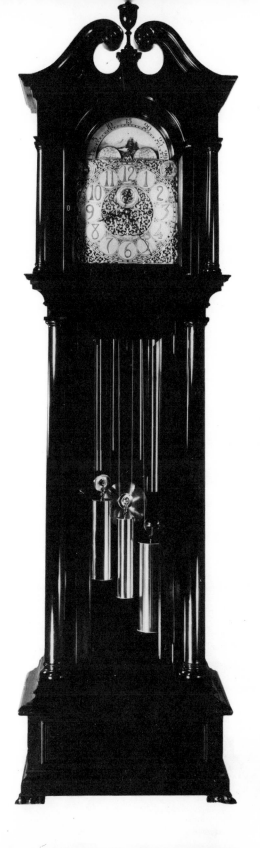

investigation. If the answer is a number, as in this investigation, it is a good idea whenever possible to give its percentage error as well. After you have done each investigation, you should come to a conclusion and include it in your written report.

Sample problem

A recording timer makes 125 dots in 2.5 s. What are (a) its period and (b) its frequency?

(a) Period

$$T = \frac{2.5 \text{ s}}{125}$$

$$= 0.020 \text{ s}$$

(b) Frequency

$$f = \frac{125}{2.5 \text{ s}} \qquad \text{or} \qquad f = \frac{1}{T}$$

$$= 50 \text{ c/s} \qquad \qquad = \frac{1}{0.020 \text{ s}}$$

$$= 50 \text{ Hz} \qquad \qquad = 50 \text{ Hz}$$

Practice

1. A recording timer makes 540 dots in 4.0 s. What is its period?

(0.0074 s)

2. A recording timer has a period of 0.025 s. How many dots does it make in 0.80 s?

(32)

3. A recording timer has a period of 0.04 s. How many dots does it make in 0.20 s?

(5)

4. A recording timer makes 465 dots in 8.5 s.
(a) Calculate its period. (0.018 s)
(b) Its actual period is 0.020 s. Calculate the percentage error.

(−10%)

The unit for frequency is named after Heinrich Hertz (1857-1894). In 1887, when he was 30 years old, he was generating high-frequency radio waves.

A positive percentage error indicates a measurement greater than the actual value. A negative percentage error indicates a measurement less than the actual value.

1.4 Motion in a Straight Line

In Chapters 1 and 2 we will examine the motion of objects moving in a straight line, such as a train travelling back and forth along a straight railway track.

What we want is a record of the distance of the train from its starting point at regular time intervals. This information will then be used to draw a distance-time graph.

The recording timer provides exactly what we need. Attach one end of the paper tape to the object and start the timer. Each different kind of motion will produce a different pattern of dots on the tape.

Remember that the time between dots is constant, usually 1/60 s, if you have a timer like the one shown.

For the next investigation, try to imagine what kind of pattern will be produced by an object with uniform motion, that is, an object that travels the same distance in every second.

Investigation: Uniform Motion

Problem:
How does a distance-time graph show uniform motion?

Materials:
recording timer
1 m ticker tape

Procedure
1. Set up the timer and thread one end of the tape into it.
2. Holding on to the end of the tape, walk several steps while your partner operates the timer. Pull the tape as smoothly and steadily as possible.

Analyse the tape as follows:
3. Select a convenient unit of time. A timer may have a period of 1/60 s. Then six dots would represent 0.10 s, a convenient unit.
4. Draw a line across the tape through the first dot on the tape.
5. Draw a line through every sixth dot all the way along the tape.

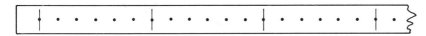

6. Now measure, in centimetres, the total distance travelled from the first dot up to the end of each marked time interval.

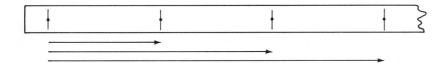

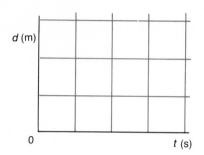

7. Record this information in a data table similar to this:

time (s)	0	0.10	0.20	0.30	0.40	0.50	0.60	1.40	1.50
distance (cm)	0								

8. Draw a distance-time graph, with time plotted horizontally and distance vertically. Make the graph as large as possible. (See Appendix D)

Questions

1. Find the average speed for the trip by dividing the total distance travelled by the total time taken. Be sure to use the correct unit for the speed.

2. Draw a straight line from the first point on the graph to the last point on the graph. Recall the definition of "slope" from your knowledge of mathematics and find the slope of this line. What does this slope tell you?

3. What shape would the graph have if the motion were absolutely uniform?

4. What shape would the graph have if the motion were uniform, but faster? Slower?

Speed

The **speed** of an object moving with uniform motion is the distance it travels each second, and is calculated by dividing the distance travelled by the time taken.

$$\text{speed} = \frac{\text{distance}}{\text{time}}$$

The equation may be used if the object is not moving uniformly, to calculate the average speed of the object.

The highest speed ever recorded for a wheeled vehicle was achieved by "The Blue Flame" driven by Gary Gabelich at the Bonneville Salt Flats, Utah, on October 23, 1970. Powered by a liquid natural gas-hydrogen peroxide rocket, this car had an average speed for two runs in opposite directions over 1 km of 1014.5 km/h, or 281.81 m/s.

Sample problem

A car travels 100 km in 2.5 h. Calculate its speed.

$$\text{speed} = \frac{\text{distance}}{\text{time}}$$
$$= \frac{100 \text{ km}}{2.5 \text{ h}}$$
$$= 40 \text{ km/h}$$

The race lap record for the Indianapolis 500 is 47.02 s, set by Wally Dallenbach driving a turbo-charged Eagle-Offenhauser on May 26, 1974. This corresponds to 308.0 km/h or 85.57 m/s.

Practice

1. What is the speed of a train that travels 480 km in 8.0 h?
(60 km/h)

2. How fast is an airplane moving when it travels 580 m in 2.50 s?
(232 m/s)

3. An ant moves 29.4 mm in 72.8 s. How fast is it moving?
(0.404 mm/s)

4. A car goes 25 km in 0.70 h, then travels 35 km farther in the next 1.50 h. What is its average speed for the entire trip?
(27 km/h)

1.5 Slope and Distance-Time Graphs

In mathematics, the **slope** of a straight line is calculated as follows:

$$\text{slope} = \frac{\Delta y}{\Delta x}$$

where $\Delta y = y_2 - y_1$
and $\Delta x = x_2 - x_1$

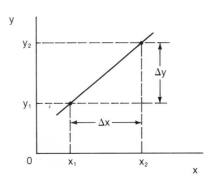

The idea of slope may have come from carpentry, where it is used to describe the steepness of a roof.

Here, Δy is called the **rise**,
and Δx is called the **run**.

$$\text{slope} = \frac{\text{rise}}{\text{run}}$$

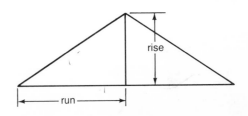

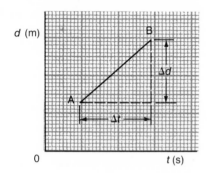

The slope of a distance-time graph is found in the same way as the slope of any other graph, but it means something special. In the previous investigation, you found that the slope of a distance-time graph tells you the speed of the object, v.

Δd = the distance travelled between A and B.

Δt = the time required to travel from A to B.

$$\text{speed} = \frac{\text{distance}}{\text{time}}$$

$$v = \frac{\Delta d}{\Delta t}$$

= slope of the graph

Speed is equal to the slope of a distance-time graph.

$$v = \frac{\Delta d}{\Delta t}$$

This equation can be rearranged to calculate either Δd or Δt, using the rules of algebra.

Multiply both sides of the equation by Δt

$$v\,\Delta t = \frac{\Delta d\,\Delta t}{\Delta t}$$

then $\Delta d = v\,\Delta t$

Divide both sides of the equation by v

$$\frac{\Delta d}{v} = \frac{v\,\Delta t}{v}$$

then $\Delta t = \frac{\Delta d}{v}$

Traditionally, for straight-line motion, values of Δd, and hence v, have always been positive. To allow for more interesting problems where the motion reverses its direction, the authors have chosen to introduce negative values of Δd and v as well. Because of this, distance, d, will represent the distance away from the starting point at any time. This permits the introduction of negative slopes on distance-time graphs.

Sample problem

The graph at the right shows the motion of three runners, A, B, and C.
What is the speed of runner A?

$$v = \frac{\Delta d}{\Delta t}$$
$$= \frac{(6.0 - 2.0) \text{ m}}{(12.0 - 4.0) \text{ s}}$$
$$= \frac{4.0 \text{ m}}{8.0 \text{ s}}$$
$$= 0.50 \text{ m/s}$$

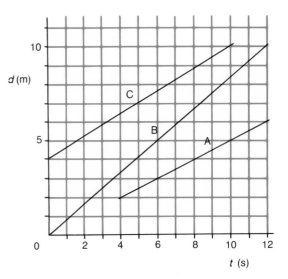

Practice
1. What, according to the above graph, is the speed of:
   (a) runner B   (0.83 m/s)
   (b) runner C   (0.60 m/s)
2. How far will a plane get, flying at 230 m/s for 10.0 min?   (1.38×10^5 m)
3. How long will it take a boy on a bicycle, moving at 13.0 m/s, to go 195 m?   (15.0 s)

1.6 Motion at Changing Speed

So far, our moving objects have all had a constant speed. In the next investigation, we are going to examine the motion of an object that changes speed after it has been moving for a time. In this case, as you pull the paper tape, you must move at one speed for the first half of the trip and then try to double the speed for the remainder of the trip.

Investigation: Motion at Two Different Speeds

Problem:
How are different speeds represented on a distance-time graph?

Materials:
recording timer
1 m ticker tape

Procedure

1. Set up the recording timer and thread one end of the tape into it.
2. Turn on the timer and pull the tape through, smoothly. About half way down the tape, suddenly double the speed and continue pulling evenly, to the end of the tape.
3. As before, divide the tape into convenient time intervals and measure the distance travelled up to the end of each interval.
4. Draw a distance-time graph.
5. Select the straightest portion of the graph in each half of the trip and find its slope. What was the speed in each half?
6. Calculate the average speed for the whole trip.

Questions

1. Describe briefly the kind of motion that is taking place in each of the situations represented by these distance-time graphs.

(a)
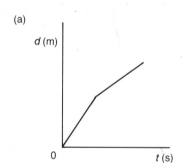

(b)
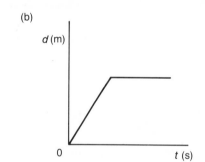

(c)
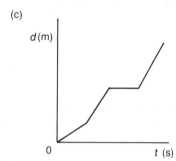

2. Describe briefly the motions represented by each of these graphs. If the speed is changing, state whether it is increasing or decreasing.

(a)
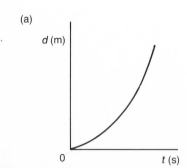

(b)
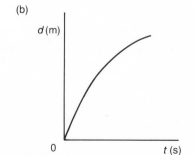

(c)
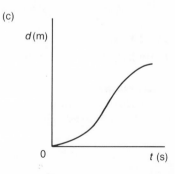

3. Describe the motion represented by each of these distance-time graphs.

(a)

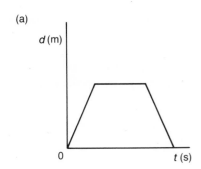

(b)

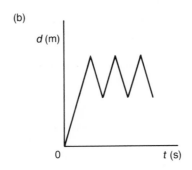

(c)

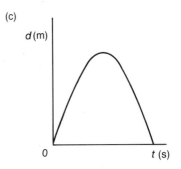

Sample problem: Rest Stops and Return Trips

Examine carefully the following distance-time graph. Find the speed of the object in each lettered section.

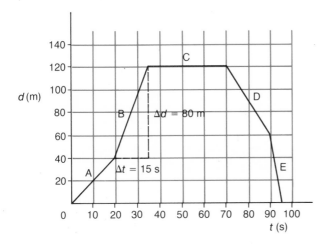

	A	B	C	D	E
Δd (m)	40	80	0	− 60	− 60
Δt (s)	20	15	35	20	5
v (m/s)	2.0	5.3	0	−3.0	−12

You are already familiar with graphs like sections A and B. The steeper slope indicates that the object travelled faster in section B than it did in section A. Since, in section C, it is always 120 m away from the starting point, the object is not moving. The speed and the slope in this part of the graph are zero.

In the last two intervals, the object is returning towards its starting point. The graph in section D shows the object moving from a point 120 m from its starting point to a point 60 m from its starting point. The graph is falling instead of rising. We will call this a rise of −60 m.

If Δd is negative, then the slope is negative and we say that the speed is negative. **Positive speeds** indicate motion away from the starting point, and **negative speeds** indicate motion in the opposite side, that is, back towards the starting point.

Practice

This distance-time graph shows the motion of a delivery truck whose driver is trying to find a certain house on a long dark street.

Remember, *d* represents the distance away from the starting point. Therefore, positive values of Δd represent distances moved forward and negative values of Δd represent distances moved backwards.

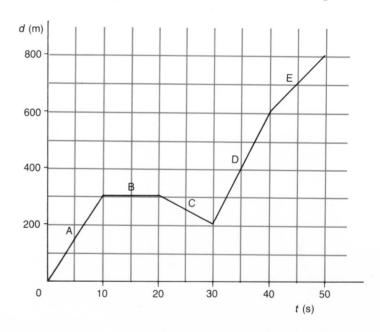

1. How far is the truck from its starting point after:
   (a) 10 s   (b) 15 s   (c) 30 s   (d) 43 s   (e) 50 s
                          (300 m, 300 m, 200 m, 660 m, 800 m)
2. What is the truck's speed in each of the lettered intervals?   (30 m/s, 0 m/s, −10 m/s, 40 m/s, 20 m/s)

Average Speed

So far, all the objects studied have been travelling at constant speeds, shown on distance-time graphs as straight lines. The slope of the straight line tells you the speed. If the slope changes, then the speed of the object has changed.

Sometimes, when an object's speed changes several times during a trip, it is useful to be able to calculate its **average speed**. In words, this may be expressed as follows:

$$\textbf{average speed} = \frac{\textbf{total distance travelled}}{\textbf{total time for the trip}}$$

$$\textit{or} \ \ v = \frac{\Delta d}{\Delta t}$$

This definition of average speed applies only to an interval of motion in which the direction of motion does not change. For such an interval a positive value of average speed represents forward motion whereas a negative value represents backward motion.

Sample problem

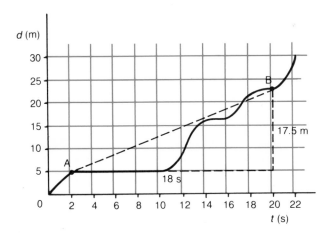

The graph represents the motion of an object that is moving very irregularly. Only where the line is straight is the speed constant. Suppose that you needed to know the average speed between points A and B. The distance between these two points is:

$$\Delta d = 22.5 \text{ m} - 5.0 \text{ m} = 17.5 \text{ m}$$

The time the object takes to go from A to B is:

$$\Delta t = 20 \text{ s} - 2 \text{ s} = 18 \text{ s}$$

The average speed between the two points is:

$$v = \frac{\Delta d}{\Delta t}$$

$$= \frac{17.5 \text{ m}}{18 \text{ s}}$$

$$= 0.97 \text{ m/s}$$

Now, look at the graph once more, at the straight line joining A and B.

The slope of this line is also found by dividing 17.5 m by 18 s.

Average speed is equal to the slope of the line joining two points on a distance-time graph.

Practice

1. From the graph, calculate the average speed for the entire 22 s trip.   (1.4 m/s)

2. Find the average speed for each of the following time intervals on the graph.

    (**a**) from 0 s to 2 s   (2.5 m/s)

    (**b**) from 6 s to 10 s   (0 m/s)

    (**c**) from 15 s to 18 s   (1.7 m/s)

    (**d**) from 6 s to 15 s   (1.3 m/s)

1.7 Speed at a Point

When an object's speed changes, the object is accelerating. If its speed changes continuously, it may have a different speed at every moment in time. You now know how to find the average speed between any two points on a distance-time graph, but how can you determine the speed at a certain point? If you were in an accelerating car, you could simply look down at the speedometer. How do you get this information from a distance-time graph? That is the subject of the next investigation.

Investigation: Motion with Changing Speed

Problem:

How can you determine the speed of an accelerating object?

Materials:
recording timer
2 m ticker tape
lead mass

Procedure
1. Set up the recording timer. Attach the ticker tape to the lead mass.
2. Clamp the timer vertically to the edge of the desk so that the lead mass will pull the tape smoothly after it, as it falls.
3. This time, it may be necessary to measure the distance for every dot, to get enough points to plot a graph.
4. Draw a distance-time graph as before.

Questions
1. What happens to the slope of your graph, as time passes?
2. What happens to the speed of the lead mass?
3. Locate the point on the graph that represents the position of the lead mass when half the total time of the trip has elapsed. Mark it with an X. Draw a straight line touching the graph at point X with the same slope as the graph at point X. Determine the slope of this line.
4. Calculate the average speed for the trip. Compare this with the speed at point X.
5. How would you find the speed of the lead mass when one-third of the trip has been completed?

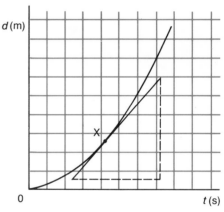

Motion with changing speed

Slope and Changing Speed

Constant speed is shown on a distance-time graph by a straight line. When a car accelerates, its speed changes and its distance-time graph will be curved. The driver can read the speed of the car from the speedometer. How would you find out the speed from a distance-time graph?

Here is a typical example of increasing speed. At first, the object is at rest, so the graph is horizontal. Then the car accelerates—its speed is increasing, and the slope of the graph also increases.

Look at point A on the graph. How fast is the car moving at that moment? It is necessary to determine the slope of the graph at that moment, but we only know how to find the slope of a straight line.

Through point A draw a straight line that has the same slope as the graph at point A. If the line is drawn at the wrong angle, it will

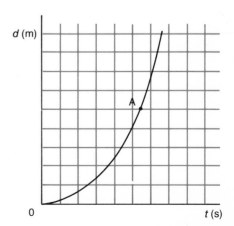

cross the graph at point A. The line you want just touches the graph at point A. Such a line is called a **tangent**.

Find the slope of this tangent and you will have the speed of the car.

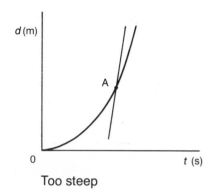

Too steep

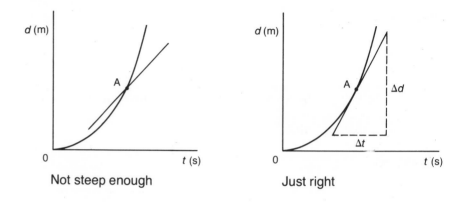

Not steep enough

Just right

Speed is equal to the slope of the tangent to a distance-time graph.

Sample problem

On the following distance-time graph, find the speed at points A, B, and C by finding the slope of the tangent to the graph at each of the points.

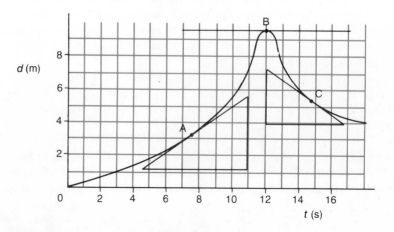

For point A: $v = \dfrac{\Delta d}{\Delta t}$

$= \dfrac{4.4 \text{ m}}{6.5 \text{ s}}$

$= 0.68 \text{ m/s}$

For point B: $v = \dfrac{\Delta d}{\Delta t}$

$= \dfrac{0 \text{ m}}{10 \text{ s}}$

$= 0 \text{ m/s}$

For point C: $v = \dfrac{\Delta d}{\Delta t}$

$= \dfrac{-3.2 \text{ m}}{5.5 \text{ s}}$

$= -0.58 \text{ m/s}$

Practice

Plot a graph of the data tabulated at the right.

1. What is the average speed for the first 2.5 s? (4.0 m/s)
2. What is the average speed from the 2.5 s mark to the 7.5 s mark? (−4.0 m/s)
3. What is the speed at the 2.5 s mark? (0.0 m/s)
4. At what other time is the speed zero? (7.5 s)
5. What are the speeds at each of the following times?
   (a) 1.0 s (5 m/s)
   (b) 3.0 s (−2 m/s)
   (c) 5.0 s (−6 m/s)
   (d) 1.7 s (3 m/s)

d (m)	t (s)
10.0	0.0
13.1	0.5
15.9	1.0
18.1	1.5
19.5	2.0
20.0	2.5
19.5	3.0
18.1	3.5
15.9	4.0
13.1	4.5
10.0	5.0
6.9	5.5
4.1	6.0
1.9	6.5
0.5	7.0
0.0	7.5
0.5	8.0
1.9	8.5
4.1	9.0
6.9	9.5
10.0	10.0

1.8 Summary

1. In a repeated motion, one complete motion is called a cycle.
2. The period is the time needed to complete one cycle, in seconds (s).
3. The frequency is the number of cycles in one second, measured in hertz (Hz).
4. Period (T) and frequency (f) are related by the equations:

$$T = \dfrac{1}{f} \quad \text{or} \quad f = \dfrac{1}{T}$$

5. In the drawing of a distance-time graph, all the distances are measured on the ticker tape from the starting point of the motion.

6. On distance-time graphs, a straight line shows that the object is moving at a constant speed. The speed of the object is equal to the slope of the straight line.

$$v = \frac{\Delta d}{\Delta t}$$

7. A negative slope on a distance-time graph indicates motion back towards the starting point and, hence, a negative speed.

8. For irregular motions, the average speed is the distance travelled divided by the time taken.

9. The speed at any point on a curved distance-time graph is equal to the slope of the tangent to the curve at that point.

1.9 Review

1. A spinning top makes one revolution every 0.080 s. What is its frequency?

2. A record-player turntable makes 33.3 r/min. What is its period in seconds?

3. An electric clock motor rotates 1200 times in 240 s.
   (a) What is its frequency?
   (b) What is its period?

4. What is the period of the minute hand of a clock?

5. The crankshaft of a car engine is turning at 3.6×10^2 r/min. Four of its eight spark plugs fire during each revolution, at equal time intervals. The coil provides the sparks for all the plugs.
   (a) How many sparks does the coil produce per second?
   (b) What is the time between sparks?

6. Here are some world record times for various track and field events (as of November 30, 1975):

Race	Time (s)	Held by
(a) 100 m	9.90	Steven Williams (United States)
(b) 200 m	19.5	Tommie Smith (United States)
(c) 400 m	43.9	Donald Quarrie (Jamaica)

   Calculate the average speed for each race. Can you explain the result?

7. Viking I, the first spacecraft to land on Mars, travelled 7.00×10^8 km in 303 d. Calculate its average speed, in kilometres per second.

8. How long does it take a girl, riding her bike at 2.50 m/s, to travel 1800 m?

Some real-life problems that are not exactly motion in a straight line may be treated as if they were.

9. How far will a woman travel in 15 min, driving her car down the highway at 24 m/s?

10. The speed limit on expressways is 100 km/h. If you see something on the road ahead of you, as you are driving along, it usually takes about 1.0 s for the brakes to be fully applied. How far will the car travel in that time, in metres?

11. The speed limit on suburban streets is 50 km/h. You are travelling at the limit when a boy jumps out from behind a parked car 5 m in front of you. How long will it be before you hit him?

Donald Quarrie of Jamaica (at the left), in the honour round after winning the men's 200 m dash at the Montreal Olympics. The United States runners with him are Millard Hampton and Dwayne Evans (left to right).

12. Calculate the speed of the object in each of these distance-time graphs.

(a)

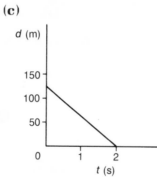

(b)

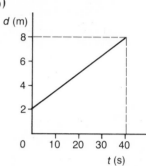

(c)

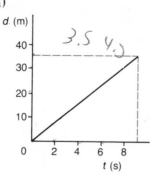

(d)

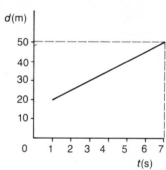

13. Calculate the speed of this automobile in each part of its trip.

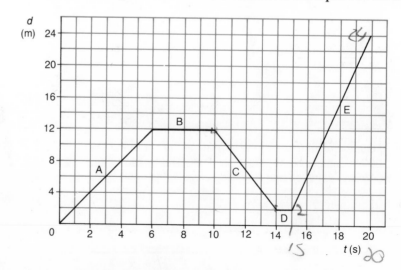

14. None of the following could be a distance-time graph for a moving object. Explain why, in each case.

(a)

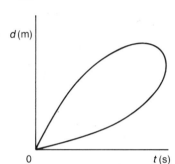

(b)

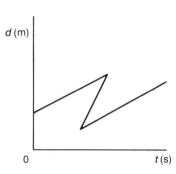

(c)

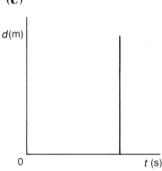

(d)

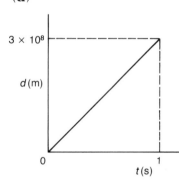

15. Draw a distance-time graph for a runner who goes at 5 m/s for 10 s, then at 2 m/s for 20 s, then at -9 m/s for 10 s.

16. Draw a distance-time graph using the following data:

d (km)	0	0.5	1.0	1.5	2.2	3.2	4.2	5.2	5.7	5.8	5.8
t (h)	0	0.1	0.2	0.3	0.4	0.5	0.6	0.7	0.8	0.9	1.0

How fast was the object moving after
(a) 0.1 h?   **(b)** 0.5 h?   **(c)** 1.0 h?
What was the average speed for
(d) the first 0.5 h? **(e)** the last 0.5 h? **(f)** the whole hour?

17. Harry gives Sam a 30 m head start in the 100 m dash. Harry can run at 10 m/s, while Sam only runs at 6.0 m/s.
  (a) Draw a distance-time graph for a 100 m dash, plotting both runners on it.

Numerical Answers to Review Problems
1. 12 Hz
2. 1.80 s
3. (a) 5.00 Hz
    (b) 0.200 s
4. 3600 s
5. (a) 24
    (b) 0.042 s
6. (a) 10.1 m/s
    (b) 10.3 m/s
    (c) 9.11 m/s
7. 26.7 km/s
8. 720 s
9. 2.2×10^4 m
10. 28m
11. 0.4 s
12. (a) 4.0 m/s
    (b) 0.15 m/s
    (c) -62 m/s
    (d) 5 m/s
13. 2 m/s, 0 m/s, -2.5 m/s
    0 m/s, 4.4 m/s
16. (a) 5.0 km/h
    (b) 10 km/h
    (c) 0 km/h
    (d) 6.4 km/h
    (e) 5.2 km/h
    (f) 5.8 km/h
17. (b) Harry passes Sam at 7.5 s, 75 m
    (c) 40 m
18. (a) 360 m/s
    (b) 1.09×10^3 m/s
    (c) 3.30×10^3 m/s
    (d) 3.38×10^3 m/s
19. 24 min
20. 1.2 min
21. (a) 1.0 km
    (b) 15 min
    (c) 3.5 km

(**b**) Does Harry win? If so, at what time and place does he catch up to Sam?

(**c**) How much of a head start would Sam need to win the race?

18. A rocket took off straight up, heading for the moon. The following data were recorded. Draw a distance-time graph.

d(m)	0	10	80	270	640	1250	2160	3430	5120	7290	10 000	13 300
t(s)	0	1	2	3	4	5	6	7	8	9	10	11

(**a**) What was the average speed for the first 6.00 s?

(**b**) What was the speed exactly 6.00 s from the start of the trip?

(**c**) What was the average speed for the 11th second? (10.0 s to 11.0 s)

(**d**) What was the speed 10.5 s after the start of the trip?

19. Toronto is about 50 km from Hamilton. A freight train starts out from Hamilton for Toronto at 50 km/h. At the same time, a passenger train leaves Toronto for Hamilton at 75 km/h. How much time passes before they meet one another, in minutes?

20. Two trains, each 1.0 km long, are heading towards each other at 50 km/h. At a certain moment, their locomotives are right beside one another (they are on parallel tracks). How much time passes before their cabooses are beside one another, in minutes?

21. A boy runs out the door and starts down the road for school at 10 km/h. Six minutes later, his mother discovers that he has forgotten his lunch, and she runs after him at 14 km/h.

(**a**) How far does he get in 6.0 min? $d = 10 \times .1 = 1 \, km$

(**b**) How long does it take her to catch him, in minutes?

(**c**) How far from home is he when she catches him?

$d = 14 \times .25 = 3.5$

$t_B = t_m + .$

(20) either 1 km in 50 km/hr or 2 km at 100 km/hr.

$d = v \times t$

$1 = 50 \times t$

$\frac{1 km}{50 km/hr} = t$

$.02 h = t = 1.2 min$

(21) $d_B = d_m$

$v_B \times t_B = v_m \times t_m$

$10 \times (t_m + .1) = 14 \times t_m$

$1 + 10 t_m = 14 t_m$

$1 = 4 t_m$

$1/4 = t_m = .25$

[handwritten at top:]

$d_B = d_m$

$v_B \times t_B = v_m \times t_m$

$10 \times (t_m + 6\,min) = 14 \times t_m$

1.10 Learning Objectives

1. Given the information about some repeated event, to calculate its period or frequency.
2. Given the frequency, to calculate the period of a repeated motion, and vice versa.
3. Given a paper tape from a recording timer, to make measurements of distance and time, draw up a table of values, and make an accurate distance-time graph.
4. Given any two of the speed, the distance, and the time, to calculate the third.
5. On a distance-time graph, to distinguish between and to calculate both positive and negative constant speeds.
6. To calculate the average speed of a trip from its distance-time graph.
7. To distinguish between increasing and decreasing speeds on distance-time graphs.
8. To calculate the speed at any point on a curved distance-time graph.

The preferred unit for speed is metres per second, but highway speeds are given in kilometres per hour.

According to SI, "m/s" should be used for all speeds.

[handwritten work:]

$v_1 = 50$
$v_2 = 75$

(19)

$d_1 = v_1 \times t_1$

$t_1 = \dfrac{d_1}{v_1}$

$d_2 = v_2 \times t_m$

$t_2 = \dfrac{d_2}{v_2}$

$d_1 + d_2 = 50\,km$

$d_1 + 1.5 d_1 = 50$

$2.5 d_1 = 50$

$d_1 = 20$

$d_1 + d_3 = 50$

$t_1 = t_2$

$v_1 \times t_1 = d_1$

$v_2 \times t_2 = d_2$

$v_1 t + v_2 t = 50$

$50t + 75t = 50$

$t_1 = d_2$

$\therefore \dfrac{d_1}{v_1} = \dfrac{d_2}{v_2}$

$\dfrac{v_2}{v_1} = \dfrac{d_2}{d_1}$

$\dfrac{d_2}{d_1} = \dfrac{75}{50} = 1.5$

$d_2 = 1.5 d_1$

$d_1 = v_1 \times t_1$

$20 = 50 \times t_1$

$\dfrac{20}{50} = t_1 = .4 = 24\,min$

check

$d_2 = v_2 \times t_2$

2 Speed and Acceleration

2.1 Changing Speeds

By means of distance-time graphs, we can analyse the motion of objects with either constant or changing speeds. By calculating the slope of these graphs, we can determine what the speed is, and whether it is increasing or decreasing. The next step is to determine the rate at which the speed increases or decreases. This is called the **acceleration** of the object. Two cars may both be able to reach a speed of 120 km/h, but one may be able to reach it twice as fast as the other. One may accelerate steadily while the other's acceleration varies. In this chapter, you will learn what is meant by acceleration, what unit is used to measure it, and how to measure the acceleration of ordinary moving objects.

2.2 Speed-Time Graphs

Distance-time graphs are useful for representing the motion of objects travelling at a constant speed or changing from one constant speed to another, but the motion of objects whose speed is constantly changing is more easily represented by a speed-time graph. To draw a speed-time graph you need a record of the speed of an object at different times. For example, you could sit in the back seat of a car with a stopwatch, look over the driver's shoulder at the speedometer, and record the speed of the car every five seconds. By plotting this data, you could produce a speed-time graph.

The same kind of information can be obtained from a paper tape run through a recording timer, by analysing the distances between the dots in a different way. Instead of measuring the total distance from the starting point to the end of each time interval, measure only the distance travelled during each time interval.

Investigation: Motion with Increasing Speed

Problem:
How is constant acceleration represented on a speed-time graph?

Materials:
recording timer
2 m ticker tape
cart
ramp

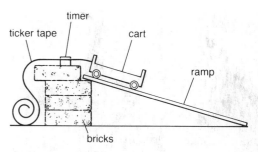

Accelerating a cart down a ramp

Procedure
1. Set up the ramp, making it steep enough that the cart will speed up considerably on the way down. Use the recording timer to make a record of this motion on a 2 m length of ticker tape.
2. To analyse the tape, divide it into convenient time intervals, as in Section 1.4. This time, hovever, measure the distance travelled during each interval, and not the total distance for the trip.
3. If each time interval consists of six dots, each representing 1/60 s, then each interval lasts for 0.10 s (6 × 1/60 s = 0.10 s). This is the time that must be used to calculate the speed for each interval.
4. Record your distance and time measurements in a data table such as this:

time	t (s)	0.1	0.2	0.3	0.4	0.5	0.6	0.7
distance per interval	Δd (cm)	1.7	3.0	3.9	4.9			
speed	v (cm/s)	17	30	39	49			

130 90 100

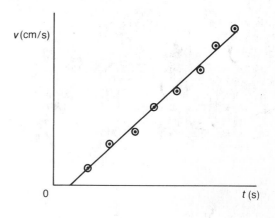

5. Complete the table by calculating the average speed for each interval.
6. Use this table to plot a graph of speed against time, with time plotted horizontally, as before.
7. Your graph should be almost a perfect straight line. Use a ruler to draw the best straight line possible through the points. (The best straight line is the one that comes as close as possible to as many points as possible.)

Here, you are plotting the speed at the end of each time interval. In fact, these are more accurately described as the speeds in the middle of each time interval.

Questions
1. Calculate the slope of your speed-time graph. Be sure to use the correct unit for this slope.
2. By how much did the cart's speed increase per second? This is called its acceleration.
   What is the connection between the acceleration of an object and the slope of its speed-time graph?

In this chapter, the definition of acceleration is only valid for motion in a straight-
line forward direction. A more complete
definition of acceleration is introduced in
Section 3.7.

Dragsters accelerate from a standing start
over a $^1/_4$-mile course (402.336 m). The
lowest recorded elapsed time for a
piston-engined dragster is 5.637 s, driven
by "Big Daddy" Garlits at the Ontario
Motor Speedway, California, on October
11, 1975. His top speed was 403.45 km/h,
or 112.07 m/s. His average acceleration
was 19.88 m/s^2.

Acceleration

If the speed of an object changes by the same amount each second,
it has a constant acceleration. The acceleration is the change in
speed per second and is calculated by dividing the total change in
speed by the time for the acceleration.

$$\text{acceleration} = \frac{\text{change in speed}}{\text{time for the change}}$$

Sample problem

What is the acceleration of a car whose speed increased steadily
from 25 m/s to 65 m/s in 8.0 s?

The car's speed increased by 40 m/s in 8.0 s.

$$\text{In one second it increased} \quad \frac{40 \text{ m/s}}{8.0} = 5.0 \text{ m/s}$$

The acceleration of the car was 5.0 m/s/s.

This is usually written as 5.0 m/s^2, for convenience.

Practice
1. A bicycle rider accelerates from 5 m/s to 15 m/s in 4.0 s. What
   is his acceleration?　　　　　　　　　　　　　　　　(2.5 m/s^2)
2. A jet plane accelerates from rest to 750 km/h in 1.20 h. What is
   its acceleration?　　　　　　　　　　　　　　　　　(625 km/h^2)
3. A runner accelerates from 0.52 m/s to 0.78 m/s in 0.050 s.
   What is her acceleration?　　　　　　　　　　　　　(5.2 m/s^2)

2.3 Acceleration and Slope

In the last investigation, you saw that the speed-time graph of an
object with constant acceleration is a straight line. The slope of the
line is equal to the object's acceleration. The equation for acceleration may be found from the speed-time graph on page 27.

As usual, to find the slope, first pick two points on the line as far
apart as possible, say A and B.

The change in speed between points A and B is Δv.
The time interval between points A and B is Δt.
The object's acceleration, using our definition for acceleration, must be:

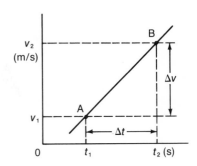

$$a = \frac{\Delta v}{\Delta t}$$

where a is the acceleration, in m/s^2
Δv is the change in speed in m/s
Δt is the time interval for the acceleration in s

This is also the slope of the line between points A and B.

Acceleration is equal to the slope of a speed-time graph.

In addition, by multiplying both sides of the equation by Δt,

$$\Delta v = a \, \Delta t$$

and, by dividing both sides of the last equation by a,

$$\Delta t = \frac{\Delta v}{a}$$

Sample problem

Determine the acceleration of this object for the first 10 s of its motion, using the slope of its speed-time graph.

In the first 10 s of the motion, the object accelerates from 0 m/s to 25 m/s.

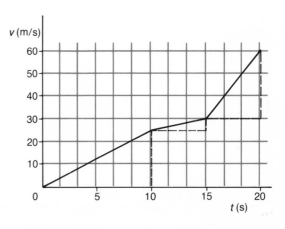

$$\Delta v = 25 \text{ m/s} - 0 \text{ m/s}$$
$$= 25 \text{ m/s}$$
$$\Delta t = 10 \text{ s}$$
$$a = \frac{\Delta v}{\Delta t}$$
$$= \frac{25 \text{ m/s}}{10 \text{ s}}$$
$$= 2.5 \text{ m/s}^2$$

Practice

1. Calculate the acceleration of the object in the sample problem for each of the following time intervals.
   (a) from 10 s to 15 s   (1.0 m/s²)
   (b) from 15 s to 20 s   (6.0 m/s²)
2 A car accelerates from rest at 50.0 cm/s² for 12.5 s. How fast is it moving then?   (625 cm/s)
3. A turtle wants to accelerate from 2 mm/s to 8 mm/s. How long will it take it, if its maximum acceleration is 3 mm/s²?   (2 s)

2.4 Positive, Negative, and Zero Accelerations

Examine the following speed-time graph. On it you will find examples of three different kinds of acceleration. The object starts off from rest (at zero speed) and accelerates steadily for a while. After 10 s, it stops accelerating and then travels at a constant speed for 10 s. The slope of this part of the graph is zero, telling you that the acceleration is zero. Now the object slows down. In each second, it loses the same amount of speed. The slope of the graph in this section is going to be negative, making the acceleration negative. A **negative acceleration** is often called a **deceleration.**

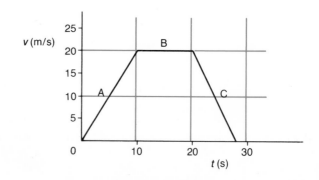

The acceleration for each section is:

A: $\Delta v = 20$ m/s   B: $\Delta v = 0$ m/s   C: $\Delta v = -20$ m/s
     $\Delta t = 10$ s $\Delta t = 10$ s $\Delta t = 8$ s

$$a = \frac{20 \text{ m/s}}{10 \text{ s}} \qquad a = \frac{0 \text{ m/s}}{10 \text{ s}} \qquad a = \frac{-20 \text{ m/s}}{8 \text{ s}}$$

$$= +2.0 \text{ m/s}^2 \qquad = 0 \text{ m/s}^2 \qquad = -2.5 \text{ m/s}^2$$

increasing speed   constant speed   decreasing speed

Sample problem

A car travelling at 50 m/s slows down to 18 m/s in 16 s. What is its acceleration?

$$\Delta v = v_2 - v_1$$
$$= 18 \text{ m/s} - 50 \text{ m/s}$$
$$= -32 \text{ m/s}$$
$$\Delta t = 16 \text{ s}$$
$$a = \frac{\Delta v}{\Delta t}$$
$$= \frac{-32 \text{ m/s}}{16 \text{ s}}$$
$$= -2.0 \text{ m/s}^2$$

Practice

1. How long will it take a truck travelling at 35 m/s to stop if it accelerates at -5.0 m/s^2? (7.0 s)
2. A plane landing accelerates at -1.5 m/s^2 for 1.0 min until it stops. How fast was it going as it started to slow down? (90 m/s)
3. A car hitting a tree loses 40.0 m/s in 0.100 s. What is its acceleration? (-400 m/s^2)
4. Calculate the acceleration of the object, in each of the lettered sections on the graph at the right.
   (A: 0 m/s^2; B: -1.5 m/s^2; C: 0 m/s^2; D: 2.5 m/s^2;
   E: -1.5 m/s^2)

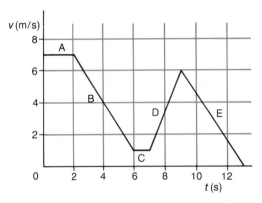

2.5 Changing Acceleration

Just as speeds are not all constant, so accelerations are not all constant either. Speed-time graphs are not all straight lines. Sometimes the acceleration increases and sometimes it decreases. You can probably think of several examples of each. Consider a car accelerating from rest. At first it picks up speed easily, accelerating quickly. Later on, its acceleration is less – the increase in speed per second is not as great. Eventually, the car's acceleration is zero – it has reached its top speed.

In the next investigation you will analyse the acceleration of a chain sliding over the edge of the desk. You will find that its acceleration changes as less and less of it remains on the desk and more and more of it is in mid-air, falling to the floor.

Investigation: Changing Acceleration

Problem:
How is a changing acceleration represented by a speed-time graph?

Materials:
recording timer
2 m ticker tape
1 m chain with 2-3 cm links

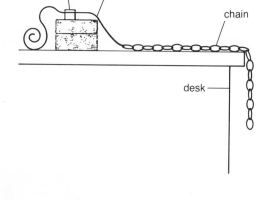

Procedure
1. Attach the paper tape to one end of the chain. Place the chain at right angles to the edge of the desk, with its free end hanging over the edge. Connect the recording timer to the paper tape.
2. Pull the hanging end of the chain over the edge of the desk until the chain starts to move by itself. Immediately start the timer, shutting it off as soon as all of the chain has left the desk. For your graph, use only the part of the tape where the chain is falling under its own weight with some of the chain still on the desk. This usually means discarding parts at the beginning and end of the tape.
3. Divide the tape into convenient time intervals (use 0.1 s if possible) and make the necessary measurements to draw a speed-time graph.
4. Join the first and last points on your graph with a straight line and calculate its slope. This tells you the average acceleration of the chain during its motion.

Questions
1. Is the slope of the line increasing, constant, or decreasing?
2. Is this an example of increasing, constant, or decreasing acceleration?
3. How do you calculate the average acceleration of an object whose acceleration is not constant?
4. Classify each of the following as representing constant, increasing, or decreasing acceleration.

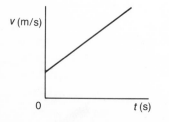

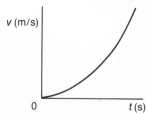

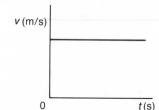

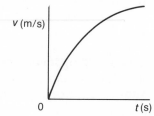

Sample problem

Use the following speed-time graph to calculate the average acceleration of a train for the first hour of its motion.

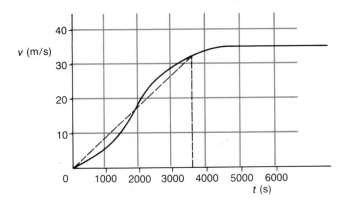

For the first hour:

$$\Delta t = 3600 \text{ s}$$
$$\Delta v = 33 \text{ m/s}$$
$$a = \frac{\Delta v}{\Delta t}$$
$$= \frac{33 \text{ m/s}}{3600 \text{ s}}$$
$$= 9.2 \times 10^{-3} \text{ m/s}^2$$

Practice
Using the above graph, find the train's average acceleration for the following time intervals.
(a) 0 s to 5000 s $(7.0 \times 10^{-3} \text{ m/s}^2)$
(b) 2000 s to 6000 s $(3.8 \times 10^{-3} \text{ m/s}^2)$
(c) 20 min to 90 min $(6.4 \times 10^{-3} \text{ m/s}^2)$

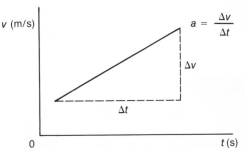

2.6 Acceleration at a Point

Constant accelerations are shown on speed-time graphs as straight lines. The slope of the line is equal to the object's acceleration (see graph at right).

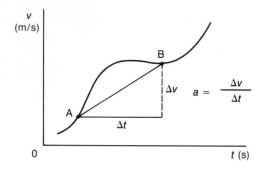

When the speed-time graph is a curve, the acceleration is no longer constant. It has a different value at every point on the line. You know how to find the average acceleration between any two points on the line. It is equal to the slope of the straight line joining the two points (see graph at left).

To find the acceleration at any point on the line, you must be able to find the slope of the line at that point. As explained in Chapter 1, this is done by drawing a tangent to the curve at the point and calculating its slope:

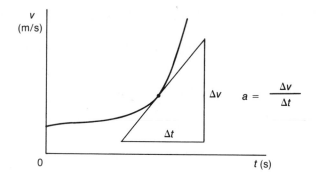

Acceleration is equal to the slope of the tangent to a speed-time graph.

Sample problem

On this speed-time graph, we are going to find constant acceleration, average acceleration, and acceleration at a given point.

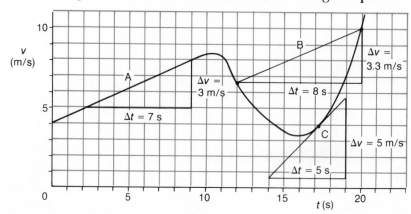

1. The acceleration in section A is constant. Its value is:

$$a = \frac{\Delta v}{\Delta t} = \frac{3.0 \text{ m/s}}{7.0 \text{ s}} = 0.43 \text{ m/s}^2$$

2. The motion between 12 s and 20 s is not uniform. The speed decreases and then increases again. The average acceleration between these two times is:

$$a = \frac{\Delta v}{\Delta t} = \frac{3.3 \text{ m/s}}{8.0 \text{ s}} = 0.41 \text{ m/s}^2$$

3. The motion around 17.4 s is not uniform. The speed is increasing, and so is the acceleration. The acceleration at 17.4 s is:

$$a = \frac{\Delta v}{\Delta t} = \frac{5.0 \text{ m/s}}{5.0 \text{ s}} = 1.0 \text{ m/s}^2$$

Practice

Examine the following speed-time graph.

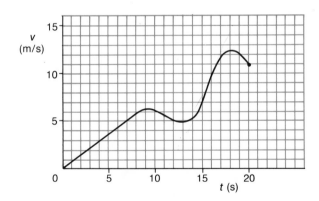

1. At what times is the acceleration zero? (9.2 s, 12.7 s, 18.1 s)
2 What is the acceleration for the first 7.0 s?   (0.71 m/s^2)
3. What is the average acceleration for each of the following time intervals?
   (a) 5.0 to 15.0 s   (0.33 m/s^2)
   (b) 9.0 to 13.0 s   (−0.35 m/s^2)
   (c) 15.0 to 20.0 s   (0.71 m/s^2)
4. What is the acceleration at each of the following times?
   (a) 15.0 s   (1.2 m/s^2)
   (b) 11.0 s   (0.50 m/s^2)
   (c) 17.0 s   (1.2 m/s^2)

2.7 The Pendulum

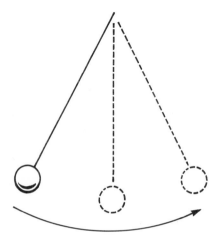

In the next investigation, you will study the motion of a pendulum by drawing both distance-time and speed-time graphs of its motion. To start a pendulum, you move it to one side and release it. At the instant when you let go of it, its speed is zero, but its acceleration is not. After all, if an object had both zero speed and zero acceleration, it could never start moving. It would have to stay at rest.

The pendulum then accelerates down to the bottom of its swing, reaching its maximum speed. Is this also the point of maximum acceleration? Consider that it has just finished speeding up and is now going to slow down. What is the value of its acceleration?

After passing the mid point of its trip, the pendulum rises, slows down, and stops. How does its final acceleration compare with its initial acceleration? How does its speed on one side of the mid point compare with its speed at the same distance on the other side of the mid point?

Other questions can be answered by comparing your results with the graphs of others with pendulums of different amplitudes. How does the amplitude affect the maximum speed and the acceleration? What is the effect of the amplitude on the period of the pendulum?

Before you do the investigation, sketch the distance-time and speed-time graphs that you expect will represent the motion of the pendulum.

Investigation: Motion of a Pendulum

Problem:
How do both speed and acceleration vary as a pendulum swings?

Materials:
recording timer
large pendulum (at least 2 m long)
2 m ticker tape

Procedure
1. Feed the paper tape into the timer. Move the pendulum bob over to the timer and attach it to the paper tape. Release the bob and record only its forward motion as it moves away.
2. Draw both distance-time and speed-time graphs of the motion. On the distance-time graph, mark the positions of both zero

and maximum speed. On the speed-time graph, mark the positions of both maximum and zero acceleration.

Questions
1. What is the average speed of the pendulum?
2. What is the average acceleration of the pendulum?
3. What is the period of the pendulum?
4. What is the maximum speed of the pendulum?
5. What is the initial acceleration of the pendulum?
6. What is the final acceleration of the pendulum?
7. Is the speed-time graph symmetrical? What does this indicate about the speeds and accelerations on opposite sides of the mid point?

Assume that the pendulum bob moves forward in a straight line.

While the motion of a pendulum fascinated Galileo, 300 years ago, it may not have the same appeal today. For those interested in more practical matters, we will examine a road test of a motorcycle – one of the most powerful 175 cm³ motorcycles available, the Can-Am T'NT.

2.8 Road Test of a Can-Am Motorcycle

The Can-Am motorcycle is, along with the snowmobile, one of the few Canadian-designed and -manufactured vehicles. The road test shown here is probably one of the first all-metric road tests.

Two graphs are plotted. The first is for road speed in kilometres per hour against time in seconds. The second is for road speed in kilometres per hour against engine speed in revolutions per minute – one graph for each gear.

Speed-time graphs are an important part of every vehicle test. At a glance, you can compare the accelerations in the different gears, the speed at which each gear change occurs, the top speed, and even the distance travelled in each gear.

At some point in each gear, as the vehicle accelerates, the acceleration decreases. Before the acceleration decreases too much, the rider should change up into the next gear. If the gear change is too extreme, the engine will be turning over too slowly and the acceleration will be too low. On a speed-time graph, the slope should be a maximum just after each gear change. It is difficult to do anything about the gearbox after you have bought a vehicle; with the help of speed-time graphs you can compare different makes before you buy, to be sure of getting one that will do what you want it to do.

CAN-AM T'NT SI CYCLE WORLD TEST
SPECIFICATIONS

Suspension, front	telescopic fork	Gear ratios, overall	:1
Suspension, rear	swing arm	6th	9.01
Tire, front	3.00-21	5th	10.28
Tire, rear	4.00-18	4th	12.30
Brake, front	150 mm drum	3rd	15.77
Brake, rear	150 mm drum	2nd	21.69
Total brake swept area,		1st	31.92
mm^2	24 300	Front fork rake angle,	
Brake loading, N/m^2	75 800	degrees	25-31, adjustable
(73 kg rider)		Curb mass (w/half-tank fuel)	
Engine type—		kg	115
rotary valve, two-stroke single		Mass bias, front/rear,	
Bore × stroke, mm	62 × 57.5	percentage	44.5/55.5
Piston displacement, cm^3	173.6	Test mass	
Compression ratio	13:1	(fuel and rider), kg	188
Claimed kW @ r/min	18 @ 8500		
Carburetion	32 mm Bing	Performance	
Ignition	CDI	Engine r/min @ 97 km/h	7100
Oil system	automatic injection	Piston speed @ 9000 r/min)	
Oil capacity, L	2.2	m/s	17.25
Fuel capacity, L	9.5	kg/kW (73 kg rider)	5.84
Recommended fuel	premium	Fuel consumption, km/L	27.8
Starting system	primary kick	Speedometer error	
Lighting system	12 V alternator	64 km/h indicated, actually	56
Air filtration	oil-wetted foam	80	76
Clutch	wet, multi-disc	97	96
Wheelbase, mm	1400	Braking distance:	
Seat height, mm	840	from 48 km/h, m	11.6
Seat width, mm	190	from 97 km/h, m	45.1
Handlebar width, mm	860	Standing 400 m, s	17.00
Footpeg height, mm	300	Terminal speed, km/h	117.25
Ground clearancce, mm	230	Top speed (actual @ 9000 r/min)	
Primary drive	straight cut gear	km/h (after 800 m)	122
Final drive	# 520 chain		

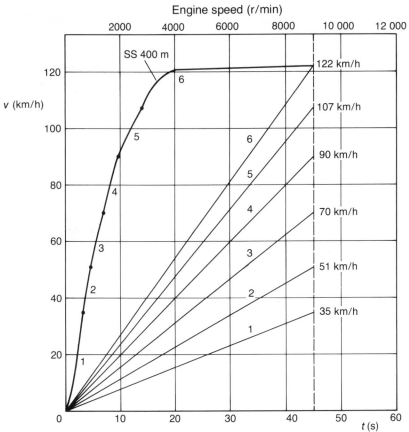

Speed versus time and engine speed

Gear	Speed @ 9000 r/min
6	122 km/h
5	107 km/h
4	90 km/h
3	70 km/h
2	51 km/h
1	35 km/h

Questions

1. What gear was the motorcycle in at (**a**) 50 km/h (**b**) 80 km/h (**c**) 100 km/h?   (2, 4, 5)
2. How much time did it take to reach (**a**) 50 km/h (**b**) 80 km/h (**c**) 100 km/h?   (4.5 s, 7.5 s, 11 s)
3. What was the average speed for the first 400 m?
                                                   (24 m/s or 85 km/h)
4. What was the average acceleration for the first 400 m?
                                          (6.9 km/h/s or 1.9 m/s²)
5. For each gear, state whether the acceleration was (**a**) increasing, (**b**) decreasing, or (**c**) constant.   (a, b, b, b, b, b)
6. The rider changed gears each time the engine reached 9000 r/min, but what was the engine speed just after he changed gears each time? (For example, when he changed from first gear into second gear, the engine speed fell from 9000 r/min to 6200 r/min.)   (6200, 6600, 7000, 7500, 7900)

2.9 Distance and Acceleration

The distance covered by an object travelling at a constant speed is easy enough for us to calculate. The equation is:

$$\Delta d = v \, \Delta t$$

For example, in 10 s, a bicyclist pedalling at 5.0 m/s will go:

$$\Delta d = v \, \Delta t$$
$$= (5.0 \text{ m/s}) (10 \text{ s})$$
$$= 50 \text{ m}$$

It is not possible to use this equation if the object is accelerating. Suppose you wanted to know how far a bus went in 10 s, beginning at 2.0 m/s and accelerating steadily at 1.0 m/s². Which speed would you use in the equation? The bus starts at 2.0 m/s and works its way up to 12 m/s. At one time or another it has every possible speed between 2.0 m/s and 12 m/s, including 3.5 m/s and 8.766 m/s. What we need to know is the average speed of the bus.

Look at the speed-time graph of this motion. Because of the constant acceleration, it is a straight line.

The bus is going at 2 m/s to start with and at 12 m/s at the end of the trip. The average of the two speeds is:

$$\frac{2 \text{ m/s} + 12 \text{ m/s}}{2} = 7.0 \text{ m/s}$$

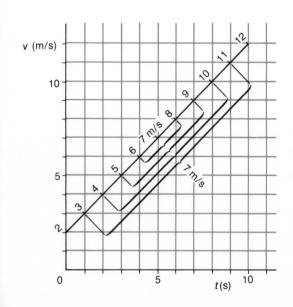

One second from the beginning and one second from the end of the trip, the speeds are 3 m/s and 11 m/s. The average of these two speeds is:

$$\frac{3 \text{ m/s} + 11 \text{ m/s}}{2} = 7.0 \text{ m/s}$$

Two seconds from the start and two seconds from the end, the speeds are 4 m/s and 10 m/s. The average of these speeds is again 7.0 m/s.

Every pair of speeds at equal intervals from the start and the end of the trip will have an average of 7.0 m/s, which is also the speed of the bus at 5 s, the halfway point of the trip.

The average speed of the bus, and of every other object with constant acceleration, is:

$$v_{average} = \frac{v_1 + v_2}{2}$$

where v_1 is the beginning or initial
       speed of the object
and v_2 is the final speed of the
       object

For our bus example,

$$v_{average} = \frac{v_1 + v_2}{2}$$
$$= \frac{2 \text{ m/s} + 12 \text{ m/s}}{2}$$
$$= 7.0 \text{ m/s}$$

The distance travelled by any object with a constant acceleration is:

$$\Delta d = v_{average} \, \Delta t$$
$$\text{or}$$
$$\Delta d = \left(\frac{v_1 + v_2}{2}\right) \Delta t$$

For our accelerating bus:

$$\Delta d = \left(\frac{v_1 + v_2}{2}\right) \Delta t$$
$$= \left(\frac{2.0 \text{ m/s} + 12 \text{ m/s}}{2}\right) (10 \text{ s})$$
$$= (7.0 \text{ m/s}) (10 \text{ s})$$
$$= 70 \text{ m}$$

Note that this equation is correct only for constant accelerations, when the speed-time graph is a straight line. If the graph is a curve, the speeds calculated by the above method will not all be the same. You will be unable to tell which speed is the proper average speed. You can see this on the following graph.

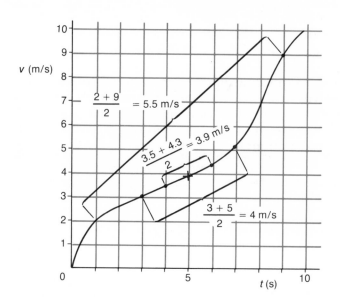

Sample problem

A car rolling down a hill accelerates from rest to 22 m/s in 40 s. Calculate:

(a) the average speed of the car
(b) the distance the car rolls down the hill

(a) average speed

$$v_{average} = \frac{v_1 + v_2}{2}$$

$$= \frac{0 \text{ m/s} + 22 \text{ m/s}}{2}$$

$$= 11 \text{ m/s}$$

(b) distance

$$\Delta d = v_{average} \, \Delta t$$
$$= (11 \text{ m/s})(40 \text{ s})$$
$$= 4.4 \times 10^2 \text{ m}$$

Practice

1. What is the average speed of a ball bearing rolling down a ramp, accelerating steadily from 8.0 m/s to **(a)** (12 m/s? **(b)** 18 m/s? **(c)** 24 m/s?   (10 m/s, 13 m/s, 16 m/s)
2. How far does a dragster travel in 6.00 s, accelerating steadily from zero to 90.0 m/s?   (270 m)
3. Two skateboarders accelerate steadily from 4.5 m/s to 11.5 m/s in 6.0 s. How far do they travel?   (48 m)

Constant Acceleration from Rest—a Special Case

The distance travelled by an object that accelerates steadily, starting from zero speed, can be calculated using the equation just developed:

$$\Delta d = \left(\frac{v_1 + v_2}{2}\right) \Delta t$$

Another equation can also be used. To obtain it, recall the shape of the speed-time graph of a constant acceleration, starting from rest.

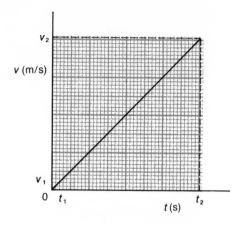

If you start from rest at time zero,

$$v_1 = 0 \quad \text{and} \quad v_2 = v \quad \text{so that} \quad \Delta v = v$$
$$d_1 = 0 \qquad\qquad d_2 = d \qquad\qquad \Delta d = d$$
$$t_1 = 0 \qquad\qquad t_2 = t \qquad\qquad \Delta t = t$$

now

$$a = \frac{\Delta v}{\Delta t}$$
$$= \frac{v}{t}$$

therefore $v = at$

Substitute into the original equation:

$$\Delta d = \left(\frac{v_1 + v_2}{2}\right) \Delta t$$
$$d = \left(\frac{0 + at}{2}\right) t$$
$$= \tfrac{1}{2} at^2$$

The distance travelled by an object with constant acceleration from rest is:

$$d = \tfrac{1}{2}\, at^2$$

Sample problem

How far down a smooth ramp does a 5.0 kg cart roll in 8.0 s, accelerating from rest at 2.5 m/s²?

$$d = \tfrac{1}{2} at^2$$
$$= \tfrac{1}{2}(2.5 \text{ m/s}^2)\,(8.0 \text{ s})^2$$
$$= 80 \text{ m}$$

Practice

1. A skier accelerates at 1.20 m/s² down an icy slope, starting from rest. How far does she get in
   (a) 5.0 s? (b) 10.0 s? (c) 15.0 s?   (15 m, 60.0 m, 135 m)
2. What is the acceleration of an object that accelerates steadily from rest, travelling 10 m in 10 s?   (0.20 m/s²)
3. How long does it take an airplane, accelerating from rest at 5.0 m/s², to travel 360 m?   (12 s)

2.10 Summary

1. To draw a speed-time graph, the distance travelled in each time interval is measured. The distance divided by the time for an interval gives the average speed for the interval.
2. On speed-time graphs, a straight line shows that the object has a constant acceleration. The acceleration of the object is equal to the slope of the speed-time graph.

$$a = \frac{\Delta v}{\Delta t}$$

3. A negative slope on a speed-time graph indicates decreasing speed, or deceleration. A deceleration is a negative acceleration.
4. For irregular motions, the average acceleration is the slope of the straight line joining any two points on the speed-time graph.
5. The acceleration at any point on a curved speed-time graph is the slope of the tangent to the curve at that point.
6. If an object has a constant acceleration, the distance travelled in any time interval is:

$$\Delta d = \left(\frac{v_1 + v_2}{2} \right) \Delta t$$

7. If an object starts from rest and accelerates steadily, the distance travelled in a certain time is:

$$d = \tfrac{1}{2} at^2$$

2.11 Review

1. A dragster accelerates from 0 to 90 m/s in 6.0 s. What is its acceleration?
2. A rocket accelerates at 40 m/s^2 for 3.0 min. What is its change in speed?
3. How long will it take a falling rock, accelerating at 10 m/s^2, to reach 112 m/s, if it starts from rest?
4. A car enters a tunnel at 24 m/s and accelerates steadily at 2.0 m/s^2. At what speed does it leave the tunnel, 8.0 s later?
5. The driver of a truck moving at 18 m/s throws on its brakes and stops it in 4.0 s. What is the acceleration of the truck?

6. A motorcycle stuntman accelerates from rest to a maximum speed of 35.2 m/s at the top of the take-off ramp, then swoops up and over 20 cars. Calculate how long it takes him to accelerate, at an acceleration of 8.8 m/s².

7. A car accelerates from rest to 8.8 m/s in 3.0 s in first gear, then changes into second gear. After 8.0 s from the start of the trip, the car reaches 22.0 m/s and is shifted into third gear. After 7.0 s in third gear, it reaches 41.8 m/s. Calculate the acceleration in each gear.

8. Here is the speed-time graph of a trip on a bicycle.
   How fast is the bicycle moving at each of the following times?
   (a) 4 s (b) 6 s (c) 10 s (d) 12 s
   What is the acceleration of the bicycle at each of these times?
   (e) 2 s (f) 5 s (g) 7 s (h) 14 s

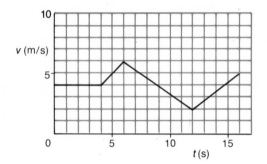

9. Draw the speed-time graph of the motion of a bus that accelerates from rest at 1.0 m/s² for 6.0 s, then continues on at a constant speed for 6.0 s, then accelerates at −2.0 m/s² for 3.0 s.

10. An arrow shot straight up into the air at 50 m/s accelerates at −10 m/s² until it stops. Draw a speed-time graph of this motion.

11. Two runners accelerate uniformly from rest at 1.40 m/s² for 8.00 s.
    (a) What is their final speed?
    (b) What is their average speed?
    (c) How far do they travel?

12. A ball accelerates steadily down a ramp, starting from rest. It goes 2.0 m in 4.0 s.
    (a) What is its average speed?
    (b) What is its final speed?
    (c) What is its acceleration?

13. A car accelerates from rest at 6.00 m/s². How far does it get between 10.0 and 15.0 s?

14. A skier accelerates steadily down a hill from 3.50 m/s to 11.40 m/s in 4.20 s.
    (a) What is the average speed for the trip?
    (b) What distance is travelled?

15. Runner A runs at 6.0 m/s for 10 s. Runner B accelerates from 4.0 m/s to 10.0 m/s, steadily, in 10 s.
    (a) How far does runner A go?
    (b) How far does runner B go?
    (c) How much farther does runner B travel than runner A?

16. Jack and Jill ran down the hill. Both started from rest and accelerated steadily. Jack accelerated at 0.25 m/s² and Jill at

0.30 m/s². After running for 20 s, Jill fell down.
(a) How far did Jill get before she fell?
(b) How far had Jack travelled when Jill fell?
(c) How fast was Jack running when Jill fell?
(d) How long was it after Jill fell that Jack ran into her and broke his crown (to the nearest second)?

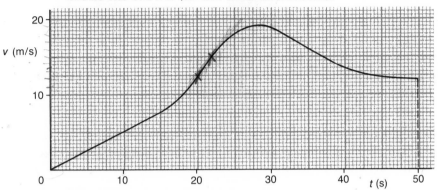

17. The graph shows the motion of a small bird flying down a long, straight, narrow cage.
(a) What is the bird's acceleration for the first 10 s of the trip?
(b) At what time is the bird's acceleration at its maximum?
(c) What is this maximum acceleration?
(d) At what time(s) is the bird's acceleration zero?
(e) At what time(s) is the bird's speed zero?

2.12 Learning Objectives

1. Given the paper tape of the motion of an object, to measure distance and time and construct a speed-time graph.
2. To calculate the average acceleration of an object from its speed-time graph.
3. Given any two of acceleration, time, and change in speed, to calculate the third.
4. To distinguish between increasing, decreasing, constant, positive, and negative accelerations on a speed-time graph.
5. Given any three of initial speed, final speed, time, distance, and acceleration, to calculate a fourth.
6. To calculate the acceleration at a point on a speed-time graph by measuring the slope of the tangent at that point.

Numerical Answers to Review Problems
1. 15 m/s²
2. 7.2×10^3 m/s
3. 11 s
4. 40 m/s
5. -4.5 m/s²
6. 4.0 s
7. 2.9 m/s², 2.6 m/s², 2.8 m/s²
8. (a) 4 m/s
   (b) 6 m/s
   (c) 3.3 m/s
   (d) 2 m/s
   (e) 0 m/s²
   (f) 1.0 m/s²
   (g) -0.67 m/s²
   (h) 0.75 m/s²
11. (a) 11.2 m/s
    (b) 5.60 m/s
    (c) 44.8 m
12. (a) 0.50 m/s
    (b) 1.0 m/s
    (c) 0.25 m/s²
13. 375 m
14. (a) 7.45 m/s
    (b) 31.3 m
15. (a) 60 m
    (b) 70 m
    (c) 10 m
16. (a) 60 m
    (b) 50 m
    (c) 5.0 m/s
    (d) 2 s
17. (a) 0.50 m/s²
    (b) 22 s
    (c) 1.7 m/s²
    (d) 28 s, 50 s
    (e) 0 s

3 Vectors

3.1 Distance and Direction

The direction of a trip is usually just as important as its length. A trip of 100 km to the north is quite different from a trip of 100 km to the south or east. In physics, two such trips are said to be of the same distance but of different displacements.

Quantities that express only magnitude, such as time or distance, are called **scalar quantities**.

Quantities that express both magnitude and direction are called **vector quantities**. The combination of distance and direction is the vector quantity called **displacement**.

The symbols for vector quantities are usually written with a small arrow over them.

[N] north
[E] east
[W] west
[S] south

All directions are put in square brackets in vector quantities. To go [30° S of E], you first point yourself east, then turn 30° towards the south.

	Distance	Displacement
symbol	d	$\vec{d}$
example	10 km	5 km[E]

Vector quantities are often represented by arrows, called vectors, in vector diagrams. The length of the arrow indicates the magnitude of the vector in the direction in which the arrow is pointing. Since most vectors are larger than the pages of this book, they will usually have to be drawn on a reduced scale. Here are some examples of displacement vectors:

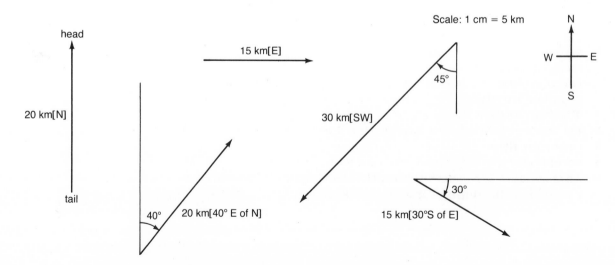

3.2 Vector Addition

If you went on a trip of 30 km[N], followed by a trip of 40 km[E], the sum of the distances you travelled is 70 km.

However, you would not be 70 km from your starting point. Your distance from that point may be obtained from a vector diagram by "adding" together the two displacement vectors. The first step is to set up a proper scale and a set of directions.

(a) To add vectors, draw both of them to the same scale and connect them together, tail to head.

Here $\vec{d_1}$ = 30 km [N]
$\vec{d_2}$ = 40 km [E]
The total displacement of these two, $\vec{d_3}$, is shown as:

$$\vec{d_3} = \vec{d_1} + \vec{d_2}$$

This equation tells you to add the two vectors together using a vector diagram, and not just to add their magnitudes together.

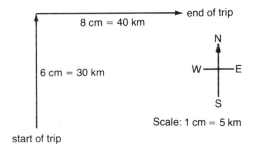

(b) The total displacement is represented by a vector drawn from the tail of the first displacement vector to the head of the second displacement vector. Measure the length and direction of this vector and calculate the displacement, using the scale. The total displacement is 50 km[53° E of N].

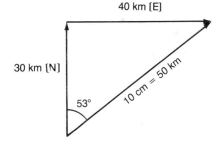

Practice

1. What is the total displacement of two trips, one of 10 km[N], and the other of 24 km[E]?   (26 km[67° E of N])
2. What is the total displacement of a trip of 50 km[W] followed by a trip of 100 km[30° E of N]?   (87 km[N])
3. Do you get the same displacement if you add the vectors in reverse order?
4. What is the total displacement of a trip to the store by a small boy who goes 2 blocks[N], 3 blocks[E], 1 block[S], 5 blocks[W], 4 blocks[S], and then 2 blocks[E]?   (3 blocks[S])

3.3 Speed and Velocity

The speed of a car, as given by its speedometer, is a scalar quantity. The car could be going east or west, uphill or downhill—you just can't tell. The combination of speed and direction is called **velocity**, another vector quantity.

	Speed	Velocity
symbol	v	$\vec{v}$
example	25 km/h	100 km/h[W]

Velocity vectors may also be represented by arrows. All that is needed is a proper scale, and a north-pointing arrow to establish direction. Here are some examples:

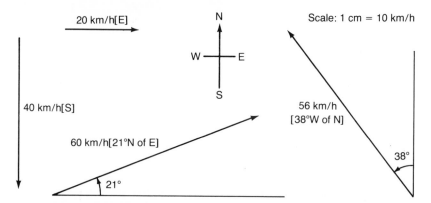

Velocity vectors are added together in exactly the same way as displacement vectors. As you will see, the vector diagrams that are produced are useful in a wide variety of boat, balloon, and airplane navigation problems.

3.4 Train Problems

A passenger walking inside a moving train has different velocities relative to the train and the ground. On a train moving at 20 km/h[N], all the seated passengers are at rest relative to the train, but are moving at 20 km/h[N] relative to the ground.

If a passenger on this train walks towards the front of the train at a normal pace, say 3 km/h, the passenger's velocity is 3 km/h[N] relative to the train and 23 km/h[N] relative to the ground. The passenger's velocity relative to the ground is found by adding the passenger's velocity relative to the train to the train's velocity relative to the ground.

$$\vec{v_1} = 20 \text{ km/h[N]} \qquad\qquad \vec{v_2} = 3 \text{ km/h[N]}$$

$$\vec{v_1} + \vec{v_2} = 23 \text{ km/h[N]} \qquad\qquad \text{Scale: 1 cm = 2 km/h}$$

When the vectors to be added are in the same direction, you can combine them by adding their magnitudes together.

$$\vec{v_1} + \vec{v_2} = 20 \text{ km/h[N]} + 3 \text{ km/h[N]}$$
$$= 23 \text{ km/h[N]}$$

If a passenger is walking towards the back of the train with a velocity of 3 km/h[S], the passenger's velocity relative to the ground is 17 km/h[N]. This velocity is found in the same way as in the previous example, by adding the passenger's velocity relative to the train to the train's velocity relative to the ground.

$$\vec{v_1} = 20 \text{ km/h[N]} \qquad\qquad \text{Scale: 1 cm = 2 km/h}$$

$$\vec{v_1} + \vec{v_2} = 17 \text{ km/h[N]} \qquad\qquad \vec{v_2} = 3 \text{ km/h[S]}$$

When vectors to be added are in opposite directions, you can combine them by adding their magnitudes together, provided that you change the form of one of them so that it has the opposite direction. When you change its sign as well as its direction, the vector still represents the original velocity.

$$\vec{v_1} + \vec{v_2} = 20 \text{ km/h[N]} + 3 \text{ km/h[S]}$$
$$= 20 \text{ km/h[N]} + (-3 \text{ km/h[N]})$$
$$= 17 \text{ km/h[N]}$$

Practice

1. A baseball pitcher is warming up on an airplane on the way to a game. The plane is flying at 400 km/h[W] and the pitcher can throw the ball at 150 km/h. What is the velocity of the ball relative to the ground, if the pitcher throws the ball
   (a) towards the front of the plane?   (550 km/h[W])
   (b) towards the rear of the plane?   (250 km/h[W])
2. A jet plane travelling horizontally at 1200 km/h[E] fires a rocket forwards at 1100 km/h relative to itself. What is the velocity of the rocket relative to the ground?   (2300 km/h[E])
3. A bowler is practising his game on a railway flatcar travelling at 50 km/h[N]. If the velocity of the ball is 60 km/h[S] relative to the flatcar, what is its velocity relative to the ground?
                                                          (10 km/h[S])

4. A boat is travelling upstream at 5 km/h relative to the shore. If there is a current in the river of 7 km/h, how fast is the boat moving relative to the water?   **(12 km/h)**

3.5 River-crossing Problems

A swimmer jumps into a river and swims for the opposite shore. In still water she can swim at 4 km/h[N]. There is a current in the river pushing her downstream at 3 km/h[E]. As a result, she does not actually go north, but moves at an angle to the bank of the river. The swimmer's velocity is found by adding her velocity relative to the water to the velocity of the water relative to the bank.

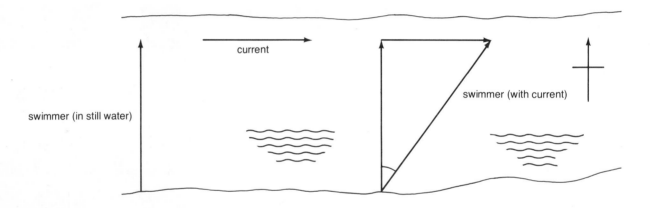

current

swimmer (in still water)

swimmer (with current)

To draw a proper vector diagram, first decide on a north point and a suitable scale. Then draw the vectors, connecting the tail of the second to the head of the first. The swimmer's velocity is represented by the vector drawn from the tail of the first vector to the head of the second.

N

W — E

S

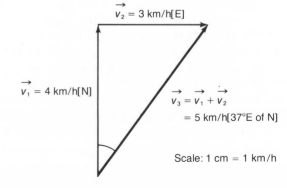

$\vec{v}_2 = 3$ km/h[E]

$\vec{v}_1 = 4$ km/h[N]

$\vec{v}_3 = \vec{v}_1 + \vec{v}_2$
$= 5$ km/h[37°E of N]

Scale: 1 cm = 1 km/h

Practice
1. A swimmer jumps into a river and swims straight for the other side at 3 km/h[N]. There is a current in the river of 4 km/h[W]. What is the swimmer's velocity?   (5 km/h[53° W of N])
2. A conductor in a train travelling at 12.0 km/h[N] walks across the aisle at 5.0 km/h[E] to punch a ticket. What is his velocity relative to the ground?   (13 km/h[23° E of N])
3. A small plane with a top speed of 100.0 km/h in still air is flown straight north. Unknown to the pilot, a 50.0 km/h wind is blowing to the west. What is the plane's velocity relative to the ground?   (112 km/h[27° W of N])

3.6 Airplane Navigation Problems

Flying objects are affected by the wind in the same way that floating or swimming objects are carried downstream by the current.

An airplane that can fly at 250 km/h in still air will only travel at 200 km/h if flying into a 50 km/h wind. Flying in the same direction as this wind will increase the plane's velocity by 50 km/h.

The plane's velocity relative to the ground is found by adding the plane's velocity relative to the air to the velocity of the air relative to the ground. Pilots have special names for each of these vectors, as shown in the table.

Symbol	Velocity vector	Speed	Direction
$\vec{v_a}$	plane's velocity relative to air	air speed	heading
$\vec{v_w}$	wind velocity (velocity of air relative to ground)	wind speed	wind direction
$\vec{v_g}$	plane's velocity relative to ground	ground speed	track

Air navigation problems are solved with vector diagrams in exactly the same way as river-crossing problems, though in this section the vectors will not always be at right angles to one another the way they were in the last section.

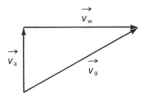

$$\vec{v_g} = \vec{v_a} + \vec{v_w}$$

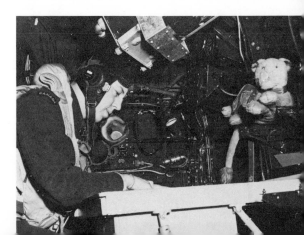

Scale: 1 cm = 20 km/h

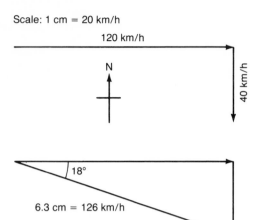

6.3 cm = 126 km/h

ground speed = 126 km/h

track = [18°S of E]

Sample problems

1. An airplane is heading east with an air speed of 120 km/h. A 40 km/h wind is blowing towards the south. Calculate the ground speed and the track for the plane's trip.
   (a) Draw the vectors to scale, connecting them head to tail to add them together (upper diagram at left).
   (b) The ground velocity vector is represented by a line connecting the tail of the first vector to the head of the second. Measure its length and its direction to get the ground speed and the track (lower diagram at left).

The wind is going to increase the plane's speed from 120 km/h to 126 km/h, but the plane is going to go [18° S of E] instead of east.

2. A pilot wants to fly west. The airplane has an air speed of 100 km/h. There is a 10 km/h wind blowing north. Calculate the pilot's proper heading and ground speed.
   (a) Draw the wind velocity vector, and, at its tail, a line to the west (in the direction the plane is supposed to go).

Scale: 1 cm = 10 km/h

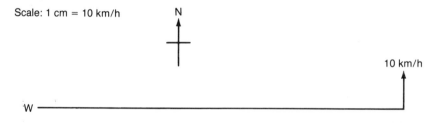

   (b) Using a ruler, fit a vector 10 cm long (100 km/h) from the head of the wind vector to the line going west. Now you can measure the heading and the ground speed.

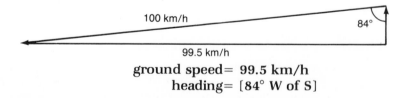

ground speed= 99.5 km/h
heading= [84° W of S]

Practice

1. A balloon pilot wants to travel north. The balloon can move at 26 km/h in still air. There is a wind of 10 km/h[E].
   (a) What is the heading? (That is, which way should the pilot point the balloon?)　　　　　　　　　　　　　　　([23° W of N])
   (b) How fast will the balloon travel relative to the ground?　　　　　　　　　　　　　　　(24 km/h)

2. An airplane pilot wants to fly east. The plane has an air speed of 500 km/h. A wind is blowing at 50.0 km/h[N]. Calculate:
   (**a**) the proper heading   ([6° S of E])
   (**b**) the ground speed (the speed relative to the ground)
                                           (**497 km/h**)

3.7 Velocity Changes and Acceleration Vectors

Acceleration was originally defined as the rate of change of speed. Gradually, physicists came to realize that the rate of change of velocity is even more important. An object's velocity always changes when either its speed or its direction changes. A car going around a corner at a constant speed undergoes a change in velocity and is accelerating.

We defined acceleration (in Chapter 2) as:

$$a = \frac{\Delta v}{\Delta t} \qquad \text{where} \quad \Delta v = v_2 - v_1$$

Now, using vectors, we must change this definition to:

$$\vec{a} = \frac{\Delta \vec{v}}{\Delta t} \qquad \text{where} \quad \Delta \vec{v} = \vec{v}_2 - \vec{v}_1$$

If there is a change in direction, a vector diagram is needed to calculate $\vec{a}$.

First, find $\Delta \vec{v}$.

$$\text{If} \quad \Delta \vec{v} = \vec{v}_2 - \vec{v}_1$$

$$\text{then} \quad \Delta \vec{v} = \vec{v}_2 + (-\vec{v}_1)$$

But what is the vector $(-\vec{v}_1)$?

It is simply $\vec{v}_1$ with its direction reversed.

If you know the time interval for the change in velocity, then:

$$\vec{a} = \frac{\Delta \vec{v}}{\Delta t}$$

Sample problem

What is the acceleration of a ball that is thrown up into the air at a velocity of 20 m/s[up] and comes back 4.0 s later, with a velocity of 20 m/s[down]?

$$\Delta \vec{v} = \vec{v}_2 - \vec{v}_1$$
$$= 20 \text{ m/s [down]} - 20 \text{ m/s [up]}$$
$$= 20 \text{ m/s [down]} - (-20 \text{ m/s [down]})$$
$$= 40 \text{ m/s [down]}$$

$$\vec{a} = \frac{\Delta \vec{v}}{\Delta t}$$
$$= \frac{40 \text{ m/s [down]}}{4.0 \text{ s}}$$
$$= 10 \text{ m/s}^2 \text{ [down]}$$

Practice

1. A train slows down from 50 m/s[E] to 34 m/s[E] in 4.0 s. What is its acceleration?   (4.0 m/s²[W])
2. A car changes velocity from 25 m/s[E] to 40 m/s[W] in 10 s. What is its acceleration?   (6.5 m/s²[W])
3. A ball is rolled up a ramp and has an initial velocity of 5.0 m/s[up]. 4.0 s later, it has a velocity down the ramp of 3.0 m/s[down].
   (a) What is its acceleration?   (2.0 m/s²[down])
   (b) At what moment during its trip was the ball stationary?   (2.5 s)

3.8 Acceleration at Constant Speed

One of the remarkable results of the study of vectors was that acceleration was found to be not the rate of change of speed with time but the rate of change of velocity with time. Acceleration is a vector. If your velocity changes, you are accelerating. Velocities have both magnitude and direction. Acceleration occurs during a change in direction and during a change of speed.

A car going around a corner at a constant speed is accelerating because its velocity is changing. When a car accelerates forwards, loose objects inside the car are thrown backwards and you feel yourself pressed into the seat. Similarly, when you go around a corner in a car, loose objects are thrown outwards and you feel yourself pushed outwards. The car is accelerating inwards, towards the centre of the corner.

The Jam-jar Accelerometer

How can a vehicle accelerate without changing speed? If an object is moving in a circle at a constant speed, how could it possibly be accelerating?

What we need is an independent witness, one who knows nothing about vector diagrams, or changes in direction, but can identify accelerations. You can make such a "witness" with a jar and a cork.

Get a jar with a tightly fitting screw-on lid and solder a small loop of copper wire to the centre of the inside of the lid. Tie one end of a short string to the loop and the other end to a cork. Fill the jar with water, screw on the lid, and turn the jar upside down.

This instrument is called an accelerometer. When the jar is stationary, the cork is straight up and down. Accelerate the jar horizontally. The cork always points in the direction of the acceleration. Try it a few more times to make sure.

Now for the acid test. Hold the jar at arm's length and turn it round and round at a steady speed. Which way should the cork point? What should happen if there is really no acceleration at all?

The inward acceleration of objects moving at constant speed in a circle is called **centripetal acceleration.**

Incidentally, the angle of the cork from the vertical is a measure of the amount of acceleration. With the proper equation, you could use the jar to measure the accelerations of carts, trains, or cars.

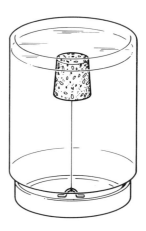

A jam-jar accelerometer

Which way is this cart accelerating?

3.9 Summary

1. Scalars are quantities that have magnitude only.
2. Vectors are quantities that have both magnitude and direction.
3. A displacement vector includes a direction as well as a distance.
4. A velocity vector includes a direction as well as a speed.
5. An acceleration vector includes a direction as well as an acceleration.
6. Vectors are represented by arrows. The length of the arrow is proportional to the magnitude of the vector.
7. Vectors are added by joining them head to tail. The total is represented by a line drawn from the tail of the first to the head of the second.
8. In navigation problems, the net velocity of an object is its own velocity and the velocity of the wind or the current, added together as vectors.
9. A change in direction produces both a change in velocity and an acceleration.
10.
$$\vec{\Delta v} = \vec{v_2} - \vec{v_1}$$
11. Acceleration is the rate of change of velocity.
$$\vec{a} = \frac{\vec{\Delta v}}{\Delta t}$$
12. An object moving at a constant speed in a circle has an acceleration towards the centre of the circle. This is called a centripetal acceleration.

3.10 Review

1. A plane flying a triangular pattern flies first 150 km[N], then 400 km[E].
   (a) What is its total displacement after these two legs?
   (b) What third displacement would complete the trip back to the starting point?
2. A boat sails 120 km[60° N of E], then 60 km[W]. What is its displacement?
3. A balloon drifts 20 km[60° E of S], then its engines are turned on and it flies 20 km[60° W of S]. What is its total displacement?
4. A man inside a plane flying at 400 km/h[W] fires a gun eastwards. The muzzle velocity of the gun is 450 km/h. What is the velocity of the bullet relative to the ground?

5. A street car accelerates from rest at 2.5 m/s²[W]. A woman inside the street car is walking at 5.0 m/s[E] relative to the street car. What is her velocity relative to the ground at:
(a) 0 s? (b) 1 s? (c) 2 s? (d) 3 s? (e) 4 s?

6. A man is walking inside a railway boxcar at 3 m/s[N] relative to the boxcar. The boxcar is rolling along a ferryboat at 5 m/s[S] relative to the ferryboat. The ferryboat is heading north at 4 m/s. What is the velocity of the man relative to
(a) the ferryboat? (b) the ground?

7. A boy and a girl both swim at 3.0 m/s. They jump into a river 1.0 km across, with a current of 2.0 m/s[E].
(a) The boy faces due north at all times. What is his velocity relative to the ground?
(b) The girl swims straight across. What is her velocity relative to the ground?
(c) How long (in minutes) does each take to cross the river?

8. A motorboat is headed [30° N of E] with its engine set to move the boat at 30 km/h in still water. There is a current of 15 km/h[S]. What is the velocity of the boat?

9. A boy in a car moving at 10 km/h[N] wants to throw a ball to a girl standing on the right-hand side of the road. He is able to throw the ball at 20 km/h. He wants the ball to go straight east, directly to her.
(a) Which way should he throw the ball in order to do this?
(b) How fast will the ball travel to reach her?

10. A pilot wants to fly north. The plane has an air speed of 350 km/h. There is a 25 km/h wind blowing to the west.
(a) What is the plane's ground speed?
(b) What is its heading?

11. A small plane is flying east at 100 km/h, in a wind blowing at 20 km/h[S].
(a) What is the plane's ground speed?
(b) What is its heading?

12. A pilot flies 300 km[E] and then back home 300 km[W] at an air speed of 300 km/h. A 30 km/h wind is blowing to the east.
(a) What is the pilot's ground speed for each leg of the trip?
(b) What is the time for each leg of the trip, in minutes?
(c) How long would the trip take if there were no wind, in minutes?

13. A ball rolls up a hill, starting at 10 m/s[up] and accelerating at −3 m/s²[up]. What is its velocity after
(a) 1 s? (b) 3 s? (c) 4 s?

14. A ship travels at 30 km/h[30° E of N] for 10 h, then at 20 km/h[60° S of W] for 17 h. What is its total displacement?

58 Fundamentals of Physics

15. A man is standing on the deck of a freighter heading north at 10 km/h. He measures the wind velocity and gets a reading of 10 km/h[E]. What is the actual wind velocity?

16. A pilot wants to fly a huge square path, 100 km[N], 100 km[W], 100 km[S], and then 100 km[E]. His plane has an air speed of 100 km/h. A 50 km/h wind is blowing to the south. For each leg of the trip, calculate
(a) the ground speed
(b) the heading
(c) the time, in minutes
Finally,
(d) What would be the saving in time if there were no wind?

17. A wheel with a radius of 50 cm is rolling along the ground at 10 m/s[E]. That is, the centre point of the wheel is moving at 10 m/s[E].
(a) What are the velocities of the top, bottom, front, and back points of the wheel, relative to the centre of the wheel?
(b) What are the velocities of those four points relative to the ground?

3.11 Learning Objectives

1. To draw displacement vectors and velocity vectors to scale, given their magnitude and direction.
2. To add displacement vectors, by means of a vector diagram, in order to find the total displacement.
3. To add velocity vectors, by means of a vector diagram, to solve river-crossing and navigation problems.
4. To calculate both the change in velocity and the acceleration of an object moving back and forth along a straight line.

4 The Acceleration of Gravity

4.1 Gravity

Sir Isaac Newton (1642-1727)

Isaac Newton, so the story goes, discovered gravity one afternoon while sitting under an apple tree. An apple fell and struck him on the head. All at once he realized that the Earth was pulling down on the apple, and that that was why it fell. Before Newton made his discovery, falling was considered just another "natural" motion that needed no explanation. Apples fell, smoke rose, and the moon circled the Earth, because of their natures.

Newton suggested that the Earth, because of its great mass, exerted a strong inward pull on all nearby objects, such as apples and moons. This inward force he called the **force of gravity.**

Aristotle wrote, about 350 B.C., that the speed of a falling body is proportional to its mass. In other words, a 2 kg rock should fall twice as fast as a 1 kg rock. This was generally believed for nearly 2000 years, until Galileo, in 1590, suggested a simple experiment which you can try. Drop two objects of equal mass and similar shape side by side. They will fall at the same rate. Now, tie the two objects together with a short length of string. This gives you a single object with twice the mass of either of the original objects, and it will fall at the same rate as either of the original objects. This is how Galileo concluded that all freely falling objects fall at the same rate.

You can test Galileo's theory of gravity by doing the following investigation.

Aristotle (384-322 B.C.)

Investigation: Gravity

Problem:
What factors influence the motion of falling objects?

Materials:
this book
a large rubber stopper
a piece of paper slightly smaller than the cover of the book

Galileo Galilei (1564-1642)

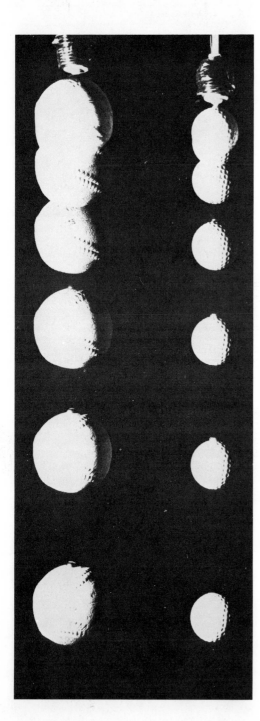

Procedure

1. The mass of this book is many times the mass of the rubber stopper. Hold the book horizontally at exactly the same height as the stopper and release them both simultaneously. Drop the book carefully so that it lands flat on its cover, and not on a corner. Note whether there is any great difference between the times the book and the stopper take to fall. Repeat several times to make sure of your observations.
2. Drop the book and the piece of paper, both held horizontally, from the same height. Then shield the piece of paper from the air by placing it on top of the book, hold the book and paper horizontally, and drop them again. Compare the rates at which they fall each time.
3. Crumple the paper into a tiny ball and drop it side by side with the book. Note what happens.

Questions

1. Why does the ball of paper keep up with the book, whereas the sheet of paper doesn't?
2. What is the rule for falling objects, when there is little or no air resistance?
3. According to your results, if you held the moon and an apple side by side and dropped them, which would hit the Earth first? Explain.

4.2 Gravity and Free Fall

From the last investigation, it is apparent that the motion of a freely falling object is an acceleration. But is the acceleration constant, or is it increasing or even decreasing? And how can you measure it?

In earlier investigations, you measured the motions of various moving objects by fastening a paper tape to them. However, if you do this with a rock, the rock is no longer a freely falling object. The tape will slow it down a little.

In this investigation, we will photograph the motion of a falling ball-bearing with a strobe light that flashes at regular intervals. We must use a black background, and hold the camera shutter open for the entire fall. Each time the strobe flashes, an image of the ball-bearing will form on the film.

Once the print has been developed, the distances between the images can be measured. These distances are very small and will have to be measured with the help of a magnifying glass. Your school will have magnifiers with tiny scales built into them for measuring tenths of a millimetre. An alternative, if you have the proper equipment, is to make an enlarged print of the film to make the measuring easier.

Another problem is that the distances on the film are not full size. So that you can determine the scale, include a metre stick in the photograph, in the same plane as the falling object.

On the print, measure the length of the metre stick in millimetres. Suppose it is 40 mm long. Then every measurement made on the print in millimetres should be multiplied by $\dfrac{1000 \text{ mm}}{40 \text{ mm}}$, or 25, to convert it into its actual length in millimetres.

Investigation: Acceleration Due to Gravity

Problem:
What is the acceleration of a freely falling object?

Materials:
13 mm ball-bearing
strobe light
Polaroid camera and tripod
metre stick
magnifier with scale (0.1 mm graduations)

Procedure
1. Set up the camera and the strobe light. Focus the camera and set the exposure controls. Set the strobe flash at some convenient frequency.
2. Turn out the lights, open the shutter, drop the ball, watch it fall to the floor, and close the shutter. Develop the picture.
3. The picture should reveal a number of dots, just as the ticker tape did. Use the magnifier to measure the distance between dots, and then draw a speed-time graph.

Questions
1. What does the shape of the graph tell you about acceleration due to gravity?
2. Use the slope of the graph to calculate the acceleration in m/s^2.
3. The acceleration due to gravity is important enough to have its own symbol, g. The correct value of g is about 9.8 m/s^2. What is the percentage error of your measurement?
4. Could you use a styrofoam ball in this investigation? Explain your answer.

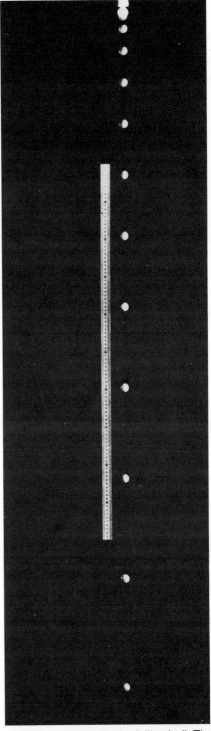

A strobe photograph of a falling ball. The time between flashes is 0.05 s. A metre stick is included, to show the scale of the photograph.

Other Ways to Measure g

If you have no Polaroid camera or strobe light, you can measure g in various other ways—even with a recording timer. Stand the timer on edge, so that the tape runs through it vertically. Attach the tape to a heavy object, and let the object fall. Make sure that the tape runs through the timer smoothly, so as to reduce the timer's effect on the motion.

Some schools have a special apparatus consisting of an electric stopclock, a magnetic target switch, and an electromagnet that holds a ball-bearing directly above the switch. When the current to the electromagnet is shut off, the ball falls and the clock starts. When the ball hits the switch, the clock stops. This gives you the time an object takes to fall a certain distance. By changing the distance, you can collect enough information for a speed-time graph, or you may calculate the acceleration directly, using the equation:

$$d = \tfrac{1}{2}\, at^2$$

Or you could use the strobe photograph reproduced on page 61. Its caption gives the time between flashes and the scale of the photograph. An analysis of the distance between its dots will give you a good value for g, the acceleration of a freely falling object.

4.3 Gravimetry

The study of acceleration due to gravity, and the measurement of this acceleration, are a major part of the science of gravimetry. The most accurate measurements are made at the International Bureau of Weights and Measures (BIPM), which is in France. Three methods have been used.

Starting in 1888, g was calculated at BIPM from measurements of the periods of pendulums. The relationship between the period of a simple pendulum and g is given in one of the investigations that follow. The best value for g that has been obtained at BIPM by this method is 9.809 398 m/s². This method is no longer used, chiefly because of the difficulty in allowing for changes in the length of a pendulum as it swings back and forth; even a steel pendulum will stretch a little.

The second method, brought into use in 1951, involves photographing a falling metre stick. The metre stick is made of platinum and iridium and is graduated in millimetres. It falls inside a cylindrical vacuum chamber. The scale on the stick is illuminated by a quartz-controlled spark gap, which gives out light flashes at regular intervals. A camera records about 50 images per fall, and these are then analysed to provide the value of g. The temperature of the chamber is measured, so that any expansion or contraction of the scale may be allowed for. The value of g, at BIPM with this apparatus, is 9.809 280 m/s^2.

The third method, in use since 1960, involves an object launched upwards by means of an elastic band and allowed to fall back again. The time for the trip up should be the same as the time for the trip back down. Once again, the whole apparatus is enclosed in a vacuum chamber to eliminate air resistance. The projectile has an arrangement of three mirrors at each end. Laser light is reflected from the object constantly as it moves. The distance the object falls may then be measured in terms of the wavelength of the light, to an accuracy of about 10^{-9} m. To ensure accuracy, steps have to be taken to cushion the instrument from ground vibration and from the shock of launching.

The results obtained since 1966 show an average value for g of 9.809 260 m/s^2, slightly less than the value obtained by the earlier methods. One outcome of the new, more accurate, measurements is the discovery of variations in g of about 0.000 000 4 m/s^2. The origin of these variations is not known.

Galileo and his inclined plane (see page 64)

4.4 Diluting Gravity

Galileo made many measurements with balls rolling down ramps. His only clocks were water clocks, special containers filled with water. A small hole in the bottom let the water drip out slowly. The volume of water collected in a certain time was a rough measure of the time that had elapsed. Such clocks are not accurate enough to be used to measure the accelerations of freely falling objects, but can be used for slower motions, such as that of a ball rolling down a ramp.

Galileo realized that the pull of gravity is "diluted" when a ball is rolled down a ramp, rather than dropped in free fall. The ball still accelerates steadily, but not as rapidly as in free fall. The degree of "dilution" depends on the steepness of the ramp: the greater the slope, the greater the acceleration. The equation is:

$$a = g\left(\frac{h}{d}\right)$$

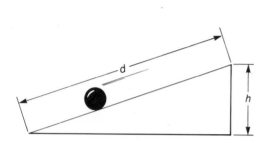

(See photograph on page 63)

Although $\vec{a}$ and $\vec{g}$ are both vectors, they do not act in the same direction, as this equation might imply. The equation only gives the magnitude of the acceleration down the ramp.

where g is the acceleration due to gravity
       a is the acceleration rate down ramp
       h is the vertical height of ramp
       d is the length of ramp

If you measure the time a toy car takes to roll down a ramp, you can calculate its acceleration by using the equation:

$$d = \frac{1}{2}at^2$$

In the next investigation, we will use these two equations to calculate g.

Investigation: Diluting Gravity

Problem:
How is g determined by rolling a toy car down a ramp?

Materials:
2 m wooden track
toy car
stopwatch
supports for track

Procedure
1. Make a long ramp, by supporting the track with books or

bricks. Record the length of the ramp and its height.
2. Release the car at the top of the ramp, and record the time it takes the car to reach the bottom. Repeat twice more.
3. Repeat the procedure for two other ramp heights. You should now have three times for each of three different heights.
4. Calculate the average time for each height.
5. Calculate the acceleration for each height, using:

$$a = \frac{2d}{t^2}$$

6. Calculate d/h for each height.
7. Calculate g for each height, using:

$$g = a\left(\frac{d}{h}\right)$$

8. Calculate the average of the three values of g.
9. Calculate the percentage error of g. (Its true value is 9.8 m/s².)
10. Record all your measurements and calculations in a data table:

t (s)	$t$average (s)	d (cm)	h (cm)	$\dfrac{d}{h}$	a (m/s²)	g (m/s²)	$g$average (m/s²)
1.5 1.4 1.3	1.4	200	35				

Sample problem

A toy car is rolled down a ramp 200 cm long and 40 cm high. What is its acceleration?

$$a = g\left(\frac{h}{d}\right)$$
$$= (9.8 \text{ m/s}^2)\left(\frac{40 \text{ cm}}{200 \text{ cm}}\right)$$
$$= (9.8 \text{ m/s}^2)(0.20)$$
$$= 2.0 \text{ m/s}^2$$

Practice
1. A car rolls down a sloping driveway 20 m long and raised 0.20 m at one end. What is the car's acceleration? (0.098 m/s²)
2. A skier slides down an icy hill 500 m long and 200 m high. At what rate does the skier accelerate?   (3.9 m/s²)
3. A piece of drapery track 3.5 m long is used as a ramp for ball-bearings. If we want the ball-bearings to accelerate at 1.4 m/s², how high should we raise one end of the track?   (0.50 m)

4.5 Gravity and the Pendulum

Make a simple pendulum by attaching a small, heavy mass such as a few large washers to the end of a long piece of string. Fasten the other end of the string to something sturdy, and start the pendulum swinging.

The period of the pendulum is the time required for one complete cycle; the pendulum must go all the way across from one side of its swing to the other and all the way back again.

The amplitude of the pendulum is the maximum sideways displacement of the bob from its rest position.

The mass hanging at the end of the string is called the bob.

The period of the pendulum depends only on its length, and on g. It does not matter what the mass of the bob is, as long as it is not too small, or what the amplitude is, as long as it is not too large. As long as the bob is compact and dense, air resistance will not affect the pendulum significantly.

The equation for calculating the period of a pendulum is:

$$T = 2\pi\sqrt{\frac{l}{g}}$$

where T is the period of the pendulum

       l is the length of the pendulum, measured from the top end of the string down to the centre of the bob

       g is the acceleration due to gravity

       $\pi = 3.14$

Note: if $T = 2\pi\sqrt{\dfrac{l}{g}}$ (first square both sides)

      then $T^2 = 4\pi^2\dfrac{l}{g}$ (now muliply both sides by g)

      and $gT^2 = 4\pi^2 l$ (now divide both sides by T^2)

      so that $g = \dfrac{4\pi^2 l}{T^2}$

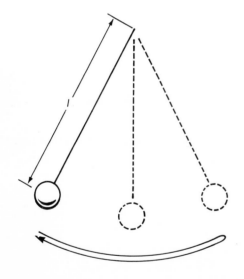

Investigation: Gravity and the Pendulum

Problem:

What is the value of g as calculated from the period of a pendulum?

Materials:
1.5 m string
6 large washers
stopwatch
metre stick

Procedure
1. Make a pendulum about 1.5 m long, and measure its length carefully in metres. Measure from the top end of the pendulum to the centre of the bob.
2. Start the pendulum swinging and measure the time for 20 complete swings.
3. Calculate the time for one swing.
4. Calculate g, using:

$$g = \frac{4\pi^2 l}{T^2}$$

5. Repeat, using two other lengths, say 1.0 m and 0.5 m.
6. Calculate your average value of g.
7. Calculate your percentage error for g.
8. If you have time, see whether the period is affected by the use of nine or 12 washers for the bob, instead of six.
9. Of all the methods you have used to find g, which is the most accurate?

Sample problem

What is the period of a pendulum 1.0 m long?

$$T = 2\pi\sqrt{\frac{l}{g}}$$
$$= 2\pi\sqrt{\frac{1.0 \text{ m}}{9.8 \text{ m/s}^2}}$$
$$= 2\pi\sqrt{0.102 \text{ s}^2}$$
$$= 2(3.14)\,(0.319 \text{ s})$$
$$= 2.0 \text{ s}$$

A pendulum 1.0 m long is used in some grandfather clocks. Each time it swings across, it counts off one second. A clockwork motor gives the pendulum a small push at the right moment during each swing, to keep it going.

Practice

1. What is the period of a pendulum
   (**a**) 4 m long? (**b**) 9 m long? (**c**) 16 m long?   (**4 s, 6 s, 8 s**)
2. What is the period of a pendulum 1 m long on the moon, where
   g is one-sixth of that on Earth?   (**4.9 s**)
3. How long must a pendulum be to have a period of
   1.0 s?   (**0.25 m**)
4. What is the acceleration due to gravity on the planet Needleep if
   a 2.5 m pendulum on that planet has a period of 5.0 s?

(**4.0 m/s^2**)

4.6 Projectiles

What happens when a ball is thrown up into the air – straight up or
at an angle? How high will a batted ball go? How far will it go, and
how long will it stay in the air?

What happens when a cannon is fired or when you shoot an
arrow? At what angle should the shot be thrown in the shot-put to
make it go the greatest distance? Is the same angle also the best one
in javelin throwing or discus throwing?

A simple example of a projectile is an object that is fired horizontally and then falls freely. To see what happens in such a case, get
two pennies and balance one of them on the edge of a desk. Place
the other nearby, and then flick it with your finger, so that it shoots
off the table, just grazing the first one on the way past. The idea is to
get one penny simply to fall off the table while the other is shot off
horizontally. Listen for two sounds as the pennies hit the floor. You
will hear only one.

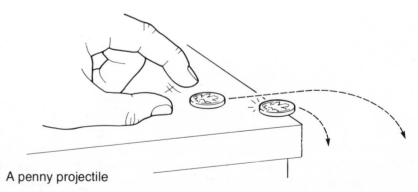

A penny projectile

The surprising thing is that the pennies hit the ground at the
same time. Both have the same vertical acceleration, g.

Examine the photograph carefully. A grid of squares has been superimposed. Notice that the two objects fall the same vertical distance in the same time. Notice also that the projected object travels the same horizontal distance in each second. It is travelling at a constant speed horizontally – the speed at which it was projected.

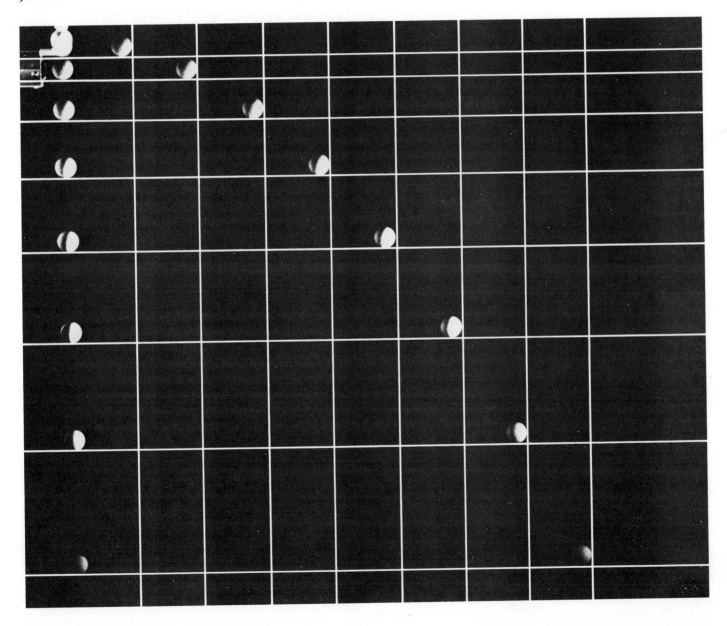

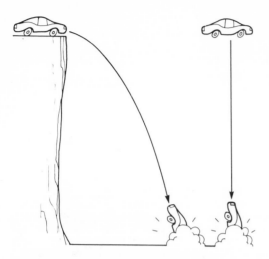

A car projected horizontally and a car
dropped vertically fall the same distance
vertically in the same time.

Sample problems

1. A car travelling at 72 km/h drives off a cliff 400 m high.
   (a) How long does it take to hit the ground?
   (b) How far from the base of the cliff does it hit the ground?
   (c) How fast is it going when it hits the ground?

   (a) We must calculate how long a freely falling object takes to
   fall straight down 400 m.

   $$d = \tfrac{1}{2} at^2$$
   $$t^2 = \frac{2d}{a}$$
   $$t = \sqrt{\frac{2d}{a}}$$
   $$= \sqrt{\frac{2(400 \text{ m})}{9.8 \text{ m/s}^2}}$$
   $$= \sqrt{81.63 \text{ s}^2}$$
   $$= 9.0 \text{ s}$$

   Therefore, it takes the car 9.0 s to hit the ground.
   (b) While the car is falling, it is travelling horizontally at 72 km/h.

   $$v = 72 \text{ km/h}$$
   $$= 72\ 000 \text{ m/h}$$
   $$= \frac{72\ 000}{3600} \text{ m/s}$$
   $$= 20 \text{ m/s}$$
   $$\Delta d = v\,\Delta t$$
   $$= (20 \text{ m/s})\,(9.0 \text{ s})$$
   $$= 180 \text{ m}$$

   (c) After falling vertically for 9.0 s, a freely falling object is
   going:

   $$v = a\,\Delta t$$
   $$= (9.8 \text{ m/s}^2)\,(9.0 \text{ s})$$
   $$= 88 \text{ m/s[down]}$$

   At the same time, it is going 20 m/s [horizontally].
   These two velocities must be added as vectors.
   The final speed will be 90 m/s.

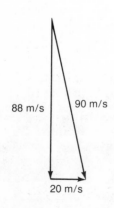

88 m/s   90 m/s

20 m/s

2. A baseball was hit out into centre field. It was in the air for 4.0 s.
   What was its maximum height?

   The ball went up for 2.0 s and then down for 2.0 s. While falling,
   it accelerated downwards at 9.8 m/s². How far did it fall?

$$d = \frac{1}{2}at^2$$
$$= \frac{1}{2}(9.8 \text{ m/s}^2)(2.0 \text{ s})^2$$
$$= 20 \text{ m}$$

Therefore, the ball rose 20 m into the air, and then fell 20 m back to the ground.

Practice

1. A ball is thrown horizontally at 10.0 m/s. It is in the air for 5.00 s.
   (a) How far does it fall vertically? (122 m)
   (b) How far does it travel horizontally? (50.0 m)
   (c) How fast is it moving vertically when it hits the ground? (49.0 m/s)
   (d) What is its speed when it hits the ground? (50.0 m/s)
2. A bullet is fired horizontally at 300 m/s from a height of 2.00 m. How far does it go before it hits the ground? (192 m)
3. An arrow is shot straight up into the air at 30 m/s. How long will it take to come back down? (6.1 s)

4.7 Summary

1. All freely falling objects accelerate downwards at the same rate.
2. Acceleration due to gravity is approximately constant near the Earth's surface, with a value of:
$$g = 9.8 \text{ m/s}^2$$
3. The distance an object falls from rest may be calculated by:
$$d = \frac{1}{2}gt^2$$
4. The speed of an object falling from rest, after t seconds, is:
$$v = gt$$
5. The acceleration of an object moving down a smooth ramp is:
$$a = g\left(\frac{h}{d}\right) \qquad \text{where } h \text{ is the height of the ramp}$$
$$d \text{ is the length of the ramp}$$
6. The period of a pendulum is given by:
$$T = 2\pi\sqrt{\frac{l}{g}}$$

7. If the air resistance is negligible, an object projected horizontally and an object dropped from rest will fall the same vertical distance in the same time.
8. If the air resistance is negligible, projectiles all accelerate downwards at the same rate, the acceleration due to gravity, and move horizontally at a constant speed.

4.8 Review

Note: $g = 9.8 \text{ m/s}^2$

1. What is the speed of a freely falling object after each of these times?
   (a) 2.0 s (b) 4.0 s (c) 6.0 s (d) 15 s

2. How long does it take a freely falling object to reach each of these speeds?
   (a) 24.5 m/s (b) 88.2 m/s (c) 63.7 m/s (d) 100 km/h

3. How far does a freely falling object fall in each of these times?
   (a) 1.0 s (b) 2.0 s (c) 3.0 s (d) 5.83 s

4. Which would reach the ground first, if dropped from the same height at the same time: a quarter or a feather? Explain, if you are on
   (a) the Earth. (b) the moon.

5. The CN tower in Toronto is 533.33 m high.
   (a) How long would it take a rock dropped from the top to reach the ground?
   (b) How fast would the rock be moving as it hit the ground (in m/s and km/h)?
   (c) Would the rock actually reach the speed calculated in (b)? Discuss.

6. How much farther does a freely falling object fall in 10 s than in 1 s? (Divide one distance by the other to get a ratio.)

7. How long does it take a freely falling object to fall each of these distances?
   (a) 1.0 m (b) 3.0 m (c) 9.0 m (d) 75 m

8. A ramp 5.00 m long is used to accelerate rolling objects. Calculate the acceleration produced by rolling an object from each of the following ramp heights.
   (a) 50 cm (b) 25 cm (c) 12.5 cm (d) 2.5 m

9. What ramp height would be needed for a ramp 3.00 m long to produce each of the following accelerations?
   (a) 1.0 m/s² (b) 4.9 m/s² (c) 0.01 m/s² (d) 9.0 m/s²

10. Calculate the period of a simple pendulum with each of the following lengths.
    (a) 1.5 m (b) 15 m (c) 150 m

11. What pendulum lengths would give the following periods?
    (a) 4.0 s (b) 9.5 s (c) 22.8 s

12. Calculate the length of the pendulum needed for a grandfather clock (period = 2.0 s) on the moon, where g is one-sixth of that on the Earth.

13. A ball-bearing is shot horizontally at 30 m/s and falls for 5.0 s.

(a) How far does it fall vertically?
(b) How far does it travel horizontally?
(c) How far is it from its starting point after 5.0 s?
14. A car goes off a cliff horizontally at 49 m/s and falls for 5.0 s.
(a) What is the vertical speed of the car after 5.0 s?
(b) What is the horizontal speed of the car after 5.0 s?
(c) What is the actual speed of the car after 5.0 s?

4.9 Learning Objectives

1. Given a strobe photograph or a ticker tape of a freely falling object, to draw a speed-time graph and find the acceleration due to gravity.
2. Given any two of the time to fall, the acceleration, the distance of the fall, and the speed of fall (starting from rest), to calculate the others.
3. Given any three of the acceleration due to gravity, the height of a ramp, the length of the ramp, and the acceleration down the ramp, to calculate the other quantity.
4. Given any two of the length of a pendulum, its period, and the acceleration due to gravity, to calculate the third.
5. Given the initial horizontal speed of a projectile, to calculate the vertical distance fallen and the speed attained, the horizontal distance travelled and the speed attained, and the net velocity of the projectile at any time.
6. To list and explain at least three different ways of finding the acceleration due to gravity.

Numerical Answers to Review Problems
1. (a) 20 m/s
   (b) 39 m/s
   (c) 59 m/s
   (d) 1.5×10^2 m/s
2. (a) 2.5 s
   (b) 9.0 s
   (c) 6.5 s
   (d) 2.8 s
3. (a) 4.9 m
   (b) 20 m
   (c) 44 m
   (d) 1.7×10^2 m
5. (a) 10 s
   (b) 1.0×10^2 m/s, 3.7×10^2 km/h
6. 100
7. (a) 0.45 s
   (b) 0.78 s
   (c) 1.4 s
   (d) 3.9 s
8. (a) 0.98 m/s^2
   (b) 0.49 m/s^2
   (c) 0.25 m/s^2
   (d) 4.9 m/s^2
9. (a) 0.31 m
   (b) 1.5 m
   (c) 0.31 cm
   (d) 2.8 m
10. (a) 2.5 s
    (b) 7.8 s
    (c) 25 s
11. (a) 4.0 m
    (b) 22 m
    (c) 1.3×10^2 m
12. 0.17 m
13. (a) 1.2×10^2 m
    (b) 1.5×10^2 m
    (c) 1.9×10^2 m
14. (a) 49 m/s
    (b) 49 m/s
    (c) 69 m/s

5 Forces

5.1 Force

The simple definition of a **force** is a push or a pull. Forces make things happen. They speed things up, slow them down, push them around corners and up hills. Forces can distort matter by compressing, stretching, or twisting. Forces are the agents that objects use to interact with one another.

Kinds of Force

Though there seem to be a great many different kinds of forces, physicists believe that there are at most four basic forces: the force of gravity, the electric force, the strong nuclear force, and the weak nuclear force.

The force of gravity is important for large objects like stars, planets, and moons. It holds them together and controls their motions in the same way that it controls the motion of falling objects.

The electric force is the force between electric charges. It is the force that holds atoms and molecules together, making diamonds hard and rubber weak. It tenses muscles, explodes sticks of dynamite, and supports floating ships. Even the force of magnetism is electric—produced by electric charge in motion. Indeed, most common forces are electric.

The strong and weak nuclear forces act between the particles that make up atoms. The nucleus of an atom is composed of positively charged particles, called protons, and neutral particles, called neutrons. Though the force of repulsion between protons that are so close together is considerable, they are held together by the strong nuclear force, a much stronger but short-range force that acts only when the particles are close together.

There are many more "elementary" particles besides the proton, the neutron, and the electron. Many of them, including the neutron, are unstable and break up. The force responsible for this is the weak nuclear force.

Physicists are now working on "unified field theories", which, they hope, will replace the four forces with a single force. Scientists have always believed that the universe is simple rather than complicated. They try to reduce the number of laws required to explain what happens in the universe to a minimum. More often than not, this has led them closer to the truth.

Measuring Force

In the International System of Units, the unit of force is the **newton** (N), named after Isaac Newton, the famous English physicist. Forces are often measured by means of a spring balance calibrated in newtons. To see how much force is needed to make a newton, obtain a spring balance and pull on it until it reads 1 N. Use the spring balance to find the force of gravity pulling on a 100 g mass. If your school has a newton bathroom scale, stand on it to find the force of gravity pulling down on you in newtons.

5.2 The Force of Gravity

The Earth is surrounded by a gravitational force field. This means that every small mass will feel a force pulling it towards the Earth, no matter where it is in the space on or above the Earth's surface. The **gravitational field strength** is the amount of force acting on an object per kilogram of mass, and is measured in newtons per kilogram. The gravitational field strength is not the same everywhere. It depends on how close the object is to the centre of the Earth; it is greater in valleys and less on mountaintops. In the next investigation, you will measure the gravitational field strength at your position on the Earth's surface.

Investigation: Mass and the Force of Gravity

Problem:
How does the force of gravity on an object depend on its mass?

Materials:
spring balance calibrated in newtons (0 N to 5 N)
five 100 g masses

Procedure
1. Make sure the spring balance reads zero with no mass attached. If it does not, ask your teacher to fix it, or make a note of the reading so that you can correct the readings you make in the investigation.

Just after Isaac Newton graduated from Cambridge University, in 1665, England was struck by the plague. Tens of thousands died. All the schools were closed down, and the pupils were sent home. For the next two years, with sickness and death all around, Newton worked quietly at home, developing many of the fundamental laws of physics and several important mathematical theorems.

In 1669, the professor of mathematics at Cambridge gave up his position to Newton, to enable him to devote more time to his theories. Newton never married, cared little about clothes or food, and was known to laugh only once—at a friend who complained he did not see the value of geometry.

The gravitational field surrounding the Earth

2. Hang various combinations of 100 g masses (from one to five) on the spring balance, and measure the force of gravity each time. Jiggle the balance before each reading to make sure it doesn't stick. Record your observations in a data table drawn up in your notebook.

3. Plot a graph of force against mass, with mass plotted horizontally. This graph should be a straight line. Use a ruler to draw the best straight line possible, as close to, or through, as many points as possible. Don't forget to plot the point (0,0) as part of your graph.

Questions

1. Determine the slope of your graph. This is the value of the gravitational field strength. What are the units of this slope? You have seen this value before in connection with gravity, but with different units. What were those units?

2. Make up an equation for calculating F, the force of gravity, when you are given m, the mass of the object, and g, the gravitational field strength.

3. If you did this investigation on top of Mount Everest, would the line be straight? Would it have the same slope? Explain your answers.

Gravitational Field Strength

The gravitational field strength is the gravitational force acting on a 1 kg mass. Its value is represented by the symbol g. As you have just seen, the force of gravity varies directly with the mass of the object. If the mass is doubled, the force also doubles. The graph of force versus mass should be a straight line through the origin. The equation of this straight line should be:

$$F = mg$$

where F is the force of gravity on an object, in newtons

m is the mass of the object, in kilograms

g is the gravitational field strength, in newtons per kilogram

You have measured g, the slope of the graph, and found it to be approximately 9.8 N/kg. It is this value of g that you should use in problems, unless otherwise instructed.

Sample problem

What is the force of gravity on a 1250 kg automobile?

$$F = mg$$
$$= (1250 \text{ kg}) (9.8 \text{ N/kg})$$
$$= 1.2 \times 10^4 \text{ N}$$

Practice
1. What is the force of gravity on a 4.5 kg block of concrete? (44 N)
2. What is the mass of an object that is pulled down by a force of gravity of 167 N at the Earth's surface?   (17 kg)
3. The force of gravity on a 250 kg spacecraft on the moon is 408 N. What is the gravitational field strength there? (1.63 N/kg)

Mass and Weight

Weight is a commonly used term that is often confused with **mass**. Weight and mass are quite different things.

"Mass" is used to describe the amount of matter in an object. It is measured in kilograms. As long as the amount of matter in an object remains the same, its mass stays the same. The label on a kilogram of hamburger should say "mass: 1 kg".

"Weight" is used to describe the force of gravity on an object. Since gravity is a force, weight is measured in newtons, not in kilograms. Since the force of gravity can vary, the weight of an object will also vary, depending on its location. On the Earth's surface an object's weight does not vary much, but astronauts on a trip to the moon find their weight slowly decreasing towards zero.

Astronaut's location	Astronaut's mass	Astronaut's weight
On the surface of the Earth	60 kg	590 N
150 km above the Earth	60 kg	560 N
9/10 of the way to the moon	60 kg	0 N
On the surface of the moon	60 kg	98 N

Note that the point about 9/10 of the way to the moon is special. There, the pull of the earth is balanced by the pull of the moon to give a net weight of zero.

5.3 Variations in Gravitational Field Strength

The Earth is not a sphere. Because it rotates on an axis through its north and south poles, it bulges out slightly at the equator. A boat floating at the north pole is about 21 km closer to the centre of the Earth than a boat floating in the ocean at the equator. The gravitational field strength at the north pole is greater, though not by much, than the gravitational field strength at the equator, as shown in the table.

Newton was the first to explain how the rotation of the Earth produces a bulging out at the equator. You feel the same effect on a merry-go-round moving quickly; you feel yourself being pulled steadily outwards. The Earth seems solid enough, but even it slowly gave way to the immense forces involved. The effect is greater at the equator because the speed of the turning Earth is greatest there.

Latitude (°)	g^* (N/kg)	Distance to centre (km)*
0 (equator)	9.7805	6378
15	9.7839	6377
30	9.7934	6373
45	9.8063	6367
60	9.8192	6362
75	9.8287	6358
90 (north pole)	9.8322	6357

*all measurements made at sea level

The height above sea level also affects the gravitational field strength, as shown below. Once again, the farther from the centre of the earth you get, the smaller the gravitational field strength becomes.

Location	Latitude (°)	g at sea level (N/kg)	Altitude (m)	g (N/kg)
Toronto	44	9.8054	162	9.8049
Mount Everest	28	9.7919	8848	9.7647
Dead Sea	32	9.7950	−397	9.7962

The tables show that the gravitational field strength does vary, but only slightly, for different locations on the Earth's surface. To one decimal place, the value of g is 9.8 N/kg everywhere. Usually we consider g to be constant on the Earth's surface.

On the other hand, farther out in space, the value of g decreases considerably. The table shows the force of gravity on an object at various distances from the centre of the Earth. The force of gravity on this object is 900 N at the Earth's surface.

The table shows that the force of gravity on an object depends on its distance from the Earth, decreasing as the distance increases. An object on the Earth's surface is about 6400 km from its centre. At twice this distance from the centre, the force of gravity on the object is not one-half as much, but $(1/2)^2$, or one-quarter as much. At 10 times the distance, the force is reduced to $(1/10)^2$ or $1/100$ of its original value. This is called the Inverse Square Law for Force. The force depends inversely on the square of the distance from the Earth's centre. Inverse square laws turn up often in physics, describing such things as light intensity, magnetism, and electric forces, as well as gravity.

Distance to centre of Earth (Earth radii)	Force of gravity (N)
1	900
2	225
3	100
4	56
5	36
6	25
7	18
8	14
10	9
30	1

$$F_1 \propto \frac{k I}{d_1{}^2} \qquad F_2 = \frac{k I}{d_2{}^2}$$

$$F_1 d_1{}^2 = F_2 d_2{}^2$$

$$\frac{F_1}{F_2} = \frac{d_2{}^2}{d_1{}^2}$$

The force of gravity on a 92 kg object at various distances from the Earth

Sample problem

The force of gravity on a rocket 10 000 km from the centre of the Earth is 900 N. What will the force of gravity on the rocket be when it is 30 000 km from the centre of the Earth?

$$\text{ratio of distances} = \frac{d_2}{d_1}$$
$$= \frac{30\ 000\ \text{km}}{10\ 000\ \text{km}}$$
$$= 3$$

$$\text{therefore, ratio of forces} = \left(\frac{1}{3}\right)^2$$

$$= \frac{1}{9}$$

$$= \frac{F_2}{F_1}$$

$$\text{this means that } F_2 = \frac{1}{9} F_1$$

$$= \frac{1}{9} (900 \text{ N})$$

$$= 100 \text{ N}$$

Practice

1. The force of gravity on the average person is about 700 N at the Earth's surface. Calculate the force of gravity on a person at 10 times that distance from the centre of the Earth.   (7.0 N)
2. If the Earth's radius is 6400 km, calculate the force of gravity on a 100 000 kg space station situated
   (a) on the Earth's surface.   (9.8×10^5 N)
   (b) 128 000 km from the centre of the Earth.   (2.5×10^3 N)
   (c) 384 000 km from the centre of the Earth (about the distance to the moon).   (2.7×10^2 N)
   (d) 1.5×10^8 km from the Earth's centre (about the distance to the sun).   (1.8×10^{-3} N)
3. The force of gravity on a meteorite approaching the Earth is 50 000 N at a certain point. Calculate the force of gravity on the meteorite when it reaches a point one-quarter of this distance from the centre of the Earth.   (8.0×10^5 N)
4. The gravitational field strength is also governed by an inverse square law. What is the gravitational field strength 200 km above the Earth's surface, at the altitude of many manned space flights?   (9.2 N/kg)

From the radius and period of the moon's orbit, Newton calculated its acceleration as 0.0027m/s². This meant that the gravitational field strength of the Earth, acting on the moon, was 0.0027 N/kg – far less than its value of 9.8 N/kg at the Earth's surface. Newton knew that the moon was about 60 times as far away from the centre of the Earth as an object at the Earth's surface, so he said that the value of g on the moon should be:

$$g = \frac{9.8 \text{ N/kg}}{60^2} = 0.0027 \text{ N/kg}$$

This was proof enough for him that the force of gravity depends inversely on the square of the distance between the objects.

Gravitational Field Strength and Free Fall

In Chapter 4, we said that freely falling objects accelerate downwards at g, an acceleration equal to 9.8 m/s², and now we are saying that g, the gravitational field strength, is equal to 9.8 N/kg.

The two are, indeed, equivalent. They have the same value, and the units are really the same. If the gravitational field strength at a point out in space is 5 N/kg, then a freely falling object at that point will accelerate downwards at 5 m/s².

Everything we have said about variations in the gravitational field strength also applies to the acceleration of a freely falling object.

5.4 Satellites in Orbit and Projectiles

It was Newton who first saw the connection between falling objects, projectiles, and satellites in orbit. The example he gave is still as good an explanation as any of this relationship.

Imagine a large cannon on the top of a high mountain firing cannon balls horizontally at greater and greater speeds. At first the cannon balls fall quickly to the ground. As their initial speed increases, the cannon balls travel farther and farther.

At very high speeds a new factor affects the distance. Since the Earth is round, it curves downwards. The cannon balls must travel down and around before landing.

When a certain critical speed is reached, the cannon ball's path curves downwards at the same rate as the Earth curves. The cannon ball is then in orbit, perpetually falling towards the Earth, but never landing.

A satellite in circular orbit 100 km above the surface of the Earth is travelling at about 7900 m/s (or 28 400 km/h), and takes about 86 min for each orbit.

5.5 The Law of Universal Gravitation

You have already heard the story of Newton, the apple, the moon, and the force of gravity. To explain both the motion of the falling apple and the orbiting of the moon, he concluded that the Earth must exert a force of attraction on all objects around it, a force that decreases as an object's distance from the Earth increases.

Now, if the Earth attracts people and apples, what about the moon? If an apple were dropped near the surface of the moon, wouldn't it fall to the moon? What holds the atmospheres of Jupiter and Saturn in? Surely these planets are surrounded by gravitational fields too!

If you hold two apples side by side and let go, they will both fall to the Earth. What would happen if you tried this deep in outer space, far from the Earth or any other large object? Would the apples fall towards each other? Why should large objects have a force of attraction but not small ones?

Newton decided that every apple, every rock, every particle in the universe attracts, and is attracted to, every other particle in the universe. The strength of the attraction depends on the masses of the objects and on the distance between them. The equation Newton gave for this force is:

The first artificial Earth satellite, launched by the Russians on October 4, 1957, was a spherical metal instrument package 60 cm in diameter with a mass of 83.5 kg. Its orbit was elliptical, with a perigee, or closest approach to the Earth, of 228 km, an apogee of 946 km, and an orbital period of about 96 min. Slowed by air resistance in the upper atmosphere, it descended towards the Earth after about three months and burned up, vaporized by the heat generated by air resistance in the denser air.

$$F = \frac{Gm_1m_2}{d^2}$$

where F is the force of attraction
between two objects, in newtons
m_1 is the mass of one object, in kilograms
m_2 is the mass of the other object, in kilograms
d is the distance between the objects
measured centre to centre, in metres
$G = 6.67 \times 10^{-11}$ N·m²/kg²

There are several important points here. First, the equation gives us two equal but opposite forces. The Earth pulls down on the moon; and the moon pulls up on the Earth with an equal force. At the Earth's surface, the Earth pulls down on a 1 kg mass with a force of 9.8 N. Newton's equation also requires that the 1 kg mass must pull upwards on the Earth with a force of 9.8 N.

Second, the forces of attraction are governed by an inverse square law. If an object is moved 10 times as far from the centre of the Earth as the Earth's surface, the force of gravity is reduced to $\left(\frac{1}{10}\right)^2$, or 1/100, of what it was at the Earth's surface. The forces decrease rapidly as objects are moved apart.

On the other hand, there is no value of d, no matter how great, that would reduce the forces of attraction to zero. Every object in the universe exerts a force on all other objects, near and far.

Third, the constant, G, has a very small value. The force of gravity is significant only if one or both of the objects is massive. It takes the whole Earth, with a mass of 5.98×10^{24} kg, to exert 9.8 N of force on a 1 kg mass. The force operating between relatively small objects, such as two cars on the road, is negligible.

Sample problem

What is the force of attraction between two apples, each with a mass of 0.50 kg, held 10 cm apart?

$$m_1 = 0.50 \text{ kg}$$
$$m_2 = 0.50 \text{ kg}$$
$$d = 10 \text{ cm}$$
$$= 0.10 \text{ m}$$
$$G = 6.67 \times 10^{-11} \text{ N·m}^2/\text{kg}^2$$

$$F = \frac{Gm_1m_2}{d^2}$$

$$= \frac{\left(6.67 \times 10^{-11} \frac{\text{N} \cdot \text{m}^2}{\text{kg}^2}\right)(0.50 \text{ kg})(0.50 \text{ kg})}{(0.10 \text{ m})^2}$$

$$= 1.7 \times 10^{-9} \text{ N}$$

You can see that, while the force of gravity between ordinary-sized objects is small, it is not zero.

Practice
1. What is the force of attraction (gravitational) between a 60 kg girl and a 70 kg boy standing 1.0 m apart? $(2.8 \times 10^{-7} \text{ N})$
2. What is the force of attraction between two 2000 kg cars side by side, 2.5 m apart? $(4.3 \times 10^{-5} \text{ N})$
3. What is the force of gravity acting on a 1.00 kg mass 20 000 km from the centre of the Earth? (1.00 N)

5.6 Frictional Forces

There are various kinds of friction. There is **static friction**, the force that keeps a stone from rolling down a sloping roof, and there is **sliding friction**, the force opposing a toboggan sliding down a hill. There is **rolling friction**, the force resisting the motion of a bicycle wheel, as well as **air resistance**, the force opposing the flight of a jumbo jet, and the **viscous force** that affects the motion of a ship through the water. Frictional forces always act opposite to the direction of motion.

Most frictional forces are complex, depending on the nature of the materials involved and the size, shape, and speed of the moving object. We shall consider only the force of friction acting on an object sliding along a horizontal surface.

Investigation: Sliding Friction

Problem:
What factors affect the force of friction on a sliding wooden block?

Materials:
3 wooden blocks
spring balance

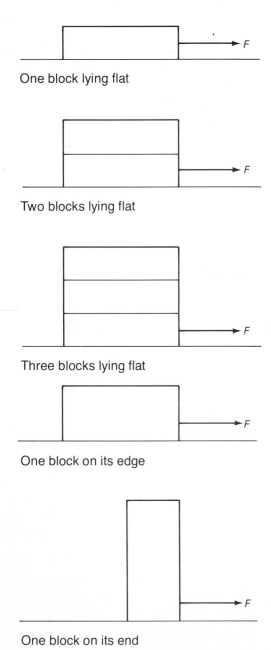

One block lying flat

Two blocks lying flat

Three blocks lying flat

One block on its edge

One block on its end

Procedure
1. Measure the length, width, and height of a block. Calculate the area of each face.
2. Use the spring balance to find the weight of a block, in newtons.
3. Pull one block along the desk on its largest face at a steady speed, and record the force required.
4. Repeat, using piles of two and three blocks, at the same speed as in step 3.
5. Pull one block along, first on its edge and then on its end, again at the same speed. Record the force required each time.
6. Pull one block along, first at half the original speed and then at twice the original speed. Record the force required each time.

Questions
1. Does the speed of the block have a significant effect on the force of friction? For example, to go twice as fast, do you have to apply twice the force?
2. Does the area in contact with the desk affect the force of friction significantly? When the area is twice as much, does the force double?
3. When you double or triple the number of blocks, what happens to the force of friction?
4. The coefficient of friction, represented by the Greek letter μ, is calculated by dividing the force of friction by the weight of the object, both expressed in newtons. Calculate the coefficient of friction for each of the above cases. It should be the same in each case, though there is usually a large percentage error in this investigation.
5. Find the average value of the coefficient of friction for the kind of wood you are using, sliding on the kind of desk you have. Each different combination of materials will have its own coefficient of friction.
6. If you were to make the desk or the block smoother, what effect would this have on the coefficient of friction?

The Coefficient of Friction

The coefficient of friction is a number used to calculate the force of friction acting on an object sliding along a horizontal surface. The equation for the coefficient of friction is:

$$\mu = \frac{F_f}{F_g}$$

where F_f is the force of friction, in newtons

F_g is the weight of the object, in newtons

μ is the coefficient of friction, and has no units

A rearrangement of this equation will give the equation for calculating the force of friction.

$$F_f = \mu \, F_g$$

The force of friction depends on μ, the coefficient of friction, which is determined by the two materials in contact, their smoothness and cleanness, and by the weight of the object, which is the force pushing the two surfaces together. The force of friction does not depend on the speed of the object or on the extent of the area in contact.

Materials	μ
oak on oak, dry	0.30
steel on steel, dry	0.41
greasy	0.12
steel on ice	0.010
rubber on asphalt, dry	0.40
wet	0.20
rubber on concrete, dry	0.70
wet	0.30
rubber on ice	0.005
leather on oak, dry	0.50

Sample problems

1. It takes 50 N to pull a 6.0 kg object along a desk. What is the coefficient of friction?

$$\mu = \frac{F_f}{F_g}$$
$$= \frac{F_f}{mg}$$
$$= \frac{50 \text{ N}}{(6.0 \text{ kg}) (9.8 \text{ N/kg})}$$
$$= 0.85$$

2. The coefficient of friction between two materials is 0.35. A 5.0 kg object made of one of the materials is being pulled along a table made of the other material. What is the force of friction?

$$F_f = \mu \, F_g$$
$$= \mu \, mg$$
$$= (0.35) \, (5.0 \text{ kg}) \, (9.8 \text{ N/kg})$$
$$= 17 \text{ N}$$

Practice

1. A 70 kg hockey player is skating on steel skates. What is the force of friction of the ice?   (6.9 N)
2. The driver of a 1500 kg car puts on the brakes on a concrete road. Calculate the force of friction (a) on a dry road and (b) on a wet road.   (1.0×10^4 N, 4.4×10^3 N)
3. A tractor ploughing a field is pulling with a force of 880 N on a 100 kg plough. What is the coefficient of friction?   (0.90)

5.7 Elastic Forces

If you try to stretch, compress, or twist most materials, they will resist with an opposing **elastic force**. This is the kind of force you feel when you stretch a rubber band and the kind that holds you up when you walk across the floor. You may not feel the floor move, but it does, and if it is subjected to too great a load it will flex so much that it will break. Elastic forces are important to engineers designing all kinds of things, from skyscrapers to cars and toasters.

Investigation: Stretching a Rubber Band

Problem:
What is the relationship between the length of a rubber band and
its elastic force?

Materials:
large rubber band
spring balance
metre stick

Procedure
1. Place the metre stick flat on the desk. Hook one end of the
   rubber band around the end of the metre stick and hook the
   other end onto the spring balance.
2. Stretch the rubber band by pulling on the spring balance until it
   is about twice its natural length. As you do this, stop every few
   centimetres and record the length of the rubber band, in
   metres, and the elastic force, in newtons. You will need at least
   10 readings.
3. Plot a graph of elastic force against length. The first part of this
   graph should be a straight line. Draw this straight line back to
   cross the horizontal length axis. The point where it crosses will
   tell you the length of the rubber band if no force is stretching it,
   that is, when it is its natural length.
4. Calculate the slope of the straight-line part of the graph. This is
   called the spring constant of the rubber band, and it is measured in newtons per metre.

Questions
1. What would the graph look like if a stronger, thicker rubber
   band were used? How does the spring constant change when a
   stronger rubber band is used?
2. What would the graph look like if the elastic force were plotted
   against the increase in length, instead of against the total length,
   of the rubber band (increase in length = total length − natural
   length)?

Hooke's Law

As long as the increase in length is not too great, the elastic force of
a rubber band, or a steel spring, or almost anything stretched or
compressed, will vary directly with the increase in length. A graph

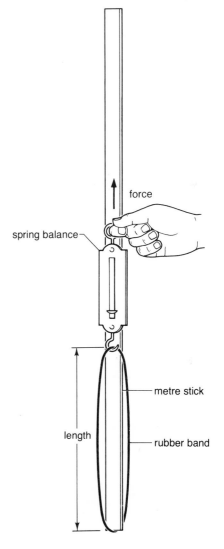

Measuring the length of a rubber band as
the force acting on it increases

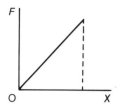

of the elastic force plotted against the increase in length will be a straight line through the origin. The equation of this straight line will be:

$$F = kx$$

where F is the elastic force, in newtons
x is the increase in length, in metres
k is the spring constant, in newtons per metre
(and also the slope of the graph)
The value of the spring constant depends on the dimensions of the object being stretched and the nature of the material from which it was made. If you were to make a bar measuring 1 cm by 1 cm by 1 metre of each of the materials listed and stretch it, you would find the spring constants that are given in the table.

Material	Spring constant (N/m)
rubber	700
plastic	140 000
wood	1.4×10^6
lead	1.5×10^6
bone	2.8×10^6
magnesium	4.2×10^6
glass	6.9×10^6
aluminum	7.0×10^6
copper	12×10^6
mild steel	21×10^6
diamond	120×10^6

Sample problem

How much force would it take to stretch a steel bar 1.0 cm $\times$ 1.0 cm $\times$ 1.0 m long until it is 1.0 mm longer?

$$x = 1.0 \text{ mm}$$
$$= 0.0010 \text{ m}$$

$$k = 21 \times 10^6 \text{ N/m}$$
$$F = kx$$
$$= (21 \times 10^6 \text{ N/m}) (0.0010 \text{ m})$$
$$= 2.1 \times 10^4 \text{ N}$$

Robert Hooke (1635-1703) published the law of elastic force in 1678. The equation you have just developed is known to this day as Hooke's Law.

Practice
1. A steel spring has a spring constant of 40 N/m. How much force would it take to stretch it by 10 cm?   (4.0 N)
2. A garage door has a spring constant of 600 N/m. How much will it stretch if a 150 N force is applied to it?   (0.250 m)
3. What is the spring constant of a car spring, if a 2500 N force compresses it from a length of 50 cm to a length of 40 cm?
                                                        (2.5×10^4 N/m)

5.8 Adding Vectors

In engineering and physics, it is often necessary to find the total force acting on an object. This is called the **net force** or the **unbalanced force**. When finding the unbalanced force, the directions of the forces are important, as well as their magnitudes.

A quantity with both magnitude and direction is called a **vector quantity**. You may have studied displacement and velocity vectors already this year. If so, you know that "10 N[E]" represents a force of 10 N acting in an easterly direction on an object.

A vector quantity is represented in a "vector diagram" by an arrow. The direction of the arrow shows the direction of the force and the arrow's length represents its magnitude. Each centimetre of length would represent a certain amount of force, according to some convenient scale.

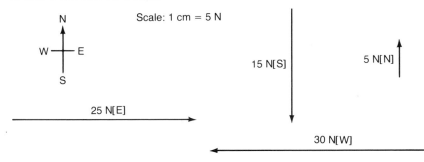

When the forces are acting along a straight line, the unbalanced force is easily found. For example, if forces of 10 N[E] and 20 N[E] are acting on an object, the unbalanced force is 30 N[E].

When vectors are added, they are joined head to tail. Their total is represented by a vector drawn from the tail of the first vector to the head of the last vector.

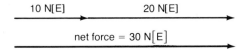

If forces of 20 N[E] and 5 N[W] are acting on an object, the unbalanced force is 15 N[E].

This result may be obtained from a vector diagram, using the same rule for adding as before.

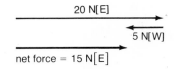

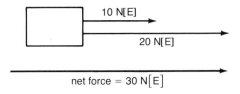

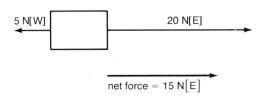

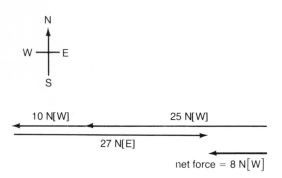

Sample problem

What is the unbalanced force acting on an object pulled west by a force of 25 N, east by a force of 27 N, and west by a force of 10 N?

The total force acting west is: 25 N[W] + 10 N[W] =   35 N[W]
The total force acting east is: 27 N[E]
The unbalanced force is: 8 N[W]
This result can also be obtained using a vector diagram.

Practice

1. What is the net force on an object being pulled east by a 55 N force, west by a 67 N force, west by a 34 N force, east by a 75 N force, and west by a 24 N force?   (5 N[E])
2. What additional force would it take to make the net force in the previous question (a) 0 N? (b) 20 N[E]? (c) 20 N[W]?
(5 N[W], 15 N[E], 25 N[W])

5.9 Summary

1. Force is a push or pull, measured in newtons with a spring balance.
2. Mass is the amount of matter in an object, measured in kilograms.
3. Weight is the force of gravity on an object, measured in newtons.
4. The gravitational field strength at a given point is the force of gravity on a 1 kg mass, and is represented by the symbol g.
5. At the surface of the Earth, g = 9.8 N/kg.
6. The force of gravity, F_g, on a mass, m, is found by the equation
$$F_g = mg$$
7. The gravitational field strength varies with the distance to the centre of the Earth.
8. The gravitational field strength, g, is inversely proportional to the square of the distance to the centre of the Earth, d.

$$g \propto \frac{1}{d^2}$$

9. The gravitational field strength at a given point and the acceleration of a freely falling object at that point are the same.
$$g = 9.8 \text{ N/kg} = 9.8 \text{ m/s}^2 \text{ at the Earth's surface}$$
10. According to Newton's Law of Universal Gravitation, there is a force of gravitational attraction between every pair of objects

in the universe. This force varies directly with the masses of the objects and inversely with the square of the distance between them.

$$F = \frac{Gm_1m_2}{d^2} \qquad \text{where} \qquad G = 6.67 \times 10^{-11} \text{ N·m}^2/\text{kg}^2$$

11. Sliding friction depends on the roughness of the surface and on the weight of the object. It does not depend on the speed of the motion or the area in contact.
12. The coefficient of sliding friction on a level surface is μ, where

$$\mu = \frac{F_f}{F_g}$$

13. For elastic materials, the amount of stretch varies directly with the applied force. The equation for this is:
$$F = kx$$
14. When adding forces along the same straight line, consider all the forces in one direction as being positive, and all the forces in the opposite direction as being negative; then add them all together to find the unbalanced, or net, force.

5.10 Review

Use $g = 9.80$ N/kg

1. What is the force of gravity at the Earth's surface on each of the following masses?
   (a) 75.0 kg (b) 454 g (c) 2.00 t (d) 3.14 kg
2. What is the weight of each of the following masses?
   (a) 25 g (b) 102 kg (c) 12 mg (d) 0.382 kg
3. Use these forces of gravity to determine the masses of the objects on which they act.
   (a) 0.98 N (b) 100 N (c) 62 N (d) 44.5 MN
4. Calculate the gravitational field strength at the surface of each of the following planets.

Planet	Mass on planet's surface (kg)	Force of gravity on this mass (N)
(a) Mercury	57	201
(b) Venus	29	247
(c) Earth	83	813
(d) Mars	453	1688
(e) Pluto	82	656

5. Why is the gravitational field strength half way up Mount Everest the same as at sea level at the equator?

6. Why is the gravitational field strength at the south pole less than the field strength at the north pole?

7. The force of gravity on an astronaut is 600 N at the Earth's surface. What is his weight at each of the following distances from the centre of the earth, measured in multiples of the Earth's radius?
   (a) 2 (b) 5 (c) 10 (d) 20

8. The force of gravity on a spacecraft some distance from the Earth is 800 N. What would that force be if its distance to the Earth's centre were
   (a) one-half as great? (b) one-third as great? (c) one-tenth as great? (d) one-quarter as great?

9. A 20 kg object out in space is attracted to the Earth by a force of gravity of 100 N. How fast will this object accelerate towards the Earth, if it is falling freely?

10. Two of the largest oil tankers in the world, the *Batilus* and the *Bellaya*, have masses of 492 000 t, fully loaded. If they were moored side by side, 1.0 m apart, their centres would be 64 m apart. Calculate the force of gravity between them.

11. Sirius is the brightest star in the night sky. It has a radius of 2.5 × 10^9 m and a mass of 5.0 × 10^{31} kg. What is the gravitational force on a 1.0 kg mass at its surface?

12. Sirius B is a white dwarf star, in orbit around Sirius, with a mass of 2.0 × 10^{30} kg (approximately the mass of the sun), and a radius of 2.4 × 10^7 m (approximately one-thirtieth of the radius of the sun). (a) What is the force on a 1.0 kg mass on the surface of Sirius B? (b) What is the acceleration due to gravity on the surface of Sirius B?

13. A 1000 kg communications satellite in synchronous orbit 42 400 km from the Earth's centre has a period of 24 h. Placed in orbit above the equator, and moving in the same direction as the Earth is turning, it stays above the same point on the Earth at all times. This makes it useful for the reception and retransmission of telephone, radio, and TV signals.
    (a) Calculate the force of gravity acting on the satellite.
    (b) What is the gravitational field strength at this altitude?

14. A 20.0 kg toboggan is pulled along by a force of 30.0 N.
    (a) What is the force of gravity on the toboggan?
    (b) What is the coefficient of friction?
    (c) How much force is needed to pull the toboggan if two 60.0 kg girls are sitting on it?

15. It takes a 5.0 N force to pull a 2.0 kg object along the ground.

What is the coefficient of friction?

16. How much force does it take to pull a 100 kg packing crate along a rough floor, given each of the following coefficients of friction?
    (a) 0.10 (b) 0.20 (c) 0.50 (d) 0.90

17. If the coefficient of friction is 0.25, how much force is needed to pull each of the following masses along a rough desk?
    (a) 25 kg (b) 15 kg (c) 200 g (d) 3.5 t

18. A 10 N force stretches a length of fishing line by 10 cm. What is the line's spring constant?

19. A 20 N force is used to stretch various rubber bands. Calculate the amount of stretch that will occur, given each of the following spring constants.
    (a) 200 N/m (b) 100 N/m (c) 400 N/m (d) 750 N/m

20. An archer pulls back with a force of 240 N, moving the arrow 60 cm. What is the spring constant of the bow?

21. Find the unbalanced force for each of the following combinations of forces.
    (a) 20 N[E], 30 N[W], 50 N[E]
    (b) 27.3 N[N], 2.8 N[S], 13.5 N[S]
    (c) 50 N[E], 20 N[W], 5 N[E], 35 N[W]

Numerical Answers to Review Questions

1. (a) 735 N (b) 4.45 N (c) 1.96×10^4 N
    (d) 30.8 N
2. (a) 0.25 N (b) 1.00×10^3 N
    (c) 1.2×10^{-4} N (d) 3.74 N
3. (a) 0.10 kg (b) 10.2 kg (c) 6.3 kg
    (d) 4.54×10^6 kg
4. (a) 3.5 N/kg (b) 8.5 N/kg
    (c) 9.8 N/kg (d) 3.73 N/kg
    (e) 8.0 N/kg
7. (a) 150 N (b) 24.0 N (c) 6.00 N
    (d) 1.50 N
8. (a) 3.20×10^3 N (b) 7.20×10^3 N
    (c) 8.00×10^4 N (d) 1.28×10^4 N
9. 5.0 m/s^2
10. 3.9×10^3 N
11. 5.3×10^2 N
12. (a) 2.3×10^5 N (b) $2.3 \times 10^5 \text{ m/s}^2$
13. (a) 222 N (b) 0.222 N/kg
14. (a) 196 N (b) 0.153 (c) 210 N
15. 0.26
16. (a) 98 N (b) 2.0×10^2 N
    (c) 4.9×10^2 N (d) 8.8×10^2 N
17. (a) 61 N (b) 37 N (c) 0.49 N
    (d) 8.6×10^3 N
18. 1.0×10^2 N/m
19. (a) 0.10 m (b) 0.20 m (c) 0.050 m
    (d) 0.027 m
20. 4.0×10^2 N/m
21. (a) 40 N[E] (b) 11.0 N[N] (c) 0 N

$$2.3 \times 10^5 = F_g = mg$$

$$F_g = F_g = mg$$

$$\boxed{\frac{G m_1 m_2}{d^2}} = \boxed{mg}$$

$$g = \frac{G m_1}{d^2}$$

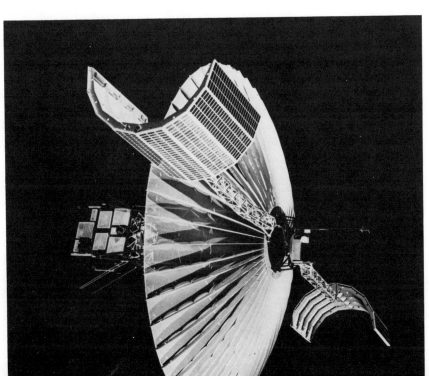

5.11 Learning Objectives

1. To measure forces in newtons with a spring balance.
2. To distinguish between mass and weight, measuring each in the correct unit.
3. Given any two of the mass of an object, the object's weight, and the gravitational field strength, to calculate the third.
4. To explain variations in the Earth's gravitational field strength due to latitude and height above sea level.
5. To calculate the new weight of an object, given its old weight and the ratio of the new distance from the centre of the Earth to the old distance from the centre of the Earth.
6. Given the field strength at the Earth's surface, the radius of the Earth, and the distance from the centre of the Earth, to calculate the gravitational field strength at any point above the Earth's surface.
7. To give the gravitational field strength, given the acceleration of a freely falling object, and vice versa.
8. Given the masses of two objects, the distance between them, and the gravitational constant, to calculate the force of gravity between the objects.
9. Given any two of the force of friction on an object, the force of gravity on the object, and the coefficient of friction, to calculate the third.
10. To list two factors that do not significantly affect the force of friction and two factors that do.
11. Given any two of the elastic force of an object, the amount of stretch (or compression), and the spring constant, to calculate the third.

6 Newton's Laws

6.1 Why Do Things Move?

Two thousand years ago, Aristotle thought he knew the answer to this question. An object moves, he said, when you push hard enough on it. If you push harder, it will move farther, and if you stop pushing, it will soon stop moving. The explanation sounded so reasonable that few scholars questioned it—until Galileo came along.

Galileo felt that Aristotle was wrong, because his law of motion did not cover every possible situation involving force and motion. Galileo could imagine objects that were moving with no force acting on them, and that would never stop once in motion.

Motion with No Force

Imagine a wooden block and a rubber ball being pushed along a desk, both at the same speed. If the pushing forces are removed, the ball will travel much farther than the wooden block before it stops.

Galileo saw that the force of friction, opposing the motion, slowed down both objects, but that the force of friction on the ball was much less than that on the block. He then asked himself what would happen if there was no force of friction acting on the ball. He concluded that the ball would travel on forever, at a constant speed, in a straight line.

It is impossible to demonstrate this because there are forces acting on all objects at all times. We can, however, do something similar. Several devices are available that can slide along a smooth surface with almost no friction. One of them consists of a circular metal disc, or "puck", with a small hole through its centre. Gas is pumped through the little hole at a pressure sufficient to raise the puck off the table a millimetre or so. The puck slides along the table on a cushion of gas. In one type of puck designed for this purpose, the gas is air from an inflated ballcon attached to it. Another type has a small electric air pump mounted on it, to pump air through the little hole.

Aristotle (384-322 BC) put it this way: "If, then, A has moved B a distance C in a time D, then in the same time the same force A will move ½B twice the distance C, and in ½D it will move ½B the whole distance C."

Galileo wrote: "Any velocity once imparted to a moving body will be rigidly maintained as long as the external causes of acceleration or retardation are removed, a condition found only on horizontal planes; for in the case of planes which slope downwards there is already present a cause of acceleration, while on planes sloping upwards there is a retardation; from this it follows that motion along a horizontal plane is perpetual."

This "frictionless" puck has a built-in flashing light on top for making strobe photographs.

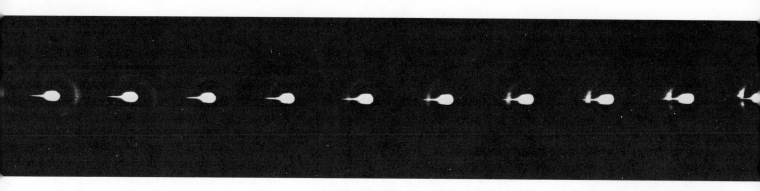

Some high-school physics labs have air tracks and air tables. An air track is a hollow beam with a pattern of tiny holes drilled in it. Air pumped into one end of the beam escapes through the holes, supporting small plastic riders on a layer of air. An air table allows nearly friction-less motion in two dimensions. The surface of such a table is covered with tiny holes. Plastic pucks glide across it, colliding with each other and demonstrating what happens in all kinds of collisions.

Galileo explained his theory of motion by saying that every object possesses a quantity of inertia, a property that resists changes in motion. Objects with greater mass were supposed to possess more inertia.

Newton wrote, in Latin: "LAW I: Every body continues in its state of rest, or of uniform motion in a straight line, unless it is compelled to change that state by forces impressed upon it."

The strobe photograph shows one of these pucks moving across a smooth, level surface. You can see, by measuring the distances travelled in equal time intervals, that the speed is quite constant, and in a straight line. Can you tell which way the puck is going?

Once an object is moving, it needs no force to keep it moving, as long as no other force acts on it.

Motion with Balanced Forces

When equal forces act in opposite directions on an object, the forces are "balanced", and the net force is zero. Surely this situation is identical to one in which no forces are acting on the object. After all, which of the two equal forces would speed up the object if it was in motion, or slow it down? The object must keep on going at a constant speed.

6.2 Newton's First Law of Motion

In 1667, Newton published one of the greatest scientific works ever written, *The Mathematical Principles of Natural Philosophy*. In it, he set down his basic principles of motion, particularly the motion of heavenly bodies such as the moon and the planets. He stated three laws of motion, the first being:

If no net force acts on an object, it maintains its state of rest or its constant speed in a straight line.

If you have ever had to push a stalled car off the road, you have experienced this law of motion. You have to push very hard to get the car moving, but once it is moving you can relax a little: you only have to push hard enough to balance the force of friction.

Demonstrations of Newton's First Law of Motion

1. Cut a small square of cardboard 4 cm by 4 cm. Balance the card on your left index finger. Now place a nickel on the card so that it balances, too. Aim carefully, then flick one corner of the card with your right index finger. If you hit the corner squarely, the card will spin out from under the nickel, leaving the nickel balanced on your finger. The force is applied to the card, not the nickel. The nickel "maintains its state of rest".

2. In a car travelling at constant speed, flip a coin straight up into the air. It should appear to come straight back down again. In fact, if the coin is in the air for 0.5 s, and the car is travelling at 50 km/h, the coin will travel almost 7 m horizontally while in the air. The force applied to the coin is vertical. There is no force acting horizontally on the coin, which "maintains a constant speed" horizontally, keeping up with your hand and the car. You can imagine what would happen if the car stopped abruptly while the coin was in the air. It would hit the front of the car at 50 km/h. It is Newton's first law that explains why it is important for you to keep your seat belt fastened. A car's brakes will stop the car but they will not stop you unless you are buckled in.

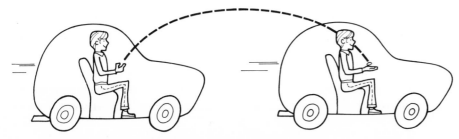

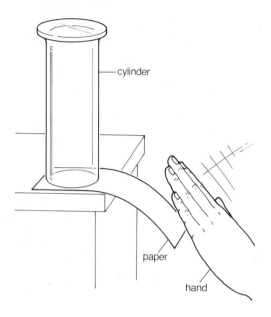

3. On the edge of your desk, place one end of a sheet of paper, using a graduated cylinder turned upside down as a weight to hold it there. Bring the palm of your hand down quickly, striking the paper so that it is pulled out from under the cylinder. Why didn't the cylinder tip over?

Sample problem

The driver of a car travelling along an icy road tries to turn suddenly. The car keeps going straight ahead and lands in the ditch. Why?

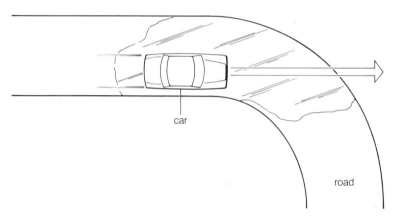

A car on an icy curve

Because of the ice, there is no force of friction on the car's wheels to make it turn. The only forces that are acting are balanced – the road pushing up on the car and gravity pulling down on it. The car keeps on going at a steady speed, in a straight line, right off the road, according to Newton's first law of motion.

Practice
1. A jet plane is travelling at a constant speed in a straight line in level flight. What does this tell you about the forces acting on it?
2. A woman pushes a refrigerator across the floor at a steady speed of 20 cm/s. If she has to push with a force of 400 N to keep it moving, what is the force of friction on the refrigerator: (**a**) more than 400 N? (**b**) less than 400 N? (**c**) 400 N?
3. A 1200 kg boat accelerates steadily at 0.05 m/s² in a straight line. Are the forces on this boat balanced or unbalanced?

6.3 Motion with Unbalanced Forces

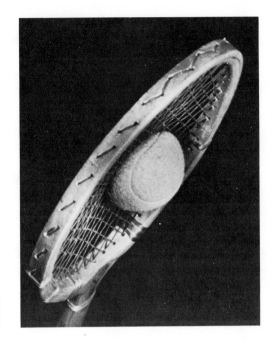

When the forces acting on a stationary object are balanced, it will remain at rest. If the forces acting on a moving object are balanced, it will continue to move at a constant speed in a straight line. This is Newton's first law of motion.

If the forces acting on an object are not balanced, the object will accelerate in the direction of the net force. To accelerate a golf ball north, you must strike it with a golf club moving north.

The amount of acceleration depends on the amount of the unbalanced force and on the mass of the object being accelerated. In the next investigation, carts of different masses will be accelerated by varying amounts of force to clearly demonstrate this relationship.

The carts have low friction roller skate wheels. If the frictional force is very small, the unbalanced force will be almost exactly equal to the force applied to accelerate the cart.

The first mass to be accelerated is a cart carrying three 100 g masses. Forces to accelerate this mass are produced by attaching one or more of its 100 g masses to the end of a string attached to the cart and running over a pulley attached to the edge of the desk.

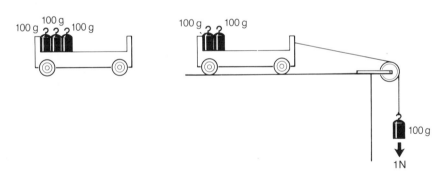

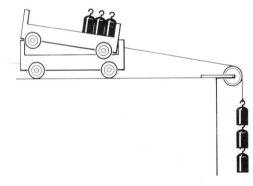

Each 100 g mass will pull on the cart with the same force, almost exactly 1 N. The total mass being accelerated will always be the same, one cart and three 100 g masses.

To accelerate twice as much mass, a second cart and three more 100 g masses are piled on the first cart.

Three times the original mass would be three carts and nine 100 g masses.

The amount of acceleration for each combination of force and mass is calculated from measurements made on a ticker-tape record of the trip. The acceleration could be obtained by drawing a

speed-time graph and finding its slope, but there is a simpler way, using the equation:

$$d = \tfrac{1}{2}at^2$$

This means that:

$$a = \frac{2d}{t^2}$$

You will recall that t is the time for an object to travel a distance d, starting from rest, accelerating steadily.

When you have calculated the acceleration of a single mass acted upon by several different forces, and the acceleration of several different masses, acted upon by the same force, the relationship between these quantities should become clear.

Investigation: Newton's Second Law

Problem:
What is the relationship between force, mass, and acceleration?

Materials:
 3 carts
 nine 100 g masses
 recording timer
 pulley and string
 clamp for pulley

Procedure
1. Set up the recording timer at one end of the desk and clamp the pulley to the edge of the other end of the desk.
2. Tie a piece of string to one end of one of the carts. Put two 100 g masses on the cart and hook a third to the other end of the string, running the string over the pulley.
3. Tape a piece of ticker tape to the other end of the cart and run it through the recording timer.

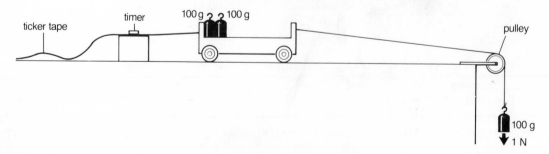

4. Start the timer, release the cart, and catch it before it hits the pulley.
5. Repeat, using two of the 100 g masses to accelerate the cart, and then repeat once more, using all three 100 g masses.
6. Now add a second cart and three more 100 g masses to double the mass being accelerated. Use three of the six 100 g masses to accelerate this combination.
7. Finally, add a third cart and three more 100 g masses to triple the original mass. Use three of the nine 100 g masses to accelerate this mass also.
8. Analyse each of the five tapes to find the acceleration in each case as follows. Starting with the first dot on each tape, mark off a convenient time interval, such as 30 dots (30 dots = 30 × $^1/_{60}$ s = 0.5 s). Measure the distance travelled in this time interval, in metres. Now calculate the acceleration of the cart. Record all your measurements and calculations in a data table such as the following.

F (N)	m (carts)	d (m)	t (s)	a (m/s²)	ma
1	1		0.5		
2	1		0.5		
3	1		0.5		
3	2				
3	3				

In the last column of the table, calculate the product of mass (in carts) and acceleration (in m/s²).
9. Draw a graph of force versus acceleration, for the motion of a single cart.
10. Draw a graph of mass versus acceleration, for motions involving the 3 N force.
11. Draw a graph of force versus ma, the product of mass and acceleration, for all cases.

Questions
1. If the unbalanced force on an object is doubled, what change in acceleration is produced?
2. What is the relationship between the unbalanced force acting on an object and its acceleration?
3. If the mass of an object is doubled, but the unbalanced force acting on it remains the same, what change in acceleration is produced?
4. What is the relationship between the mass of an object and its acceleration?

5. What is the relationship between the unbalanced force acting on an object and *ma*, the product of its mass and its acceleration?

6. If a 1 N force accelerates one cart at 0.5 m/s², what acceleration will a 5 N force produce on a stack of five carts?

Force, Mass, and Acceleration

A graph of the relationship between *F*, the unbalanced force acting on an object, and *ma*, the product of its mass and its acceleration, is a straight line through the origin. The equation of this straight line will be:

$$F = kma$$

where *F* is the unbalanced force, in newtons

$\quad$ *m* is the mass of the object, in carts

$\quad$ *a* is the acceleration of the object, in metres per second per second

$\quad$ *k* is a constant, the slope of the graph

In SI, mass is measured in kilograms, not in "carts" as in your investigation. If kilograms were used in your investigation, you would find that the slope of the graph of force versus *ma* would be exactly 1.

This is no accident. The unit of force, the newton, was carefully chosen so that an unbalanced force of one newton accelerates a one kilogram object at one metre per second per second. This makes the value of *k* equal to 1.

In metric units, the equation relating force, mass, and acceleration is:

$$\mathbf{F = ma}$$

This is Newton's second law of motion.

6.4 Newton's Second Law of Motion

If an unbalanced force acts on an object, the object accelerates in the direction of the force.
The acceleration varies directly with the unbalanced force.
The acceleration varies inversely with the mass of the object.

Newton wrote: "LAW II: The change of motion is proportional to the motive force impressed, and is made in the direction of the straight line in which the force is impressed."

In the last investigation, the accelerating force was supplied by the force of gravity on 100 g masses. We assumed that this was the unbalanced force even though a small force of friction acts on the cart as it rolls. When this investigation is done more carefully, this force of friction and the force of friction of the pulley on the string must be taken into account. It is the unbalanced force that must be used in the equation for Newton's second law of motion.

Sample problems

1. What is the acceleration of a 70 kg skater, acted upon by an unbalanced force of 161 N?

$$a = \frac{F}{m}$$
$$= \frac{161 \text{ N}}{70 \text{ kg}}$$
$$= 2.3 \text{ m/s}^2$$

2. What is the acceleration of a 1000 kg car, if its engine pushes with a force of 500 N against a 100 N force of friction?

Find the net force
$$F = 500 \text{ N} - 100 \text{ N}$$
$$= 400 \text{ N}$$

Calculate the acceleration
$$a = \frac{F}{m}$$
$$= \frac{400 \text{ N}}{1000 \text{ kg}}$$
$$= 0.400 \text{ m/s}^2$$

Practice

1. The net force on a 5.0 kg bowling ball is 20 N. What is its acceleration? (4.0 m/s^2)
2. A baseball hit by a bat with a force of 1000 N accelerates at $4.0 \times 10^3 \text{ m/s}^2$. What is the ball's mass? (0.25 kg)
3. What unbalanced force is needed to accelerate a $3.0 \times 10^4 \text{ kg}$ spacecraft at 2.5 m/s^2? $(7.5 \times 10^4 \text{ N})$
4. How much force is needed to accelerate a 2.0 kg block of wood at 4.0 m/s^2 along a rough table, against a 10 N force of friction? (18 N)

6.5 Newton's Third Law of Motion

The third law of motion is familiar to many people:

For every action force, there is an equal and opposite reaction force.

Newton's original version is: "LAW III: To every action there is always opposed an equal reaction; or, the mutual actions of two bodies upon each other are always equal, and directed to contrary parts."
In the discussion that followed, he added: "If you press a stone with your finger, the finger is also pressed by the stone. If a horse draws a stone tied to a rope, the horse (if I may say so) will be equally drawn back towards the stone."

This law means that, if you kick a rock (an action force), the rock will "kick" back with an exactly equal force (the reaction force).

Everyone has blown up a balloon and released it suddenly to fly about the room. The elastic forces in the balloon itself push the air out in one direction, and the escaping air pushes the balloon in the opposite direction.

We have had many examples of action and reaction forces in our study of gravity. The Earth pulls downwards on the moon (an action force), holding it in orbit around the Earth. The equal and opposite (reaction) force is that of the moon pulling upwards on the Earth.

The upward pull of the moon has its effects on the Earth. For one thing, it combines with the force of the sun on the Earth, to produce the tides. The water in the part of the ocean that faces the moon is pulled outwards towards the moon, raising the water level and creating a high tide there. There is also a high tide on the side of the Earth farthest from the moon. The force of attraction of the moon is least there and the water bulges out away from the Earth.

As the Earth turns, the bulges remain fixed in relation to the moon. To someone on the Earth, the bulges seem to travel around it, creating a series of regularly spaced high and low tides at each point on the surface of the Earth.

Without the pull of gravity of the moon, the depth of the ocean at any particular place would remain fairly constant.

The effect of the moon's gravity is strongest on the ocean at point A, weaker on the Earth at point B, and weakest on the ocean on the far side of the Earth at point C.

There is always a high tide at points A and C, and a low tide at points D and E. Every day, a point fixed on the Earth's surface would rotate around and pass through the bulges at A and C, experiencing two high tides.

Twice a month, when the sun, moon, and Earth are lined up, the high tides are higher and the low tides lower. These are called **spring tides.** When the sun, Earth, and moon form a right angle, the effects of the sun and the moon tend to cancel each other, and the tides are minimized. These are called **neap tides.**

Practice
1. What is the reaction force to the action force in each of the following situations?
   (**a**) A football player kicks the football with a force of 500 N[N].
   (**b**) A book pushes down on a desk with a force of 25 N.
   (**c**) A crane lifts a steel girder with a force of 6000 N[up].
   (**d**) A gun fires a bullet with a force of 1000 N[E].
   (**e**) The Earth pulls down on an apple with a force of 10 N.
2. When you drop a tennis ball, it bounces back up off the ground. Explain in detail the force that causes this.
3. Explain how a person trapped, motionless, in the centre of a frictionless ice rink can get to the side of the rink and escape.
4. A man wants to test a rope. He ties one end to a telephone pole and the other to a horse and makes the horse pull as hard as it can. It is not quite strong enough to break the rope. The man brings in a second horse of identical strength to take the place of the telephone pole. Will the rope break when the two horses pull in opposite directions as hard as they can? Explain your answer.

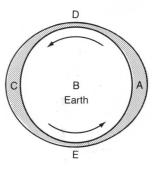

If Newton was correct, then, if you jumped upwards as hard as you could, the Earth would move away in the opposite direction. If you jumped 1 m, with a mass of 60 kg, then the Earth would move:

$$1 \text{ m} \times \frac{60 \text{ kg}}{6 \times 10^{24} \text{ kg}} = 10^{-23} \text{ m}$$

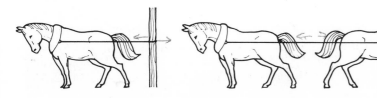

An Action-Reaction Problem

Many people accept the fact that there is a reaction for every action, but don't see why it must be an exactly equal force. This problem demonstrates that, at least for accelerating objects, the two must be exactly equal.

Imagine two boxes labelled A and B and tied together by a piece of string on a frictionless table. Box A has a mass of 10 kg and box B has a mass of 20 kg. A force of 60 N pulls on box A, which drags box B along behind it.

The acceleration of the boxes is:

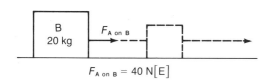

$$a = \frac{F}{m}$$

$$= \frac{60 \text{ N } [E]}{30 \text{ kg}} \qquad \text{(Use the total mass of the two boxes.)}$$

$$= 2.0 \text{ m/s}^2 \text{ [E]}$$

Now consider box B alone. It accelerates because the string connecting it to box A is pulling on it. How much force does the string exert? According to Newton's second law of motion:

$$F_{A \text{ on } B} = ma$$
$$= (20 \text{ kg}) (2.0 \text{ m/s}^2 \text{ [E]}) \qquad \text{(Use the mass of box B.)}$$
$$= 40 \text{ N [E]}$$

Notice that the full force of 60 N is not acting on box B. If it did, B would accelerate much faster than 2.0 m/s².

Next, we need to determine the net force on box A. Again, according to Newton's second law:

$$F = ma$$
$$= (10 \text{ kg}) (2.0 \text{ m/s}^2 \text{[E]}) \qquad \text{(Use box A's mass.)}$$
$$= 20 \text{ N[E]}$$

If there is a 60 N force acting east on box A, why is the net force only 20 N[E]? There must be another force acting, the force of box B, pulling backwards on A. It must be a force of 40 N[W], to make the net force on box A 20 N[E].

If box A pulls on box B with a force of 40 N[E], then box B pulls back on box A with a force of 40 N[W]. This is Newton's third law of motion.

Practice

1. Find the action and reaction between two 10 kg boxes accelerated together on a frictionless table by a force of 40 N acting on one of them.   **(20 N)**
2. Repeat the first practice problem with three 10 kg boxes accelerated by a 45 N force.   **(15 N, 30 N)**

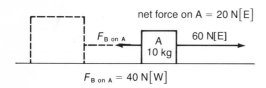

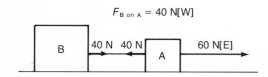

3. Repeat the first practice problem again, assuming that there is a
force of friction of 6.0 N acting on the first box, and a force of
friction of 4.0 N acting on the second box.   (**19 N**)

Walking, Flying, Driving, and Swimming

If there were no reaction forces, it would be impossible to do any of
the things mentioned in the title of this section.

1. Walking

When you want to walk, you push with your feet, but your feet do
not push on you, they push on the ground. They are not responsible for your movement. We need to find a force that acts forwards,
and acts on you. This force is the reaction force of the ground. Your
feet push backwards on the ground and the ground pushes you
forwards. The next time someone asks you why you can walk, tell
them the ground pushes you forwards.

2. Driving

It is the same with a car. The engine turns the driveshaft, the
driveshaft turns the wheels, and the wheels push backwards on
the ground. If you have ever stood behind a car accelerating on
gravel, you will appreciate this. Why does the car move forwards?
The ground pushes it forwards, providing the reaction force to the
force of the turning wheels.
   Consider what happens to a car on slippery ice. There is nothing
wrong with the car's engine, but it can't make the car go forwards.
There is no reaction force, because the ice is slippery.

3. Swimming

It is the water that pushes you forwards. Of course, you must first
push backwards on the water, but then the water's reaction force
pushes you forwards.

4. Flying

If you have a propeller on your plane, it pushes air backwards, like a giant fan. This air pushes forwards on the propeller, which moves ahead, dragging the plane along behind it.

5. A Challenge

If a car is pushed forwards by the road, a swimmer by the water, and a plane by the air, what pushes a rocket forwards, in the vacuum of outer space?

6.6 Testing Newton's Laws

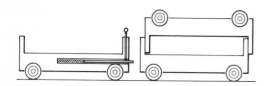

It is possible to test all three of Newton's laws of motion in one investigation, using spring-loaded carts. These carts have a spring-loaded plunger that can be depressed and locked in the "loaded" position, ready to fire when a wooden "trigger" is struck by a metre stick.

A kind of explosion can be created by placing a loaded cart against one or more other carts. When the spring is released, the carts move off in opposite directions, at various speeds, according to the laws of motion.

Newton's Third Law of Motion

When the spring in the first cart is released, its plunger pushes on the second cart with a certain force. According to Newton's third law of motion, the second cart should push back with an exactly equal force. Also, the two forces should act for exactly the same length of time, while the carts are in contact.

Newton's Second Law of Motion

The acceleration of each of the carts is determined by its mass and the force acting on it. Since the forces on the carts are equal, their accelerations are determined by their masses. Three stacked carts should have one-third of the acceleration of a single cart. Since the forces act for the same length of time, the single cart should reach three times the speed of the three carts.

Newton's First Law of Motion

Once the spring stops pushing, the carts should continue to move across the desk at a constant speed, provided that there is not much friction.

In the next investigation, you will examine such explosions between carts. You can test your predictions by using two bricks, one at either end of the desk. You must set up the carts and the bricks so that the carts collide with the bricks simultaneously. An example will show you what we mean.

Sample problem

Three carts repel a single cart. If the single cart travels 45 cm to hit its brick, how far must the other carts travel?

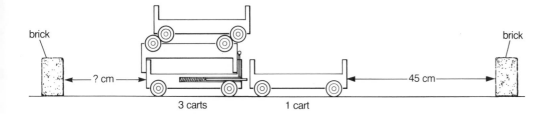

The cart with three times the mass of a single cart will have one-third the acceleration and a top speed one-third as great. Moving at a constant speed, it will travel only one-third as far as the single cart in the same time. Its brick must be placed $\frac{45 \text{ cm}}{3}$, or 15 cm, away.

In the same way, you can predict and test explosions between any number of carts.

Investigation: Exploding Carts

Problem:
Do Newton's laws work for exploding carts?

Materials:
5 carts
2 bricks
metre stick

Procedure
1. Set a stack of carts on the desk next to a single cart. Place bricks at opposite ends of the desk so that the carts will hit them simultaneously. You might put one brick 40 cm from the stacked cart. Then, use Newton's laws of motion to predict the distance the single cart should travel. Record this prediction in a data table.

Number of carts in stack	Distance stack of carts travels (cm)	Predicted distance single cart will travel (cm)	Actual distance single cart travels (cm)	Error (%)
1				
2				
3				

2. Release the spring in the single cart by hitting the trigger with the metre stick. Do the carts hit their bricks simultaneously? If they do not, move the brick hit by the single cart until they do. Record this distance and calculate the percentage error between your predicted distance and the actual distance.
3. Repeat, using a different number of carts in the stack.
4. Calculate the average percentage error of the experiment.

Questions
1. In this explosion, when a large mass and a small mass travel out in opposite directions, which mass:
   (a) has the greatest speed?
   (b) travels the greatest distance to reach its brick?
   (c) takes the longest time to reach its brick?
2. What is the relationship between the ratio of the masses of the two carts and the ratio of their speeds?

6.7 Summary

1. **Newton's First Law of Motion:**
   If no net force acts on an object, it maintains its state of rest or its constant speed in a straight line.
2. **Newton's Second Law of Motion:**
   If an unbalanced force acts on an object, the object accelerates in the direction of the force. The acceleration varies directly with the unbalanced force and inversely with the mass of the object.

$$F = ma$$

3. One newton is the unbalanced force that accelerates a one kilogram object at one metre per second per second.

$$1 \text{ N} = 1 \text{ kg} \cdot \text{m/s}^2$$

4. **Newton's Third Law of Motion:**
   For every action force, there is an equal and opposite reaction force.

6.8 Review

1. What is the reaction force in each of the following cases?
   (a) A canoe paddle pushes on water with a force of 150 N[E].
   (b) A bulldozer pushes a large rock with a force of 10^4 N[W] at 0.2 m/s.
   (c) A baseball hits a window with a maximum force of 400 N[S] and breaks it.
   (d) The wheels of a car push on a road with a force of 250 N[S] and 2500 N[down].
2. Use Newton's first law of motion to explain what will happen in each of the following situations.
   (a) A car attempts to stop at a traffic light on an icy street.
   (b) A truck attempts to turn a corner on an icy expressway.
   (c) A passenger in a car does not have the seat belt buckled when the car runs into a snowdrift.
   (d) An airline passenger attempts to sip a cup of coffee when the airplane suddenly drops one metre.
3. Harry is pushing a car down a level road at 2.0 m/s with a force of 243 N. The total force acting on the car in the opposite direction, including road friction and air resistance, is one of the following. Which one?
   (a) slightly more than 243 N
   (b) exactly equal to 243 N
   (c) slightly less than 243 N

Numerical Answers to Review Questions

3. 243 N
4. (a) 2.0 N (b) 4.0 N (c) 6.0 N
5. (a) 20 m/s² (b) 10 m/s² (c) 6.7 m/s²
6. 0.250 m/s²
7. 1.86×10^3 N
8. (a) 6.0 m/s², 4.0 m/s² (b) 0.60 m/s, 0.40 m/s
9. (a) 5.0 m/s²[E] (b) 2.5 s
10. (a) 2.86×10^7 N (b) 4.78×10^6 N[up] (c) 1.64 m/s²
11. 10.2 m/s², 53.3 m/s²
12. 49 N
14. 60 m/s
15. 1.6×10^4 N[S]
16. 5.0 s
17. 1.5×10^4 N[W]
18. 44.0 m/s[S]
19. 18 N[up]
20. 44 m/s[down]

4. What force would be required in each case to accelerate a 0.50 kg grapefruit at:
(**a**) 4.0 m/s²? (**b**) 8.0 m/s²? (**c**) 12 m/s²?

5. What acceleration would an unbalanced force of 84 N produce on each of the following masses?
(**a**) 4.2 kg (**b**) 8.4 kg (**c**) 12.6 kg

6. A 1200 kg car travelling at 50 km/h experiences an air resistance of 5000 N and road friction of 2200 N. If the wheels push with a force of 7500 N, what is the car's acceleration?

7. An 1100 kg car accelerates at 3.40 m/s². If the wheels exert a force of 5600 N on the road, calculate the force resisting the motion.

8. Two boys, one with a mass of 60 kg and the other with a mass of 90 kg, are standing side by side in the middle of an ice rink. One of them pushes the other with a force of 360 N for 0.10 s. Assuming that the ice surface is frictionless:
(**a**) What is the acceleration of each boy?
(**b**) What speed will each reach after the 0.10 s?
(**c**) Does it matter which boy did the pushing?

9. A block of wood of mass 6.0 kg sliding along a skating rink at 12.5 m/s[W] slides onto a rough part of the ice, which exerts a 30 N force of friction on the block of wood. Calculate:
(**a**) the acceleration of the block of wood
(**b**) the time it takes the block of wood to stop

10. A fully loaded Saturn V rocket has a mass of 2.92×10^6 kg. Its engines have a thrust of 3.34×10^7 N.
(**a**) What is the downward force of gravity on the rocket at blast-off?
(**b**) What is the unbalanced force on the rocket at blast-off?
(**c**) What is the acceleration of the rocket as it leaves the launching platform?
(**d**) As the rocket travels upwards, the engine thrust remains constant, but the mass of the rocket decreases. Why?
(**e**) Does the acceleration of the rocket increase, decrease, or remain the same as the engines continue to fire?

11. Calculate the initial acceleration of a 13 140 kg V-2 rocket bomb fired vertically, if the thrust of its engines is 2.63×10^5 N. Then calculate the rocket's acceleration near "burn-out", when its mass is only 4170 kg.

12. A 5.0 kg stone is sinking in water at a constant speed of 5.0 m/s. What is the upward force of the water on the stone?

13. The hero in a cartoon has a sailboat but no wind. To make a quick escape, the ingenious character attaches an electric fan to the back of the boat to blow air into the sails. Why would this not work, even if there was an extension cord long enough?

14. What change in velocity would be produced by an unbalanced force of 2.0×10^4 N acting for 6.0 s on a 2000 kg dragster?

15. Calculate the unbalanced force acting on a 4000 kg truck that changes speed from 22.0 m/s[N] to 8.0 m/s[N] in 3.50 s.

16. How long does it take a 50 kg rider on a 10 kg bicycle to accelerate from rest to 4.0 m/s[E] if the unbalanced force acting on the bicycle is 48 N[E]?

17. What is the unbalanced force accelerating a 5.0 kg cannonball from rest to 150 m/s[W], if the force acts for 0.050 s?

18. What is the final velocity of a 150 kg motorcycle driven by a 50 kg rider, accelerated from rest for 11.0 s by an unbalanced force of 800 N[S]?

19. A 0.50 kg model rocket accelerates from 20 m/s[up] to 45 m/s[up] in 0.70 s. Calculate the unbalanced force acting on it.

20. A 2.0 kg sponge is dropped from rest, pulled down by gravity. How fast will it be travelling in 6.0 s, if a 5.0 N force of air resistance acts on it?

Would a sailboat work better with a fan?

6.9 Learning Objectives

1. To use Newton's first law of motion to explain the motion of objects at rest or with uniform motion.
2. Given any two of the mass of an object, its acceleration, and the unbalanced force acting on it, to calculate the third.
3. Given any force, to state the reaction force to it, the magnitude of the reaction force, and its direction.

7 Momentum

7.1 Motion and Momentum

If someone threw you a shot of the sort used in shot putting, you would get out of the way – quickly. But you would have no hesitation about reaching out to catch a rubber ball. What are the properties of a hurtling shot that make you avoid it? One is its velocity. A shot at rest would be of no concern. The other is its mass. Having a larger mass, a shot is a greater threat than the rubber ball, even though the two may be travelling at the same speed. On the other hand, if the ball was shot at you from a gun, it would be a serious threat.

Newton related a moving object's mass to its velocity in what he called "quantity of motion". We now call this quantity "momentum" and give it the symbol p.

The momentum of a moving object is given by the equation

$$p = mv$$

where p is the object's momentum, in kilogram metres per second
m is its mass, in kilograms
v is its velocity, in metres per second

Momentum is a vector quantity and always has the same direction as the velocity. The unit of momentum, kilogram metres per second, is a derived unit. It has no special name.

Sample problem

What is the momentum of a 1000 kg car travelling along a highway at 15 m/s?

$$p = mv$$
$$= (1000 \text{ kg}) (15 \text{ m/s})$$
$$= 1.5 \times 10^4 \text{ kg} \cdot \text{m/s}$$

Practice

1. Calculate the momentum of each of the following moving objects.
   (a) a 0.50 kg ball thrown at 30 m/s   (15 kg·m/s)
   (b) a 2000 kg railway car moving at 10 m/s $(2.0 \times 10^4$ kg·m/s)
   (c) an electron (mass = 9.1×10^{-31} kg) moving at a speed of 10^7 m/s $(9.1 \times 10^{-24}$ kg·m/s)
   (d) the Earth, of mass 6.0×10^{24} kg, moving along its solar orbit at a speed of 3.0×10^4 m/s $(1.8 \times 10^{29}$ kg·m/s)
2. The momentum of a 7.3 kg shot is 22 kg·m/s. What is its speed?
                                                    (3.0 m/s)
3. A bullet travelling at 900 m/s has a momentum of 4.5 kg·m/s. What is its mass? $(5.0 \times 10^{-3}$ kg)

7.2 Change in Momentum

Since an object's momentum has been defined as the product of its mass and its velocity, then the object will experience a change in momentum whenever its velocity or its mass changes. The change in momentum may be expressed as:

$$\Delta p = \Delta (mv)$$

Sample problems

1. A ball of mass 2.5 kg speeds up from 6.0 m/s to 8.0 m/s. Determine its change in momentum.

   $\Delta p = \Delta (mv)$
   $\quad = mv_2 - mv_1 \qquad$ since m remains constant
   $\quad = (2.5$ kg$)(8.0$ m/s$) - (2.5$ kg$)(6.0$ m/s$)$
   $\quad = 20$ kg·m/s $- 15$ kg·m/s
   $\quad = 5$ kg·m/s

2. A wagon of mass 10 kg is rolling along at a speed of 3.0 m/s when a small girl of mass 30 kg jumps onto it. The wagon continues to move on at the same speed. Determine the change in momentum of the wagon.

$$\Delta p = \Delta\,(mv)$$
$$= m_2 v - m_1 v \quad \text{since } v \text{ remains constant}$$
$$= (40\ \text{kg})\,(3.0\ \text{m/s}) - (10\ \text{kg})\,(3.0\ \text{m/s})$$
$$= 120\ \text{kg}\cdot\text{m/s} - 30\ \text{kg}\cdot\text{m/s}$$
$$= 90\ \text{kg}\cdot\text{m/s}$$

7.3 Impulse and Momentum

Impulse and momentum units are the same.

$$\text{N}\cdot\text{s} = (\text{kg}\cdot\text{m/s}^2)\,(\text{s})$$
$$= \text{kg}\cdot\text{m/s}$$

In Chapter 6, it was shown that, when an object is acted upon by a net force, it is accelerated, and that the relationship between an object's mass, its acceleration, and the force acting on it is expressed by the equation $F = ma$ (Newton's Second Law). In fact, Newton did not originally think in terms of an object's acceleration. He said that the rate of change in the momentum of an object is directly proportional to the force applied, and that the change in momentum is in the same direction as the applied force.

$$F = \frac{\Delta p}{\Delta t}$$
$$\text{or } F\,\Delta t = \Delta p$$

This form of the equation can be quite useful. For example, when a golf ball is about to be hit by a golf club, it has zero momentum. After contact, the ball has a momentum in the same direction as the force of the club on the ball. How much momentum the ball gains depends on two factors–the magnitude of the force of the club on the ball and the duration of the club's contact with the ball.

Forces that act for a duration that is short compared with the duration of observation of a system are called impulse forces.

Whenever there is an impact, or collision, between objects, the product $F\,\Delta t$ has great significance. This product is given the name "impulse".

$$\text{impulse} = F\,\Delta t$$
where F is the net force acting on
the object, in newtons
Δt is the time for which the force
acts, in seconds

Usually, when an object is hit, the duration of contact is very brief. If the duration can be extended, a greater change in momentum will result. Baseball batters or golfers are advised to "follow through", to maximize the duration of contact, thereby increasing the speed of the ball and hence the distance it will travel.

Substituting units into the equation, we find that the unit for impulse is newton seconds ($\text{N}\cdot\text{s}$). It can easily be shown that this is the same as the unit for momentum ($\text{kg}\cdot\text{m/s}$). For an object's momentum to change, the object must receive an impulse equal to its change in momentum. This becomes clear when we combine the previous equations, as follows:

$$\text{impulse} = \text{change in momentum}$$
$$F\,\Delta t = \Delta p$$

Sample problems

1. What is the impulse exerted on a golf ball by a club if they are in contact for 0.005 s and the club exerts a force of 500 N on the ball?

$$\text{impulse} = F\,\Delta t$$
$$= (500 \text{ N})\,(0.005 \text{ s})$$
$$= 2.5 \text{ N} \cdot \text{s}$$

2. What velocity will a 40 kg child on a 10 kg wagon attain if pushed from rest with a force of 75 N for 2.0 s?

$$F\,\Delta t = \Delta p$$
$$= mv_2 - mv_1 \quad \text{where } v_1 = 0$$
$$\therefore v_2 = \frac{F\,\Delta t}{m}$$
$$= \frac{(75 \text{ N})\,(2.0 \text{ s})}{50 \text{ kg}}$$
$$= 3.0 \text{ m/s}$$

3. What force is required to stop a 1000 kg car in 15 s if the car is travelling at 22 m/s?

$$F\,\Delta t = mv_2 - mv_1$$
$$\therefore F = \frac{mv_2 - mv_1}{\Delta t}$$
$$= \frac{(1000 \text{ kg})\,(0 \text{ m/s}) - (1000 \text{ kg})\,(22 \text{ m/s})}{15 \text{ s}}$$
$$= \frac{-22\,000 \text{ kg} \cdot \text{m/s}}{15 \text{ s}}$$
$$= -1.5 \times 10^3 \text{ N}$$

The negative sign indicates that the direction of the force is opposite to that of the car's initial velocity.

Notice the temporary deformation of a baseball when its momentum is changed by the impulse of a bat striking it.

Practice

1. What impulse is exerted in each of the following cases?
   (a) a force of 25 N pushing on a cart for 3.2 s   (80 N·s)
   (b) a tennis racquet exerting a force of 60 N on a tennis ball during the 0.04 s they are in contact   (2.4 N·s)
   (c) the Earth pulling down on a 12 kg rock during the 3.0 s it takes to fall from a cliff.   (3.6×10^2 N·s)

2. A billiard ball of mass 200 g is rolling towards the right-hand cushion of a billiard table at 2.0 m/s and rebounds straight back at 2.0 m/s.
   (a) What is its change in momentum as a result of the collision?   (−0.8 kg·m/s)
   (b) What impulse is exerted on the ball?   (−0.8 N·s)

3. A puck of mass 0.20 kg is sliding along a smooth flat section of ice at 18 m/s when it encounters some snow. After 2.5 s of sliding through the snow, it returns to smooth ice, continuing at a speed of 10 m/s.
   (a) What is the change in momentum of the puck?   (−1.6 kg·m/s)
   (b) What impulse is exerted on the puck by the snow? (−1.6 N·s)
   (c) What average force does the snow exert on the puck?   (−0.64 N)

4. A frictionless disc of mass 0.50 kg is moving in a straight line across an air table at a speed of 2.4 m/s when it bumps into an elastic band stretched between two fixed posts. If the elastic band exerts an average opposing force of 1.2 N on the disc for 1.5 s, what will be the final velocity of the disc?   (−1.2 m/s)

5. A skateboard of mass 2.0 kg is rolling along a smooth flat floor when a small girl pushes it, causing it to speed up to 4.5 m/s in 0.5 s. If the force exerted by the girl on the skateboard, in its direction of motion, was 6.0 N, with what initial velocity was it moving?   (3.0 m/s)

7.4 Transfer of Momentum

The momentum of a moving object may change when the object collides or interacts with a stationary object or another moving object. The following investigation will show how momentum is transferred in a simple interaction between a moving cart and a stationary brick.

Investigation: The Brick-Cart Interaction

Problem:
How does a brick dropped onto a moving cart affect the total momentum?

Materials:

cart   string and retort stand
brick   scissors
ticker-tape timer

Procedure

1. Tie the brick with the string so that it will hang perfectly level and parallel to the desk.
2. Attach a paper tape to the cart and feed the tape into the timer.
3. Tie the string to the retort stand so that the brick is suspended with its underside just above the level of the top of the cart.
4. Start the timer and send the cart across the desk at a steady speed so that it passes directly under the brick. As it passes, cut the string so that the brick drops vertically onto the cart. If the brick does not land squarely on the cart, repeat the procedure.
5. Measure the mass of the brick and of the cart, in kilograms.
6. Using the ticker tape, determine the speeds of the cart just before and just after the brick was dropped, in metres per second.

Questions

1. What is the momentum of the brick before it is dropped? Why?
2. Our system consists of the cart and the brick. What is the total momentum of the system just before the brick is dropped?
3. What is the momentum of the cart and brick together, after the brick has landed on the cart?
4. Compare the combined momentum of the cart and brick before and after the interaction.
5. The values of momentum before and after the interaction should be nearly equal. Calculate the experimental error in your determination of the total momentum. Can you explain why the two values of momentum might not have been precisely equal?

$$I = \Delta P$$
$$I = P_f - P_i$$
$$Ft = mv_f - mv_i$$

The most important property of momentum comes from Newton's Laws. In Section 6.6, you performed an investigation with exploding carts, to verify Newton's Laws. One of the most significant results of that investigation is related to the momentum of the exploding carts.

See Section 6.5 — Newton's Third Law of Motion.

It was shown that

$$F_1 = -F_2$$

(the carts exert equal forces on each other, in opposite directions)

If the time during which the carts are in contact is Δt,

Then
$$F_1 \Delta t = -F_2 \Delta t$$

But we now know that $F \Delta t = \Delta p$

$$\therefore \Delta p_1 = -\Delta p_2$$

or
$$\Delta p_1 + \Delta p_2 = 0$$

Stated in simple terms, this means that the total change in momentum of the system of two exploding carts is zero. As the carts explode, one acquires momentum in one direction while the other acquires an equal amount of momentum in the opposite direction (negative momentum), so that the total change in momentum during the explosion is zero.

Newton first expressed this relationship in the Law of Conservation of Momentum, as follows:

> If no net external force acts on an object, or system of objects, the momentum of the system remains constant, i.e., $\Delta p_{\text{TOTAL}} = 0$ for an isolated system.

In the simplest terms, "The total momentum of a system before any interaction occurs is equal to the total momentum of the system after the interaction."

Any object or group of interacting objects may be thought of as a "system", whose momentum remains the same.

This relationship is very useful in predicting what will happen whenever objects collide or explode.

A Simple Collision

Suppose a loaded railway car rolling to the right collides with an empty railway car rolling to the left on the same smooth, level railway track. They stick together and roll along, but at what speed and in what direction? We need some numbers to determine in which direction and with what speed the pair move off.

Suppose car A has a mass of 6000 kg and a velocity of 2 m/s. Car B has a mass of 3000 kg and a velocity of 3 m/s. First, find the momentum of each car.

$$p_A = (6000 \text{ kg}) \, (2 \text{ m/s}) = 12\,000 \text{ kg} \cdot \text{m/s}$$
$$p_B = (3000 \text{ kg}) \, (-3 \text{ m/s}) = -9000 \text{ kg} \cdot \text{m/s}$$

Now find the total momentum of the "system" consisting of the two cars. Remember that momentum is a vector.

$$p_{\text{TOTAL}} = 12\,000 \text{ kg} \cdot \text{m/s} + (-9000 \text{ kg} \cdot \text{m/s})$$
$$= 12\,000 \text{ kg} \cdot \text{m/s} - 9000 \text{ kg} \cdot \text{m/s}$$
$$= 3000 \text{ kg} \cdot \text{m/s}$$

The velocity of the two cars hooked together is easy to find. All 9000 kg of mass is going at the same velocity. Its momentum is the total momentum of the two cars before the collision. Its velocity is:

$$v = \frac{p_{\text{TOTAL}}}{m}$$
$$= \frac{3000 \text{ kg} \cdot \text{m/s}}{9000 \text{ kg}}$$
$$= 0.33 \text{ m/s}$$

The total momentum of the two cars is the same before and after the collision. There has been no change in the total momentum. The cars pushed on each other, but no outside force acted on the system of the two cars, so that the Law of Conservation of Momentum was applicable.

When objects collide, they may not "touch". For example, two oppositely charged objects or two like magnetic poles can repel one another without actually touching (see sections 11.1 and 13.1).

The principles of jet and rocket propulsion are based on the Law of Conservation of Momentum. A rocket, using its engines, ejects mass (usually hot gases from combustion) backwards at a high speed. The rocket thereby acquires an equal amount of momentum in the opposite direction (forward), which causes its velocity to increase. Retro-rockets, as the name implies, do the opposite. Fired forward, they cause the rocket to lose momentum, and hence speed.

Sample problem

A 60 kg halfback running at 20 m/s runs into an 80 kg tackle running in the opposite direction at 15 m/s. What happens in the collision?

1. Total momentum before collision

momentum of halfback	$p_h = 1200 \text{ kg} \cdot \text{m/s}$
momentum of tackle	$p_t = -1200 \text{ kg} \cdot \text{m/s}$
total momentum	$p_{\text{TOTAL}} = 0 \text{ kg} \cdot \text{m/s}$

Remember, for this type of straight-line problem, motion in one direction is considered to be positive (+), and motion in the opposite direction is considered to be negative (−).

When you jump, you exert an impulse on the Earth, and the Earth exerts an impulse on you, giving you upward momentum. The Earth must have a momentum equal to yours, but its mass is so great that its velocity is too small to measure.

2. Total momentum after collision = 0 kg·m/s, according to the Law of Conservation of Momentum. Actually, the players will probably stop only momentarily. Whoever can push the hardest will get into motion again, acquiring momentum by exerting an impulse on the Earth in the opposite direction.

Practice

1. A 5000 kg boxcar runs into a stationary 8000 kg tank car at 5.2 m/s. They hook together and move off down the track. How fast will they be going?   (2.0 m/s)
2. A large compressed spring is placed between a 4000 kg railway car and a 6000 kg boxcar at rest. The spring is released and the two cars move off in opposite directions. If the heavier car moves at 2.4 m/s, how fast will the other move?   (−3.6 m/s)
3. A 0.20 kg golf ball, moving at 80 m/s, hits a watermelon of 10 kg mass at rest on a frictionless table, and sticks in it. How fast does the watermelon move?   (1.6 m/s)

7.5 Summary

1. The momentum of any moving object is given by

$$p = mv$$

and is a vector quantity whose units are kilogram metres per second.
2. The impulse exerted on an object is given by

$$\text{impulse} = F\,\Delta t$$

and is a vector quantity whose units are newton seconds.
3. Newton's Second Law may be written in terms of momentum and impulse as

$$F\,\Delta t = \Delta p$$

4. The Law of Conservation of Momentum states: "In any interaction in a system of objects, when no external force acts on the system, its total momentum remains constant."

7.6 Review

1. An object is pushed with a force of 6.0 N for 0.5 s. What impulse is given to it?
2. What impulse produces a velocity change of 4.00 m/s in a 12.5 kg mass?
3. A 15 kg wagon is accelerated by a constant force of 60 N from 5.0 m/s to 13.0 m/s.
   (a) What impulse does the wagon receive?
   (b) For how long was the force acting on the wagon?
4. A freight car with a mass of 6.0×10^4 kg is rolling along a level track at 0.40 m/s, dragging a chain behind it.
   (a) If the largest force that could be applied to the chain is 320 N, how long would it take to stop the car?
   (b) How far would the car move before it could be stopped?
5. What average force will stop a hammer with a momentum of 48 N·s in 0.030 s?
6. A stone of mass 10 kg slides along the ice in a straight line with a constant velocity of 8.0 m/s. A constant force then acts on the stone for 2.5 s, changing its velocity to 2.0 m/s.
   (a) What is the momentum of the stone before and after the force acts?
   (b) Calculate the impulse acting on the stone.
   (c) What is the magnitude and direction of the force that is acting?
7. Two frictionless discs on an air table, initially at rest, are driven apart by an explosion with velocities of 9.0 m/s and 5.0 m/s. What is the ratio of their masses?
8. In an experiment similar to Investigation 6.6, two dynamics carts are at rest with a compressed spring between them. When the spring is allowed to expand, the carts move apart. Both hit bricks at either end of the table, simultaneously, but cart A moves 0.60 m while cart B moves 0.90 m. What is the ratio of:
   (a) the speed of A to the speed of B after the explosion?
   (b) their masses?
   (c) the impulses applied to the carts?
   (d) the accelerations of the carts while the spring was pushing them apart?
9. A proton of mass 1.67×10^{-27} kg, travelling with a speed of 1.0×10^7 m/s, collides with a helium nucleus at rest. The proton rebounds straight back with a speed of 6.0×10^6 m/s while the helium nucleus moves forward with a speed of 4.0×10^6 m/s.
   (a) What was the total momentum before the collision?

Numerical Answers to Review Questions
1. 3.0 N·s
2. 50.0 N·s
3. (a) 1.2×10^2 N·s (b) 2.0 s
4. (a) 75 s (b) 15 m
5. 1.6×10^3 N
6. (a) 80 kg·m/s, 20 kg·m/s (b) −60 N·s
   (c) −24 N
7. 0.56
8. (a) 0.67 (b) 1.5 (c) 1.0 (d) 0.67
9. (a) 1.67×10^{-20} kg·m/s
   (b) -1.0×10^{-20} kg·m/s
   (c) 2.67×10^{-20} kg·m/s (d) 6.68×10^{-27} kg
10. 2.7 m/s
11. (a) 10 kg·m/s (b) 7.5 kg·m/s
    (c) 1.0 m/s (d) 4.0 m/s
12. 0.50 m/s
13. 0.22 m/s
15. −1.5 m/s

(b) What was the momentum of the proton after the collision?

(c) What was the momentum of the helium nucleus after the collision?

(d) Determine the mass of the helium nucleus.

10. A stationary flatcar of mass 4.0×10^4 kg is rammed by a locomotive with a mass of 6.0×10^4 kg and a velocity of 4.5 m/s. If they stick together, with what velocity will they continue to move?

11. Two 2.5 kg carts are moving along together with a velocity of 2.0 m/s when a spring compressed between them expands rapidly. The front cart continues with a velocity of 3.0 m/s, in the same direction.

(a) What was the momentum of the two carts before the explosion?

(b) What was the momentum of the front cart after the explosion?

(c) What was the velocity of the second cart after the explosion?

(d) What velocity would the front cart have had to acquire for the second cart to remain stationary after the explosion?

12. A 1.5 kg brick is dropped vertically onto a 2.5 kg toy truck, which is moving across a level floor at 0.80 m/s. With what velocity do the truck and brick continue to move, after the brick has landed on the truck?

13. Explain how an astronaut who is stranded in free space a short distance from his spacecraft might employ his knowledge of momentum to return safely to the craft. Why must he be very careful about his momentum?

14. A sandbag is mounted on a cart that is at rest on a horizontal frictionless surface, and their total mass is 4.5 kg. What will be the velocity of the cart and sandbag if a bullet of mass 2.0 g is fired into the sandbag with a horizontal velocity of 500 m/s?

15. Two boys of mass 45 kg and 60 kg, respectively, are sitting on 15 kg wagons, facing each other and holding a rope taut between them. The lighter boy pulls on the rope and acquires a velocity of 2.0 m/s. What is the velocity of the other boy?

7.7 Learning Objectives

1. Given any two of mass, velocity, and momentum, to calculate the third.
2. Given any two of force exerted, duration of force exerted, and impulse exerted, to calculate the third.
3. To state Newton's Second Law in terms of impulse and momentum.
4. Given any four of force applied, time, mass, initial velocity, and final velocity, to calculate the fifth.
5. To state the Law of Conservation of Momentum and to identify systems of interacting objects to which it applies.
6. For interactions between two objects, given any five of their masses, their initial velocities, and their final velocities, to calculate the sixth.

8 Work, Energy, and Power

8.1 Work

Work is done whenever a force makes something move. It is done by a car's engine to make the car accelerate, by a crane lifting a steel beam for a new building, by an archer bending his bow as he pulls an arrow back, and by the bow when the archer releases the arrow. Work is also being done when a chicken is roasted in an oven, though in this case it is not so obvious what the force is, and what it is that is being made to move.

Measuring Work

The standard amount, or unit, of work is called a **joule** (J). You can do 1 J of work by pushing on a small object with a force of exactly 1 N, moving that object exactly 1 m.

If you move the same object twice as far, you will have done twice as much work. The amount of work done varies directly with the distance the object moves.

If you use twice as much force to move this object the original distance, again you will have done twice as much work. The amount of work done varies directly with the amount of force acting on the object.

Here are the results of an imaginary experiment with work (W), distance (d), and force (F).

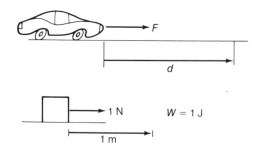

Force F (newtons)	Distance d (metres)	Work W (joules)
1	1	1
1	2	2
1	5	5
2	1	2
5	1	5
2	2	4
5	5	25

In each case, the amount of work done is calculated by multiplying the force that was applied by the distance the object moved.

$$W = Fd$$

where F is the force applied, in newtons
  d is the distance moved, in metres
  W is the work done, in joules

There are three special cases that must be mentioned. The first is when movement occurs even though no force is applied. Once set in motion, an object on a frictionless surface keeps on moving. Though work was done to start it moving, no further work is necessary to keep it moving. If the applied force is zero, no work is done, even on a moving object.

In the second situation, force is exerted but there is no motion. For example, you could exhaust yourself by pushing hard against a brick wall, but the wall would not budge. If the distance moved is zero, the equation states that no work was done on the wall. In this case, you would have done work, not on the wall, but on yourself, producing heat. The equation gives the amount of work done by the force that is applied, on the object to which it is applied.

The third situation occurs when force is applied at right angles to the direction of motion of the object. It does no work. It neither helps to speed up the object nor does it slow it down.

In the problems in this book, the force that is applied will always be in the same direction as the direction of motion.

Sample problems

1. How much work is done by a boy pushing a car with a force of 800 N for a distance of 200 m?

$$W = Fd$$
$$= (800 \text{ N}) (200 \text{ m})$$
$$= 1.60 \times 10^5 \text{ J}$$

2. How much work is done by a girl pushing a 100 kg refrigerator across a rough floor for 10 m using a force of 900 N against a force of friction of 900 N?

The refrigerator will move at a constant speed because the forces on it are balanced, but the work done is not zero. When you calculate work, you use the applied force, not the net force. The friction could not conceivably reduce the amount of work done.

The joule is named after James Prescott Joule (1818-89), owner of a Manchester brewery, who was determined to prove that heat was not "caloric fluid" (a substance) but a form of energy that could be produced by doing work. He found that the heat produced by stirring water or mercury is proportional to the amount of work done in the stirring.

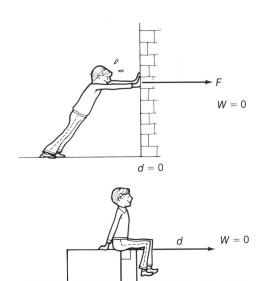

Here, work is defined for straight-line motion only, where the force is in the direction of motion of the object.

$$W = Fd$$
$$= (900 \text{ N}) (10 \text{ m})$$
$$= 9000 \text{ J}$$
$$= 9.0 \times 10^3 \text{ J}$$

Practice

1. A force of 20 N was used to push a box along the floor for a distance of 8.0 m. How much work was done? $(1.6 \times 10^2 \text{ J})$
2. A 2.0 kg puck accelerated at 5.0 m/s^2 for 0.50 m across a frictionless air hockey table. How much work was done on the puck? (5.0 J)
3. A bulldozer pushed a large rock with a force of 5000 N at 2.0 m/s for 20 s. How much work was done? $(2.0 \times 10^5 \text{ J})$
4. How much work is required to lift a 50 kg object straight up 10 m? $(4.9 \times 10^3 \text{ J})$

Note that, according to the laws of motion, you only need to balance the force of gravity in order to keep an object moving straight up at a constant speed. Of course, a bit more force is necessary at the beginning of the trip to get the object moving, but, on the other hand, less force is needed at the end of the trip as the object stops. It can be shown that the small amount of extra work at the beginning is offset exactly by the slight reduction at the end. When something is being lifted in our problems, we will assume that the force needed is equal to the force of gravity on the object and that it is constant for the whole trip.

8.2 Power

''Work'' and ''power'' are often used interchangeably in everyday life, but in physics each has a distinct meaning. **Power** is defined as the rate at which work is done. The machine that can do a certain amount of work the fastest is developing the most power.

For machines working steadily, the power is calculated by dividing the work done by the time taken to do the work. The standard amount of power is a joule per second, which, in SI units, is one watt (W).

$$1 \text{ J/s} = 1 \text{ W}$$

$$P = \frac{W}{t}$$

where W is the work done, in joules
t is the time taken, in seconds
P is the power, in watts

In 1782, James Watt (1736-1819) introduced a new, improved version of the steam engine that changed its status from that of a minor gadget to that of a universal work horse. First used to pump water from coal mines, it soon powered steamships, locomotives, shovels, tractors, cars, and any number of mechanical devices.

In 1807, Robert Fulton, the American inventor, launched the first commercially successful steamboat.

George Stephenson built the first practical steam locomotive in 1814. The 7 t engine pulled 48 t at a speed of 25 km/h from Darlington to Stockton, in the north of England.

Sample problem

What is the power of a bulldozer that does 5.5×10^4 J of work in 1.1 s?

$$P = \frac{W}{t}$$
$$= \frac{5.5 \times 10^4 \text{ J}}{1.1 \text{ s}}$$
$$= 5.0 \times 10^4 \text{ W}$$

Practice

1. How much power does a crane develop, doing 60 000 J of work in 5.00 min? (200 W)
2. How long does it take a 2.5 kW electric motor to do 75 000 J of work? (30 s)
3. How much work can a 500 W electric mixer do in 2.5 min? (7.5×10^4 J)

The world's largest power station, a hydro-electric station on the Yenisey River in the U.S.S.R., can develop 6×10^9 W of power.

Investigation: Power Running Up Stairs

Problem:
What is the maximum power that a physics student can develop running up stairs?

The record for stair-climbing is held by Dr. Randolph Seed who, in February 1972, climbed the 100-storey John Hancock Building in Chicago in 14 min 29 s. Assuming a mass of 70 kg for the doctor and a height of 4.5 m for each storey, Dr. Seed developed an average power of 355 W.

Materials:
physics student(s)
kilogram bathroom scale
metre stick
stopwatch

Procedure
1. Measure the mass of the physics student (or students, if you want to make this a competition), in kilograms. Set up a suitable table in your notebook and start recording your data.
2. Calculate the force of gravity on the student, using $F_g = mg$. Use this value for force in your work calculation.
3. Measure the height of one step. Count the number of steps and multiply to find the vertical height the student will rise, in metres.
4. With the stopwatch, measure the time the student takes to run up the stairs, from a standing start, in seconds.
5. Calculate the power developed.

A steam locomotive built in the U.S. in 1929, a Northern Pacific 2-8-8-4, could develop more than 3×10^7 W of power — a record.

Questions
1. What are the physical characteristics of the more powerful students in your class? Do they tend to be tall, or strong, or heavy?
2. In which sports must a person be able to generate a lot of force? Do much work? Develop great power?

Sample Problem

How much power is developed by a 60 kg boy running up a 4.5 m high flight of stairs in 3.0 s?

$$F_g = mg \qquad \qquad \text{(He is doing work against the}$$
$$= (60 \text{ kg}) (9.8 \text{ N/kg}) \qquad \text{force of gravity.)}$$
$$= 588 \text{ N}$$
$$W = Fd$$
$$= (588 \text{ N}) (4.5 \text{ m})$$
$$= 2646 \text{ J}$$
$$P = \frac{W}{t}$$
$$= \frac{2646 \text{ J}}{3.0 \text{ s}}$$
$$= 8.8 \times 10^2 \text{ W}$$

Practice
1. How much power is developed by a 70.0 kg girl running up a 3.00 m high flight of stairs in 2.20 s?   (935 W)
2. How long will it take the girl in question 1 to run up a flight of stairs 4.5 m high?   (3.3 s)
3. A boy who can generate 500 W runs up a flight of stairs in 5.0 s. How high are the stairs if the boy has a mass of 50 kg? (5.1 m)

8.3 Another Unit for Work

The unit for work is the joule, which is the amount of work done by a force of 1 N pushing an object for a distance of 1 m. The joule is a very small quantity of work. Even a small machine, such as the fan on a furnace, does several million joules of work in a day.

There is a larger unit that is used to measure work called the kilowatt hour. It is the amount of work done by a machine with a power of 1 kW, in 1 h.

To calculate the work done in 1 h by a machine working at a rate of 1 kW, we will use the equation:

$$P = \frac{W}{t}$$

This means that $\qquad W = Pt$

Now, to calculate the work done in each of the units:

$P = 1 \text{ kW}$	or	$P = 1000 \text{ W}$
$t = 1 \text{ h}$	or	$t = 3600 \text{ s}$
$W = Pt$		$W = Pt$
$= (1 \text{ kW})(1 \text{ h})$		$= (1000 \text{ W})(3600 \text{ s})$
$= 1 \text{ kW·h}$		$= 3\ 600\ 000 \text{ J}$

$$1 \text{ kW·h} = 3\ 600\ 000 \text{ J}$$
$$= 3.6 \text{ MJ}$$

Kilowatt hours are commonly used to measure energy, especially electrical energy. Eventually, however, the megajoule will be used for large amounts of energy.

$$1 \text{ MJ} = 10^6 \text{ J}$$

When amounts of work are to be calculated in kilowatt hours, it is simpler to use kilowatts instead of watts for the power and hours instead of seconds for time. The units of work will then be kilowatt hours instead of joules.

Sample problem

How much work is done by a 25 kW water pump running steadily for a week, in kilowatt hours?

$$W = Pt$$
$$= (25 \text{ kW})(7 \times 24) \text{ h}$$
$$= (25 \text{ kW})(168 \text{ h})$$
$$= 4.2 \times 10^3 \text{ kW·h}$$

Practice
1. How much work (in kilowatt hours) is done by a 6000 W electric generator, running 8.0 h a day for a year? (1.8×10^4 kW·h)
2. How long (in hours) will it take a 500 W power drill to do 100 kW·h of work? (200 h)
3. How much power is being developed by a machine that can do 600 kW·h of work in 12 h? (50 kW)

8.4 Energy

No machine can operate without fuel. Just as gasoline is the fuel for automobiles, food is the fuel for the human body. Food somehow gives you the ability to do work; it gives you energy. **Energy** is the ability to do work.

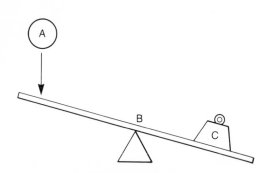

When falling object A does work on lever
B, which does work on object C, energy is
transferred from A to B to C.

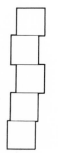

This is not the complete story. Suppose that you do some work on a large rock, by lifting it straight up into the air. You have used some of your energy supply. But that energy has not vanished. It has not been "used up", but transferred (most of it) to the rock. And the rock can now do something it could not do before. If you let go of it, it will fall back to its original position, and, as it falls, it can do work. It might be made to push down on a lever, lifting some other object. Or you could tie a rope to the rock and run the rope over a pulley, so that, as it fell, the rock would lift some other object or pull it along the ground. Each time work is done, energy is transferred from the object doing the work to the object being worked on. **Work** is the transfer of energy.

It is convenient to measure both work and energy in the same unit, the joule. If you do 5000 J of work on an object, you have transferred 5000 J of your energy to it. Doing work on an object increases its energy. Mathematically, this is expressed as:

$$W = \Delta E$$

where W is the work done on an object, in joules
ΔE is the change in energy of the object, in joules

Kinds of Energy

Energy is transferred when work is done, but it is also, usually, transformed from one kind of energy to another. There are many kinds of energy, some obvious, and some not so obvious. It took many scientists many years to discover the various forms we know. The secret is to remember that anything that can do work has energy. The following is a description of the more important kinds of energy.

1. **Gravitational Potential Energy:** Any raised object, such as the rock you lifted, has energy and can do work as it falls.
2. **Kinetic Energy:** Any moving object, such as a fast-moving baseball, has energy and can do work on any object it hits.

3. **Heat Energy:** Hot objects have energy and can do work. It is easiest to show this with a very hot object, such as a boiler full of superheated steam, but even water at room temperature can do work.

4. **Chemical Potential Energy:** Atoms join together in various combinations to form many different kinds of molecules, involving varying amounts of energy. In chemical reactions, new arrangements of atoms are formed and energy is absorbed or released. A stick of dynamite releases chemical energy and can do work when it explodes. You release chemical energy when you burn coal, flex a muscle, or turn on a flashlight.

5. **Elastic Energy:** Any object that is compressed, stretched, or twisted can do work and therefore has energy.

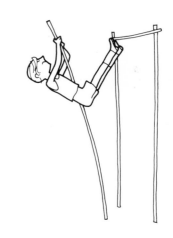

6. **Light:** It is not easy to show directly that light can do work. Ordinarily, heat energy is produced when sunlight is absorbed. When light strikes a photocell, electrical energy is produced. However, in a famous experiment, a tiny piece of metal foil in a vacuum was made to move by a beam of light shining on it. The beam of light did work, so it must have had energy.

7. **Electrical Energy:** Electric currents make motors turn and lights flash. There are electric clocks and dishwashers, elevators, streetcars, pencil-sharpeners, and stoves. Almost every conceivable kind of work can be done by electricity. Even our bodies use electrical impulses to send messages back and forth. Electric currents can do work because they have energy.

8. **Nuclear Energy:** The nucleus of every atom has energy. The energy released by the fission of a kilogram of uranium atoms in a nuclear reactor is more than the energy released in the burning of thousands of tonnes of coal in a conventional thermal generating station.

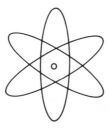

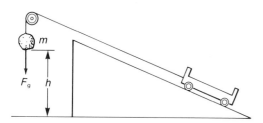

8.5 Gravitational Potential Energy

Imagine a rock with a mass, m, tied to the end of a long rope. The rope runs up over a pulley and the other end is tied to another object, or to a spring, or perhaps to a wagon on a ramp.

If you let go of the rock, it will fall, pulling on the rope, and do work. The rock will pull downwards with a force equal to the force of gravity.

The work done by the rock depends on how far it falls. Suppose that it falls a distance, h. Then the work done will be:

$$W = Fd$$
$$= (mg)(h) \qquad \text{since} \quad F = mg$$
$$= mgh \qquad \text{and} \quad d = h$$

This is also the amount of energy that will be transferred to whatever is attached to the other end of the rope, provided that the rope and the pulley are frictionless. The higher the rock is lifted in the first place, the more work it will be able to do, and the more energy will be stored in it. When the rock falls, this energy is released.

The energy stored in an object due to its distance above the surface of the Earth is called **gravitational potential energy**, E_p. The change in gravitational potential energy of an object is given by the equation:

$$\Delta E_p = mgh$$

where m is the mass of the object, in kilograms
g is the gravitational field strength, in newtons per kilogram
h is the vertical distance the object is moved, in metres
ΔE_p is the object's change in energy, in joules

Sample problems

1. How much gravitational potential energy does a 4.0 kg rock gain if it is lifted 25 m?

$$\Delta E_p = mgh$$
$$= (4.0 \text{ kg})(9.80 \text{ N/kg})(25 \text{ m})$$
$$= 9.8 \times 10^2 \text{ J}$$

2. How much potential energy is lost by a 61.2 kg boy falling 0.500 m out of bed?

$$\Delta E_p = mgh$$
$$= (61.2 \text{ kg})(9.80 \text{ N/kg})(-0.500 \text{ m})$$
$$= -300 \text{ J}$$

A negative change in energy is a decrease in energy.

Practice

1. A crane lifts a 1500 kg car 20 m straight up.
   (a) How much potential energy does the car gain?
   $$(2.9 \times 10^5 \text{ J})$$
   (b) How much potential energy does the crane transfer to the car?
   $$(2.9 \times 10^5 \text{ J})$$
   (c) How much work does the crane do?
   $$(2.9 \times 10^5 \text{ J})$$

2. A 4.00 kg rubber ball drops from a height of 5.00 m to the ground and bounces back to a height of 3.00 m.
   (a) How much potential energy does the ball lose on the trip down?
   (196 J)
   (b) How much energy does the ball regain on the trip back up?
   (118 J)
   (c) What is the net loss of potential energy during the bounce?
   (78 J)

Relative Potential Energy

The equation just developed may be used to determine the change in an object's potential energy as it is moved towards or away from the Earth.

In practice, it is useful to select a position at which an object's potential energy is zero. Usually we pick the lowest point in the problem. The potential energy at any other point is measured relative to the zero position. Then the equation for the gravitational potential energy is:

$$E_p = mgh$$

where h is measured vertically from the zero position in metres

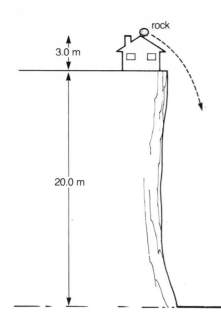

Remember, the distance, h, in the equation $E_p = mgh$ is the vertical straight-line distance of the object above the chosen reference plane, since the force is also vertical.

Sample problem

A 10.0 kg rock is on top of a house 3.00 m high on the edge of a cliff 20.0 m high. What is the gravitational potential energy of the rock
(a) relative to the roof of the house?
(b) relative to the floor of the house?
(c) relative to the bottom of the cliff?

(a) The zero point is the roof.
$$E_p = mgh$$
$$= (10.0 \text{ kg}) (9.80 \text{ N/kg}) (0 \text{ m})$$
$$= 0 \text{ J}$$
(b) The zero point is the floor of the house.
$$E_p = mgh$$
$$= (10.0 \text{ kg}) (9.80 \text{ N/kg}) (3.00 \text{ m})$$
$$= 294 \text{ J}$$
(c) The zero point is the bottom of the cliff.
$$E_p = mgh$$
$$= (10.0 \text{ kg}) (9.80 \text{ N/kg}) (23.0 \text{ m})$$
$$= 2254 \text{ J}$$
$$= 2.25 \times 10^3 \text{ J}$$

Practice

1. A man on a flying trapeze stands on a platform 20 m above the ground holding the trapeze. The trapeze is 10 m long and is attached to a kite 26 m above the ground. The man swings down and lets go of the rope on the upswing. He has a mass of 60 kg. Calculate his potential energy relative to the ground when he is at each of the following heights.
   (a) 20 m (on platform) $(1.2 \times 10^4 \text{ J})$
   (b) 16 m (bottom of swing) $(9.4 \times 10^3 \text{ J})$
   (c) 18 m (lets go of trapeze) $(1.1 \times 10^4 \text{ J})$
   (d) 9.0 m (halfway to ground) $(5.3 \times 10^3 \text{ J})$
2. Repeat the previous question, calculating his potential energy relative to a point 16 m above the ground.
   $(2 \times 10^3 \text{ J}, 0 \text{ J}, 1 \times 10^3 \text{ J}, -4 \times 10^3 \text{ J})$

8.6 Kinetic Energy

Kinetic energy is the energy of a moving object. A bowling ball headed down an alley will be able to do work on the pins because it is moving. The amount of kinetic energy in the ball depends on how fast the ball is moving, and on its mass. A tennis ball moving down the alley at the same speed could do very little work on the pins.

The kinetic energy of any object is a result of work being done on it. If we could determine how much work it took to accelerate a bowling ball up to a certain speed, then we would know how much kinetic energy had been given to the ball.

Imagine a bowling ball with mass, m, accelerated by a bowler with a force, F, pushing on it for a distance, d, down a frictionless alley.

Force F acts for distance d on bowling ball, mass m.

The work done on the bowling ball is:

$$W = Fd$$

The relationship between the force, the mass of the ball, and the acceleration of the ball, since there is no friction, is:

$$F = ma$$

By substitution, we now have:

$$W = (ma)(d)$$
$$= mad$$

The speed-time graph of an object accelerating from rest is a straight line for a constant acceleration.

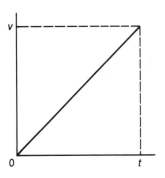

The speed of the ball changes from 0 to v in a time, t. The acceleration is the slope of the graph:

$$a = \frac{\Delta v}{\Delta t}$$
$$= \frac{(v - 0)}{(t - 0)}$$
$$= \frac{v}{t}$$

The distance travelled by the accelerating bowling ball is:

$$\Delta d = \left(\frac{v_1 + v_2}{2}\right) \Delta t$$
$$= \left(\frac{0 + v}{2}\right)(t - 0)$$
$$= \frac{vt}{2}$$

Now we substitute into the equation for work:

$$W = mad$$

$$= m\left(\frac{v}{t}\right)\left(\frac{vt}{2}\right)$$
$$= \tfrac{1}{2}mv^2$$

Doing work on the object by accelerating it has transferred energy to it. The only change between the object now and before the work was done on it is its increased speed. The energy the ball now has is energy of motion, or **kinetic energy**, written as E_k.

$$E_k = 1/2\,mv^2$$

where m is the mass of the object, in kilograms
v is the speed of the object, in metres per second
E_k is the kinetic energy, in joules

Sample problem

What is the kinetic energy of a 6.0 kg curling stone sliding at 4.0 m/s?

$$E_k = 1/2\,mv^2$$
$$= 1/2\ (6.0\ \text{kg})\ (4.0\ \text{m/s})^2$$
$$= 48\ \text{J}$$

Practice

1. What is the kinetic energy of a 0.500 kg ball thrown at 30.0 m/s?   (225 J)
2. What is the kinetic energy of a 25.0 g bullet travelling at 3600 km/h?   (1.25×10^4 J)
3. What is the mass of an object travelling at 20 m/s with a kinetic energy of 4000 J?   (20 kg)
4. What is the speed of a 1.5 kg rock falling with a kinetic energy of 48 J?   (8.0 m/s)
5. A 0.50 kg rubber ball is thrown into the air. At a height of 20 m above the ground, it is travelling at 15 m/s.
   (a) What is the ball's kinetic energy?   (56 J)
   (b) What is its gravitational potential energy relative to the ground?   (98 J)
   (c) How much work was done by someone at ground level throwing the ball up into the air?   (1.5×10^2 J)

Investigation: Kinetic Energy in Elastic Collisions

Problem:

Is kinetic energy conserved in a collision between air pucks?

Materials:

2 low-friction pucks with ring magnets
strobe light

Polaroid camera
metre stick
synchronizing strobe disk

Procedure

1. Either use the photograph printed here or make your own strobe photo of a collision between two magnetic pucks. Do not push the pucks so fast that they actually touch each other.
2. Make measurements so as to be able to calculate the speeds of the pucks before and after the collision.
3. Measure the masses of the pucks.

The pucks moved as follows:

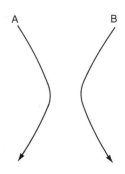

The strobe flashed every 0.10 s.
The photograph is one-tenth of full size.
Each puck has a mass of 0.10 kg.

Questions

1. Calculate the kinetic energy of each puck before and after the collision. Draw a data table in which to record your results.
2. Calculate the total kinetic energy before the collision and after the collision.
3. How much energy is gained or lost? If this were a perfectly **elastic collision** no kinetic energy would be lost. What is the gain or loss as a percentage of the total kinetic energy before the collision?
4. If some energy is lost, where might it have gone?

Sample problem

A 6.0 kg magnetic puck hits a stationary 2.0 kg magnetic puck head-on at 6.0 m/s. The first puck continues on, slowing to 3.0 m/s, and the second puck moves forwards at 9.0 m/s. Is kinetic energy lost in this collision?

The kinetic energy before the collision is:
$$E_k = 1/2\ mv^2$$
$$= 1/2\ (6.0\ kg)\ (6.0\ m/s)^2$$
$$= 108\ J$$

The kinetic energy after the collision is:
$$E_k = 1/2\ (6.0\ kg)\ (3.0\ m/s)^2 + 1/2\ (2.0\ kg)\ (9.0\ m/s)^2$$
$$= 27\ J + 81\ J$$
$$= 108\ J$$

No kinetic energy is lost.

Practice

1. A 2.0 kg puck hits a stationary 6.0 kg puck head-on at 6.0 m/s. The 2.0 kg puck bounces straight back at 3.0 m/s and the 6.0 kg puck goes forwards.
   (a) If the collision is elastic, what energy does the 6.0 kg puck receive?   (27 J)
   (b) How fast must the 6.0 kg puck go?   (3.0 m/s)
2. A 6.00 kg ball of putty moving at 10.0 m/s runs head-on into another 6.00 kg ball of putty. They stick together and move ahead at 5.00 m/s.
   (a) Calculate the total kinetic energy before the collision. (300 J)
   (b) Calculate the total kinetic energy after the collision. (150 J)
   (c) Was the collision elastic?   (no)
   (d) What percentage of the original kinetic energy was lost?   (50%)

8.7 Conservation of Energy

Imagine a large rock inside a tall vacuum chamber. The rock is released at the top of the chamber and falls, accelerating at 9.8 m/s². As it falls, its gravitational potential energy decreases, and its kinetic energy increases. (Fortunately, there is no air resistance in a vacuum, and no heat energy is produced.) Is the increase in kinetic energy equal to the decrease in potential energy?

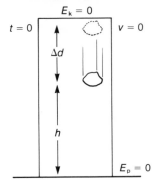

Object with mass m falling in a vacuum

Suppose that the rock has a mass of 2.0 kg, that it falls from a height of 490 m, and that its gravitational potential energy is zero at the bottom of the chamber.

1. Since the rock falls from rest with an acceleration of 9.8 m/s², its speed at the time, t, will be:
$$v = gt$$

2. The distance it has fallen at that time will be:
$$\Delta d = \left(\frac{v_1 + v_2}{2}\right) \Delta t$$
$$= \left(\frac{0 + v}{2}\right) t$$
$$= \frac{vt}{2}$$

3. Its height above the ground at that time will be:
$$h = 490 - \Delta d$$

4. Its kinetic energy will be:
$$E_k = \tfrac{1}{2} mv^2$$

5. Its gravitational potential energy will be:
$$E_p = mgh$$

6. Its total energy will be:
$$E_t = E_k + E_p$$

The table summarizes the results of all the calculations for the fall of the rock.

time (s)	1 speed (m/s)	2 distance fallen (m)	3 height (m)	4 kinetic energy (J)	5 potential energy (J)	6 total energy (J)
0	0	0	490.0	0	9604	9604
1	9.8	4.9	485.1	96	9508	9604
2	19.6	19.6	470.4	384	9220	9604
3	29.4	44.1	445.9	864	8740	9604
4	39.2	78.4	411.6	1537	8067	9604
5	49.0	122.5	367.5	2401	7203	9604
6	58.8	176.4	313.6	3457	6147	9604
7	68.6	240.1	249.9	4706	4898	9604
8	78.4	313.6	176.4	6147	3457	9604
9	88.2	396.9	93.1	7779	1825	9604
10	98.0	490.0	0	9604	0	9604

Since the total amount of energy remained constant, the potential energy lost as the rock fell was converted into kinetic energy. This appears to happen during every kind of energy transfer or transformation, even though more than these two kinds of energy may be involved. This principle is called the Law of Conservation of Energy.

In any transfer or transformation of energy, the total amount of energy remains constant.

The Law of Conservation of Energy was proposed by Heinrich von Helmholtz (1821-1894) in 1847, suggesting that energy could neither be created nor destroyed.

Sample problem

A 20 kg rock falls 50 m in a vacuum, from rest.
(a) What is the rock's loss in gravitational potential energy?
(b) What is its gain in kinetic energy?
(c) What is the final speed of the rock?

(a) $\Delta E_p = mgh$
$= (20 \text{ kg}) (9.8 \text{ N/kg}) (50 \text{ m})$
$= 9.8 \times 10^2 \text{ J}$

(b) $\Delta E_k = \Delta E_p = 9.8 \times 10^2 \text{ J}$

(c) $E_k = \frac{1}{2}mv^2$
$v^2 = \frac{2E_k}{m}$

$$v = \sqrt{\frac{2E_k}{m}}$$
$$= \sqrt{\frac{2(9.8 \times 10^2 \text{ J})}{20 \text{ kg}}}$$
$$= \sqrt{980 \text{ J/kg}}$$
$$= 31 \text{ m/s}$$

Practice

1. What is the speed of a 70.0 kg rock after it has fallen freely for 1000 m?   **(140 m/s)**
2. How far would a 1.00 kg ball have to fall freely to reach a speed of 100 km/h?   **(39.4 m)**
3. How fast would you have to throw a 2.0 kg rock straight up so that it would reach a height of 20 m?   **(20 m/s)**

Total Energy of a Toy Car

The Law of Conservation of Energy was arrived at by experiment. One interaction after another was studied; energies were measured and totalled. When the total energy was not constant, invariably a new form of energy was discovered to account for the difference. A big step forward was the acceptance of heat as a form of energy. The force of friction, which slows objects down, also generates heat. Kinetic energy is being changed to heat energy.

The next investigation involves a strobe photograph of a toy car moving down a curved ramp. Measurements of the distance travelled between dots will enable you to calculate the speed and the kinetic energy of the car at various times. Measurements of the car's height above the desk at these same times will enable you to calculate the corresponding gravitational potential energy. Adding these results together will give the total energy, unless some of it is being transformed into another kind of energy, such as heat.

Investigation: Total Energy of a Toy Car

Problem:
Is the total energy of a toy car on a ramp constant?

Materials:
accurate metric scale
onionskin paper

Procedure

1. Draw a straight line across a sheet of onionskin paper to serve as a zero line for potential energy.
2. Place the onionskin paper over the photograph with the straight line lined up with the lower edge of the photograph. Assume that the lower edge of the photograph is horizontal.
3. Put a small dot in the centre of the little square on the top of each image of the car.
4. Number the dots, as shown in the photograph.

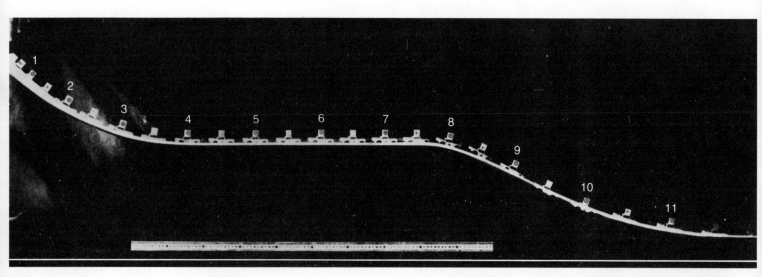

5. Measure the height above the zero line of each numbered dot and correct for the scale of the photograph (1 cm = 10 cm). Set up a suitable table in your notebook and begin to record your observations.

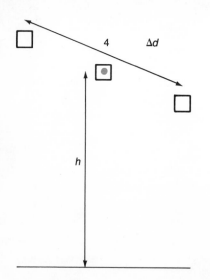

interval	h (m)	Δd (m)	v (m/s)	E_p (J)	E_k (J)	$E_t = E_p + E_k$ (J)
1						
2						

6. Measure the distance travelled between the two dots on either side of each numbered dot, and correct for the scale of the photograph.

7. Divide each distance travelled by the time interval. The time between dots is 0.05 s. The time interval here is 2 × 0.05 s = 0.10 s. This gives you the average speed for each numbered interval.
8. Calculate the kinetic energy, the potential energy, and the total energy for each numbered interval. The mass of the car is 100 g.
9. On a single set of axes, draw graphs of each type of energy plotted against time.

Questions

1. What does the shape of the graph of potential energy against time resemble? Why?
2. What does the shape of the kinetic energy graph resemble? Why?
3. What should the graph of total energy against time look like if the sum of the kinetic energy and potential energy is constant?
4. What percentage of the sum of the original kinetic energy and potential energy remains at the end of the trip?
5. What other energy transformations could have taken place as the car went down the ramp?

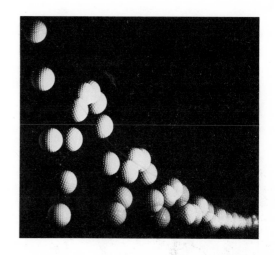

$E_h = E_k + E_p$

Temp-ave E/molecule

8.8 Heat Energy

Heat is energy that is stored inside matter, the total of the kinetic energy of its molecules as they move – colliding, spinning and vibrating – and their potential energy as they move closer together or farther apart.

Temperature is a measure of the average energy per molecule. A cup of tea may be at the same temperature as a bathtub full of water, but the total amount of heat in each is quite different.

The total amount of heat needed to raise the temperature of an object may be shown to depend on three quantities: the mass of the object, the desired temperature change, and the specific heat capacity of the material.

It takes about 4200 J of heat energy to raise the temperature of 1 kg of water by 1°C. Other materials require different amounts of heat to undergo the same change. The specific heat capacity of water is said to be 4200 J/(kg·°C)

This is read as "four thousand two hundred joules per kilogram per degree Celsius".

The specific heat capacities of some common materials are shown in a table.

$4/500 = 5.820 / 15$

Material	Specific heat capacity J/(kg·°C)
water	4200
alcohol, methyl	2380
kerosene	2100
concrete	880
asbestos	820
ice	2040
aluminum	900
copper	430
iron	450
steel	480
lead	130

If it takes 4200 J of heat energy to raise the temperature of 1 kg of water by 1°C, then it will take twice as much heat energy to heat up 2 kg of water by 1°C. The heat required will be proportional to the mass of the object.

Also, if the specific heat is a constant, it will take twice as much heat to heat up 1 kg of water by 2°C. The amount of heat required is proportional to the required temperature change.

This means that the equation for calculating the heat required to change the temperature of an object is:

$$\Delta E_h = mc\Delta T$$

where m is the mass of the object, in kilograms
ΔT is the temperature change, in degrees Celsius
c is the specific heat capacity, in joules per kilogram per degree Celsius
ΔE_h is the heat energy added, in joules

Sample problem

How much heat does it take to raise the temperature of 100 g of lead shot (tiny beads of lead) from 20°C to 33°C?

$$m = 100 \text{ g}$$
$$= 0.100 \text{ kg}$$
$$\Delta T = (33 - 20)°C$$
$$= 13°C$$
$$c = 130 \text{ J/(kg·°C)}$$
$$\Delta E_h = mc\ \Delta T$$
$$= (0.100 \text{ kg}) (130 \text{ J/kg·°C})) (13°C)$$
$$= 1.7 \times 10^2 \text{ J}$$

Practice

1. How much heat energy does it take to raise the temperature of 10 kg of water from 5°C to 95°C?   (3.8×10^6 J)

2. A 500 g block of aluminum cools from 50°C to 20°C. How much heat does it lose?   (1.4×10^4 J)

3. If 15 000 J of heat are absorbed by a 2.0 kg block of copper, by how much will its temperature rise?   (17°C)

4. If 25 000 J of heat energy are absorbed by 5.0 kg of a substance, its temperature rises by 20°C. What is the specific heat of the substance?   (2.5×10^2 J/(kg·°C))

8.9 Efficiency

According to the Law of Conservation of Energy, the amount of energy present before an energy transformation is equal to the amount of energy present after that energy transformation. Unfortunately, sometimes, some of the energy is not in a useful form and is wasted. Some transformations are more efficient than others. The efficiency of an energy transformation is calculated as follows:

$$\textbf{efficiency} = \frac{\textbf{useful energy output}}{\textbf{energy input}} \times \textbf{100\%}$$

Automobiles are highly inefficient. Suppose that an amount of fuel containing 1000 J of chemical energy is fed into an automobile's engine. In an internal combustion engine, the fuel is vaporized and mixed with air in the carburetor, then drawn into a cylinder containing a piston. A spark from the spark plug ignites the fuel mixture, producing very high temperatures and pressures. The pressure of the gases so produced pushes down on the piston, which turns the crankshaft, and thus, through the transmission, turns the wheels, which makes the car move forwards. If you calculate the work done by multiplying the force of the wheels moving the car by the distance the car moves, you will get far less than the original 1000 J. Perhaps only 100 J remain. The rest is lost as heat energy.

Much of this heat is carried away by the exhaust gases. When the exploded fuel gases have done their job, they are pushed out through the exhaust valve, which opens as the piston starts back up the cylinder.

Some of the heat is conducted through the walls of the cylinders to the rest of the engine. To keep the engine from getting too hot, a mixture of water and anti-freeze is pumped through special passages inside the engine to pick up heat and carry it to the car's radiator, where a large fan blows air past the mixture to cool it down. Not only is this heat energy lost, but energy is used to run the water pump and the fan.

As the energy is transferred to the car's driving wheels, friction in the crankshaft bearings, transmission, differential, and rear wheel bearings generates more heat energy, decreasing the useful energy available.

By the time all these losses have been subtracted, perhaps only 250 of the 1000 J reaches the transmission and only 100 J is delivered to the wheels. The other 900 J is lost as heat.

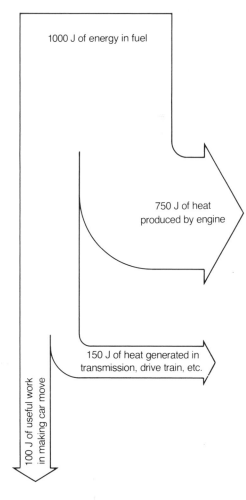

Heat loss in a typical car

The efficiency of the car is $\dfrac{100 \text{ J}}{1000 \text{ J}} \times 100\%$, or 10%

Investigation: Efficiency of a Kettle

Problem:
How much of the electrical energy used by a kettle is transferred to the water?

Materials:
electric kettle
thermometer
stopwatch

Procedure
1. Empty the kettle. Look on the bottom to find out how much electric power the kettle uses. Note the power in watts.
2. Put a known mass of water in the kettle. (1000 mL of water have a mass of 1 kg.)
3. Measure the temperature of the water, then plug in the kettle and start the stopwatch. Keep track of the temperature and the time, in your notebook in a suitable table.

Mass of water (kg)	Temperature of water (°C)		Temperature change (°C)	Time for heating (s)	Power of kettle (W)
	initial	final			

4. When the temperature is around 60°C, start looking at the stopwatch, and, when it indicates the end of the next full minute, pull out the plug. Stir the water thoroughly. Wait a few seconds after pulling out the plug for the temperature to stop rising. Record the final temperature of the water.

Questions
1. How much electrical energy was used by the kettle?
2. How much heat energy was absorbed by the water?
3. What is the efficiency of the kettle?
4. Where did the rest of the energy go?

Sample problem

A 1500 W kettle heats 1.5 kg of water from 18°C to 59°C in 3.0 min.
(a) How much electrical energy was used by the kettle?
(b) How much heat energy was delivered to the water?
(c) What is the efficiency of the kettle?

(a) $\Delta E_e = Pt$
$= 1500 \text{ W} \times 180 \text{ s}$
$= 2.7 \times 10^5 \text{ J}$
(b) $\Delta E_h = m \, \Delta Tc$
$= (1.5 \text{ kg})((59 - 18)°C)(4200 \text{ J}/(\text{kg} \cdot °C))$
$= (1.5 \text{ kg})(41°C)(4200 \text{ J}/(\text{kg} \cdot °C))$
$= 2.6 \times 10^5 \text{ J}$
(c) efficiency $= \dfrac{2.6 \times 10^5 \text{ J}}{2.7 \times 10^5 \text{ J}} \times 100\%$
$= 96\%$
Any kettle with an efficiency of over 90% is a good one.

The Efficiency of Some Common Machines

Machine	Efficiency (%)
electric generator	99
large electric motor	92
dry cell	91
home gas furnace	85
storage battery	72
home oil furnace	65
small electric motor	62
liquid fuel rocket	47
steam power plant	41
diesel engine	38
diesel locomotive	35
internal combustion engine	25
fluorescent lamp	20
solar cell	10
steam locomotive	9
incandescent lamp	4

Practice

1. How much electrical energy does a 1200 W electric kettle use in each of the following times?
   (a) 1.0 s (b) 1.0 min (c) 1.0 h (d) 1.0 d
   $(1.2 \times 10^3 \text{ J}, 7.2 \times 10^4 \text{ J}, 4.3 \times 10^6 \text{ J}, 1.0 \times 10^8 \text{ J})$
2. How much heat energy does it take to heat 2.0 kg of water from 10°C to 100°C? $(7.6 \times 10^5 \text{ J})$
3. How long would it take a 1000 W kettle to do the job described in question 2, assuming that it is 100% efficient? (760 s)

8.10 Summary

1. Work is calculated by multiplying the applied force by the distance the object moves. (If the force is in newtons and the distance in metres, the work done will be in joules.)
$$W = Fd \qquad\qquad 1 \text{ J} = 1 \text{ N} \cdot \text{m}$$
2. Power is the rate at which work is done. It is determined by dividing the work done by the time required. If the work is in joules and the time in seconds, the power will be in watts.
$$P = \frac{W}{t} \qquad\qquad 1 \text{ W} = 1 \text{ J/s}$$
3. Work is measured in joules and kilowatt hours.
$$1 \text{ kW} \cdot \text{h} = 3.6 \times 10^6 \text{ J}$$

4. Energy is the ability to do work.
5. Work is the transfer of energy.
6. Energy is measured in joules, the same unit that is used to measure work.
7. Gravitational potential energy is the energy of objects raised above the Earth's surface.

$$E_p = mgh$$

8. Kinetic energy is the energy of moving objects.

$$E_k = \tfrac{1}{2}\,mv^2$$

9. In elastic collisions, the total kinetic energy remains constant.
10. According to the Law of Conservation of Energy, in any transfer or transformation of energy the total amount of energy remains constant. However, it may be in any one of a number of different forms.
11. The heat energy required to change the temperature of an object depends on the mass of the object, the temperature change, and the object's specific heat capacity.

$$\Delta E_h = mc\,\Delta T$$

12. The efficiency of an energy transformation is calculated from the energy input and the useful energy output. The useful energy is the energy that is actually used for some purpose and not wasted.

$$\text{Efficiency} = \frac{\text{useful energy output}}{\text{energy input}} \times 100\%$$

8.11 Review

Use $g = 9.80$ N/kg

1. Calculate the work done by a 47 N force pushing a pencil 0.26 m.
2. Calculate the work done by a 47 N force pushing a 0.025 kg pencil 0.25 m against a force of friction of 23 N.
3. Calculate the work done by a 2.4 N force pushing a 400 g sandwich across a table 0.75 m wide.
4. How far can mother push a 20.0 kg baby carriage, using a force of 62 N, if she can only do 2920 J of work?
5. How much work is it to lift a 20 kg sack of potatoes vertically 6.5 m?

6. If a small motor does 520 J of work to move a toy car 260 m, what force does it exert?

7. A girl pushes her little brother on his sled with a force of 300 N for 750 m. How much work is this if the force of friction acting on the sled is (a) 200 N, and (b) 300 N?

8. A 75.0 kg man pushes on a 500 000 t wall for 250 s but it does not move. How much work does he do on the wall?

9. A boy on a bicycle drags a wagon full of newspapers at 0.80 m/s for 30 min using a force of 40 N. How much work has the boy done?

10. What is the gravitational potential energy of a 61.2 kg person standing on the roof of a 10-storey building relative to each of the following levels (each storey is 2.50 m high)?
    (a) the 10th floor
    (b) the sixth floor
    (c) the first floor

11. A 10 000 kg airplane lands, descending a vertical distance of 10 km while travelling 100 km measured along the ground. What is the plane's loss of potential energy?

12. A coconut falls out of a tree 12.0 m above the ground and hits a bystander 3.00 m tall on top of the head. It bounces back up 1.50 m before falling to the ground. If the mass of the coconut is 2.00 kg, calculate the potential energy of the coconut relative to the ground at each of the following times.
    (a) while it is still in the tree
    (b) when it hits the bystander on the head
    (c) when it bounces up to its maximum height
    (d) when it lands on the ground
    (e) when it rolls into a groundhog hole and falls 2.50 m to the bottom of the hole

13. Calculate the kinetic energy of a 45 g golfball travelling at:
    (a) 20 m/s (b) 40 m/s (c) 60 m/s

14. When the speed of an object doubles, does its kinetic energy double? Explain your answer.

15. How fast must a 1000 kg car be moving to have a kinetic energy of:
    (a) 2.0×10^3 J (b) 2.0×10^5 J (c) 1.0 kW·h

16. How high would you have to lift a 1000 kg car to give it a potential energy of: (a) 2.0×10^3 J (b) 2.00×10^5 J (c) 1.00 kW·h

17. A 50 kg bicyclist on a 10 kg bicycle speeds up from 5.0 m/s to 10 m/s.
    (a) What was the total kinetic energy before accelerating?

Numerical Answers to Review Questions

1. 12 J
2. 12 J
3. 1.8 J
4. 47 m
5. 1.3×10^3 J
6. 2.00 N
7. (a) 2.25×10^5 J (b) 2.25×10^5 J
8. 0 J
9. 5.8×10^4 J
10. (a) 1.50×10^3 J (b) 7.50×10^3 J
    (c) 1.50×10^4 J
11. 9.80×10^8 J
12. (a) 235 J (b) 58.8 J (c) 88.2 J
    (d) 0 J (e) -49.0 J
13. (a) 9.0 J (b) 36 J (c) 81 J
14. $\times$ 4
15. (a) 2.0 m/s (b) 20 m/s (c) 85 m/s
16. (a) 0.20 m (b) 20.4 m (c) 367 m
17. (a) 7.5×10^2 J (b) 3.0×10^3 J
    (c) 2.2×10^3 J
18. (a) 147 J (b) 562 J (c) 710 J
    (d) 710 J (e) 392 J (f) 318 J
    (g) 710 J
19. 500 W
20. 300 s
21. 1.3×10^6 J
22. (a) 3.1×10^2 J (b) 12 W (c) 5.0 N
23. 86.4 kW·h
24. (a) 48 J (b) 12 J (c) 12 J (d) 36 J
    (e) 12 J
25. (a) 8.0 J (b) 8.0 J (c) 6.0 J
27. 26 J
28. 3.3°C
29. 1.4×10^3 J/(kg·°C)
30. 7.5°C
31. (a) 32 m³ (b) 3.2×10^4 kg
    (c) 1.9×10^3 kW·h
32. (a) 2.0 h (b) 40 km

(b) What was the total kinetic energy after accelerating?

(c) How much work was done to increase the kinetic energy of the bicyclist?

(d) Is it more work to speed up from 0 to 5.0 m/s than from 5.0 to 10.0 m/s?

18. At the moment when a shotputter releases a 5.00 kg shot, the shot is 3.00 m above the ground and travelling at 15.0 m/s. It reaches a maximum height of 8.00 m above the ground and then falls to the ground. If air resistance is negligible,

(a) What was the potential energy of the shot as it left the hand, relative to the ground?

(b) What was the kinetic energy of the shot as it left the hand?

(c) What was the total energy of the shot as it left the hand?

(d) What was the total energy of the shot as it reached its maximum height?

(e) What was the potential energy of the shot at its maximum height?

(f) What was the kinetic energy of the shot at its maximum height?

(g) What was the kinetic energy of the shot just as it struck the ground?

19. A power mower does 9.00×10^5 J of work in 0.500 h. What power does it develop?

20. How long would it take a 500 W electric motor to do 1.50×10^5 J of work?

21. How much work can a 22 kW car engine do in 60 s if it is 100% efficient?

22. A force of 5.0 N moves a 6.0 kg object along a rough floor at a constant speed of 2.5 m/s.

(a) How much work is done in 25 s?

(b) What power is being used?

(c) What force of friction is acting on the object?

23. How much electrical energy (in kilowatt hours) would a 60.0 W light bulb use in 60.0 d if left on steadily.

24. A 6.0 kg metal ball moving at 4.0 m/s hits a 6.0 kg ball of putty at rest and sticks to it. The two go on at 2.0 m/s.

(a) What is the kinetic energy of the metal ball before it hits?

(b) What is the kinetic energy of the metal ball after it hits?

(c) What is the kinetic energy of the putty ball after being hit?

(d) How much energy does the metal ball lose in the collision?

(e) How much kinetic energy does the putty ball gain in the collision?

(f) What happened to the rest of the energy?

25. A 3.0 kg metal ball, at rest, is hit by a 1.0 kg metal ball moving at 4.0 m/s. The 3.0 kg ball moves forwards at 2.0 m/s and the 1.0 kg ball bounces back at 2.0 m/s.

(a) What is the total kinetic energy before the collision?

(b) What is the total kinetic energy after the collision?

(c) How much energy is transferred from the small ball to the large ball?

26. Two balls with the same mass, one of wood and the other a ping-pong ball partly filled with sand, are rolled along a desk. The wooden ball rolls along nicely, but the ping-pong ball stops in a few centimetres. What happened to its kinetic energy? Was the kinetic energy changed to heat energy by the force of friction between the ball and the desk? Explain your answer.

27. How much heat energy is needed to raise the temperature of 50 g of lead by 4.0°C?

28. By how much would 1500 J of heat energy raise the temperature of 0.50 kg of aluminum?

29. What is the specific heat capacity of a material if 2000 J of heat energy can raise the temperature of 10 g of it by 140°C?

30. Suppose that your car has a mass of 1000 kg and is made completely of steel. What temperature change would 1.0 kW·h of heat energy produce in it?

31. A large tank of water in the basement of a solar home measures 4.0 m × 4.0 m × 2.0 m. The density of water is 1000 kg/m^3. The temperature of the water is 70°C.

(a) What volume of water can be stored in the tank?

(b) What is the mass of this water?

(c) How much heat energy will be released by the water as it cools from 70°C to room temperature (20°C), in kilowatt hours?

32. A 12 V car battery is found to be capable of storing 2.0 kW·h of electrical energy. For a certain electric car, it is necessary to develop 10 kW of power to drive at 20 km/h.

(a) Suppose that the car has 10 such batteries. How long (in hours) could it run if all 10 of them released all their energy?

(b) How far (in kilometres) can the car go on its 10 batteries if they are all fully charged?

8.12 Learning Objectives

1. Given any two of applied force, distance, and work, to calculate the third.
2. Given any two of work, time, and power, to calculate the third.
3. To convert from joules to kilowatt hours, and the reverse.
4. To state the energy transferred, given the work done.
5. Given any three of mass, gravitational field strength, height above reference point, and gravitational potential energy, to calculate the fourth.
6. Given any two of mass, speed, and kinetic energy, to calculate the third.
7. Given the masses and speeds of objects in collision, to determine whether the collision is elastic.
8. To use the Law of Conservation of Energy to calculate kinetic and potential energies, speeds, and heights, given an initial set of masses, heights, and speeds (or energies).
9. Given any three of heat energy, mass, temperature change, and specific heat capacity, to calculate the third.
10. Given any two of energy input, energy output, and efficiency, to calculate the third.

9 Energy and Our Society

9.1 Energy

Few of us would want to return to the way of life of primitive man, hunting for food with bow and arrow or spear, huddled around a fire in a damp, dark cave, constantly at the mercy of wind and rain.

We take for granted the comforts of modern living, such as central heating, refrigerators, hot and cold running water, cars, and subways, not to mention such luxuries as air-conditioning, automatic dishwashers, electric can-openers, and electronic air cleaners.

We have learned how to change our environment to suit our tastes and needs, but only recently have we begun to realize the tremendous price, in energy and material, that we are paying and will continue to pay for our ingenuity.

Energy Consumption

Primitive man, say a million years ago, had only the energy of the food he ate. This might amount to 2 kW·h/d per person. Hunting man, 100 000 years ago, used wood for heat and cooking as well, increasing consumption to 6 kW·h/d per person. By 5000 B.C., primitive agricultural man was growing crops and using some animal energy, bringing consumption up to approximately 14 kW·h/d per person. Around 1400 A.D., in northern Europe, advanced agricultural man was using coal for heating, animals for transportation, and water power and wind power to run simple machines, and energy consumption then totalled about 30 kW·h/d per person.

The Industrial Revolution began at the end of the 18th century with the invention of the steam engine and the blast furnace. Coal mines, kept dry by steam pumps, produced coal for steam locomotives, ships, and other machines. Blast furnaces provided steel with which to build buildings, boilers, and bridges. Energy consumption rose to 90 kW·h/d per person by 1875.

In the 20th century, coal was largely replaced by oil, natural gas, and electricity. The generation of electricity by hydro-electric, thermal, and, recently, nuclear power plants expanded rapidly. Diesel locomotives replaced steam locomotives, and, most important of all, the automobile replaced the horse and buggy. A revolution in electricity and electronics produced, first, the electric light,

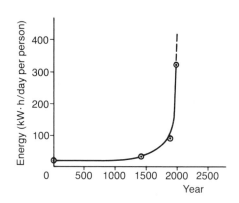

Energy consumption in industrialized nations

the phonograph, and the telephone; then came radio and television; and now the pocket computer. Men went into space and landed on the moon. Energy consumption in North America was about 325 kW·h/d per person in 1975 and it continues to increase steadily.

World Energy Consumption

Energy consumption varies considerably from country to country. The United States, with 6% of the world's population, uses 35% of its energy. In 1975, Americans used 335 kW·h/d per person of energy, the world's highest rate of consumption. Canada was second with 240 kW·h/d per person. But not all countries were as fortunate. India, for example, used only about 20 kW·h/d per person, and the world average was 100 kW·h/d per person.

How can we justify our high rate of energy use? Sweden is a highly industrialized country like Canada, with just as cold a climate, yet the Swedes use only 150 kW·h/d per person. Do Canadians use too much energy? Do they waste too much? Can we cut down on our use of energy without lowering our standard of living?

The Increasing Demand for Energy

For the last 20 years, energy use in Canada has increased by about 5% per year. If this rate of increase continues, we will be using 3.4 times as much energy in the year 2000 as we did in 1975. If we take 1975 as the base year, we will use 11.5 times as much energy in 2025, 38.8 times as much in 2050, and 131.5 times as much in 2075, a century from now. Altogether, in the next 100 years, we will use 2610 times as much energy as we did in the year 1975. Where will all this energy come from?

Practice
1. What fuel did coal replace as the primary fuel?
2. What replaced coal as the primary fuel?
3. State three reasons why Canadians use more energy per day per person than the Swedes.
4. State three reasons why Americans use more energy per day per person than we do in Canada.
5. In 1976, there were 23 000 000 people in Canada. They consumed the following resources:

Oil	5.9×10^8 barrels
Natural gas	6.0×10^{10} m^3
Electricity	2.3×10^{11} kW·h
Coal	3.5×10^7 t

The figure for electrical energy includes only hydro-electric and nuclear power plants. The electrical output from thermal plants was obtained by burning part of the coal shown in the table.

(a) Use the following information to calculate the energy content of the oil, natural gas, and coal used in 1976.

  1 barrel of oil contains 1700 kW·h of energy
  1 m^3 of natural gas contains 10.7 kW·h of energy
  1 t of coal contains 7.38×10^3 kW·h of energy
  (1.0×10^{12} kW·h, 6.4×10^{11} kW·h, 2.6×10^{11} kW·h)

(b) What was the total amount of energy consumed in Canada in 1976?   (2.1×10^{12} kW·h)

(c) How much energy was consumed per day per person?
                                                (254 kW·h)

9.2 Sources of Energy

Sources of energy are classified as renewable or non-renewable. Non-renewable fuels such as coal, oil, natural gas, and uranium are widely used in Canada. We also use one important renewable energy source, water power, to generate electricity.

Oil

In 1975, oil wells in western Canada produced 1.6 billion barrels of crude oil, or petroleum, per day. For many years none of this oil was pumped any farther east than Sarnia. About 700 thousand barrels per day were exported south from Alberta to the United States, and 815 thousand barrels per day were brought into the St. Lawrence, imported from Venezuela and the Middle East. Two factors changed all this. First, whereas a barrel of imported oil delivered in Montreal cost $2.50 in 1970, by 1976 the price had risen to $12.50 and threatened to go higher. Second, in 1973 certain Middle Eastern countries stopped exporting oil to certain other countries for political reasons and thus made it obvious that Canada should be as independent as possible of outside suppliers. Oil exports to the United States were reduced, and the pipeline has been extended so that oil can now be pumped all the way from Alberta to Montreal.

1 barrel = 35 gallons
          = 159 L

If a barrel of crude oil costs $12.50, then
  1 L costs 8¢
  1 gallon costs 36¢
Why does gasoline cost so much more
than that?

Canada's energy reserves include about
8% of the world's coal and 5% of the
world's petroleum.

We tend to forget that the Earth is in a
state of constant change. Every place
where coal and oil are found today was
once the bottom of an ancient sea. What
will the world look like by the time the
next batch of fossil fuel is ready?

Unfortunately, oil production is expected to decline in Canada, even including production from established areas, from new wells, from heavy oil deposits, from oil shale, and from the oil sands of Alberta. The oil sands contain an estimated 250 billion barrels of crude oil, but the process for extracting the oil from the sand is very expensive.

The Northwest Territories may be able to fill part of our added requirement, but, even if it is decided that the reward will be worth the high cost of development and the risk of injuring the fragile arctic environment, it may well be the year 2000 before discoveries in the Mackenzie Delta or the Beaufort Sea or the arctic islands can become productive.

Natural Gas

At present, Canada produces more natural gas than it needs for its own use. Before anyone started worrying about future energy supplies, Canada signed long-term contracts to supply natural gas to the United States. In 1975 we exported 40% of the natural gas we produced, most of it to California and the northwestern United States.

Coal

Coal is no longer used by the railways or for home heating, but it continues to be an essential fuel and raw material for the steel industry and an important fuel for the generation of electricity.

As of 1974, we imported much of the coal needed by Ontario's generating stations from the United States, while at the same time exporting to Japan half the coal produced in western Canada. New facilities are being built to transport coal from the west to the Lakehead by rail, then by ship to the generating plants on the shores of the Great Lakes.

Western North America has great reserves of coal, much of it quite near the surface. Huge earthmovers scrape away the topsoil and then the coal is scooped into railway cars. When the coal supply has been exhausted, the landscape looks like the far side of the moon. Strip mine operators are required to replace the topsoil and plant new vegetation, but they cannot restore the area to its original condition.

Coal is one possible answer to the problem of declining energy resources. It represents nearly 90% of the world's recoverable fossil fuel reserves. At the moment, the total reserves are estimated to be about 6×10^{16} kW·h.

Electricity

Three methods are used to generate large amounts of electrical energy in Canada. The traditional source is the gravitational potential energy of falling water. Until 1941, the world's largest hydro-electric generating station was the Sir Adam Beck No. 1 station at Niagara Falls, which can generate 404 MW of power. Water is taken from the Niagara River upstream from the falls and fed along a canal to the station. There the water falls down through huge passageways called **penstocks**, finally reaching the **turbines** at the bottom. The swiftly moving water sets the turbine blades spinning, the rotating shaft of the turbine turns the generator on the floor above, and electric power is produced.

There are still some good undeveloped hydro-electric sites in Canada but most of them are in the north, far from where the power is needed. Though the problem of transmitting electric power long distances efficiently seems to have been solved, there are the additional problems of damage to the environment from the damming of rivers, the building of reservoirs, and the construction of lengthy transmission lines.

Thermal power stations supply the next largest amount of electrical energy. Steam, from water heated by burning fossil fuels, primarily coal, but also some oil and gas, drives turbines, which then turn generators. A major problem here is the control of the resultant atmospheric pollution. The principal waste is carbon dioxide, which may have serious long-term effects on the world's climate. The burning of coal also produces sulphur dioxide gas, which causes certain respiratory diseases, nitrogen oxides, the major pollutant in automobile exhausts, and quantities of benzpyrene, the main cancer-causing agent in cigarettes.

The third and newest source of electric power is nuclear energy. Canadian scientists and engineers have developed one of the world's most reliable nuclear generating systems, the CANDU reactor. The nuclear power station at Pickering, near Toronto, is one of the world's largest, with four CANDU reactors generating a total of 2160 MW of power. In spite of extensive precautions, there is still public concern about the danger of leakage of radioactive sub-

World Fossil Fuel Reserves	
	%
coal	88.8
natural gas	4.7
crude oil	5.2
tar sands oil	0.8
shale oil	0.5
	100.0

The Sir Adam Beck Generating Station at Niagara Falls

In American nuclear reactors, the uranium fuel rods are enclosed in a single large vessel containing coolant at high pressure and temperature. Each fuel rod in a CANDU reactor is in a separate pressure tube. The failure of one or more of these small tubes would not be as serious as the failure of a single large pressure vessel.

The sun produces its energy by a process known as fusion. Hydrogen atoms are forced together at extreme pressures and temperatures to form helium atoms, and they release energy. Scientists have been able to produce fusion by aiming laser beams at tiny fuel pellets containing hydrogen. If a process can be perfected for doing this on a large scale, it could solve all our energy problems. The necessary fuel, hydrogen, is found in every molecule of water!

Canadian Electrical Generating Capacity (1975) (megawatts)

Hydro	32 688
Thermal	18 819
Nuclear	2 665
Total	54 172

stances from nuclear stations into the environment, and about the safe disposal of the spent fuel, which presents problems yet to be solved.

The CANDU reactor uses rods of uranium oxide for fuel. In 1974, Canada used about 500 t of uranium oxide and exported 4200 t more. Known Canadian reserves of uranium oxide are about 400 000 t, and actual reserves may be about double that amount. Obviously, they will not last forever.

The nuclear generating station at Pickering, near Toronto

Practice

1. List five renewable and four non-renewable sources of energy.
2. Many countries would be happy to buy oil and gas from Canada at top prices. Should we sell it to them?
3. Why was western Canadian oil shipped south to the United States instead of east to Montreal before 1975?
4. Why was natural gas sold to the United States instead of being left in the ground?
5. What are the advantages of oil and natural gas over coal for home heating?
6. To replace the electrical energy generated from coal, oil, and gas would require about seven times the present nuclear generating capacity.
   (a) At present, we use about 500 t of uranium oxide fuel per year. How much would we be using per year if all our thermal power plants had to be shut down for lack of fuel,

and replaced by nuclear power plants?   (3500 t)
(**b**) How long would our known recoverable reserves of uranium oxide last?   (114 years)

9.3 The Flow of Energy

Clearly, alternative sources of energy will have to be found to meet the predicted future demand in Canada. We are using our remaining coal, gas, oil, and uranium at an ever-increasing rate. The major renewable source of energy, falling water, is already being almost fully exploited.

To see what other kinds of energy are available, let us examine the flow of energy to and from the Earth's surface, as shown in the chart.

More than 99% of the incoming energy comes from the sun as solar radiation. About 30% of this radiation is reflected immediately back out into space, while another 47% is absorbed by the oceans, continents, and atmosphere, and converted into heat energy. Another 23% is used in the water cycle, to evaporate water that will later fall as rain or snow. A small fraction drives the winds, waves, and currents. An even smaller fraction is used in photosynthesis, to supply energy to growing plants. A small fraction of this last amount of energy may eventually be found as oil, gas, or coal. These fossil fuels are formed by the action of extreme temperature and pressure on dead plants and animals buried deep beneath the Earth's surface.

The sun and the moon both transfer energy to the Earth in another way. The forces of gravity of these objects, pulling on the oceans, generate tidal energy in the form of tides and tidal currents.

The only other flow of energy to the Earth's surface comes from its interior as heat. The centre of the Earth is a large mass of molten iron. As it cools, heat is conducted upwards to the surface.

In addition, heat is being generated throughout the Earth by the decay of radioactive elements. This heat is also conducted upwards.

At the surface we see evidence of this underground activity in volcanoes and hot springs. In a volcano, molten rock is escaping upwards through cracks in the rocks from deep underground. In hot springs, surface water seeps down into hot underground formations where it is heated, often far above its boiling point. The heated water returns to the surface as steam, or hot water.

The total energy flow to the Earth's surface is about 1.2×10^{17} W, after subtracting the radiation reflected back immediately into space. In a day, this would amount to 2.88×10^{15} kW·h of energy. In 1977, there were about 4×10^9 people on the Earth. Each person's share was equal to 720 000 kW·h/d, if only it could have been transformed into more useful forms of energy.

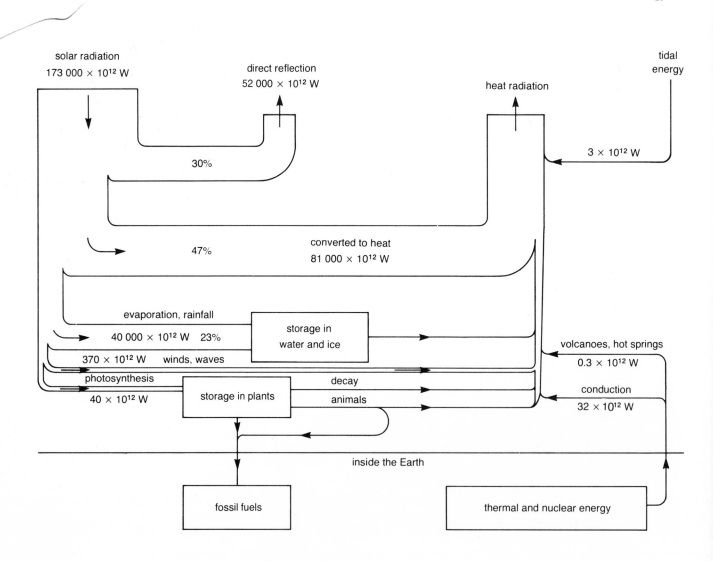

The flow of energy

9.4 Alternative Sources of Energy

Tidal Energy

A potential new source of energy is the ocean tides and tidal currents caused by the gravitational fields of the moon and sun. The French have built the world's first tidal generating station at the mouth of the Rance River in Brittany. Water passes through gates in a large dam as the tide comes in. At high tide the gates are closed and the water is trapped. About three hours after high tide, the water is allowed to start escaping through a powerhouse in which it turns turbines that generate electricity. There are 24 generators, capable of producing a total of 240 MW of electric power. In a typical year, the plant can produce 500 000 kW·h of electrical energy.

The Bay of Fundy has the largest tides in the world. Plans have been made to build a 2200 MW generating station there, but no decision has been made to go ahead with them.

Wave Energy

There have been many ambitious schemes for extracting energy from ocean waves, but none has so far been implemented. The latest, put forward by a group in Scotland, would involve the construction of a floating wave machine offshore. Moving segments would pump water into a floating generator to produce electric power. Such an installation might be extremely useful in Canada in view of our thousands of kilometres of coastline.

Wind Energy

Windmills were in use thousands of years ago, transforming the energy of the wind into useful work. At the end of the 19th century, in northern Europe, some 24 000 were in operation. Most of them were eventually replaced by steam engines.

In the early part of this century, thousands of windmills were in operation in rural North America, some of them capable of generating as much as 3000 W of electric power. They disappeared gradually as electric transmission lines were extended throughout the country.

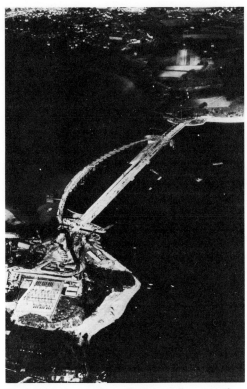

The tidal generating station at the mouth of the Rance River in France

The tides at the mouth of the Rance River average 8.1 m. Those in the Bay of Fundy can reach 13 m. Tides vary considerably, depending on the position of the sun and moon, the wind, and the atmospheric pressure.

Average wind speed	(km/h)
St. John's	24.3
Montreal	15.8
Toronto	17.2
Churchill	23.7
Winnipeg	19.3
Calgary	21.4
Regina	21.6
Vancouver	12.1

A vertical axis wind generator

Geothermal energy

Recently, people have started to buy wind generators for their cottages, homes, or farms. A typical system includes a small generator and some storage batteries. The generator charges the batteries whenever the wind is blowing.

Quebec Hydro has installed a large wind generator on the Magdalen Islands, in the Gulf of St. Lawrence. It is called a vertical axis turbine. It stands 50 m tall and has a maximum output of 200 kW. More such generators may be built in isolated areas now serviced by diesel generators.

Geothermal Energy

More and more countries are starting to install power plants that make use of geothermal energy—the energy of hot springs and geysers.

Steam from geysers can be used to drive turbines and generate electricity. Such plants have been built in Italy, Australia, New Zealand, Iceland, and the United States. A plant at Lardarello, Italy, is able to generate 370 MW of power. A plant in California produces 396 MW of electric power. Unfortunately, the number of good sites in Canada is very limited.

Biomass Energy

Biomass energy is the chemical potential energy that is stored in plants and animals. Some useful sources of biomass energy are wood, crop wastes, animal wastes, forestry waste, and garbage.

In India, thousands of methane gas digesters use a mixture of animal manure and crop waste to generate methane gas for home heating and cooking. The sludge that remains is an excellent fertilizer. Some experiments have been carried out at the University of Manitoba with digesters suitable for large livestock farms. While this process will never be a major power producer, it is feasible and it does have a useful by-product.

Alcohol is produced by the action of yeast on sugar, which is found in sugar cane, beets, potatoes, corn, and wheat. In Brazil, suppliers have been mixing alcohol with gasoline for several years, and the plan is to have all gasoline sold in Brazil 20% alcohol by 1980.

Heating municipal solid wastes in the absence of oxygen, a process called "pyrolysis" or destructive distillation, produces a mixture of gases and liquids that can be processed into fuels. It has been estimated that if 75% of the municipal wastes in Canada's largest cities were pyrolysed, they could be producing 10^{10} kW·h of energy per year by 1990. Such plants are already planned for several cities in the United States.

Gasification is the burning of biomass material in a controlled supply of air to produce fuel gases. Here the heat energy is supplied by the partial burning. The process has long been used with coal, coke, and charcoal, especially in Great Britain. Small biomass generators have been built for cars, trucks, and buses; they work best in constant-speed operation such as cross-country trucking.

Finally, a country like Canada should be able to provide a large amount of wood for burning in stoves and furnaces. As the cost of fossil fuels rises, the cost of firewood is going to seem more and more reasonable. Even rolled-up newspapers burn quite well in an enclosed stove or fireplace. Newer improved designs for fireplaces, grates, and stoves have greatly increased efficiencies. Most of the heat used to go up the chimney.

Solar Energy

The average solar power received at ground level in Toronto or Montreal is about 150 W/m². Most of this energy is absorbed as heat during the day and radiated back out into space at night. If this energy could be captured by some kind of solar panel working at 100% efficiency, Canada's energy needs could be fully satisfied by a single solar power plant covering an area of about 100 km².

Many scientists believe that solar energy will find its greatest use on a small scale, for heating homes and offices and producing hot water. About 32% of the energy consumed in Canada is used to heat living and working areas and to produce hot water. Despite our cold winters, solar energy could largely replace gas and oil.

9.5 Solar Homes

Several solar-heated homes have already been built in Canada. One such heating system consists of an array of solar radiation collecting panels on the roof and a large water storage tank in the basement. When the sun is shining, water is pumped from the tank up through pipes into the solar panels. As the water passes through the solar panels, it is heated. The water returns through a second set of pipes to the tank. The temperature of the water in the storage tank may reach 50°C or more.

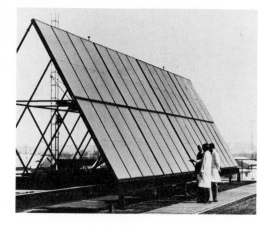

Solar collector panels on the roof of West Humber Collegiate Institute in Toronto — used for heating water

When heat is needed, hot water is pumped from the storage tank through a pipe leading into a coil of piping in the furnace called a heat exchanger. Inside the furnace, a fan blows cold air past the heat exchanger. The water gives up some of its heat energy to the air. The air is then conducted through ducts to all parts of the house, and the water returns through pipes from the heat exchanger to the storage tank.

A tank holding 20 m³ of water can store enough heat for a single-family home for three to five cloudy days, except during the coldest part of the winter. For emergencies, most solar homes have some form of auxiliary heating.

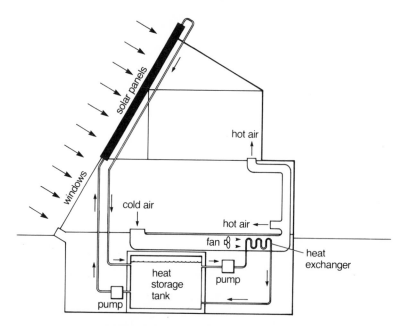

A typical solar heating system

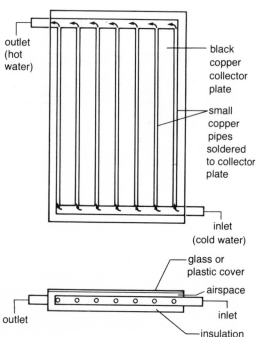

A typical solar collector panel

The solar radiation collector panels are designed to absorb and hold as much heat energy as possible from the incoming radiation. A typical collector panel is a copper plate, 1 m by 2 m, painted black to absorb solar radiation. Copper pipes run vertically up the plate every 10 cm or so, carrying water to absorb heat from the plate. These small copper pipes are joined to a larger pipe across the bottom of the panel, where the water enters, and to a larger pipe across the top of the panel, where the water leaves. The back of the collector plate is insulated to keep the heat in, and the front is covered by a thin sheet of transparent plastic or glass to allow the radiation to enter. The sheet of plastic reduces heat transfer back out of the panel by conduction, convection, and radiation.

The air trapped between the plastic sheet and the collector plate is a poor conductor of heat. Little heat is lost through conduction.

Convection occurs when hot air rises and cold air takes its place. If the top end of the panel were open, the hot air would escape up and out by convection. The plastic sheet prevents this from happening.

All hot objects radiate energy. In this case, the solar energy can pass through the plastic sheet as it enters, but the radiation from the collector plate is infrared radiation and cannot pass back out through the plastic sheet. This is called the ''greenhouse effect''; the same property of glass and plastic is used to keep a greenhouse warmer than its surroundings, to promote plant growth.

The solar home pictured here has other features designed to conserve energy. Large sliding glass doors and picture windows on the south side of the house allow solar radiation to enter and heat the living and dining areas directly. Drapes on the windows trap the heat inside at night and keep it out in the summer time.

The kitchen is on the north side of the house. The heat from the stove, refrigerator, and other appliances helps to keep it warm.

The few windows on the east, west, and north sides of the house are small to reduce heat loss.

The insulation in the walls and roof is two to three times as thick as in a normal house. This keeps the heat out in the summer as well as keeping it in in the winter.

Solar homes are expensive to build, beyond the reach of all but a few families, but when mass production of the components begins the cost will decrease. We know that solar heating works. Now it is a matter of getting organized to make the maximum use of it.

Most of the projects that have been suggested so far for exploring new sources of energy are too complex or expensive for the average person to attempt by himself. Few of us have the resources to build a solar home or convert a car to run on a biomass gasifier. Such changes depend on those who design and develop new products for us, and we should make sure that they know we are ready to buy products that use alternate forms of energy.

Practice
1. List the alternative forms of energy that are under development and have been discussed in this chapter.
2. List some possible harmful effects to the environment of:
   (a) nuclear power plants

A solar-heated home in Mississauga, near Toronto, showing the collector panels on the roof, large windows, and sliding doors

The north side of the same home has few windows.

In another design, air is used instead of water. The storage tank in the basement is filled with fist-sized rocks. A fan blows air up into the panels to be heated, then down to the basement to heat the rocks. Water holds considerably more heat per kilogram than rock at the same temperature, but water is more difficult to handle than air.

(**b**) coal-fired thermal power plants

(**c**) tidal generating stations

(**d**) hydro-electric power stations

3. (**a**) Calculate the average power received from the sun by the 30 solar panels on the roof of the solar home described in this chapter.   (9×10^3 W)

(**b**) What mass of water could be held in the storage tanks in the basement of this home?   (20 000 kg)

(**c**) If the system is only 10% efficient, how much heat energy will be stored in the tank on a sunny 10 h day?((3.2×10^7 J)

(**d**) What temperature change would one day's input of solar energy produce in the water in the storage tank?   (0.4°C)

9.6 Energy Conservation Today

There are many ways in which each of us can help to conserve energy and save money in our own homes. It has been estimated that the average home could function well with 10% to 30% less energy, if some of the following suggestions were followed.

Home Heating

The greatest user of energy in every home is the furnace. The heat energy released from oil, natural gas, or electricity is transferred to the building and its contents to keep it at a constant temperature. This heat steadily leaks out through the walls, ceiling, and chimneys, and through cracks around the doors and windows.

Here are three strategies for saving energy in home heating.

1. Keep the furnace operating at peak efficiency by having it serviced by qualified people at least twice a year. In a badly adjusted furnace, the fuel is not completely burned, and energy escapes up the chimney. Keep the motor oiled, the fan belt tight, and the air filter clean.

2. Make sure that the house is properly insulated. Even in an older home you can still usually add insulation to the attic and the basement walls and install storm windows or double-pane windows and storm doors to keep the heat in. Don't forget the basement windows.

3. Check for cracks and crevices that let in cold air. Put proper weatherstripping around doors and windows. Get a caulking gun and seal up cracks permanently. Close the fireplace damper to keep cold air out when the fireplace is not in use.

A crack 1 mm wide all around your front door is like having a hole 7.5 cm by 7.5 cm right in the middle of it.

Electric Appliances

The appliances using the most energy are, in descending order, hot-water heater, stove, refrigerator, freezer, dryer, furnace fan, and television set. Here are suggestions for each.

Insulate the hot water pipes and check the water temperature. You could consider turning the thermostat down.

Don't use the oven for small jobs. Don't bother preheating if the cooking time is more than an hour. Turn off the oven before the cooking time is up; there will be enough heat left to finish the job.

Keep the condenser coils on the back of the refrigerator clean and defrost the refrigerator regularly. When you buy a refrigerator, consider buying the standard model, instead of the frost-free type. Frost-free refrigerators use 50% more electrical energy than standard ones.

Always make sure the washer and the dryer are fully loaded. Half a load takes the same energy as a full load. Hanging the wash out to dry is free.

Many television sets have an instant-on feature that wastes energy. In fact, a part of such a set is never really off, but is using energy steadily. Perhaps the set can be plugged into an outlet that is controlled by a wall switch. Then it can easily be properly turned off when not in use.

Light bulbs use a significant amount of energy and are very inefficient. The common incandescent light bulb produces about 96% heat and 4% light. Fluorescent lights are much more efficient, producing about five times as much light as light bulbs do per watt of energy used.

Efficiency of Light Sources

Light source	Light output (lumens)	Lumens per watt
incandescent		
60 W	860	14
100 W	1740	17
fluorescent		
20 W	1600	80

You can save electrical energy by installing fluorescent lights in the kitchen, bathroom, and recreation rooms, by using low-power bulbs in hallways, basements, and bedrooms, and by turning off lights when they are not needed.

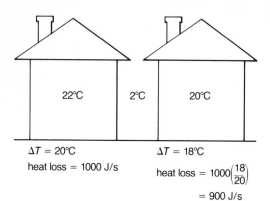

$\Delta T = 20°C$ $\Delta T = 18°C$

heat loss = 1000 J/s   heat loss = $1000\left(\dfrac{18}{20}\right)$

$= 900$ J/s

Lowering the thermostat saves heat energy.

Strangely, the R value of an air space does not depend greatly on the width of the space.

Insulation

The heat loss through the walls and ceiling depends on several factors. One of these is the temperature difference between the inside and the outside of the house. The heat flow is directly proportional to the temperature difference.

A second factor influencing the heat flow is the thermal resistance of the insulation in the walls and ceiling. The thermal resistance depends on the substance used and its thickness, as shown in the table.

Material	Thickness (cm)	Thermal resistance
brick	10	R 0.43
gypsum board	10	R 2.6
plywood	10	R 5
fibreglass	10	R 13
styrofoam	10	R 20
polyurethane	10	R 24
polyurethane	5	R 12
polyurethane	1	R 2.4
air space	2 – 10	R 1

When a wall is constructed of more than one material, the R values of the components are added together. Just a few years ago, walls were built with little or no insulation, and ceilings were given about half the amount of insulation that is used in new homes today.

Typical wall			
New house		**1950 House**	
10 cm brick	R 0.43	10 cm brick	R 0.43
2 cm plywood	R 1.0	2 cm plywood	R 1.0
8 cm fibreglass	R 10.4	air space	R 1.0
2 cm gypsum board	R 0.52	2 cm gypsum board	R 0.52
	R 12		R 3

The walls in the new house have four times the insulation value, letting through only one-fourth as much heat.

Typical ceiling			
New house		**1950 House**	
2 cm gypsum board	R 0.43	2 cm gypsum board	R 0.43
15 cm fibreglass	R 19.5	6.5 cm fibreglass	R 8.45
	R 20		R 9

heat loss through ceiling
= 2000 J/s

heat loss through ceiling
$$= 2000 \text{ J/s} \left(\frac{10}{20}\right)$$
$$= 1000 \text{ J/s}$$

More insulation reduces heat loss.

The ceilings in the new house will let through about half as much heat as the ceilings of the 1950 one.

A significant portion of each wall is composed of windows. The R value of single-pane glass is about 1. Double-pane windows and storm windows have an R value of 2 but still let through six times as much heat as the equivalent wall area. The windows and doors can be responsible for as much as 25% of the total heat loss, and even more than that with poor caulking and weatherstripping.

Increasing the thickness of the insulation in the walls and ceiling can significantly lower the cost of heating your home.

Practice

1. List five ways that are explained in the text to conserve energy at home. List another five ways.
2. Which produces more light, one 100 W light bulb or two 60 W light bulbs?
3. On a day when it is 6°C outside, what percentage of the regular fuel used would you save by lowering the thermostat setting from 21°C to 18°C?   (20%)
4. What is the R value of each of the following?
   (a) 20 cm of brick
   (b) 5.0 cm of styrofoam
   (c) 15 cm of fibreglass
   (d) 7.0 cm of polyurethane   (R 0.86, R 10, R 20, R 17)
5. The space inside the walls of an older home is usually about 9.0 cm deep. If this could be filled with polyurethane foam, by how much would the R value of the wall be increased?   (R 21)

A Conservation Project

The suggestions given in this chapter for the conservation of energy can save your family money, and conserve vital natural resources.

Procedure

1. Early one Saturday morning, record the reading on the electric meter in your home, the date, and the exact time.
2. Exactly 14 d later, read the meter again and calculate the amount of electric energy used in this period.
3. Call a family meeting to discuss possible ways to conserve electricity over the next two weeks. Use all the ideas you can collect from this and other books.
4. At the end of the second two-week period, read the meter again and see how much energy you have saved. Convert the result into dollars using the information about rates that comes with the hydro bill. Calculate how much your family could save in a year by using energy wisely.

9.7 Summary

1. Canadians use more energy per person per day than the inhabitants of any other country of the world except the United States.
2. The demand for energy in Canada has been rising at the rate of about 5% per year – faster than the rate of growth of the population.
3. Non-renewable energy sources, such as coal, oil, and natural gas, will soon have to be imported to meet Canada's needs.
4. Hydro electricity is the only renewable source of energy that is widely used in Canada.
5. The rest of the world may be running out of non-renewable energy faster than Canada.
6. The sun could supply more than enough energy for all the world's present or future needs.
7. Alternative energy sources include tidal energy, wave energy, wind energy, geothermal energy, biomass energy, and solar energy.
8. Energy conservation means using less energy, using alternative forms of energy, and using energy more efficiently.
9. The heat flow through an insulated wall varies inversely with the R value of the wall and directly with the temperature difference between the outside and the inside of the wall.

9.8 Learning Objectives

1. To list four non-renewable and one renewable source of energy used widely in Canada.
2. To explain why Canada should be self-sufficient in energy.
3. To outline why Canada is not likely to be self-sufficient in energy in the near future.
4. To describe five alternative sources of energy.
5. To describe three strategies for conserving energy.
6. To explain the operation of a typical solar home.
7. Given a table of R values for various materials, to calculate the R value of a specified wall or ceiling.

2

Electricity and Magnetism: The Energy of Electric Charge

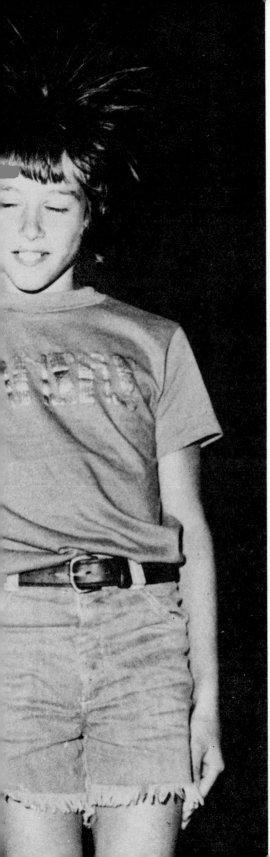

10 Electrostatics

In your work on mechanics, you learned about some of the properties of forces in general, and of the force of gravity in particular. However, gravitational forces are not the only forces that can act between objects. A small magnet will lift a nail off the ground, overcoming the gravitational attraction of the entire Earth. A comb rubbed on your sweater will lift small pieces of paper. In the first case, the force that is acting is a magnetic one; in the second case, the force is electric. These two forces form the basis for the investigations in this unit of the book. The utilization of these forces has played a major role in the evolution of life-styles in the 20th century.

10.1 Electrification

The existence of electrical forces has been known since the days of the early Greeks, when scientists observed the ability of rubbed amber to attract small bits of dried straw. They called this phenomenon the "amber effect". The Greek word for amber is "elektron", and the effect soon became known as "electriks", or electricity.

Any material that behaved like amber after being rubbed was said to be electrified, or **electrically charged**. Materials that showed no amber effect were said to be **neutral**.

The investigation that follows will show you some of the basic characteristics of the forces that act between charged objects.

Investigation: Electric Charges and Forces

Problem:
What types of electric charges are there, and what effect do they have on each other?

Materials:

ebonite rods and fur	paper
glass rods and silk	sawdust
insulated rod hanger	iron filings
suspended pith ball	

There are many common substances that behave like amber when rubbed, including:

　　orlon and other synthetic materials,
　　　after they have been in a clothes dryer
　　　(static-cling)
　　saran wrap and vinyl garbage bags
　　styrofoam packing material
　　nylon stockings and wool rugs

Such objects, when they behave like amber, are said to be "charged".

Benjamin Franklin

Procedure

1. Rub one of the ebonite rods vigorously with the fur and place it in the hanger, suspended by a thread. Then rub the other ebonite rod with fur and bring it near the suspended rod. What effect does the second rod have on the first?
2. Repeat the same procedure with the glass rods, rubbing them with the silk.
3. Suspend a glass rod rubbed with silk in the hanger and bring an ebonite rod rubbed with fur near it. What effect does the ebonite rod have on the glass rod?
4. Suspend the pith ball from a thread and touch it with your finger. Slowly bring a charged ebonite rod near to, but not touching, the pith ball, and note its effect. Describe what happens after the pith ball and the ebonite rod have touched.
5. Repeat the procedure using a charged glass rod.
6. Using first a charged glass rod and then an ebonite rod, approach each of the following in turn and note the results: small bits of paper, sawdust, iron filings, and a thin stream of water from a tap.

Questions

1. How many different types of electric charge were you able to identify?
2. Give simple descriptions of the interaction between similarly charged objects and of the interaction between oppositely charged objects.
3. What happens when a charged rod is brought near some neutral objects? Does the same thing occur with all neutral objects? If the charged rod touches a neutral object, what happens?
4. What must be true about water droplets for them to behave as they do in the presence of a charged rod?

Systematic study of electricity began only during the Renaissance, when it was found that many substances, like amber, became electrified when rubbed. It was also observed that these substances fell into two categories. When two pieces of the same material were rubbed with a third material they always repelled each other. But when each was rubbed with a different material, they either attracted or repelled one another, depending on the materials.

　There seemed to be two "electric states". Benjamin Franklin first identified these two states, and he gave them the names that we still use today—**positive charges** and **negative charges**. He concluded that all objects possess electricity and that a neutral object possesses what he called a "normal" amount. To charge an object positively, he thought, meant adding to the normal amount of electricity, whereas to charge an object negatively meant taking away from the normal amount.

For purposes of identification, he described as "negative" the charge that an ebonite rod acquires when rubbed with fur. Any other object that is repelled by a charged rod must likewise be charged negatively. Any charged object that is attracted to a charged ebonite rod, such as a glass rod rubbed with silk, must be charged positively.

Now we can state the **fundamental law of electric charges**:

Opposite electric charges attract each other.
Similar electric charges repel each other.
Charged objects attract some neutral objects.

To understand fully how a charged object can attract a neutral object, we need to understand the structure of matter. Fortunately, science met this need by providing a simple model of the structure of matter that we can use to explain electrification.

Benjamin Franklin tested his theory of electricity by means of a kite on a damp conducting string during a lightning storm. He was lucky he wasn't electrocuted.

The Principle of Conservation of Electric Charge states: "Whenever a quantity of positive charge is created in a closed system, an equal quantity of negative charge appears also."

The Law of Electric Charges

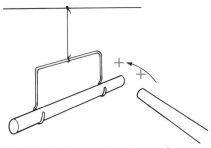

Positively charged rods repel

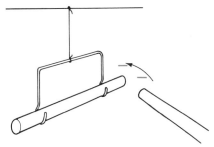

Negatively charged rods repel

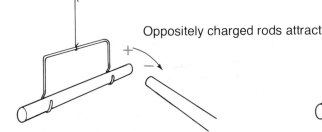

Oppositely charged rods attract

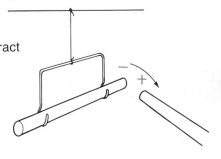

10.2 Electrical Structure of Matter

Scientists have developed highly sophisticated and extremely accurate models of the structure of solids, liquids, and gases during the last 100 years. For a basic understanding of the electrical effects under consideration here, a rather simple model often used in the early part of the century will serve well enough.

The principal concepts embodied in this model may be summarized as follows:

1. All matter is composed of sub-microscopic particles, called **atoms**.
2. Electric charges are carried by particles within the atom that are called **electrons** and **protons**.
3. Protons are found in a small central region of the atom, called the **nucleus**. They are small, heavy particles, and each one carries a positive electric charge of a specific magnitude, called the **elementary charge**.
4. Electrons move in the space around this central nucleus. They are small, very light particles (each with only slightly more than 1/2000 the mass of a proton), yet each of them carries a negative electric charge equal in magnitude to that of the proton.
5. Atoms are normally electrically neutral, because the number of positive protons in the nucleus is equal to the number of negative electrons moving around the nucleus.
6. **Neutrons** are small, heavy particles (each slightly heavier than a proton) found in the nucleus, and they carry no electric charge.
7. If an atom gains an extra electron, it is no longer neutral but has an excess of electrons and, hence, a net negative charge. Such an atom is called a **negative ion**.
8. If an atom loses an electron, it will have a deficit of electrons, and, hence, a net positive charge. Such an atom is called a **positive ion**.

Consider, first, the electrical effects in solids. The atoms of a solid are held tightly in place; their nuclei are not free to move about within the solid. Since these nuclei contain all of the protons, the amount of positive charge in a solid remains constant and fixed in position. However, it is possible for the negative charges within a solid to move, for electrons have the ability to move from atom to atom.

Objects that are charged negatively have an **excess of electrons**. Objects charged positively have a **deficit of electrons**. Both types always have their normal number of protons.

"Atom" comes from the Greek "atomos", which means, literally, "not able to be cut".

The nucleus of an atom occupies only about one part in 10^{12} of the volume of the atom. Except for the electrons, the atom consists of empty space.

All electric charges in solids are due to an excess or deficit of electrons.

Most solids fall into one of two broad categories, as far as their electrical properties are concerned—**insulators** and **conductors**.

Conductors

A conductor is a solid in which the electrons are able to move easily from one atom to another. Most metals are excellent conductors, the best being silver, copper, and aluminum. Some of the electrons in these conductors have been called "free electrons" because of their ability to move about.

Insulators

An insulator is a solid in which the electrons are not free to move easily from atom to atom. Plastic, cork, glass, wood, and rubber are all excellent insulators.

10.3 Transfer of Electric Charge

Electric charges on solid objects are due to an excess or deficit of electrons (Section 10.2). The charging of an object, then, simply requires a transfer of electrons to or away from the object. If electrons are removed from an object, it will be charged positively; if electrons are added, it will be charged negatively.

Neutral and charged objects may be represented by sketches, with positive and negative signs marked on the objects, as follows:

To determine whether a material is a conductor or an insulator, perform the following test:

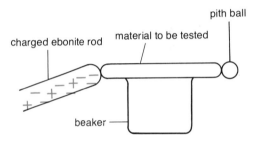

If the material is a good conductor, the pith ball will move away when contact is made with the charged ebonite rod.

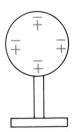

Neutral object

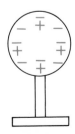

Negatively charged object

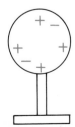

Positively charged object

Charging by Friction

In Section 10.1, you saw that some substances acquire an electric charge when rubbed with another substance. For example, an ebonite rod became negatively charged when rubbed with fur. We can explain this phenomenon with the help of the electrical structure of the atom, described in Section 10.2.

An atom holds on to its negative electrons by the force of electrical attraction of its positive nucleus. Some atoms exert stronger forces of attraction than others on their electrons. When ebonite and fur are rubbed together, some of the electrons from the fur atoms are "captured" by the ebonite atoms, which exert stronger forces of attraction on those electrons than do the fur atoms. Thus, after the rubbing, the ebonite has an excess of electrons and the fur has a deficit.

The same explanation may be applied to many other pairs of substances, such as glass and silk. The **electrostatic series** table includes many of the substances that can be charged by friction. If any two substances in the table are rubbed together, the substance that is higher in the table becomes negatively charged, while the other substance becomes positively charged. For example, an insulated brass rod becomes negatively charged when rubbed with paraffin wax, which becomes positively charged.

The rubbing action between two substances does not generate electric charge. It merely provides the very close contact necessary for electrons to transfer from one substance to the other.

The traditional method of obtaining negative and positive charges has been to use ebonite rods and glass rods, respectively. Recently, strips of vinylite and acetate, each rubbed with paper, have been used to produce negative and positive charges. Although they are easier to charge, because of their flimsiness, they are more difficult to manipulate in the laboratory.

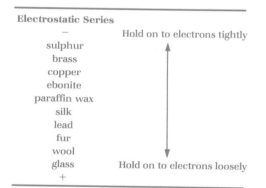

Electrostatic Series

−	Hold on to electrons tightly
sulphur	
brass	
copper	
ebonite	
paraffin wax	
silk	
lead	
fur	
wool	
glass	Hold on to electrons loosely
+	

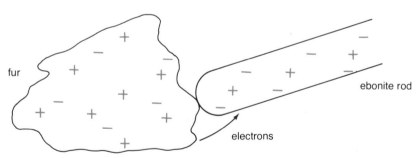

fur · ebonite rod · electrons

Transfer of electrons from fur to ebonite

Pith-ball Electroscope

An **electroscope** is a device that can be used to detect the presence of an electric charge and to determine the charge's "sign" (that is, whether it is positive or negative). A pith-ball electroscope is a light, metal-coated ball suspended on an insulating thread. If the ball is charged, it may be used to detect the presence of a charge on other objects brought near it. It will be repelled by a similarly charged object and attracted to an oppositely charged object or a neutral object.

Metal-leaf Electroscope

A metal-leaf electroscope consists of two thin metal leaves suspended from a metal rod in a glass container. A metal knob or plate is usually attached to the top of the metal rod. Since the central part of such an electroscope is made of a conducting material, any charge on it spreads out over the entire knob, rod, and leaves. Since the leaves are then charged similarly, they repel one another, thus indicating the presence of a charge. The farther apart they move, the greater the charges they are carrying.

An object that has acquired a charge by friction may be used to charge other objects, in two ways: by contact, and by induction. In the next three investigations you will charge neutral objects by contact and by induction, and use the metal-leaf electroscope to detect the presence and the sign of an electric charge.

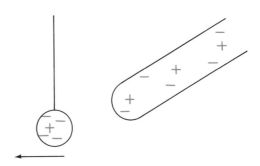

Repulsion of a negative pith ball by a charged ebonite rod

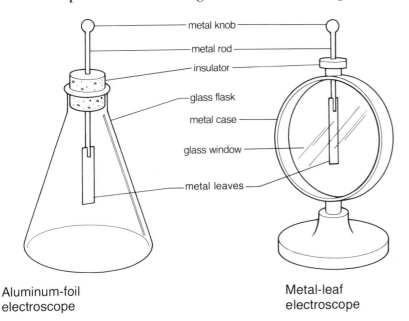

Aluminum-foil
electroscope

Metal-leaf
electroscope

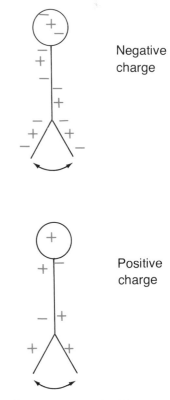

Negative charge

Positive charge

Similar net charges on a pair of leaves cause the leaves to move apart, thus indicating the presence of a charge on the electroscope.

A ping-pong ball painted with metallic aluminum paint (or wrapped in aluminum kitchen foil) and suspended by a silk thread makes a good pith ball.

To understand fully how touching something will neutralize it, look ahead to Section 10.4, on grounding.

Experiments with charged objects work best on cool dry days. Warm humid air contains many positive and negative ions. If such air comes into contact with a charged object, the ions in the air will neutralize the charged object by contact. If your electroscope seems to be "leaking" its charge, this may be due to the humidity of the surrounding air.

Investigation: Induced Charge Separation

Problem:
How can a charged object cause charges on a nearby neutral object to move?

Materials:
pith-ball electroscope   ebonite rod and fur
metal-leaf electroscope   glass rod and silk

Procedure
1. Touch the pith ball with your finger to neutralize it. Rub the ebonite rod with the fur and bring it close to the pith ball. Observe the motion of the pith ball carefully. Do not let the rod touch the pith ball.
2. Repeat the procedure using the glass rod rubbed with silk.
3. Touch the knob of the metal-leaf electroscope to neutralize it. Charge an ebonite rod, and bring it close to, but not touching, the knob of the electroscope. Observe the motion of the metal leaves as the rod is brought near, and then as it is removed.
4. Repeat, using the glass rod rubbed with silk.

Questions
1. What charge does an ebonite rod acquire when rubbed with fur? What charge does a glass rod acquire when rubbed with silk?
2. As the charged ebonite rod was brought near the pith-ball electroscope, which way did the pith ball begin to move? Why? Draw a sketch to show the pith ball, with the charged rod near it, and the effect of the rod on the positive and negative charges on the neutral pith ball.
3. Which way does the pith ball move when the charged glass rod is brought close to it? Why? Draw another sketch showing the new distribution of charge on the neutral pith ball.
4. As each rod is brought near to the knob of the metal-leaf electroscope, what happens to the leaves? Why? Draw sketches to show the distribution of charge on the knob and leaves of the electroscope, in each case.
5. What happens to the leaves when the charged rods are removed? Why? What is the net charge on the electroscope?
6. Why does touching an object with your hand ensure that it is neutral? Be sure your explanation covers both cases: when the object has an excess of electrons, as well as when it has a deficit.

7. When a nearby charged object causes a change in the distribution of charge on a neutral object, this is called an induced charge separation. Is it possible to create an induced charge separation on an insulator? On a conductor? Explain your answers.

Induced Charge Separation

The positive charges on a conductor are fixed and cannot move. The negative electrons are free to move from atom to atom. When a negatively charged ebonite rod is brought near to a neutral pith-ball or metal-leaf electroscope, some of the free electrons are repelled by the ebonite rod and move to the far side of the electroscope.

In physics, the word "induced" suggests something that is forced to happen without direct contact – something that would not happen spontaneously.

The separation of charge on the neutral pith-ball and on the neutral metal-leaf electroscope is caused by the presence of the negative ebonite rod. This separation is called an **induced charge separation**.

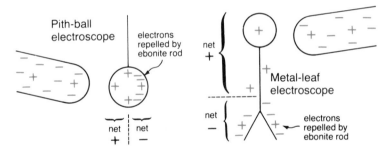

Induced charge separation caused by the presence of a charged ebonite rod

A charge separation will also result from the presence of a positively charged glass rod.

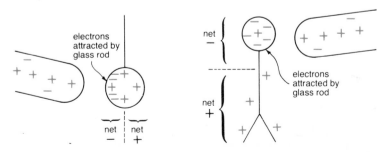

Induced charge separation caused by the presence of a charged glass rod

In both examples involving the pith-ball electroscope, the charge induced on the near side of the ball is opposite to the charge on the rod. As a result, the pith ball is attracted to the rod, whether the rod is charged negatively or positively. This is how a charged object can attract some neutral objects, as you saw in the investigation in Section 10.1.

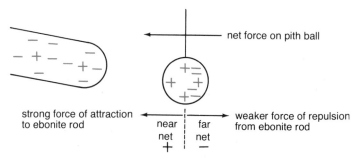

Attraction of a neutral pith ball by a charged ebonite rod

To be precise, the relationship between electric force and distance is an inverse square law; doubling the distance between two small charges decreases the magnitude of the force by a factor of four.

The strength of the electric forces depends on the distance between charges. As the distance increases, the magnitude of the force of attraction or repulsion decreases.

Investigation: Charging by Contact

Problem:
How can you charge an object by contact?

Materials:

pith-ball electroscope   ebonite rod and fur
metal-leaf electroscope   glass rod and silk

Procedure

1. Neutralize the pith-ball electroscope by touching it with your finger. Charge an ebonite rod, and touch it to the pith ball. Then bring the rod close to the pith ball again, and observe the pith ball's motion.
2. Repeat the procedure using the glass rod rubbed with silk.
3. Neutralize the metal-leaf electroscope with your finger. Now touch the knob with the (charged) ebonite rod, and observe the motion of the leaves after the rod has been removed.
4. Repeat, using the glass rod rubbed with silk.
5. Charge the metal-leaf electroscope by touching the knob with the (charged) ebonite rod. Recharge the ebonite rod and bring it

close to, but not touching, the knob. Notice the effect on the leaves. Now bring the (charged) glass rod close, and notice its effect on the leaves.

6. Repeat the same steps, but this time use the metal-leaf electroscope, charged by contact with the (charged) glass rod.

Questions

1. When the charged ebonite rod touched the pith ball, what charge did the pith ball acquire? How do you know? Which way did the electrons move? Illustrate your answers with sketches labelled "before contact", "during contact", and "after contact".
2. When the charged glass rod touched the pith ball, what charge did the pith ball acquire? Once again, draw sketches to illustrate your answers.
3. What charge did the metal-leaf electroscope acquire when it was touched with the charged ebonite rod? Draw a sketch representing the electroscope after the rod was removed.
4. What charge did the metal-leaf electroscope acquire when it was touched with the charged glass rod? Once again, draw a sketch representing the electroscope after the rod was removed.
5. When an object is charged by contact, what charge does it acquire, as compared with the charge on the rod?
6. When a rod of the same charge is brought close to the knob of a charged metal-leaf electroscope, what is the effect on the metal leaves? Draw a sketch that explains that effect.
7. When a rod of the opposite charge is brought close to the knob of a charged metal-leaf electroscope, what effect does this have on the metal leaves? Again, draw an explanatory sketch.

Charging by Contact

When a charged ebonite rod is touched to a neutral pith-ball electroscope, some of the excess electrons on the ebonite rod are repelled by their neighbours and move over on to the pith ball. The pith ball and the ebonite rod share the excess of electrons that the rod previously had. Both have negative charges. A similar sharing of electrons occurs when a charged ebonite rod touches the knob of a metal-leaf electroscope.

When a positively charged glass rod is used, some of the free electrons on the neutral pith-ball or metal-leaf electroscope are attracted over to the glass rod, until the electroscope shares the

Just before contact is made between the charged ebonite rod and the neutral electroscope, a small spark composed of "over-anxious" electrons may be observed jumping from the rod to the electroscope.

Pith-ball electroscope

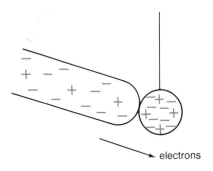

electrons

Metal-leaf electroscope

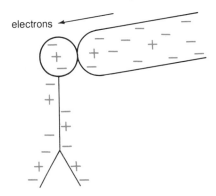

Charging by contact with a charged ebonite rod

deficit of electrons that the rod previously had. Both have positive charges.

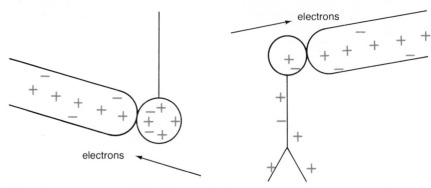

Charging by contact with a charged glass rod

An object that is charged by contact has the same charge as the charging rod.

Investigation: Charging by Induction

Problem:
How can you charge an object by induction?

Materials:
pith-ball electroscope   glass rod and silk
metal-leaf electroscope   2 short metal rods
ebonite rod and fur   2 glass beakers (250 cm³)

Procedure
1. Place a short metal rod across the top of each of the two beakers and arrange the beakers so that the ends of the rods touch. Now bring the (charged) ebonite rod near the end of one of the rods, but not touching it. Separate the two rods by moving only the far beaker, taking care not to touch the metal rod. Finally remove the ebonite rod from the vicinity. Test the metal rods, in turn, for a charge by bringing the (charged) pith-ball electroscope near them. Bring the rods into contact again, by touching only the beakers, and again test them for a charge.

2. Neutralize the metal-leaf electroscope with your finger. Bring the (charged) ebonite rod near to, but not touching, the knob. Touch the knob with your finger, and observe the leaves. Remove your finger, and then remove the rod. Observe the motion of the leaves. Bring the rod near again, and observe its effect on the leaves.

3. Repeat the entire procedure, using the (charged) glass rod.

If the rod does accidently touch the electroscope, touch the pith ball with your hand and start over again.

Questions

1. Why were the metal rods placed on glass beakers? What effect did the ebonite rod have on some electrons in the touching metal rods? Draw sketches to show the ebonite rod, the two metal rods touching, and the distribution of charge on the rods. When the rods were separated, what was the charge on each of them? What charge was on each rod after they were made to touch again? Explain your answers.

2. What would have been different about the resultant charge on each rod if a charged glass rod had been used instead of a charged ebonite rod? Illustrate your answer with a sketch.

3. Why did the leaves of the metal-leaf electroscope move apart when the charged ebonite rod was brought near? When you touched the knob with your finger, what was happening in your finger? Why were you told to remove your finger before removing the rod? Draw sketches to show what was happening before, during, and after contact with the knob by your finger.

4. Why did the leaves move apart when the charged glass rod was brought near? What was happening in your finger, this time, when it touched the knob? Again, illustrate your answers.

5. When an object is charged by induction, what charge does it acquire, compared with the charge on the rod?

Charging by Induction

A charged rod can induce a charge separation on a neutral conductor (Section 10.3). When a charged ebonite rod is brought close to the knob of a neutral metal-leaf electroscope, free electrons on the electroscope will move as far away as possible from the negative rod. If the electroscope is touched, electrons are induced to flow through the finger, thus vacating the electroscope. When the finger is removed, the electroscope is left with a deficit of electrons, and hence with a positive charge.

A positively charged rod held near the knob of an electroscope induces electrons to move through your finger on to the

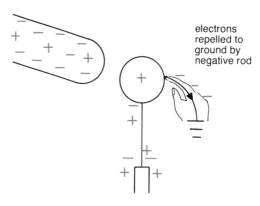

electrons repelled to ground by negative rod

Grounded electroscope in the presence of a negatively charged rod

electroscope. When you remove your finger, the electroscope is left with an excess of electrons, and hence with a negative charge.

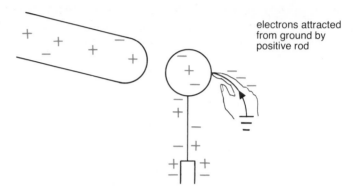

electrons attracted
from ground by
positive rod

Grounded electroscope in the presence of a positively charged rod

Notice that the leaves of the electroscope fall, indicating a neutral condition when the electroscope is grounded.

An object that is charged by induction has the opposite charge to that of the charging rod.

10.4 Electric Discharge

Many of the everyday effects of electrostatics involve a charged object losing its charge and being neutralized. This is called **electric discharge**. Some common examples are discussed below.

1. Grounding

When a charged object is "grounded", it shares its charge with the Earth, each receiving a share proportional to its size. But the Earth is very much larger than any object on it, and the share retained by the object is so small as to be negligible. We simply assume that it has been completely discharged.

The Earth is a relatively good conductor, and, because of its size, it can receive or give up a large number of electrons without becoming appreciably charged. If a negatively charged conductor is connected to the Earth, surplus electrons on the object will drain off on to the Earth until the object has discharged completely and is neutral. Similarly, a positively charged object connected to the Earth will attract electrons up from the Earth until the object is neutralized. Both of these situations are examples of discharge by **grounding**.

2. Atmospheric Discharge from the Surface of a Conductor

Because similar charges repel each other, the charge on a conductor spreads out over the entire surface. The distribution of charge over the surface of a sphere is uniform, but, for other shapes, the charge tends to be concentrated near any sharply contoured features. For example, the greatest concentration of charge occurs around sharp, pointed areas on a conductor's surface.

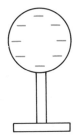

Charge distribution
is uniform over
surface of sphere.

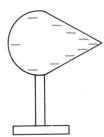

Charge distribution
becomes more concentrated
near sharp, pointed
contours.

All air contains some positive and negative ions. Moist, humid air contains many more of these ions. When ionized air comes into contact with the surface of a charged conductor, oppositely charged ions are attracted towards the conductor, and similarly charged ions are repelled. Electrons are easily transferred to and from highly charged areas of the conductor, and both the ions and the conductor will discharge as a result.

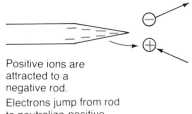

Positive ions are
attracted to a
negative rod.

Electrons jump from rod
to neutralize positive
ions.

Rod loses its negative
charge.

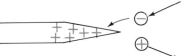

Negative ions are
attracted to a positive
rod.

Electrons jump from
negative ion to neutralize
positive rod.

Rod loses its positive charge.

Discharge of highly concentrated point-charge distributions

3. Sparks and Arcing

When a large number of electrons jump across a gap between two conductors, a tremendous amount of heat is generated. The temperatures produced can be sufficient to "weld" metals together. A device that welds metals by means of the heat generated by forming a large current across a gap in a conductor is called an "arc welder".

When an object has an excess of electrons, the electrons exert strong forces of repulsion on each other and move as far away from each other as possible. If such a charged object approaches another conductor, some electrons may even jump across the gap of air between the two. This type of discharge is called a **spark**.

As electrons jump across the gap, a cracking sound is heard and a small flash of light is often seen. The electrons ionize the air and produce a great quantity of heat. This heat causes the air to expand rapidly and thereby to produce a compression wave that spreads out at the speed of sound and is heard as a cracking noise. The heat energy is also capable of causing the air molecules to produce light energy, which we see as a flash.

This type of spark will be familiar if you have ever walked around on a rug and then touched a metal doorknob.

In hospital operating rooms, all personnel are required to wear special "conducting" boots, to eliminate the possibility that a spark caused by the build-up of static electricity will ignite the flammable gases present.

Friction between rubber tires and the road causes vehicles to be electrically charged. Gasoline trucks drag a metal chain to allow this charge to drain off to ground. Otherwise, the heat created by a spark discharge might ignite flammable vapour from the truck and cause an explosion.

4. Lightning

Properties of a Lightning Stroke
Length—from 150 m to about 3 km
Duration—from 0.002 s to as much as 1.6 s
Width—from 1 cm to about 30 cm
Temperature—up to 30 000°C
Electricity—up to 200 C of charge transferred, with a power up to many billions of kilowatts

By far the most awesome example of electric discharge is **lightning**. Rapid heating and cooling activity in the atmosphere causes clouds to become electrically charged. A charged cloud induces a strong opposite charge on the surface of the Earth directly beneath it. If the charge on the cloud increases beyond a certain point, a gigantic spark discharge occurs in the form of lightning. Surplus electrons from a negatively charged cloud may jump across the air gap to Earth; or, electrons may jump from ground across the air gap to neutralize the deficit of electrons on a positively charged cloud. Lightning strokes may also travel between two oppositely charged clouds, or between two opposite charge centres in the same cloud.

Lightning rods are not, as a rule, needed in cities. Tall buildings have sharp, pointed features that act as areas of high concentration of induced charge. As a result, lightning rarely strikes shorter objects in urban areas.

The dangers presented by lightning are immense. The discharge takes the shortest path to Earth and therefore usually strikes the tallest conductor in the vicinity. For this reason, pointed lightning rods are attached to the tops of tall buildings and connected by good conductors to the Earth. When lightning strikes such a rod, electrons are conducted to or from ground safely, with little or no danger to the building or its occupants.

Lightning discharges over the Canadian Prairies

The main function of lightning rods is to prevent lightning from occurring in their vicinity. The atmosphere contains many positive and negative ions. A negatively charged cloud will induce a positive charge on the ground and this positive charge will be concentrated in the pointed lightning rods. Negative ions in the air above the rod are attracted to it and give up their surplus electrons, which the rod conducts to ground. Positive ions in the air are repelled by the lightning rod and produce a region of positive charge in the atmosphere, below the cloud. This space charge reduces the strong electrical force between the cloud and the Earth, and this is often sufficient to prevent lightning from occurring.

10.5 Electric Fields

Electric charges exert forces of attraction and repulsion on each other, even when they are not in contact with each other. This kind of "action-at-a-distance" force is already familiar to you: the

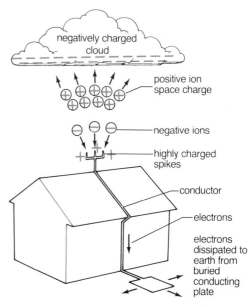

Protection of a building by a lightning rod

gravitational force existed between two masses, even though they were not touching. The gravitational force that one mass exerts on another was explained in terms of a gravitational field of force. When a mass was placed in the gravitational field of another mass, the first mass experienced a force of attraction towards the second mass.

The same kind of reasoning may be used to explain electrical forces. Every charged object creates an **electric field of force** in the space around it. Any other charged object in that field will experience a force of electrical attraction or repulsion.

The electric field may be represented by drawing a series of **field lines** around the charged object. Field lines show the direction of the electric force on a small positive test charge placed at each and every point in the field. For the sake of simplicity, field lines are drawn to show the path taken by this small positive test charge when allowed to move freely under the influence of the electric force. The strength of the electric field at any point is indicated by the relative distance between adjacent field lines.

In Chapter 5, you were introduced to g, the gravitational field strength, measured in newtons per kilogram. The electrical field strength can also be measured; it is expressed in newtons per coulomb.

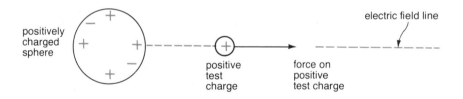

Consider, for example, what the electric field around a positively charged sphere might be like. If we place a positive test charge just to the right of the positively charged sphere, the force on it will be a repulsion, and it will move to the right.

If the positive test charge is then placed at other similar points around the sphere, and in each case a field line is drawn, the entire electric field will appear as shown at the left.

The relative distance between adjacent field lines at a given point is an indication of the strength of the electric field at that point. The electric field of a negatively charged sphere would be identical, except that the field lines would point in the opposite direction.

More complex electric fields may be created by using more than one charged object. In such cases, the positive test charge has more than one electric force acting on it. Being small, it moves in the direction of the resultant of these forces.

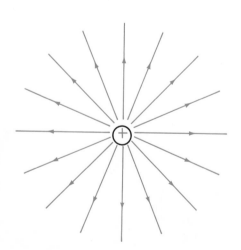

Positively charged sphere

Two positive spheres close together

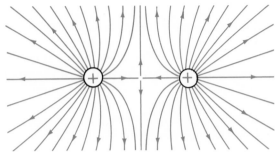

NOTE:
The electric field of two negative spheres close together is identical to this, except that the field lines point in the opposite direction.

Two oppositely charged spheres close together

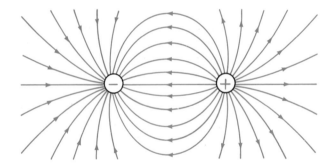

Two oppositely charged parallel plates close together

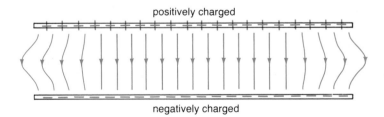

Between the plates, the field lines are straight and equally spaced, representing an electric field with a constant magnitude and direction. Such a field is called a **uniform electric field**.

Robert A. Millikan

10.6 Measuring Electric Charge

For a quantitative study of electricity, we must be able to measure the electric charge on an object. Electric charge is measured in units called coulombs (C), after the French scientist Charles Augustin de Coulomb (1736-1806). To give you an idea of the magnitude of a coulomb: 1 C of electric charge is approximately the amount that passes through a 100 W light bulb in 1 s.

Early in the century, an American physicist, Robert Andrews Millikan (1868-1953), devised and performed a series of experiments proving that there does exist a smallest unit of electric charge; all other electric charges are simple multiples of this smallest charge. He reasoned that this elementary charge is the charge on a single electron.

Millikan assumed that, when tiny oil drops are sprayed from an atomizer, they become charged by friction—some acquiring an excess of a few electrons while others have a deficit. Although there was no way of knowing how many extra electrons there were on an oil drop, or how many were missing, Millikan was able to devise a technique for measuring the *total* amount of charge on each individual drop.

Oil drops were sprayed into the space between two parallel metal plates. A light was shone on the oil drops, and they were observed through a telescope. A battery was connected to the

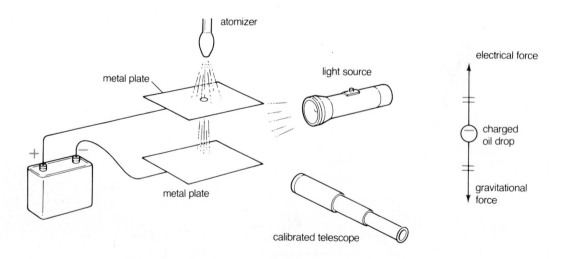

plates, creating a uniform electric field in the space between the plates. As a result, an upward electric force was exerted on those drops whose charge was the same sign as the lower plate's. By adjusting the amount of charge on the plates, it was possible to isolate a single oil drop and balance it so that the downward gravitational force and the upward electrical force were equal.

Then, using measurements of the "balancing charge", and the speed with which the drop fell when the charge was removed, Millikan was able to calculate the amount of electric charge on the oil drop, in coulombs.

By repeating this procedure many times, using the same oil drop with different amounts of charge on it, and using different oil drops, Millikan was able to compile a long list of values for the amount of charge on an oil drop. But how was he able to determine the value of the charge on an electron from this list of values for the total charge on a drop?

In the next investigation, we will perform a similar experiment. We will try to determine the mass of an individual marble by measuring the masses of a large number of bags, each containing an unknown number of identical marbles.

Millikan oil-drop apparatus

Close-up of parallel plates in Millikan apparatus

Investigation: An Experiment Similar to Millikan's

Problem:

How can we determine the mass of an individual marble using a Millikan-like technique?

Materials:

a large number of small bags, each containing an unknown number of identical marbles
triple-beam balance

Procedure

1. Without looking into the bags or in any other way trying to find out how many marbles each contains, measure the mass of each bag and record the values in a table.
2. Combine your results with those of your classmates and try to determine the value of the mass of one marble.

Questions

1. Describe your method of determining the mass of a marble. For it to be valid, what must be true about the marbles?
2. Why must a large number of values be used, to get a reliable value for the mass of a marble? What error would you make if, by chance, all the bags you measured had an even number of marbles in them?
3. In what way do the results of the Millikan experiment resemble your results?

Just as you found that the mass of each bag of marbles was a whole-numbered multiple of the mass of a single marble, so Millikan reasoned that the charge on each oil drop must be a whole-numbered multiple of some smallest amount of charge, the charge on a single electron.

Suppose that Millikan measured the charge on 12 oil drops and obtained these values:

3.2×10^{-19} C	16.0×10^{-19} C
17.6×10^{-19} C	6.4×10^{-19} C
8.0×10^{-19} C	12.8×10^{-19} C
11.2×10^{-19} C	4.8×10^{-19} C
1.6×10^{-19} C	9.6×10^{-19} C
19.2×10^{-19} C	14.4×10^{-19} C

Two observations must have been clearly evident to him from these typical values for the charge on an oil drop:

1. The smallest value for the charge on an oil drop is 1.6×10^{-19} C.

Millikan was awarded the Nobel Prize for Physics in 1923. Nobel Prizes for physics, chemistry, and other fields have been awarded almost annually since 1901, according to the terms of the will of Alfred Bernard Nobel (1833-96), the Swedish industrialist who invented dynamite. The awards are made by the Swedish Royal Academy of Sciences. Each prize has a cash value, which increases from year to year; in 1976 it was about $160 000.

2. All the other values are whole-numbered multiples of 1.6×10^{-19} C.

Our list is much shorter than Millikan's was, but it illustrates how he reached his conclusion that electric charge always occurs in multiples of a smallest unit, the charge of an electron, which he called the elementary charge (e).

$$e = 1.60 \times 10^{-19} \text{ C}$$

We can see that if one electron has a charge of 1.60×10^{-19} C, then it must take $\dfrac{1}{1.60 \times 10^{-19}}$ or 6.24×10^{18} electrons to make up 1 C of charge. For the present, we will use this as the value of a coulomb:

$$1 \text{ C} = 6.24 \times 10^{18} \, e$$

Using this value for the elementary charge, we can devise an equation to make an important calculation.

If a charged object has an excess or deficit of N electrons, each with a charge e (the elementary charge), then the total charge, Q, on the object, measured in coulombs, is given by:

$$Q = Ne$$

Sample problems

1. Calculate the charge on a metal-leaf electroscope that has an excess of 5.0×10^{10} electrons.
$$\begin{aligned} Q &= Ne \\ &= (5.0 \times 10^{10})(1.6 \times 10^{-19} \text{ C}) \\ &= 8.0 \times 10^{-9} \text{ C} \end{aligned}$$

2. How many electrons have been removed from a positively charged pith-ball electroscope if it has a charge of 7.5×10^{-11} C?
$$\begin{aligned} N &= \frac{Q}{e} \\ &= \frac{7.5 \times 10^{-11} \text{ C}}{1.6 \times 10^{-19} \text{ C}} \\ &= 4.7 \times 10^{8} \text{ electrons} \end{aligned}$$

Practice

1. In a lightning bolt, it is estimated that a charge of 20 C is transferred from a cloud to Earth. How many electrons make up the lightning bolt? $(1.2 \times 10^{20}$ electrons$)$

2. A metal-leaf electroscope is given a negative charge of 1.2 μC by induction. How many electrons move through your finger when you touch the knob of the electroscope?

$(7.5 \times 10^{12}$ electrons$)$

3. An ebonite rod with an excess of 6.4×10^8 electrons shares its charge equally with a pith ball when they touch. What is the charge on the pith ball, in coulombs? $(5.1 \times 10^{-11}$ C$)$

10.7 Summary

1. There are two types of electric charges, called negative and positive. Opposite charges attract, similar charges repel. Either type of charge will attract some neutral objects.

2. The simple electrical theory of matter states:

   (a) All matter is composed of atoms.

   (b) Electric charge, in the atom, is carried by protons and electrons.

   (c) Protons, in the nucleus, are small and heavy and carry a specific quantity of positive charge, called the elementary charge.

   (d) Electrons, moving around the nucleus, are small and light and carry an equal quantity of negative charge (the elementary charge).

   (e) In a neutral atom, the number of negative electrons is equal to the number of positive protons.

   (f) An atom with an excess of electrons is called a negative ion.

   (g) An atom with a deficit of electrons is called a positive ion.

3. All electric charges in solids are due to an excess (negative charge) or deficit (positive charge) of electrons.

4. Electrons in conductors are loosely held by their atoms and can move freely from atom to atom. Electrons in insulators are tightly held, and cannot move from atom to atom.

5. Some substances can be charged by rubbing them with another substance. An ebonite rod becomes negative and fur becomes positive when the two are rubbed together. Similarly, glass becomes positive and silk becomes negative when the two are rubbed together.

6. Electric charges may be detected and their sign identified by means of a pith-ball or metal-leaf electroscope.
7. A charged object brought close to a neutral conductor induces a separation of charge on the conductor.
8. Conductors may be charged by contact with another charged object. The charge thus acquired by the conductor is similar to the charge on the charged object.
9. Conductors may be charged by induction, by use of another charged object. The charge thus acquired by the conductor is opposite to the charge on the charged object.
10. The simple electrical theory of matter may be used to explain:
    (a) charging by both conduction and induction
    (b) the distribution of charge on a conductor
    (c) the discharging effect of points
    (d) grounding
    (e) sparks and arcing
    (f) lightning
11. Charged objects create electric fields of force in their surrounding space. Field lines, drawn to depict the electric field, represent the force on a small positive test charge at any point in the field.
12. Electric charge is measured in coulombs (C). The charge, Q, on any object is given by
$$Q = Ne$$
where N represents the number of excess or deficit electrons, and e represents the elementary charge.
13. Robert Millikan, in the oil-drop experiments that made him famous, verified that an elementary charge does exist, and that it is the charge on an electron. He found its value to be
$$e = 1.60 \times 10^{-19} \text{ C}$$
Thus, 1 C is the charge on 6.24×10^{18} electrons.

10.8 Review

1. If an ebonite rod is rubbed with fur, the rod becomes negatively charged. What is the source of this charge?
2. Two rods, one brass and the other plastic, have been charged by contact at one end while being supported by an insulator at the other end. Compare the distribution of electric charge on the two rods.

**Numerical Answers to Review
Questions**

10. (b) 8.0×10^{-8} C
11. (a) 1.9×10^{19} (b) 4.0×10^{-8} C

3. If the knob of a positively charged electroscope is approached by a negatively charged rod, what happens to the leaves of the electroscope? Why?
4. Explain fully what happens when a positively charged rod touches the knob of a neutral metal-leaf electroscope.
5. A negatively charged rod is brought near a neutral metal sphere on an insulating stand. What type of charge would you expect to find on the side of the sphere nearest the rod? On the farthest side? Explain your answers. How would these results differ if the sphere were made of plastic?
6. The CN Tower in Toronto is probably struck by lightning more than any other structure in the surrounding area. Explain why this is so, and why damage seldom results.
7. (a) Why are metallic fibres used in the pile of some carpets?
   (b) Why is it dangerous to rub clothing with the hands while it is being cleaned with kerosene or naptha?
8. (a) Define electrostatic induction.
   (b) Given a glass rod, silk, and two metal spheres mounted on insulated stands, describe how to charge the spheres oppositely by electrostatic induction.
9. Why, in winter, does a spark sometimes jump between a person's hand and a metal object he is about to touch? Why does this occur less frequently in the summer?
10. (a) What is meant by "the elementary charge"? What is its accepted value?
    (b) What is the charge on a metal-leaf electroscope with a deficit of 5.0×10^{11} electrons?
11. (a) In 5.0 s, 3.0 C of electric charge pass through the filament of a light bulb. How many electrons move through the filament in this time?
    (b) How much charge does the Earth acquire if 2.5×10^{11} electrons leave a grounded metal-leaf electroscope?

10.9 Learning Objectives

1. To identify the two types of electric charge, and to state the law of electric charges.
2. To list the main points in the simple electrical theory of matter.
3. To describe the make-up of both a positive charge and a negative charge on an object, in terms of electrons.
4. To differentiate between a conductor and an insulator.
5. To describe charging by friction, and to identify the charge on (a) an ebonite rod rubbed with fur, and (b) a glass rod rubbed with silk.
6. To explain the separation of charge on a neutral conductor when a positive and/or negative charge is brought near.
7. To describe, using diagrams, how a neutral object may be charged by (a) contact, and (b) induction; and to identify the type of charge acquired in each case.
8. To use the pith-ball electroscope and the metal-leaf electroscope to detect the presence of a charge and identify its type.
9. To state what is meant by an electric field, and to describe the electric fields around each of the following.
   (a) a single charged sphere
   (b) two oppositely charged spheres
   (c) two similarly charged spheres
   (d) two oppositely charged parallel plates
10. To name the unit of electric charge.
11. To describe briefly the results of the Millikan experiment, and to specify the value of the elementary charge.
12. To define the unit of electric charge in terms of the charge on an electron.
13. Given any two of charge on an object, elementary charge, and number of excess or deficit electrons, to determine the third.

As a result of the high temperatures created in a lightning stroke, oxygen and nitrogen in the atmosphere combine chemically to produce nitrates. These nitrates fall to Earth with the rain and replenish our supply of natural fertilizer. Ozone, which protects the Earth from harmful cosmic radiation from outer space, is also produced from oxygen atoms in the atmosphere during lightning storms.

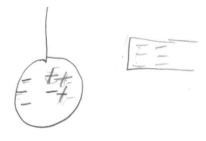

11 Current electricity

When a conductor acquires an excess or a deficit of electrons, we say it has an electric charge. We know that, because of the forces of repulsion that act between like charges, this charge distributes itself over the surface of the conductor. For this to happen, electrons must be able to move. When electric charges move from one place to another we say that they constitute an **electric current**. All electrical devices operate because of the flow of electric current through their components. Can we measure the amount of electric charge that is moving through a given component? Can we measure the rate at which it is moving? And what causes electrons to move, in the first place?

These and many more related questions will be examined in this chapter.

11.1 Moving Electrons: Electric Current

Moving electric charges constitute an electric current. In solids, these moving charges are electrons. Electric current is defined as the rate at which electric charge moves past a given point in a conductor. For example, consider a cylindrical wire such as the one shown.

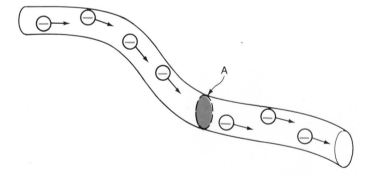

Due to the repulsion of like charges when they are moving through a conducting wire, electrons flow only on the outside "skin" of the conductor.

We may think of A as the cross-sectional area of the conductor. Then if a total charge of Q coulombs flows through the area A in a time of t seconds, the electric current, I, flowing through the wire is:

$$I = \frac{Q}{t}$$

Electric current is measured in units called **amperes** (A), after the French physicist André Marie Ampère (1775-1836). The definition of an ampere depends on a knowledge of the electromagnetic force acting between parallel conductors, but, in terms of the amount of the charge that is flowing and the time factor,

For the SI definition of the ampere, see Appendix A.

1 A is the electric current when 1 C of charge moves past a point in a conductor in 1 s.

$$1 \text{ A} = 1 \text{ C/s}$$

Sample problems

1. Calculate the amount of current flowing through an electric toaster if it takes 900 C of charge to toast two slices of bread in 1.5 min.

The definition of the coulomb of electric charge is derived from the definition of the ampere:
1 C is the amount of charge passing a point in a conductor in a time of 1 s when a current of 1 A is flowing.
$1 \text{ C} = 1 \text{ A} \cdot \text{s}$

$$t = 1.5 \text{ min}$$
$$= 90 \text{ s}$$

$$I = \frac{Q}{t}$$
$$= \frac{900 \text{ C}}{90 \text{ s}}$$
$$= 10 \text{ A}$$

2. A light bulb with a current of 0.80 A is left burning for 20 min. How much electric charge passes through the filament of the bulb?

$$t = 20 \text{ min}$$
$$= 1.2 \times 10^3 \text{ s}$$

$$Q = It$$
$$= (0.80 \text{ A}) (1.2 \times 10^3 \text{ s})$$
$$= 9.6 \times 10^2 \text{ C}$$

A multi-range DC ammeter

3. A gold-leaf electroscope with 1.25×10^{10} excess electrons is grounded and discharges completely in 0.50 s. Calculate the average current flowing through the grounding wire.

$$I = \frac{Q}{t}$$

$$= \frac{Ne}{t}$$

$$= \frac{(1.25 \times 10^{10})\,(1.6 \times 10^{-19}\ C)}{0.50\ s}$$

$$= 4.0 \times 10^{-9}\ A$$

Practice

1. How much electric current is flowing when 12 C of charge pass a point in a conductor in 4.0 s?   **(3.0 A)**
2. How much current is flowing through a light bulb when it takes 24 s for 18 C of charge to pass through its filament? **(0.75 A)**
3. How much charge enters the starting motor, if it takes 4.0 s to start a car and a current of 225 A flows during that time?
   (9.0×10^{2} C)
4. A small electric motor draws a current of 0.40 A. How long will it take for 8.0 C of charge to pass through it.   **(20 s)**
5. How many electrons pass through a light bulb in each second, if the bulb has a current of 0.50 A flowing through it?
   (3.1×10^{18})

Measuring Electric Current

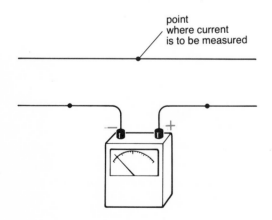

point where current is to be measured

The electric current flowing through a conductor may be measured directly with an instrument called an **ammeter**.

To measure the current flowing past a given point, the conductor must be temporarily broken at that point, and the ammeter inserted into the conducting path, as illustrated.

All the current that is flowing through the conductor must go through the ammeter. Also, the ammeter must be connected so that the electrons enter through its negative terminal and leave by its positive terminal. Can you imagine what would happen to the needle of the ammeter if you accidentally reversed the connections?

Exercises

1. Most ammeters are designed so that they can be used to measure more than one range of current values. In such ammeters, the range is determined by a dial on the case, or by a choice of terminals to be used for connecting the conductor to the ammeter. Numbers representing the various ranges of current are marked on the same scale.

   The choice of numbers, all printed on the same scale, is often confusing. A typical multi-range ammeter scale is illustrated with two sample needle positions.

   Copy the table into your notebook and determine the current reading indicated by each position of the needle for each of the six ranges of current.

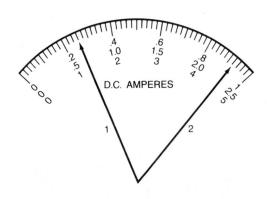

Current range	0-5 mA	0-100 mA	0-250 mA	0-1 A	0-2.5 A	0-5 A
Current reading Needle position 1						
Current reading Needle position 2						

2. Using a 6 V battery, a rheostat to regulate current, an ammeter, some wires, and a small flashlight bulb, construct an apparatus similar to the one shown. Use the range of current that results in the greatest deflection of the needle without sending the needle off the scale.

Whenever you are unsure which range to use on a multi-range meter, use the largest range first, and work down until there is a reasonable deflection of the needle.

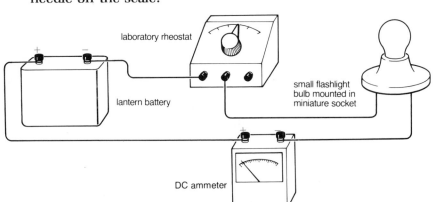

laboratory rheostat

lantern battery

small flashlight bulb mounted in miniature socket

DC ammeter

Every electrical instrument has two terminals, each with a specified polarity—either positive (red) or negative (black). For an instrument to operate as intended, electrons must enter via the negative terminal and leave via the positive terminal.

Adjust the dial on the rheostat to five or six different positions, in turn, and for each position record the reading on the ammeter and give a brief description of the brightness of the bulb.

11.2 Electric Potential

As you know, when electrons move through a conductor they constitute an electric current. You also know how to measure the amount of electric current that is flowing. But the really significant question is: what causes the electrons to move through the conductor? What could be pushing or pulling them, causing them to move?

A useful analogy is provided by a ball sitting at rest on the surface of the Earth. Work may be done on the ball to separate it from the Earth and thus give it gravitational potential energy. If the ball is then released, it will move back towards the Earth, transferring its gravitational potential energy into some other form of energy.

In physics, new situations are often explained by means of an analogy. An analogy may be thought of as a model that is familiar and easily understood and helps us to understand some similar phenomenon. (See Section 26.1)

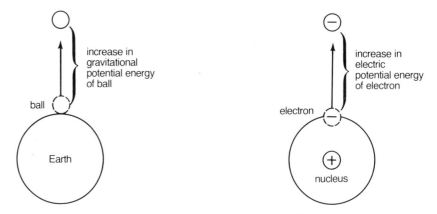

An electron moving around in an atom is in a similar position. If some force does work on the electron, overcoming its attraction to the nucleus and separating it from the atom, then the electron—like the ball—will possess potential energy, in this case of a type called **electric potential energy**. The electron will then be able to move back towards the positive nucleus in much the same way that the ball moved back towards the Earth. Electrons moving back to positive nuclei from which they have been separated, thus releasing their electric potential energy, create an electric current.

There are many devices that are capable of providing electrons with electric potential energy (as we shall see in Section 11.3), by doing work on the electrons to separate them from their atoms. The amount of work that had to be done to separate a given quantity of electric charge is equal to the electric potential energy of the charge after separation.

We define the **electric potential**, V, this way:

$$V = \frac{E}{Q}$$

where E is the work done in separating the charge, in joules

Q is the amount of charge separated, in coulombs

V is the electric potential measured in joules per coulomb, or **volts** (V)

1 V is the electric potential when 1 J of work is done in separating 1 C of electric charge.

$$1\ V = 1\ J/C$$

Allesandro Volta (1745-1827)

Because of the units in which it is measured, electric potential is often referred to as "voltage". A 12 V car battery is a battery that does 12 J of work on each coulomb of charge that it separates. "Electric potential" is the correct term and it should always be used, in preference to "voltage".

As electrons move from one point to another through a conductor they lose energy. As a result, they experience a loss in electric potential. This loss is often referred to as the **electric potential difference** or, simply, the "potential difference across the conductor".

The electrical energy lost or work done by a charge, Q, going through a potential difference, V, may be written:

$$E = QV$$

Since it is often easier to measure the current flowing and the time during which it flows, we can use the equation

$$Q = It$$

and, substituting in the first equation, we get

$$E = VIt$$

as an expression for the electrical energy lost by a current, I, flowing through a potential difference, V, for a time, t.

In practice, there are many situations in which the term "voltage" is commonly used. Whenever you see "voltage", remember that it means the same as electric potential. Increases in electric potential are often referred to as "voltage rises", and decreases are called "voltage drops".

Note that, in the equation $E = VIt$, when SI units are substituted for V, I, and t, the units of E are joules:

$E = VIt$

= (volt) (ampere) (second)

= $\frac{(joule)}{(coulomb)} \frac{(coulomb)}{(second)}$ (second)

= joule

Sample problems

1. A 12 V car battery supplies 1.0×10^3 C of charge to the starting motor. How much energy is used to start the car?

$$E = QV$$
$$= (1.0 \times 10^3 \, C)\,(12 \text{ V})$$
$$= 1.2 \times 10^4 \text{ J}$$

2. If it takes a current of 10 A flowing for 180 s to boil a kettle of water requiring 2.2×10^5 J of heat energy, what is the potential difference across the kettle?

$$V = \frac{E}{It}$$
$$= \frac{2.2 \times 10^5 \text{ J}}{(10 \text{ A})\,(180 \text{ s})}$$
$$= 1.2 \times 10^2 \text{ V}$$

Practice

1. What amount of energy does a kettle use to boil water if it has 800 C of charge passing through it with a potential difference of 120 V? $(9.60 \times 10^4 \text{ J})$
2. What is the potential difference across a refrigerator if 75 C of charge transfer 9.0×10^3 J of energy to the compressor motor? $(1.2 \times 10^2 \text{ V})$
3. An electric baseboard heater draws a current of 6.0 A and has a potential difference of 240 V. For how long must it remain on to use 2.2×10^5 J of electrical energy? $(1.5 \times 10^2 \text{ s})$
4. A flash of lightning transfers 1.5×10^9 J of electrical energy through a potential difference of 5.0×10^7 V between a cloud and the ground. Calculate the quantity of charge transferred in the lightning bolt. (30 C)
5. Calculate the energy stored in a 9.0 V battery that can deliver a continuous current of 5.0 mA for 2.0×10^3 s. (90 J)
6. If a charge of 0.30 C moves from one point to another in a conductor and, in doing so, releases 5.4 J of electrical energy, what is the potential difference between the two points? (18 V)

Measuring Electric Potential Difference

The potential difference between any two points may be measured with an instrument called a **voltmeter**. To measure a potential difference with a voltmeter, the two terminals of the voltmeter are connected between the two points, as illustrated.

A very small current must flow through the voltmeter between the two points. Also, the voltmeter must be connected so that electrons enter through its negative terminal and leave by its positive terminal.

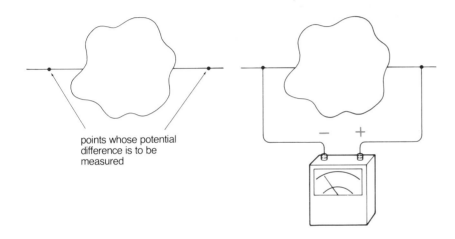

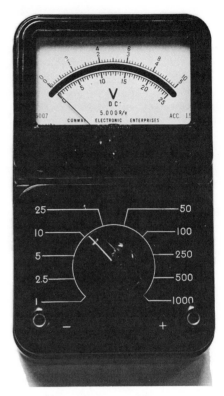

A multi-range DC voltmeter

Exercises

1. Most voltmeters may be used to measure several ranges of values of electric potential. A typical multi-range voltmeter scale is illustrated, with two sample needle positions. Copy the table into your notebook and determine the voltage reading indicated by each needle position for each of the seven ranges of electric potential.

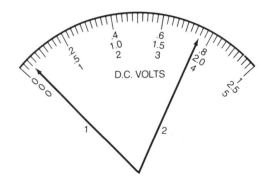

Electric potential range	0-1 V	0-2.5 V	0-5 V	0-10 V	0-25 V	0-50 V	0-100 V
Electric potential reading Needle position 1							
Electric potential reading Needle position 2							

2. Using a 6 V battery, a voltmeter, some wires, a rheostat, and a small flashlight bulb, construct the apparatus illustrated. Use whatever voltmeter range produces the greatest deflection of the needle without going off the scale.

The electric potential difference that an energy source can maintain is often described by expressions such as "6 V battery" or "115 V supply". The "voltage rating" of some common sources of electric potential difference are:

single dry cell	1.55 V
lead-acid storage cell	2.1 V
electric doorbell	12 V
automobile battery	12.6 V
telephone	24 V
normal household outlets	110 V-120 V
heavy-wiring household outlets	220 V-240 V
electric streetcar and bus supply	550 V
long-distance transmission lines	50 kV-750 kV

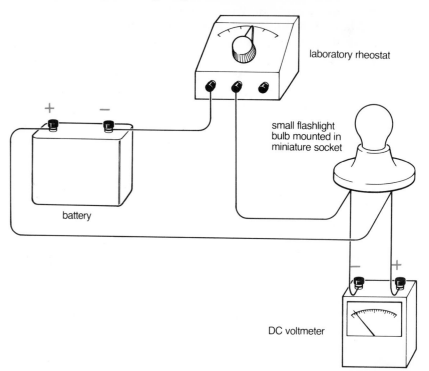

laboratory rheostat

small flashlight bulb mounted in miniature socket

battery

DC voltmeter

Adjust the dial on the rheostat to five or six different positions, in turn, and for each record the value of the potential difference across the light bulb, and give a brief description of the brightness of the bulb.

11.3 Producing Electric Potential Energy

As already shown, any device that is capable of separating electric charge (that is, removing electrons from their atoms) acts as a source of electric potential energy. At a time when meeting enormous demands for electrical energy is one of our foremost concerns, all possible sources of electric potential energy should be considered.

What follows is a review of some of the better-known sources.

1. Electrochemical Cells

(a) The Voltaic Cell

When two strips of different metals are placed in a solution of an acid, a separation of electric charge occurs. The metal strips are called electrodes and the acid is called the electrolyte. The full explanation is quite complicated but essentially what is involved is the ability of the electrolyte to dissociate (break down) into positive and negative ions. These ions move freely about in the electrolyte and react chemically with each of the electrodes. The chemical reactions result in an excess of electrons being left behind on one of the electrodes while an equal deficit of electrons occurs on the other electrode. The most common voltaic cell is made with copper and zinc electrodes and uses an electrolyte of dilute sulphuric acid; it will produce a potential difference of about 1.1 V. Although voltaic cells have great historical significance, they are no longer in common use.

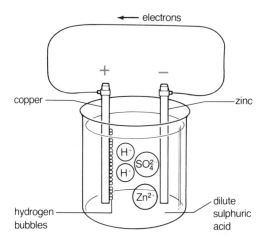

The voltaic cell

(b) The Dry Cell

The operation of a dry cell is very similar to that of a voltaic cell. The electrodes used are usually of zinc and carbon and the electrolyte is a moist paste of ammonium chloride and several other materials. The dry cell has many advantages over the voltaic cell. It is almost unbreakable and easy to handle, and it can maintain a constant potential difference of about 1.5 V. Several dry cells may be connected together to produce even greater potential differences and when this is done we call the resulting source of electric potential energy a battery of cells, or, simply, a battery.

(c) Secondary Cells

Both the voltaic cell and the dry cell will continue to separate charge and produce a potential difference only as long as there are ample quantities of each electrode and of the electrolyte. When one of these runs out, the cell will no longer operate, and we say it is "dead". The cell is now useless and must be discarded.

Many electrochemical cells in use today are called secondary or storage cells; they are cells in which the chemical reaction producing the electrical potential energy is reversible. When the cell gets weak, electrical energy may be supplied to it to produce a chemical reaction that renews the cell's ability to separate charge. Automobiles and many types of portable appliances, such as

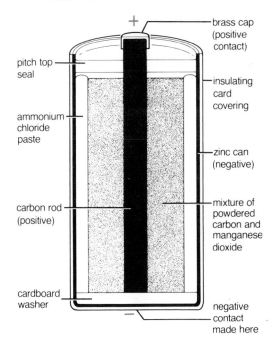

The dry cell

razors and camera flash units, rely on secondary cells for their energy. When a secondary cell loses its ability to separate charge, it requires "charging". Energy is added, during the charging process, so that the battery can continue to separate charge.

2. Electromagnetic Generators

These are a common source of electric potential energy. If a conductor is moved through a magnetic field, the electrons in the conductor experience a force that causes a charge separation and a flow of electric current. This process is called electromagnetic induction. The energy needed to move the conductor through the magnetic field is converted into electric potential energy.

Generators in a hydro-electric generating station

3. Piezoelectricity

Crystals of certain materials, such as quartz and Rochelle salt, react to mechanical pressures exerted on them by producing a small electric potential difference. The potential difference produced depends on the amount of pressure applied to the crystal. This property and the reverse (that is, vibrations of the crystal caused by the application of an electric potential to it) are called the piezoelectric effect.

A phonograph needle connected to a piezoelectric crystal can convert vibrations produced by the grooves in a record into small pulses of electric potential capable of being amplified and reproduced as sound. Also, if the crystal is connected to a diaphragm and vibrated by incoming sound waves, it will produce small electrical impulses and will act like a microphone.

Quartz crystal watches use the piezoelectric effect to keep time. A small potential difference applied to the quartz crystal by a dry cell causes the crystal to vibrate with a regular frequency, and this periodic vibration is used as a unit of time in the watch.

4. Thermoelectricity

A device called a thermocouple may be constructed by joining two wires of different metals at both ends to form a loop. If the two junctions are then exposed to different temperatures an electric potential will be developed in the loop, and a flow of electrons will result. The potential difference produced depends on the difference in temperature between the ends of the loop. This device is useful as a thermometer for measuring extremely high temperatures.

5. Photoelectricity

Light energy, too, may be used to separate charge and produce an electric potential difference. When light of a sufficiently short wavelength is used to illuminate certain metals, the surface electrons of the metal absorb its energy and are then capable of overcoming the forces binding them to their atoms. This phenomenon, called the photoelectric effect, was discovered about 1900.

More recently, solar cells have been developed to utilize the energy of the sun. Thin wafers of special materials, called semiconductors, are fused together forming a junction. When light from the sun falls on this junction, a small electric potential difference is produced. Each solar cell has an area of only a few square centimetres and produces a potential difference of less than 1 V, so it takes a large number of solar cells, connected together, to form a solar battery that will produce a large enough potential difference to be of practical value. Because of their lightness and reliability, solar cells have had extensive use as a power source on satellites and space probes.

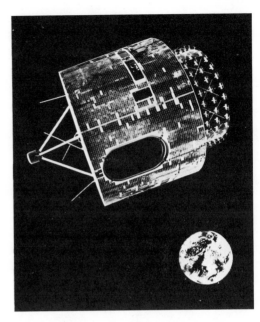

Banks of solar cells on a NASA synchronous meteorological satellite

11.4 Using Electrical Energy

Electric potential energy is used to operate an enormous range of gadgets, devices, and appliances, yet most of these make use of electrical energy for one of three basic purposes: to produce heat, to produce light, or to produce motion.

1. Heating Elements

Electrons enter a heating coil, or element, and immediately encounter opposition to their motion in the form of collisions with the atoms that make up the heating element. Other electrons coming along behind them try to push them forward, and a tremendous amount of "electrical friction" occurs as all the electrons make their way through the heating element. In so doing, the electrons transfer much of their energy to the atoms of the heating element, causing them to vibrate rapidly and hence become hot. Since the electrons have transferred a great deal of their electrical energy to the atoms with which they have collided, there is a potential difference across the element.

This chart shows wire gauges for copper and aluminum conductors, and the proper fuse to use with each.

| | Fuse required | |
Wire gauge	Copper	Aluminum
14	15 A	—
12	20 A	15 A
10	30 A	25 A
8	50 A	30 A
6	70 A	55 A

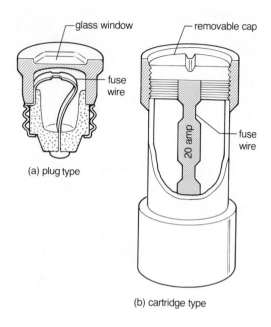

— glass window

(a) plug type

fuse wire

— removable cap

20 amp

fuse wire

(b) cartridge type

The tungsten filaments in incandescent light bulbs operate at temperatures in excess of 3000°C.

Fluorescent lights are similar to neon lights. A phosphor coating is painted on the inside of the tube. When electrons collide with this coating, they cause a fluorescence, or glowing, and white light is emitted.

It is dangerous to have more current flowing through a conductor than it can handle. Overheating may result, producing a danger of fire. As a precaution against such a mishap, a **fuse**, or **circuit-breaker**, is often included in the conducting path. These cheap, simple devices are designed to melt, or mechanically open, so that the conductor will break whenever the safe amount of current is exceeded.

For most conducting wires found in homes, 15 A fuses are used. This means that, if the current through one of the wires exceeds 15 A, a fuse will "blow" and the current will stop flowing. Thicker wires designed for higher currents may be fused at 20 A, 30 A, or even more. It is always unwise to use a larger fuse than the one specified, since doing so defeats the purpose of the fuse.

2. Light Bulbs

A similar situation occurs when electrons enter the filament of an incandescent light bulb. The electrons collide with atoms in the filament, thereby transferring some of their energy to the atoms. The atoms vibrate rapidly as they absorb this energy, and considerable heat is generated. At a sufficiently high temperature, the atoms release energy in the form of light. The greater the number of electrons going through the filament, the more energy its atoms will absorb, the higher the temperature will get, and, hence, the brighter the light produced will be.

In the case of a neon light, the process is similar, except that the electrons are moving through a gas rather than through a solid filament. An electron colliding with a (neon) gas atom causes little vibration, so that virtually no heat is produced. The electron's energy is merely transferred to the gas atom, which sends the energy out again in the form of light (Section 15.5).

3. Motors

When electrons enter a motor, they pass through a coil of wire and use their energy to create a magnetic field. This magnetic field interacts with other magnets in the motor, causing the coil to rotate. The coil will continue to rotate as long as electrons continue to flow through the magnetizing coil.

Thomas A. Edison (1847-1931)

An experimental Edison lamp (circa 1880)

We call devices that use electrical energy, **loads**, and devices that produce electrical energy for the circuit, **sources**. These electrical loads and sources take part in a transfer of energy that may occur in an electric circuit. In Chapter 12, we will consider the characteristics of electric circuits and their role in transferring electrical energy.

11.5 Summary

1. When electrons move through a conductor they constitute an electric current, I. This is expressed as:

$$I = \frac{Q}{t}$$

   where Q is the charge moving past a point in a conductor (in coulombs) and t is the time (in seconds).

   I is measured in coulombs per second or amperes, and 1 A = 1 C/s.

2. Work must be done on electrons to separate them from their atoms, and hence they acquire an electric potential. This is expressed as:

$$V = \frac{E}{Q}$$

   where E is the work done in separating charge or energy gained or lost by charge in joules and Q is the amount of charge separated (in coulombs).

   V is measured in joules per coulomb or volts, and 1 V = 1 J/C.

3. The electric current flowing through a conductor may be measured with an ammeter, and the potential difference between any two points in the conductor may be measured with a voltmeter.

4. Devices that do work to separate charge act as sources of electric potential. Some common examples are:
   (a) electrochemical cells, which use energy stored in chemicals to separate charge
   (b) electromagnetic generators, which use the force on a moving conductor in a magnetic field to separate charge
   (c) piezoelectric crystals, which convert tiny mechanical vibrations into electric potential
   (d) thermoelectric junctions, which use the energy of moving molecules to separate charge

(e) solar cells and photoelectric surfaces, which use the energy of light to produce an electric potential
5. Devices that use the energy possessed by moving electrons are called loads. Some common examples are:
    (a) coils and elements, which use electrical energy to produce heat
    (b) filaments in bulbs, which use electrical energy to produce light
    (c) motors, which use electrical energy to produce motion

When electrons flow through the conductor always in the same direction, they constitute a "direct current" (DC). When the electrons reverse their direction at regular, short intervals, they constitute an "alternating current" (AC).

11.6 Review

1. (a) What is an electric current?
   (b) Write an equation that may be used to calculate the electric current in a conductor.
   (c) What unit is used to measure electric current?
2. List three types of energy that may be used to make electrons flow through a conductor, and name a device that employs each of those three types of energy to produce an electric current.
3. What is the basic difference between a primary cell and a secondary cell? To which category does a dry cell belong? A lead-acid storage battery?
4. Describe the significance of two points in a conductor that are at the same potential. How much work must be done to move an electron between the two points?
5. What charge is transferred by a current of 0.40 A flowing for 15 min?
6. How long does it take for a current of 7.5 mA to transfer a charge of 15 C?
7. What is the potential difference between two points if 1 kJ of work is required to move 1 C of charge between the two points?
8. What is the energy of an electron accelerated through a potential difference of 1.0 MV?
9. What is the potential difference between two points when a charge of 80 C has 4.0×10^2 J of energy supplied to it as it moves between the points?
10. A current of 0.50 A flows through an incandescent lamp for 2.0 min, with a potential difference of 120 V. How much energy does the current transfer to the lamp?

**Numerical Answers to Review
Questions**

5. 3.6×10^2 C
6. 2.0×10^3 s
7. 1 kV or 1×10^3 V
8. 1.6×10^{-13} J
9. 5.0 V
10. 7.2×10^3 J
11. 1.2×10^2 V
12. 9.5 A
13. 4.5×10^4 J
14. 2.4×10^2 V
15. (a) 1.5×10^3 A **(b)** 3.0×10^9 J
16. 4.9×10^{-12} J
17. (a) 0.33 h **(b)** 2.2×10^5 C **(c)** 2.6×10^6 J

11. A current of 2.0 A flowing through a hair-blower transfers 10 800 J of energy to the blower in 45 s. What is the potential difference across the hair-blower?

12. An electric toaster operating at a potential difference of 120 V uses 34 200 J of energy during the 30 s it is on. What current is flowing through the toaster?

13. An electric drill operates at a potential difference of 120 V and draws a current of 7.5 A. If it takes 50 s to drill a hole in a piece of steel, calculate the amount of electrical energy used by the drill in that time.

14. An electric motor is used to do the 9.6×10^3 J of work needed to lift a small load. If the motor draws a current of 2.0 A for 20 s, calculate the potential difference across the motor.

15. In a lightning discharge, 30 C of charge move through a potential difference of 10^8 V in 2.0×10^{-2} s. Calculate:
   (a) the current represented by the lightning bolt
   (b) the total energy released by the lightning bolt

16. How much energy is gained by an electron accelerated through a potential difference of 3.0×10^7 V?

17. A 12 V automobile battery is rated by its manufacturer at 60 A·h. That is, it can deliver a current of 1.0 A continuously for a period of 60 h, or 60 A for 1.0 h, or any other equivalent combination, before needing to be recharged. Calculate:
   (a) how long the battery can deliver a current of 180 A
   (b) the total charge the battery is able to separate without recharging
   (c) the total amount of electrical energy that is stored in the battery

11.7 Learning Objectives

1. To define electric current and to state the unit of electric current, and its equivalent.
2. Given any two of electric current, charge, and time, to determine the third.
3. To measure accurately the electric current flowing past any point in a conductor using an ammeter.
4. To define electric potential, and to state the unit of electric potential, and its equivalent.
5. Given any two of work done (or electrical energy), charge, and electric potential difference, to determine the third.
6. To measure accurately the electric potential difference between any two points in a conductor using a voltmeter.
7. To name several types of devices that may act as sources of electric potential, and to give a brief description of the mechanism by which each produces a charge separation and a potential difference.
8. To cite several types of electric loads, and to give a brief description of the mechanism by which each uses the electrical energy of the electrons moving through it.

$$60\ Ah = t \cdot I$$
$$60\ Ah = t \cdot 180\ A$$

12 Electric Circuits

12.1 Electric Circuits

Electrons move in order to return to a positive charge from which they have been separated (Section 11.2). As a result of separation from their positive charge, the electrons possess electric potential energy that they can use to produce heat, light, and motion as they pass through various loads on their way back to the positive charge. To make it possible for electrons to do this, we connect sources of electric potential energy to electric loads by means of circuits, such as the one illustrated.

Electrons can only go through a circuit if it provides them with a complete path. Any break in the circuit will cause the flow of electric current to cease. The circuit is then said to be an "open circuit".

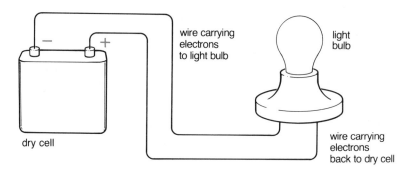

dry cell

wire carrying electrons to light bulb

light bulb

wire carrying electrons back to dry cell

As electrons go through this simple circuit (see diagram) from the negative terminal of the dry cell, through the light bulb, and back to the positive terminal of the dry cell, they transfer the electric potential energy they acquired from the dry cell to the light bulb. In a sense, then, electrons act as carriers of energy from the source of electrical energy (the dry cell) to the user of electrical energy (the light bulb).

If, by chance, two wires in a circuit touch, so that electrons can jump from one wire to the other and return to the positive terminal of the source without passing through the load, the circuit is said to be a "short circuit", or, simply, a "short".

Circuit Symbols

The various paths from source to load may be very complicated and may contain many different types of electrical devices and connectors. To simplify descriptions of these paths, circuit diagrams are drawn, using symbols and showing exactly how each device is connected to other devices. The components of an electric circuit are called elements, and the symbols most commonly used in such **schematic diagrams** are displayed here.

In the circuit diagrams in this chapter, a small dot (—•—) on a conductor will indicate a point in the circuit where a connection between two or more wires must be made. This will help you in wiring up these circuits.

Sources of electric potential

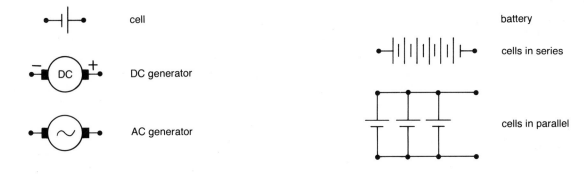

cell

DC generator

AC generator

battery

cells in series

cells in parallel

Electrical loads

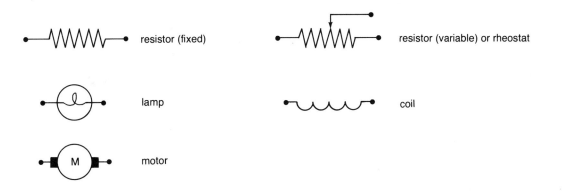

resistor (fixed)

resistor (variable) or rheostat

lamp

coil

motor

Electrical meters

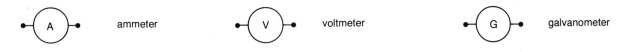

ammeter

voltmeter

galvanometer

Wiring and connectors

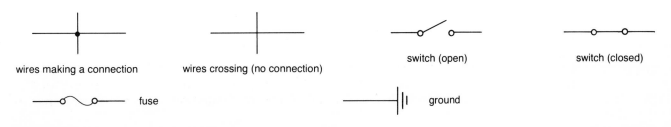

wires making a connection

wires crossing (no connection)

switch (open)

switch (closed)

fuse

ground

Series Circuits

In a series circuit, a key word to remember is "and": electrons pass through one load *and* the next load, and so on, as they return to the positive terminal of the source.

One simple way of joining several loads together is to connect them in **series** to a source of electric potential. In this type of connection, the electrons have only one path to follow through the circuit, and, as a result, each electron must go through each load in turn: every electron that goes through a series circuit goes through each load in the circuit before returning to the source. Here is an example of a series circuit:

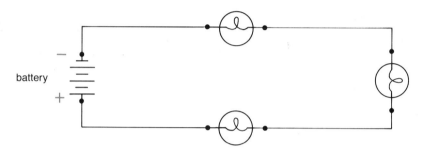

Parallel Circuits

In a parallel circuit, a key word to remember is "or": electrons pass through one load *or* the next load, and so on, as they return to the positive terminal of the source.

In a **parallel** circuit, the electrons have a choice of several paths through the circuit, and, as a result, may pass through any one of the several loads in the circuit. Every electron that goes through the parallel circuit goes through only one of the circuit's loads before returning to the source. This is how loads connected in parallel may appear:

It is easy to get the impression that electrons "race" through a circuit from the negative terminal to the positive terminal of the source. In fact, they move very slowly, and it would take a long time for any one electron to make its way completely through any practical circuit. In a copper wire with a diameter of about 1 mm and an electric current of 1 A, the electrons are drifting through the conductor with a speed of approximately 10^{-2} cm/s.

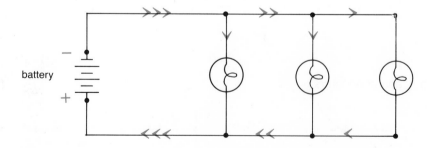

Notice that, in this circuit, there are three different paths through the circuit. Each electron will take only one of the three paths.

12.2 Kirchhoff's Laws for Electric Circuits

As electrons move through a circuit, they lose energy in the various loads they pass through, and they often have to part company and go different ways when they reach a junction of more than two wires. Two basic questions about how electric circuits operate are:

1. When electrons have several loads to pass through, what governs the amount of electric potential they will lose in each load?
2. When electrons have a choice of several possible paths to follow, what governs the number of electrons that will take each path?

An understanding of the operation of simple series and parallel circuits depends on the answers to those questions, and in the next investigation we will take the first step towards finding the answers.

Investigation: Kirchhoff's Laws

Problem:

What are the electric potential and electric current relationships in series circuits and parallel circuits?

Materials:

low-voltage DC power supply (6 or 12 V)
three different resistors (30 Ω to 100 Ω)
DC multi-range ammeter
DC multi-range voltmeter
various connecting wires

Procedure

1. Set up the series circuit shown in the diagram. Points a to h are labelled for reference only and represent junction points in the circuit.

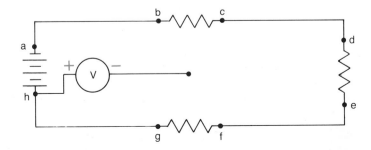

Electrical circuitry in a solid-state computer

For example, if the electric potential is 9.3 V at point d and 6.7 V at point e, then the potential difference across load de is (9.3-6.7) V, or 2.6 V.

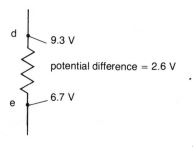

As a safety precaution, always "turn off" a circuit before making any changes or before connecting or disconnecting a meter.

When this circuit is temporarily broken at point a, and an ammeter is inserted, the circuit should look like this:

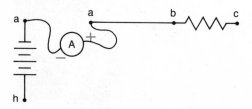

2. Connect the positive terminal of the voltmeter to point h, and then touch the negative terminal to each of the other labelled points in turn, noting and recording the reading of the voltmeter in each case. Calculate, by subtraction, the potential difference across the power source and across each load and conductor. Remove the voltmeter from the circuit.

Junction point	Electric potential	Conductor	Potential difference	Electric current
a		ab		
b		bc		
c		cd		
d		de		
e				
f				

3. Temporarily break the circuit at point a and insert an ammeter into the circuit at that point. Note and record the value of electric current flowing past point a. Remove the ammeter, reconnect point a, and then repeat the procedure at each remaining point in the circuit, noting and recording the current flowing in each case.

4. Set up the parallel circuit illustrated, using the same notation for junction points.

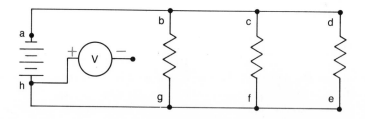

5. In the same way as before, by connecting the positive terminal of a voltmeter to point h take readings of electric potential at each point, and then calculate by subtraction the potential difference across the source and across each load and conductor.

Junction point	Electric potential		Conductor	Potential difference	Electric current
a			ab		
b			bc		
c			cd		
d			de		
e					

6. By temporarily breaking the circuit at each point and inserting an ammeter, measure the current flowing through each conductor in the circuit. Be sure when you break the circuit that you insert the ammeter into the conductor whose current you are trying to measure, and also that you reconnect the previous junction.

Questions
1. How many different paths are there for an electron to take through the series circuit? Through the parallel circuit?
2. For each possible path in each circuit, calculate the sum of the decreases in electric potential along the path, and the sum of the increases. The relationship should be evident from the data.
3. In the series circuit, how does the total current flowing from the power source compare with the currents flowing through each individual load? How do they compare in the parallel circuit?
4. At each junction point in each circuit, calculate the total current flowing into the junction and the total current flowing out. Formulate another relationship from this data.

Kirchhoff's Laws

The same electric potential and current relationships that you have just observed have been known for over a century as a result of the experimental work of a German physicist, Gustav Robert Kirchhoff (1824-87). They have since become known as **Kirchhoff's Voltage Law** (KVL) and **Kirchhoff's Current Law** (KCL).

Kirchhoff's Voltage Law
Around any complete path through an electric circuit, the sum of the increases in electric potential is equal to the sum of the decreases in electric potential.

G.R. Kirchhoff (centre) and his colleagues, R.W. Bunsen and Sir H.E. Roscoe

Kirchhoff's Current Law
At any junction point in an electric circuit, the total electric current flowing into the junction is equal to the total electric current flowing out.

These relationships are invaluable in understanding the transfer of electrical energy in a circuit and will provide the basis for our examination of electric circuit analysis, in this chapter.

✓ Sample problems

In a series circuit, each load receives *part* of the electric potential from *all* of the current flowing through the circuit.

1. Calculate the potential difference, V_2, in this circuit:

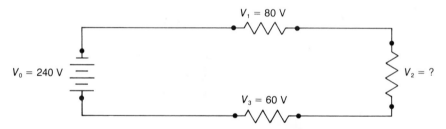

Applying KVL to the circuit,
$$V_0 = V_1 + V_2 + V_3$$
$$\therefore V_2 = V_0 - V_1 - V_3$$
$$= 240 \text{ V} - 80 \text{ V} - 60 \text{ V}$$
$$= 100 \text{ V}$$

2. Calculate the electric current, I_3, in this circuit:

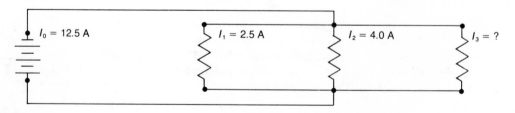

In a parallel circuit, each load receives *all* of the electric potential from *part* of the current flowing through the circuit.

Applying KCL to the circuit,
$$I_0 = I_1 + I_2 + I_3$$
$$\therefore I_3 = I_0 - I_1 - I_2$$
$$= 12.5 \text{ A} - 2.5 \text{ A} - 4.0 \text{ A}$$
$$= 6.0 \text{ A}$$

Practice

1. Find V_0 in this circuit:

Loads connected in series have the same current; loads connected in parallel have the same potential difference.

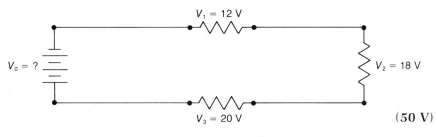

$V_1 = 12$ V

$V_0 = ?$

$V_2 = 18$ V

$V_3 = 20$ V

(50 V)

2. Find I_0 in this circuit:

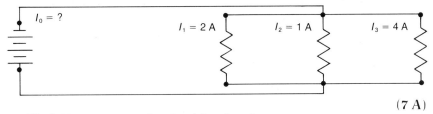

$I_0 = ?$

$I_1 = 2$ A $I_2 = 1$ A $I_3 = 4$ A

(7 A)

3. Find V_2, V_4, I_3, and I_4 in this circuit:

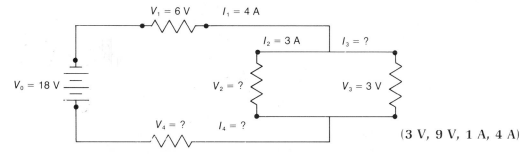

$V_1 = 6$ V $I_1 = 4$ A

$I_2 = 3$ A $I_3 = ?$

$V_0 = 18$ V $V_2 = ?$ $V_3 = 3$ V

$V_4 = ?$ $I_4 = ?$

(3 V, 9 V, 1 A, 4 A)

4. Find V_2, V_5, V_4, I_1, and I_4 in this circuit:

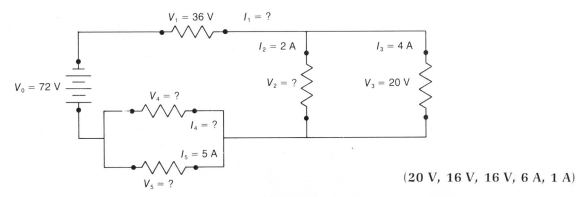

$V_1 = 36$ V $I_1 = ?$

$I_2 = 2$ A $I_3 = 4$ A

$V_0 = 72$ V $V_2 = ?$ $V_3 = 20$ V

$V_4 = ?$

$I_4 = ?$

$I_5 = 5$ A

$V_5 = ?$

(20 V, 16 V, 16 V, 6 A, 1 A)

A resistor is actually a conductor, but one of limited capability. Electrons lose energy as they pass through a resistor, because they collide with its molecules and in doing so transfer energy to them. The filament of a light bulb and the heating element in a toaster are examples of resistors.

12.3 Resistance in Electric Circuits

When electrons pass through a device that uses their electrical energy, they experience an opposition, or **resistance**, to their flow, which results in a loss of energy. This resistance may be thought of as "electrical friction" that the electrons experience as they move from molecule to molecule through a conductor. To measure the amount of resistance that a quantity of moving charge encounters, we compare the electric potential difference the charge experiences as it passes through a conductor with the amount of electric current that is flowing.

To examine electric resistance more closely, we will next investigate the relationship between potential difference and electric current for various conductors.

Investigation: Ohm's Law

Problem:
What is the relationship between the potential difference across a conductor and the electric current flowing through it?

Materials:
low-voltage variable DC power supply (6 or 12 V)
three different resistors (30 Ω to 100 Ω)
DC multi-range ammeter
DC multi-range voltmeter
various connecting wires

Procedure
1. Set up the circuit illustrated, using the largest of your three resistors. You will be told what range to use on the voltmeter and ammeter. Make sure the polarities of the meters are as shown by the + and − signs on the circuit diagrams.

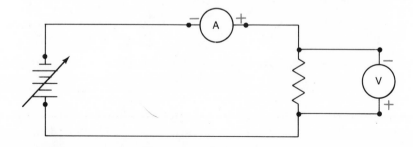

2. Adjust the power supply until the readings on both meters are the maximum ones. Record these readings and then turn the power supply down in five or six equal stages, each time recording the ammeter and voltmeter readings, until both meter readings reach zero.

Resistor	Potential difference (V)	Electric current (I)	$\dfrac{V}{I}$

3. Repeat the procedure for each of the other resistors, each time recording corresponding pairs of values for V and I. Record all the values in a table.
4. For each pair of values of V and I, calculate the ratio $\dfrac{V}{I}$ and record it in the table.
5. On one sheet of graph paper, plot graphs of V versus I for each resistor. Plot I on the horizontal axis, and label each graph.

Questions
1. For each resistor, what seems to be the significance of the ratio $\dfrac{V}{I}$?
2. Describe the shape of each graph of V versus I. What happens to the current flowing through a resistor when the potential difference is increased? What mathematical relationship between V and I is represented by such a graph?
3. What is the only significant difference between the three graphs? Calculate the slope of each graph.
4. Compare the ratio $\dfrac{V}{I}$ to the slope of its graph for each resistor.

[handwritten annotations:] CURRENT INCREASES — LINEAR EQUATION — SLOPE NOT DIFFERENCE — ONE CURVE IS WAY OUT DUE TO LOUSY CALCULATIONS

✓ Ohm's Law

Georg Simon Ohm (1787-1854), a German physicist, performed much the same experiment as you just did, and he also found that,

Not all resistances obey Ohm's Law: that is, $\frac{V}{I}$ is not a constant ratio; its value changes as V and I themselves change. A load that obeys Ohm's Law is called an "ohmic" resistance. Most metals are ohmic. Other substances are called "non-ohmic".

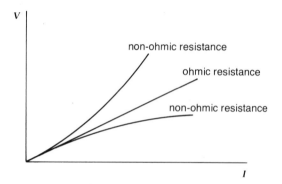

Ω is the symbol for the letter omega in the Greek alphabet, corresponding to the letter "O" in the Roman alphabet, which is used in English writing.

for a given conductor, the ratio $\frac{V}{I}$ is a constant. From this constant ratio, he formulated what we now call **Ohm's Law**:

The potential difference between any two points in a conductor varies directly as the current flowing between the two points.

This relationship may be written as

$$\frac{V}{I} = \text{constant}$$

and, since the constant depends on the properties of the particular resistor being used, we give it the symbol R and call it the resistance. Thus, Ohm's Law may be written:

$$\frac{V}{I} = R$$

V is measured in volts, and I is measured in amperes, so R is measured in volts per ampere, and this new unit, the unit of electric resistance, is called the **ohm** (Ω).

---

1 Ω is the electric resistance of a conductor that has a current of 1 A flowing through it when the potential difference across it is 1 V.

$$1\ \Omega = 1\ \text{V/A}$$

Sample problems

1. Find the resistance of an electric light bulb if a current of 0.80 A flows when the potential difference across the bulb is 120 V.

$$R = \frac{V}{I}$$
$$= \frac{120\ \text{V}}{0.80\ \text{A}}$$
$$= 1.5 \times 10^2\ \Omega$$

2. What is the potential difference across a toaster of resistance 13.7 Ω when the current flowing through it is 8.75 A?

$$V = IR$$
$$= (8.75 \text{ A}) (13.7 \text{ }\Omega)$$
$$= 120 \text{ V}$$

3. What current is flowing through an electric baseboard heater with a resistance of 38 Ω when the potential difference across it is 240 V?

$$I = \frac{V}{R}$$
$$= \frac{240 \text{ V}}{38 \text{ }\Omega}$$
$$= 6.3 \text{ A}$$

Practice

1. A portable radio is connected to a 9.0 V battery and draws a current of 25 mA. What is the resistance of the radio?
   (3.6×10^2 Ω)
2. An electric clothes-dryer is connected to a 230 V source of electric potential. If it has a resistance of 9.2 Ω, calculate the current it draws. (25 A)
3. A large tube in a television set has a resistance of 5.0×10^6 Ω and draws a current of 160 mA. What is the potential difference across the tube? (8.0×10^5 V)
4. An electric toaster has a resistance of 12 Ω. What current will it draw from a 120 V supply? (10 A)
5. What potential difference is required to produce a current of 8.0 A in a load having a resistance of 64 Ω? (5.1×10^2 V)
6. An iron, designed for use at 120 V and 5.0 A, is connected to a source of 240 V. Calculate the current the iron will draw at the higher potential, and state what will happen to the iron. (10 A)

The telephone mouthpiece (microphone), invented in 1876 and still in use today, utilizes a button of carbon granules with a potential difference across it as a detector of sound waves. Incoming sound waves hit the diaphragm, causing it to move in and compress the carbon granules. This has the effect of changing the electrical resistance of the carbon button, and the current flowing through it. This current is, then, an electrical copy of the sound-wave pattern hitting the diaphragm.

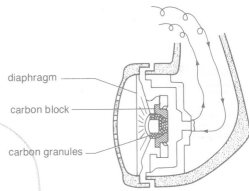

diaphragm

carbon block

carbon granules

Factors Affecting Resistance

At very low temperatures (within a few degrees of absolute zero) the electrical resistance of metals seems to disappear completely, and they become "superconductors". The field of low-temperature physics is called "cryogenics". Low-temperature electric power lines have been proposed as a way of transmitting electric power efficiently over great distances.

We have seen that the resistance of a given conductor is a constant regardless of the potential difference across it or the current flowing through it. The value of its resistance depends on the following physical properties:

1. Length
The resistance of a conductor varies directly with its length; doubling the length of a conductor doubles the resistance.

2. Cross-sectional area
The resistance of a conductor varies inversely with its cross-sectional area; doubling the cross-sectional area halves the resistance.

3. Temperature
In most materials, an increase in temperature will cause an increase in resistance. This increase will range between 3% and 5% for each 10°C increase in temperature. However, for some materials, for example, glass and carbon, an increase in temperature will cause a decrease in resistance.

The fact that resistance varies with temperature complicates the manufacturing of electrical measuring instruments that will have to be exposed to a wide range of temperatures. Alloys have been developed whose resistance is little affected by temperature. Manganin, a mixture of manganese, nickel, and copper, has a change in resistance of less than 0.01% for each 1°C change in temperature.

4. Material
The atomic structure of a material has a marked effect on its resistance. Good conductors, such as copper and aluminium, have very low resistances, whereas poor conductors, such as nichrome and mercury, have higher resistances. Insulators such as glass and rubber have very high resistances. The characteristic value of a material's resistance is called its **resistivity**. The resistivity of a given material is the resistance of a cylindrical conductor made of that material, 1 m long, with a cross-sectional area of 1 m^2, and (usually) at a temperature of 20°C.

Resistivities of Various Materials

(in $\Omega \cdot m^2/m$ at 20°C)

aluminum	2.6×10^{-8}
copper	1.7×10^{-8}
iron	10.0×10^{-8}
lead	22.0×10^{-8}
mercury	95.8×10^{-8}
nichrome	100.0×10^{-8}
platinum	10.0×10^{-8}
silver	1.5×10^{-8}
tungsten	5.5×10^{-8}

12.4 Resistance in Series and in Parallel

The currents flowing through the various branches of an electric circuit, and the differences in electric potential between various points in the circuit, depend on three relationships:

- Kirchhoff's Voltage Law (KVL): Around any complete path through an electric circuit, the total increase in electric potential is equal to the total decrease in electric potential.

- Kirchhoff's Current Law (KCL): At any junction point in an electric circuit, the total current flowing into the junction is equal to the total current flowing out of the junction.
- Ohm's Law: The potential difference between any two points in an electric circuit is directly proportional to the electric current flowing between the two points, and the resistance between the two points is given by

$$R = \frac{V}{I}$$

Most electric circuits used in homes, appliances, and automobiles contain more than one source of electric potential and many different types of loads connected together in complicated networks of conductors. No matter how complex it may be, a circuit can be "analysed" completely using the three relationships stated above. To analyse an electric circuit means to determine, for each element in the circuit:

1. the current flowing through it
2. the potential difference across it
3. the value of its resistance, if it is a load element

When there are several resistances in a circuit, the first step in the analysis of the circuit is often the calculation of the total resistance in it. The simplest situation occurs when all the resistances are connected either in series or in parallel.

Total Resistance in Series

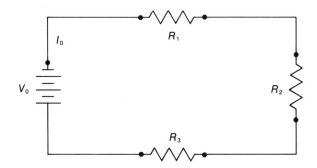
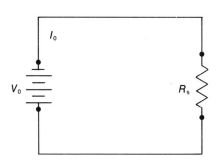

Adding resistance in series increases the total resistance in a circuit, thereby decreasing the current from the source.

The diagram shows a circuit with one source of electric potential, V_0, and three resistances, R_1, R_2, and R_3, as indicated. We would like to find the value of the total resistance of R_1, R_2, and R_3 connected in series. If we call this total resistance R_s, the circuit would simply contain the source, V_0, and the resistance, R_s. The amount of current flowing into the circuit from the source is I_0.

Applying Kirchhoff's Voltage Law to the circuit,

$$V_0 = V_1 + V_2 + V_3 \qquad (1)$$

Applying Ohm's Law to each individual resistance,

$$V_1 = I_1 R_1 \quad V_2 = I_2 R_2 \quad V_3 = I_3 R_3 \quad \text{and} \quad V_0 = I_0 R_s \qquad (2)$$

Substituting equations from (2) into (1),

$$I_0 R_s = I_1 R_1 + I_2 R_2 + I_3 R_3$$

But, applying Kirchhoff's Current Law to the circuit,

$$I_0 = I_1 = I_2 = I_3$$

Therefore, as an expression for the total resistance of R_1, R_2, and R_3, in series, we get

$$R_s = R_1 + R_2 + R_3$$

And, if the number of resistances connected in series is n, the total resistance will be given by

$$\boldsymbol{R_s = R_1 + R_2 + \dots + R_n}$$

Sample problems

1. What is the total resistance in a series circuit containing a 16 Ω light bulb, a 27 Ω heater, and a 12 Ω motor?

$$\begin{aligned} R_s &= R_1 + R_2 + R_3 \\ &= 16 \ \Omega + 27 \ \Omega + 12 \ \Omega \\ &= 55 \ \Omega \end{aligned}$$

2. A string of eight lights connected in series has a resistance of 120 Ω. If the lights are identical, what is the resistance of each bulb?

$$\begin{aligned} R_s &= R_1 + R_2 + \dots + R_8 \\ &= 8 R_1 \text{ if all are identical} \\ 120 \ \Omega &= 8 R_1 \\ R_1 &= \frac{120 \ \Omega}{8} = 15 \ \Omega \end{aligned}$$

Practice

1. Find the total resistance in each of these cases.
   (a) 12 Ω, 25 Ω, and 42 Ω connected in series
   (b) three 30 Ω light bulbs and two 20 Ω heating elements con-
       nected in series
   (c) two strings of Christmas tree lights connected in series, if
       the first string has eight 4 Ω bulbs in series, and the second
       has twelve 3 Ω bulbs in series.   (79 Ω, 130 Ω, 68 Ω)
2. Find the value of the unknown resistance in each of these cases.
   (a) a 20 Ω, an 18 Ω, and an unknown resistor connected in
       series to give a total resistance of 64 Ω
   (b) two identical unknown bulbs connected in series with a
       50 Ω and a 64 Ω heater to produce a total resistance of
       150 Ω
   (c) each light in a series string of 24 identical bulbs with a total
       resistance of 60 Ω   (26 Ω, 18 Ω, 2.5 Ω)

Total Resistance in Parallel

We can use the same approach to find the total resistance of several
resistances connected in parallel. If we call the total resistance of
$R_1, R_2,$ and R_3 connected in parallel, R_p, then the circuit appears as
shown.

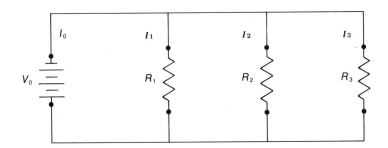
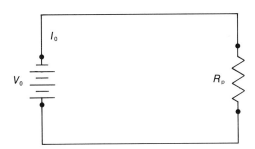

Applying Kirchhoff's Current Law to the circuit,

$$I_0 = I_1 + I_2 + I_3 \qquad (1)$$

Applying Ohm's Law to each individual resistance,

$$I_1 = \frac{V_1}{R_1} \qquad I_2 = \frac{V_2}{R_2} \qquad I_3 = \frac{V_3}{R_3} \qquad \text{and} \qquad I_0 = \frac{V_0}{R_p} \qquad (2)$$

Substituting equations from (2) into (1),

$$\frac{V_0}{R_p} = \frac{V_1}{R_1} + \frac{V_2}{R_2} + \frac{V_3}{R_3}$$

But, applying Kirchhoff's Voltage Law to the circuit,

$$V_0 = V_1 = V_2 = V_3$$

Therefore, as an expression for the total resistance of R_1, R_2, and R_3, in parallel, we get

$$\frac{1}{R_p} = \frac{1}{R_1} + \frac{1}{R_2} + \frac{1}{R_3}$$

And, if the number of resistances connected in parallel is n, the total resistance will be given by

$$\frac{1}{R_p} = \frac{1}{R_1} + \frac{1}{R_2} + \;\ldots\; + \frac{1}{R_n}$$

Adding resistance in parallel decreases the total resistance in a circuit, thereby increasing the current from the source.

Sample problems

1. Find the total resistance when a 4 Ω bulb and an 8 Ω bulb are connected in parallel.

$$\frac{1}{R_p} = \frac{1}{R_1} + \frac{1}{R_2}$$
$$= \frac{1}{4} + \frac{1}{8}$$
$$= \frac{2+1}{8}$$
$$= \frac{3}{8}$$
$$\therefore R_p = \frac{8}{3} = 2.7\ \Omega$$

2. What resistance would have to be added in parallel with a 40 Ω hair-dryer to reduce the total resistance to 8 Ω ?

$$\frac{1}{R_p} = \frac{1}{R_1} + \frac{1}{R_2}$$

$$\frac{1}{8} = \frac{1}{40} + \frac{1}{R_2}$$

$$\frac{1}{R_2} = \frac{1}{8} - \frac{1}{40}$$

$$= \frac{5 - 1}{40}$$

$$= \frac{4}{40}$$

$$= \frac{1}{10}$$

$$\therefore R_2 = 10 \ \Omega$$

Practice

1. Find the total resistance in each of these cases.
   (a) 16 Ω and 8 Ω connected in parallel
   (b) 20 Ω, 10 Ω, and 5 Ω connected in parallel   (5.3 Ω, 2.9 Ω)
2. Calculate the total resistance of two, three, four, and five 60 Ω bulbs in parallel. What is the simple relationship for the total resistance of n equal resistances in parallel?

$$(30 \ \Omega, \ 20 \ \Omega, \ 15 \ \Omega, \ 12 \ \Omega, \frac{R}{n})$$

12.5 Electric Circuit Analysis

With the information that has been presented so far about electricity, a complete analysis of any simple series or parallel electric circuit is possible, provided that you know enough about the elements in the circuit. Because so many different electric circuits are possible, there can be no standard approach to the analysing of a circuit. The steps to take in each case will depend on the information you have about the circuit, and what you want to find out.

Normally, the resistance of circuit wiring is negligible and can be overlooked when analysing circuits. In circuits that cover great distances, however, this may not be the case.

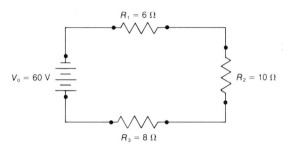

Sample circuits

1. Find: V_1, V_2, V_3
I_0, I_1, I_2, I_3

Applying Ohm's Law to the entire circuit,

$$I_0 = \frac{V_0}{R_t} \quad \text{where } R_t \text{ is the total resistance in the circuit}$$

But, since R_1, R_2, and R_3 are connected in series
$$R_t = R_1 + R_2 + R_3$$
$$= 6\ \Omega + 10\ \Omega + 8\ \Omega$$
$$= 24\ \Omega$$

Then

$$I_0 = \frac{V_0}{R_t}$$

$$= \frac{60\ \text{V}}{24\ \Omega}$$

$$= 2.5\ \text{A}$$

Using Kirchhoff's Current Law,
$$I_0 = I_1 = I_2 = I_3 = 2.5\ \text{A}$$
Then

$V_1 = I_1 R_1$	$V_2 = I_2 R_2$	$V_3 = I_3 R_3$
$= (2.5\ \text{A})\,(6\ \Omega)$	$= (2.5\ \text{A})\,(10\ \Omega)$	$= (2.5\ \text{A})\,(8\ \Omega)$
$= 15\ \text{V}$	$= 25\ \text{V}$	$= 20\ \text{V}$

As a final check, we could apply Kirchhoff's Voltage Law to the circuit, so that
$$V_0 = V_1 + V_2 + V_3$$
$$= 15\ \text{V} + 25\ \text{V} + 20\ \text{V}$$
$$= 60\ \text{V}$$
which is, in fact, the value we were given for V_0.

2. Find: V_0, V_1, V_2, V_3
I_0
R_1, R_2

Using Kirchhoff's Current Law,
$$I_0 = I_1 + I_2 + I_3$$
$$= 2\ \text{A} + 4\ \text{A} + 6\ \text{A}$$
$$= 12\ \text{A}$$

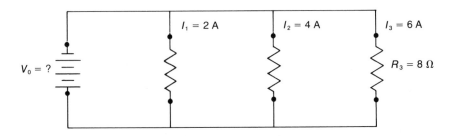

Applying Ohm's Law to R_3,

$$V_3 = I_3 R_3$$
$$= (6\text{ A})(8\ \Omega)$$
$$= 48\text{ V}$$

But, using Kirchhoff's Voltage Law around each of the three branches in the circuit,

$$V_0 = V_1 = V_2 = V_3 = 48\text{ V}$$

Then, using Ohm's Law once again,

$$R_2 = \frac{V_2}{I_2} \qquad R_1 = \frac{V_1}{I_1}$$
$$= \frac{48\text{ V}}{4\text{ A}} \qquad = \frac{48\text{ V}}{2\text{ A}}$$
$$= 12\ \Omega \qquad = 24\ \Omega$$

As a final check, we may calculate the total resistance in the circuit, R_t, using

$$\frac{1}{R_t} = \frac{1}{R_1} + \frac{1}{R_2} + \frac{1}{R_3}$$
$$\frac{1}{R_t} = \frac{1}{24} + \frac{1}{12} + \frac{1}{8}$$
$$= \frac{1 + 2 + 3}{24}$$
$$= \frac{6}{24}$$
$$= \frac{1}{4}$$

Then $\qquad R_t = 4\ \Omega$

and $\qquad I_0 = \frac{V_0}{R_t}$
$$= \frac{48\text{ V}}{4\ \Omega}$$
$$= 12\text{ A}$$

3. Find: V_1, V_2, V_3
$\quad\quad\quad I_1$, I_2, I_3
$\quad\quad\quad R_2$

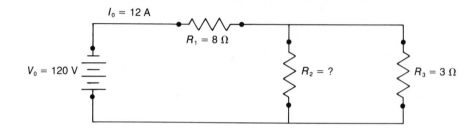

Using Kirchhoff's Current Law,
$$I_0 = I_1 = 12 \text{ A}$$
Applying Ohm's Law to the entire circuit
$$R_t = \frac{V_0}{I_0}$$
$$= \frac{120 \text{ V}}{12 \text{ A}}$$
$$= 10 \ \Omega$$

If the parallel pair of resistors R_2 and R_3 are, for the moment, thought of as one single resistor, R_4, then R_1 and R_4 are connected in series, and their total resistance is given by

$$R_t = R_1 + R_4$$
$$10 \ \Omega = 8 \ \Omega + R_4$$
$$R_4 = 2 \ \Omega$$

Then, using the relationship for the total resistance in parallel,

$$\frac{1}{R_4} = \frac{1}{R_2} + \frac{1}{R_3}$$
$$\frac{1}{2} = \frac{1}{R_2} + \frac{1}{3}$$
$$\frac{1}{R_2} = \frac{1}{2} - \frac{1}{3}$$
$$= \frac{3 - 2}{6}$$
$$= \frac{1}{6}$$
Then $\quad\quad\quad\quad\quad R_2 = 6 \ \Omega$

Using Ohm's Law,
$$V_1 = I_1 R_1$$

$$= (12 \text{ A}) (8 \text{ }\Omega)$$

$$= 96 \text{ V}$$

Then, applying Kirchhoff's Voltage Law around each of the two paths through the circuit,

$$V_0 = V_1 + V_2 \qquad\qquad V_0 = V_1 + V_3$$
$$120 \text{ V} = 96 \text{ V} + V_2 \qquad\qquad 120 \text{ V} = 96 \text{ V} + V_3$$
$$\therefore V_2 = 24 \text{ V} \qquad\qquad \therefore V_3 = 24 \text{ V}$$

and, finally,

$$I_2 = \frac{V_2}{R_2} \qquad\qquad I_3 = \frac{V_3}{R_3}$$

$$= \frac{24 \text{ V}}{6 \text{ }\Omega} \qquad\qquad = \frac{24 \text{ V}}{3 \text{ }\Omega}$$

$$= 4 \text{ A} \qquad\qquad = 8 \text{ A}$$

Practice

1. In this circuit, find V_1, V_2, I_0, I_1, and R_2.

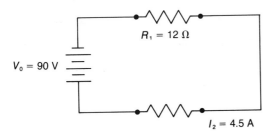

$$R_1 = 12 \text{ }\Omega$$

$$V_0 = 90 \text{ V}$$

$$I_2 = 4.5 \text{ A}$$

(54 V, 36 V, 4.5 A, 4.5 A, 8.0 Ω)

2. In this circuit, find V_0, V_1, I_2, R_1, and R_2.

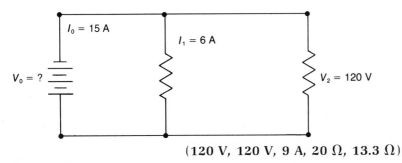

$$I_0 = 15 \text{ A}$$

$$I_1 = 6 \text{ A}$$

$$V_0 = ?$$

$$V_2 = 120 \text{ V}$$

(120 V, 120 V, 9 A, 20 Ω, 13.3 Ω)

3. In this circuit, find V_1, V_3, I_1, I_2, I_3, and R_3.

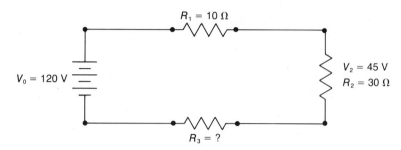

$$(15 \text{ V}, \ 60 \text{ V}, \ 1.5 \text{ A}, \ 1.5 \text{ A}, \ 1.5 \text{ A}, \ 40 \ \Omega)$$

4. In this circuit, find V_0, V_1, V_2, V_3, I_0, I_1, and I_2.

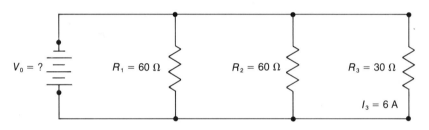

$$(180 \text{ V}, \ 180 \text{ V}, \ 180 \text{ V}, \ 180 \text{ V}, \ 12 \text{ A}, \ 3 \text{ A}, \ 3 \text{ A})$$

5. In this circuit, find V_1, V_2, V_3, I_0, I_1, I_2, and I_3.

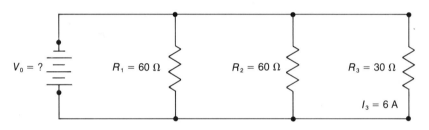

$$(30 \text{ V}, \ 30 \text{ V}, \ 90 \text{ V}, \ 6 \text{ A}, \ 1 \text{ A}, \ 5 \text{ A}, \ 6 \text{ A})$$

12.6 Power in Electric Circuits

When electrons move through a circuit, they dissipate the energy they receive from the source in the various loads they encounter. In Section 11.2, a formula for the amount of energy lost was developed: when a current, I, flows through a potential difference, V, for a time, t, the energy dissipated is given by

$$E = VIt$$

It is often more useful to know the rate at which a load uses energy. This quantity was defined in Section 8.2 in connection with mechanics, and it was called **power**. Power is the rate at which energy is used.

$$P = \frac{E}{t}$$

Substituting the expression above for electrical energy, we get

$$P = \frac{E}{t}$$

$$= \frac{VIt}{t}$$

$$= VI$$

as an expression for the electric power dissipated by a current, I, through a potential difference, V.

Note that potential difference is measured in volts (joules per coulomb) and current is measured in amperes (coulombs per second), and the unit of electric power is the product of the units of potential difference and current, namely,

$$(\text{volt})\,(\text{ampere}) = \left(\frac{\text{joule}}{\text{coulomb}}\right)\left(\frac{\text{coulomb}}{\text{second}}\right)$$

$$= \frac{\text{joule}}{\text{second}}$$

$$= \textbf{watt}$$

So electric power is measured in watts – the same unit that was used to measure mechanical power.

If the load has a resistance, R, then its power may also be expressed, using Ohm's Law, as

$$P = VI$$

But, from Ohm's Law, $\quad I = \dfrac{V}{R} \quad$ and $V = IR$

so we can write

$$P = VI$$
$$= (IR)I$$
$$= I^2R$$

as well as

$$P = VI$$
$$= V\left(\dfrac{V}{R}\right)$$
$$= \dfrac{V^2}{R}$$

Thus, to summarize, for a load with a current, I, potential difference, V, and resistance, R, the power is given by

$$\boldsymbol{P = VI}$$
$$\boldsymbol{P = I^2R}$$
$$\boldsymbol{P = \dfrac{V^2}{R}}$$

and, when proper units are used for I, V, and R, power will always be measured in watts.

The **power rating** of all electrical appliances is required by law to be indicated on a specification plate on the appliance, and some common values are shown in the table.

Appliance	Power rating	Current (with 120 V supply)
Kettle	1.5 kW	12.5 A
Stove	6 to 10 kW	*
Refrigerator	200 W	1.7 A
Toaster	1000 W	8.3 A
Vacuum cleaner	500 W	4.2 A

*Stoves operate at 240 V and draw currents in the range of 25 A to 40 A.

Sample problems

1. What is the current drawn by a 100 W light bulb operating at a potential difference of 120 V?

$$P = IV$$
$$\therefore I = \dfrac{P}{V}$$
$$= \dfrac{100 \text{ W}}{120 \text{ V}}$$
$$= 0.830 \text{ A}$$

2. What is the resistance of a 600 W kettle that draws a current of 5.0 A?

$$P = I^2R$$

$$\therefore R = \frac{P}{I^2}$$
$$= \frac{600 \text{ W}}{(5.0 \text{ A})^2}$$
$$= 24 \text{ } \Omega$$

3. What power is dissipated by an electric frying pan that has a resistance of 12 Ω and operates at a potential difference of 120 V?

$$P = \frac{V^2}{R}$$
$$= \frac{(120 \text{ V})^2}{12 \text{ } \Omega}$$
$$= 1.2 \text{ x } 10^3 \text{ W or 1.2 kW}$$

Practice

1. What is the potential difference across a 1250 W baseboard heater that draws 5.2 A? $(2.4 \times 10^2 \text{ V})$
2. If a 700 W toaster and an 1100 W kettle are plugged into the same 120 V outlet, what total current will they draw?(15.0 A)
3. What is the maximum power that may be used in a circuit with a potential difference of 120 V and a 20 A fuse?   (2.4 kW)
4. A portable heater plugged into a 120 V outlet draws a current of 8.0 A. Calculate each of the following.
   (a) the quantity of electric charge that flows through the heater in 10 min $(4.8 \times 10^3 \text{ C})$
   (b) the energy consumed by the heater $(5.8 \times 10^5 \text{ J})$
   (c) the power dissipated by the heater $(9.6 \times 10^2 \text{ W})$

The Cost of Electricity

Electric appliances get their ability to do work by using energy supplied by your local electric power system, which bases its charges on the amount of electrical energy used in a given time.

The basic unit of energy, the joule, is a very small unit, and, for this reason, the electrical energy consumed is measured by means of a larger unit derived from the joule.

Energy used may be written as
$$E = Pt$$

Then, if power is measured in kilowatts (kW) and time is measured in hours (h), electrical energy may be measured in **kilowatt hours** (kW·h).

---

1 kW·h is the energy dissipated in 1 h by a load with a power of 1 kW.

It is often useful to calculate the relationship between the joule and the kilowatt hour, using the equation

$$E = Pt$$
$$= (1\ kW)\ (1\ h)$$
$$= 1\ kW \cdot h$$
$$or = (1000\ J/s)\ (3600\ s)$$
$$= 3.6 \times 10^6\ J$$

---

1 kW·h = 3.6 × 10⁶ J = 3.6 MJ

The power dissipated by each of several appliances operating simultaneously may be added to get an expression for the total power being used. When this power is multiplied by the time for which it is used, an expression for the total energy is arrived at. The electricity system installs a meter on each house to make this measurement and to keep track of the amount of electrical energy used by the house. Then, by multiplying the number of kilowatt hours of energy used by the rate (price per kilowatt hour), the total cost of the electricity is calculated. Generally, the rate decreases as the amount of energy used increases. Typical rates charged for electricity are given in this table.

RESIDENTIAL Bi-monthly		RESIDENTIAL ALL ELECTRIC Monthly	
First 100 kW·h	@ 6.70¢	First 50 kW·h	@ 6.70¢
Next 400 kW·h	@ 3.25¢	Next 200 kW·h	@ 3.05¢
Balance	@ 2.15¢	Balance	@ 2.15¢
Minimum Bill	$7.00	Minimum Bill	$3.50

An electrician servicing a domestic electrical meter

Sample problems

Some conservationists think that the power companies encourage excessive use of energy by their rate structure: They feel that you would be more careful about using energy if the rate got higher the more you used.

1. Calculate the cost of operating a 400 W spotlight for 2.0 h a day for 30 d at a rate of 6.0¢/kW·h.

$$E = Pt$$
$$= (0.400 \text{ kW}) (60 \text{ h})$$
$$= 24 \text{ kW·h}$$
$$\text{Cost} = (24 \text{ kW·h}) (6.0¢/\text{kW·h})$$
$$= 144¢ \quad \text{or} \quad \$1.44$$

2. Find the cost of operating an oven for 3.0 h if it draws 15 A from a 240 V supply, at a rate of 5.0¢/kW·h.

$$P = IV$$
$$= (15 \text{ A}) (240 \text{ V})$$
$$= 3600 \text{ W} \quad \text{or} \quad 3.6 \text{ kW}$$
$$E = Pt$$
$$= (3.6 \text{ kW}) (3.0 \text{ h})$$
$$= 10.8 \text{ kW·h}$$
$$\text{Cost} = (10.8 \text{ kW·h}) (5.0¢/\text{kW·h})$$
$$= 54¢$$

Practice

1. Find the cost of operating an electric toaster for 3.0 h if it draws 5.0 A from a 120 V outlet. Electric energy costs 5.5¢/kW·h. (10¢)
2. What is the cost to a storekeeper of leaving a 40 W light burning near his safe over the weekend, for 60 h, if electricity costs 4.5¢/kW·h? (11¢)
3. The blower motor on an oil furnace, rated at 250 W, comes on, for an average of 5.0 min at a time, a total of 48 times a day. What is the monthly (30 d) cost of operating the motor, if electricity costs 4.2¢/kW·h? ($1.26)

12.7 Additional Investigation: Transforming Electrical Energy into Heat Energy

Problem:
Is energy conserved during its transformation from electrical energy into heat energy?

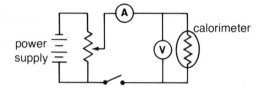

Materials:

electric calorimeter   thermometer
power source (6-12 V)   timer
ammeter   triple-beam balance
voltmeter   rheostat

Procedure

1. Measure the mass of the calorimeter cup.
2. Fill the cup about two-thirds full of cold water, and measure the mass of the cup with the water.
3. Return the cup to the calorimeter, and attach the power source to the calorimeter, as shown.
4. Close the switch and adjust the rheostat until the ammeter reads 2.0 A. Open the switch immediately.
5. Stir the water in the cup gently, and record its temperature.
6. Close the switch and start the timer. Make any adjustments necessary to keep the current constant. Record the temperature every 2 min (gently stirring each time) until the temperature of the water is as many degrees above room temperature as it was below room temperature originally. Also keep a record of the current and voltage.
7. If you are not able to keep the current and voltage constant, calculate the average value of each during the experiment.

Questions

1. What was the temperature change of the water in the calorimeter cup?
2. How much heat energy did the water gain?
3. How much heat energy did the calorimeter cup gain?
4. How much electrical energy was supplied to the water?
5. What difference is there between the energy supplied and the energy gained? Try to explain this difference if energy is conserved in any transformation.

12.8 Additional Investigation: Transforming Electrical Energy into Mechanical Energy

Problem:

Is energy conserved during its transformation from electrical energy into mechanical energy?

Materials:

small electric motor   timer
power supply   ammeter
string and small masses   voltmeter

Procedure

1. Arrange the materials as shown.
2. Start the motor running without the mass attached. Record the current and voltage used to run the motor by itself.
3. Use the string to attach a small mass to the rotor of the motor. Start the motor. If the load is too heavy to lift, immediately stop the motor and reduce the mass. If the motor accelerates the load upwards, then add more mass until the load rises at a slow, uniform rate.
4. Measure the time required for the motor to raise the load by 1.0 m at a slow, uniform speed. Also record the current and voltage used by the motor in raising the load. Repeat several times and average the results.

Questions

1. How much power is used to run the motor with no load on it?
2. How much electrical energy would be used by the motor alone during the average time needed to lift the load?
3. How much electrical energy is used by the motor, on the average, to lift the load at a uniform speed?
4. How much electrical energy is used only in lifting the load?
5. By how much is the gravitational potential energy of the load increased when it is lifted 1.0 m?
6. What difference is there between the electrical energy used to lift the load and the gravitational potential energy gained by the load? Try to explain this difference if energy is conserved during any transformation.

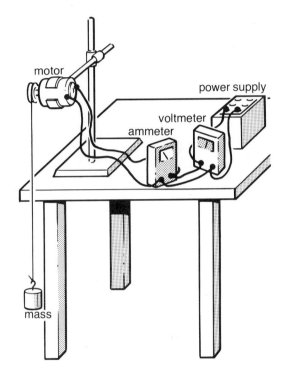

12.9 Summary

1. Loads and sources of electric potential are connected together in complete circuits by conductors. The network of conductors and circuit elements may be represented in a schematic diagram using standard symbols.
2. Circuit elements may be connected together in series (in which case all the current passes through each load in succession) or in parallel (in which case the current splits up and each part passes through a different load).

3. In every electric circuit,
    (a) around any complete path, the total increase in electric potential and the total decrease in electric potential are equal.
    (b) at any junction point, the total electric current flowing into the junction and the total electric current flowing out of the junction are equal.
    These relationships are known as Kirchhoff's Laws.
4. Between any two points in a circuit, the ratio of potential difference to current is constant, and this constant is called the resistance. This relationship, known as Ohm's Law, may be represented as
$$\frac{V}{I} = R$$
    where R, the resistance, is measured in volts per ampere, or ohms, and $1\ \Omega = 1\ V/A$.
5. The resistance of a cylindrical conductor depends on its
    (a) length
    (b) cross-sectional area
    (c) temperature
    (d) molecular structure, or resistivity
6. The total resistance of n resistances connected in series is given by
$$R_s = R_1 + R_2 + \ldots + R_n$$
    and the total resistance of n resistances connected in parallel is given by
$$\frac{1}{R_p} = \frac{1}{R_1} + \frac{1}{R_2} + \ldots + \frac{1}{R_n}$$
7. The power, or rate of energy dissipation, of an electrical device is given by
$$P = IV$$
$$P = I^2R$$
$$P = \frac{V^2}{R}$$
    where P, the power, is measured in joules per second, or watts, and $1\ W = 1\ J/s$.
8. Electrical energy may be measured as the product of power and time in units called kilowatt hours, and
$$1\ kW \cdot h = 3.6 \times 10^6\ J$$
    The cost of electric energy may be calculated by multiplying the number of kilowatt hours consumed by the price per kilowatt hour.

12.10 Review

1. Describe the current and potential difference characteristics of a series circuit, and of a parallel circuit.

2. Draw a schematic diagram of a circuit containing one resistor connected in series, two resistors connected in parallel, a fuse, a switch, a voltmeter, and an ammeter. The fuse should protect the whole circuit, the switch should interrupt the whole circuit, the voltmeter should measure the potential difference across the series resistor, and the ammeter should measure the current through one of the parallel resistors.

3. Describe the effect on the rest of the circuit when one of three lamps in a circuit burns out, if the three lamps are connected (a) in series, and (b) in parallel. Explain your answers.

4. A battery is constructed by connecting several 1.5 V dry cells together. Draw the circuit symbol of such a battery, if it consists of (a) three cells connected in series, and (b) four cells connected in parallel. What is the potential difference of the battery in each case?

5. Draw a schematic diagram for a circuit that may be used to determine the resistance of an unknown resistor.

6. Describe what is meant by resistance and list four factors that affect the resistance of a conductor. Describe the effect of each factor on the resistance of a conductor.

7. What is the effect on the total resistance in a circuit, when an extra resistor is added (a) in series, and (b) in parallel?

8. State three equations for calculating the power dissipated in a resistor, and show that, when proper units are used in these equations, the unit that results for power is watts.

9. (a) What quantity is measured in kilowatt hours?
   (b) What values of electric potential are found in the home, and where are these different values used?

10. Draw a graph of potential difference versus current for two different resistances, and indicate which has the greater resistance, and why.

11. A voltmeter connected across the ends of a heating coil indicates a potential difference of 60 V when an ammeter shows a current through the coil of 3.0 A. What is the resistance of the coil?

12. A flashlight bulb has a resistance of 7.5 Ω and is connected to a dry cell with a potential difference of 3.0 V. What current passes through the bulb?

Numerical Answers to Review Questions

4. (a) 4.5 V (b) 1.5 V
11. 20 Ω
12. 0.40 A
13. 2.4×10^2 V
14. (a) 1.6×10^2 Ω (b) 20 Ω (c) 15 V
15. (a) 20 Ω (b) 10 Ω
16. (a) 90 Ω (b) 2.5 Ω (c) 12 Ω
17. 8
18. 1.0 Ω
19. 16 Ω
20. (a) 10 Ω, 12 Ω, 4.8 V (b) 36 V, 18 Ω, 6 Ω (c) 4 Ω, 1 A, 5 A, 3.3 A, 1.6 A, 1.1 A
21. 2.2×10^4 J
22. (a) 3.00×10^3 W (b) 1.2×10^3 W (c) 60.0 W
23. (a) 3.6×10^3 W (b) 3.5 A
24. (a) 8.3 A (b) 17 A
25. $27.59

Almost everyone has experienced an electric shock without suffering any great physical damage. Except at extremely high voltages, electric potential difference causes little harm. The pain and danger of electric shock are due to electric currents that pass through parts of the body due to a potential difference applied to the body. Internal, moist flesh has a low resistance whereas the dry outer layers of skin have a high resistance and are fairly good insulators. With normal skin, shocks of 12 V or even higher cause scarcely more than a tingle, if they are felt at all. If the skin is moist, however, current can penetrate to vital organs, and even low-voltage shocks can cause serious damage and may even be fatal. Every year, many people are killed by 120 V shocks when they are in a bathtub or swimming pool, or even standing in a puddle of water.

13. What is the potential difference across a motor with a resistance of 40 Ω if the motor draws a current of 6.0 A?

14. A string of eight Christmas tree lights connected in series to a 120 V source draws a current of 0.75 A. Find
    (a) the total resistance of the string of lights
    (b) the resistance of each light
    (c) the potential difference across each light

15. (a) What is the resistance of a toaster that draws a current of 6.0 A from a 120 V source?
    (b) What resistance would have to be added in series with the same toaster to reduce its current to 4.0 A?

16 Calculate the total resistance in each of these cases.
    (a) 10 Ω, 30 Ω, and 50 Ω in series
    (b) 6 Ω, 5 Ω, and 30 Ω in parallel
    (c) 9 Ω in series, with a parallel branch of 4 Ω and 12 Ω

17. How many 160 Ω resistors must be connected in parallel to draw a current of 6.0 A from a 120 V source?

18. The potential difference across a heating coil is 6.0 V when the current passing through it is 3.0 A. What resistance must be added in series with the coil to reduce the current flowing through it to 2.0 A?

19. A portable radio is designed to operate at a potential difference of 6.0 V and a current of 250 mA, but the only source available has a potential of 10.0 V. What resistance must be added in series with the radio to make it operate properly?

20. Examine these circuits and find the values indicated.
    (a) Find: R_2, R_3, and V_3

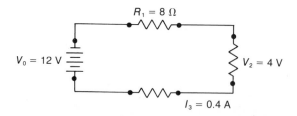

    (b) Find: V_0, R_1, R_{total}

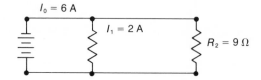

(c) Find: $R_3, I_1, I_2, I_4, I_5, I_6$

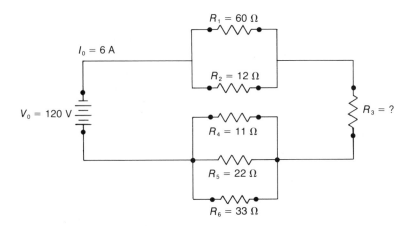

21. Calculate the electrical energy dissipated in 1.5 min when a current of 4.0 A goes through a potential difference of 60 V.
22. Calculate the power dissipated by each of the following loads.
    (a) a clothes-dryer drawing 12.5 A from a 240 V source
    (b) a kettle that draws 12.0 A and has a resistance of 8.3 Ω
    (c) a 240 Ω heating pad plugged into a 120 V source
23. (a) What maximum power can be used on a 240 V circuit with a 15 A fuse?
    (b) How much more current can safely be drawn from a 120 V outlet fused at 20 A if an 800 W toaster and an 1180 W kettle are already operating in the circuit?
24. A 1.0 kW toaster, designed to operate at 120 V, is mistakenly connected to a source of 240 V.
    (a) What current is the toaster designed to draw?
    (b) What current will it draw when connected to 240 V?
    (c) What is likely to be the result?
25. A refrigerator compressor draws 2.5 A from a 120 V source and operates for an average of 15 min out of each hour. Calculate the annual cost of operating the refrigerator if the average cost of electrical energy is 4.2¢/kW·h.

12.11 Learning Objectives

1. To identify the standard symbols used in electric circuit diagrams, and to draw and interpret the schematic diagrams for simple circuits.

2. To draw simple series and parallel circuits containing several load elements, and to describe the basic current and electric potential relationships in each type of connection.

3. To state Kirchhoff's Laws, and to use them to write equations to represent the relationships between potential differences and electric currents in simple circuits.

4. To define resistance in terms of Ohm's Law, and to state the unit of resistance and its equivalent.

5. Given any two of potential difference, electric current, and resistance, to determine the third.

6. To list four factors that affect the resistance of a cylindrical conductor, and to describe the effect of each.

7. Given the values of several resistances connected either in series or in parallel, to determine their total resistance.

8. To analyse simple series, parallel, and series-parallel circuits: that is, given sufficient information about a circuit, to calculate the potential difference across each element, the current through each element, and the resistance of each load.

9. To define electric power, and to state the unit of power, and its equivalent.

10. Given any two of power, electric current, potential difference, and resistance, to determine the other two.

11. To define the kilowatt hour as a unit of electrical energy, and, given the power and time of use, to determine the electrical energy consumed by a load, and hence the cost of operating the load.

13 Magnetism

13.1 Magnetism and Magnetic Forces

Even before 600 B.C., the Greeks had discovered that a certain type of iron ore, which later came to be known as lodestone, or magnetite, was capable of exerting forces of attraction on other small pieces of iron. Also, when pivoted and allowed to rotate freely, a piece of lodestone would come to rest in a north-south position. Because it had this property, lodestone was used widely in navigation. Chemically, lodestone consists mainly of iron oxide, a mineral that was first found near a place called Magnesia, in Greece. Hence the term **magnetism**.

Nowadays, lodestone is hardly ever used for its magnetic property. Artificial magnets are made from various alloys of iron, nickel, and cobalt, by a procedure that will be explained in Section 13.4.

When a magnet is dipped in iron filings, the filings are attracted to the magnet and concentrations of them accumulate most noticeably at the opposite ends of the magnet. We call these areas of concentrated magnetic force **poles**. When a magnet is allowed to rotate freely, one of the poles tends to ''seek'' the northerly direction and it is called the **north-seeking pole**, or more simply the **N-pole**. The other is called the **south-seeking pole**, or the **S-pole**.

When the N-pole of one magnet is brought near the N-pole of another freely swinging magnet, a force of repulsion is observed. Similarly, two S-poles repel each other. On the other hand, N-poles and S-poles always attract each other. These observations lead to what is called the Law of Magnetic Poles:

Opposite magnetic poles attract. Similar magnetic poles repel.

The iron oxide that makes up lodestone is also known as magnetite (Fe_2O_3).

Lodestone, showing magnetic attraction of iron nails

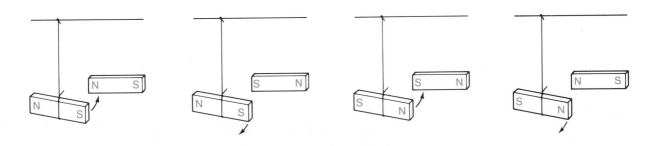

When we talk about the poles of magnets, we usually leave out the word "seeking." The pole of a magnet marked "N" is the north-seeking pole — the pole that would point to the north pole of the Earth if allowed to swing freely. So, we should not think that the N-pole of a compass pointing towards the north pole of the Earth contradicts the law of magnetic attraction of unlike poles.

13.2 Magnetic Fields

When an N-pole and an S-pole are brought close to each other, they begin to attract even before they touch. This "action-at-a-distance" type of force is already familiar, from your examination of the gravitational force (Chapter 5) and the electric force (Chapter 10). The effect of those forces was described in terms of a "field of force" in the surrounding space. Similarly, we will consider the space around a magnet, in which magnetic forces are exerted, as a **magnetic field of force**.

To detect the presence of such a magnetic field, we need a delicate instrument that is affected by magnetic forces. Small filings of iron respond to magnetic forces, but their poles are not marked and so we cannot determine which way they are pointing. A more complete observation of the magnetic force at a given point in a magnetic field can be made by means of a small test compass with clearly marked poles.

A magnetic field may be represented by a series of lines around a magnet, representing the path the N-pole of a small test compass would take if it were allowed to move freely in the direction of the magnetic force. Then, at any point in the field, a magnetic field line indicates the direction in which the N-pole of the test compass would point. In the investigation that follows, you will examine the magnetic force field that is created by a bar magnet, and the field that is created by two bar magnets placed close together.

A magnetically propelled monorail transit system

Investigation: Magnetic Fields

Problem:
What is the nature of the magnetic field in the region around a bar magnet, and in the region of a pair of bar magnets close together?

Materials:
two bar magnets
small plotting compass
iron filings
large sheets of blank paper

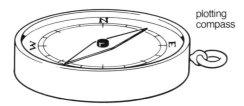
plotting compass

Procedure
1. First, check the compass and bar magnets to ensure that their polarity is correctly marked. (It is possible, as you will see in Section 13.4, to reverse-magnetize a magnet.) Place the compass several metres away from any other magnets or metallic substances, and allow it to swing freely. If the compass has been correctly magnetized, one of its poles should point north when it comes to rest. Then, this pole should point towards the S-pole of each of the bar magnets, when brought close to them. Make sure that the compass and the bar magnets are correctly magnetized before proceeding.
2. Place one of the bar magnets on a table at the centre of a large sheet of paper, mark its outline with a pencil, and label the poles on the outline. Make a small dot on the paper close to the S-pole of the magnet, and place the plotting compass on the paper so that it points directly towards this dot. Now, make a second dot exactly at the opposite end of the compass needle. Move the compass until the needle points directly towards the second dot, and make a third dot at the opposite end of the needle. Continue the procedure until the resulting line of dots either makes its way back to the magnet or runs off the edge of the sheet. Join the dots with a smooth line, and put arrows on the line pointing in the direction of the N-pole of the compass.

3. Repeat the same procedure, using other starting points near the S-pole of the magnet. Try to cover your paper with field lines.

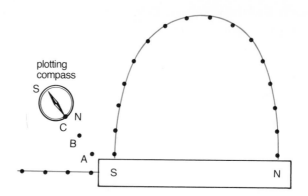

4. To get a more detailed impression of the magnetic field of a bar magnet, place the magnet *under* the same piece of paper, exactly where you drew the outline. Sprinkle iron filings gently over the entire surface of the paper, tap the paper several times, and note the relationship between the pattern of iron filings and the field lines you drew with the plotting compass. Draw a detailed sketch of the magnetic field thus revealed.

5. Under a fresh sheet of paper, place the two bar magnets in a straight line, with their opposite poles about 5 cm apart. After outlining the position of the poles on the sheet with a pencil, sprinkle iron filings on the paper and tap it gently. Draw a sketch of the magnetic field that is indicated by the position of the filings, using your compass to determine the direction of the magnetic field lines.

6. Repeat the same procedure, using two like poles, and sketch the magnetic field.

Questions

1. From what area of the magnets do field lines seem to originate? To what region do they seem to return? Which field lines, if any, leave the magnets but seem not to return? Why?

2. Do magnetic field lines ever cross each other? Could there be any magnetic lines of force in the regions of space between the field lines you have drawn? Check to see.

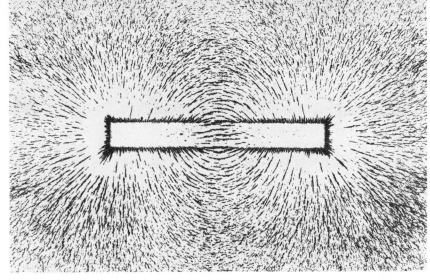

The magnetic field of a bar magnet

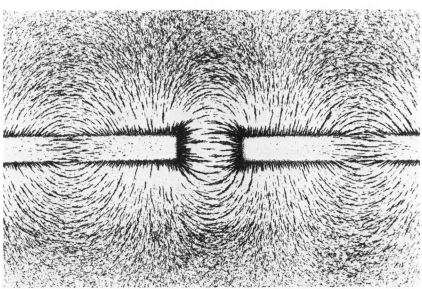
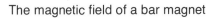

The magnetic field of a pair of opposite poles, close together

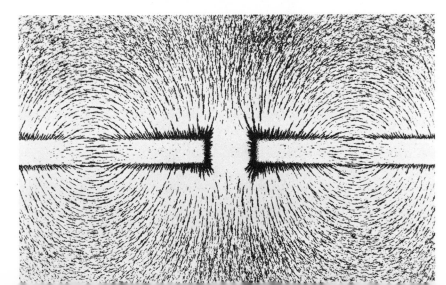

The magnetic field of a pair of similar poles, close together.

3. What do you notice about the spacing of the field lines as you move away from the poles? What does this spacing indicate about the strength of the magnetic field?
4. There is a theory of magnetism that states that every magnetic field line is a closed curve; but the field lines we have drawn seem to start at the N-pole and return at the S-pole. Draw in the remainder of each field line, to make it a closed curve. Where does the magnetic field that you have just drawn lie?

13.3 Magnetic Field of the Earth

The most up-to-date theory suggests that the Earth's magnetic field is due to the presence of swirling currents of molten magnetic iron in its interior. As this lava flows, the position of the north and south magnetic poles shifts, and the declination of any given point on the Earth's surface changes.

In the investigation in Section 13.2, you saw that a small compass in the presence of a magnetic field will rotate until its N-pole points in the direction of the field. The early navigators used this discovery to find the direction of north. But what magnetic field was their compass reacting to? In the 16th century, William Gilbert (1540-1603), a distinguished physicist who was also physician to Queen Elizabeth I, stated that the Earth itself had a magnetic field and behaved as if it had a large bar magnet in its interior, inclined at a slight angle to its axis. The diagrams show the Earth, its magnetic field, and the bar magnet that was at one time believed to be responsible for this field.

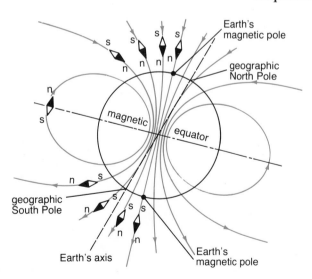

The magnetic field of the Earth

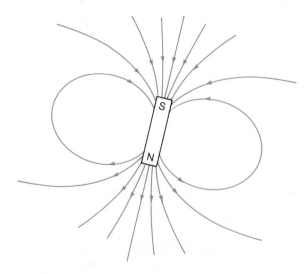

The magnetic field of an inclined bar magnet

Magnetic Declination

A magnetic compass points towards the Earth's magnetic north pole, rather than towards its geographic north pole (that is, the northern end of the Earth's axis). The angle between the geographic north, or true north, and magnetic north varies from position to position on the Earth's surface and is called the **magnetic declination**. A navigator using a magnetic compass must know the angle of declination at his location before he can find true north.

A magnetic compass used for navigation on a naval vessel

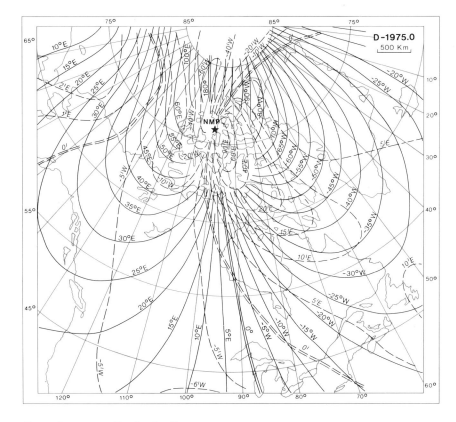

Canada: magnetic declinations

The Earth's magnetic field protects us by deflecting potentially harmful cosmic radiation from outer space. The weaker cosmic rays are shunted completely to one side, whereas the stronger ones are at least deflected to higher latitudes, where they can do less harm.

Magnetic Inclination, or Dip

The magnetic field of the Earth is not just horizontal; it has a vertical component as well. A magnetic compass gives only the direction of its horizontal component. Also, the direction of the

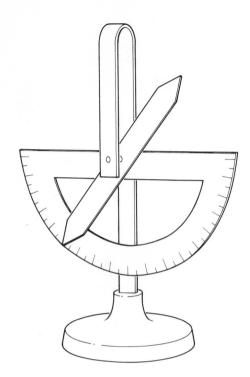

Magnetic dipping-needle

Earth's magnetic field lines varies over the Earth's surface.

The angle between the direction of the magnetic field at a given position and a horizontal line is called the **magnetic inclination** or "dip", and it may be measured with a dipping needle, which is a magnetized compass needle pivoted exactly at its centre of gravity. If there were no magnetic field it would remain horizontal. However, when aligned with a magnetic compass pointing north, the north end of the dip needle will point down towards the Earth (in the northern hemisphere), and the angle of dip may be measured on the protractor provided.

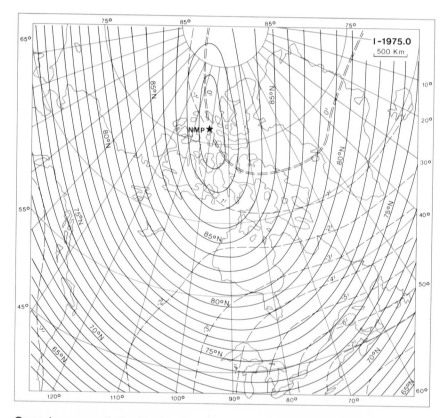

Canada: magnetic inclinations

In the southern hemisphere, the S-pole of a dipping needle points down towards the Earth.

Changes in the Earth's Magnetism

Navigators' declination charts must be revised from time to time because the declination at any given point changes gradually. Values that have been recorded for the declination at Agincourt, Ontario, include these:

Year	Declination
1750	3° 49' W of N
1800	0° 53' W of N
1900	5° 26' W of N
1965	7° 26' W of N

Scientists predict that the declination at Agincourt will again be 0° N near the beginning of the 23rd century. The changes in declination are accompanied by small changes in inclination. It is believed that these changes occur because the magnetic field of the Earth is slowly rotating about the Earth's axis, taking about 1000 years to make one rotation.

Apart from slight shifts in pole locations and a small decrease in strength, the Earth's magnetic field has remained quite constant during the seven centuries since the magnetic compass came into use. Geophysicists can discover what the Earth's magnetic field was like long before mankind existed on the planet by observing the orientation of magnetic molecules in solidified volcanic rock. These crystallized magnetic minerals aligned themselves with the magnetic field of the Earth as it was at the time of their solidification, and this time can be determined quite accurately by using the radioactive dating technique described in Chapter 16.

13.4 Magnetic Materials: Induced Magnetism

Small pieces of iron stroked in one direction with lodestone become magnetized. Even bringing a piece of iron near a magnet causes it to be magnetized. Nickel and cobalt, and any alloy containing nickel, cobalt, or iron, behave in the same way. These substances are called **ferromagnetic**, and you can induce them to become magnetized by placing them in a magnetic field.

In sketches of magnetic fields, ⊗ represents a magnetic field line pointing into the page and ⊙ represents a magnetic field line pointing out of the page.

Domain Theory of Magnetism

The atoms of ferromagnetic substances may be thought of as tiny magnets with an N-pole and an S-pole. These atomic magnets, or **dipoles**, interact with their nearest neighbouring dipoles and a group of them line up with their magnetic axes in the same direction to form a **magnetic domain**. In an unmagnetized piece of iron there are millions of these domains, but they are pointing in random directions so that the piece of iron, as a whole, is not magnetized. The diagram represents this unmagnetized condition.

When such a piece of iron is placed in a magnetic field (that is, near another magnet), the dipoles act like small compasses and rotate until they are aligned with the field. One end of the piece of

Atomic dipoles are lined up inside domains but domains are pointing in random directions.

Magnetic material in an unmagnetized state

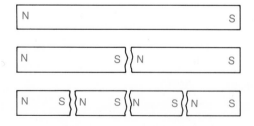

Atomic dipoles (not
domains) turn so
that all domains point in
the direction of the
magnetizing field.

Magnetic material in a magnetized state

The actual boundaries between magnetic
domains are very irregular in shape and
the domains are of varying size. These
diagrams are greatly simplified for easier
understanding.

iron will then consist of a large number of dipoles pointing north
and will become an N-pole, and the other end will become an
S-pole. The next diagram shows the same piece of iron in the
magnetized condition.

Effects of the Domain Theory

(a) Demagnetization
When a piece of iron becomes demagnetized, its aligned dipoles
return to random directions. Dropping or heating an induced
magnet will cause this to occur. Some materials, such as pure iron,
revert to random alignment as soon as they are removed from the
magnetizing field. Substances that become demagnetized spontaneously and instantly are called **soft ferromagnetic** materials.
Iron may be alloyed with certain materials, such as aluminum and
silicon, that have the effect of keeping the dipoles aligned even
when the magnetizing field is removed. These alloys are used to
make permanent magnets and are referred to as **hard ferromagnetic** materials.

(b) Reverse Magnetization
The bar magnets used in classrooms are made of hard ferromagnetic alloys, and they remain magnetized for a long time. The
letter N is stamped on that end of the magnet to which all the
N-poles of the aligned domains point. If a bar magnet is placed in a
strong enough magnetic field of opposite polarity, its domains can
turn and point in the opposite direction. In that case, the N-pole of
the magnet is at the end marked S. The magnet is reverse-
magnetized.

(c) Breaking a Bar Magnet
Breaking a bar magnet produces two pieces of iron whose dipole
alignment is identical to the original piece. Both pieces will also be
magnets, with N-poles and S-poles at opposite ends. Continued
breaking will produce the same results, since the domains within
the magnet remain aligned even when the magnet is broken.

(d) Magnetic Saturation
In most magnets, a large number of the dipoles are aligned in the
same direction, but not all.
   The strength of a bar magnet may be increased only up to a
certain level. The peak will occur when as many as possible of its
dipoles are aligned. The material is then said to have reached its
magnetic saturation.

Effect of breaking a bar magnet

(e) Induced Magnetism by the Earth

If a piece of iron is held in the Earth's magnetic field and its atoms are agitated, either by heating or by mechanical vibration (that is, by hitting the iron with a hammer), alignment of its dipoles will result. This is most easily accomplished by holding the piece of iron pointing north and at the local angle of inclination, while tapping it with a hammer.

Steel columns and beams used in building construction are invariably found to be magnetized. Steel hulls of ships and railroad tracks are also magnetized by the Earth's magnetic field.

(f) Keepers for Bar Magnets

In time, a bar magnet will become demagnetized as the poles at its ends begin to reverse the polarity of the atomic dipoles inside it. If bar magnets are stored in pairs with their opposite poles adjacent and with small pieces of soft iron (called "keepers") across the ends, demagnetization does not occur. The keepers themselves become strong induced magnets and form closed loops of magnetic dipoles, thus preventing demagnetizing poles from forming.

13.5 Summary

1. Certain materials, such as lodestone, are capable of exerting magnetic forces and are called magnets. The forces are concentrated at opposite ends of a magnet, in areas called poles.
2. There are two characteristic poles of magnetic force, called north-seeking and south-seeking. The fundamental law of magnetic poles states:

Similar poles repel.
Opposite poles attract.

3. The region of magnetic force around a magnet is called a magnetic field and is represented by magnetic field lines that show the direction of the force on the N-pole of a small test compass at each point in the field.
4. The Earth has a magnetic field similar to that of a bar magnet, with its S-pole located near the north geographic pole of the Earth. Compasses point to this pole, called the north magnetic pole, and the angle between the north magnetic pole and the north geographic pole at any point on the Earth is called the magnetic declination.
5. The Earth's magnetic field has two components, the vertical and the horizontal, and the angle between the direction of the

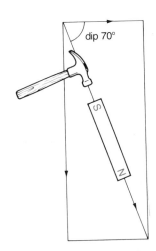

Magnetism by Earth induction

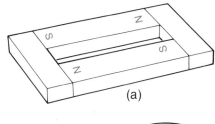

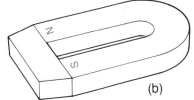

Keepers
(a) on bar magnets
(b) on a horseshoe magnet

Earth's magnetic field (which varies) and a horizontal line is called the magnetic inclination, or dip.

6. Substances containing iron, nickel, or cobalt may be induced to become magnets by being placed in a magnetic field. They are called ferromagnetic materials.

7. Induced magnetism may be explained by means of the theory of domains. Ferromagnetic materials are composed of a large number of tiny magnetic dipoles. Groups of aligned dipoles form magnetic domains that are normally oriented at random. In the presence of a magnetic field, the dipoles turn so that all domains are aligned to form a magnet.

8. The domain theory may be used to explain:
   (a) demagnetization of a temporary magnet
   (b) reverse magnetization of a bar magnet
   (c) the breaking of a bar magnet into a large number of smaller magnets
   (d) magnetic saturation
   (e) magnetism induced by the Earth
   (f) keepers for bar magnets

13.6 Review

1. What name is given to materials that are strongly attracted by a magnet? Name two such materials, other than iron and steel.

2. Describe how a screwdriver could be magnetized. What might happen if the screwdriver were heated or dropped? Explain your answer.

3. What name is given to the region in which a magnet influences other magnetic materials? How far does this region extend?

4. Describe two ways in which you could detect the presence of a magnetic field. Does any magnetic field exist in the spaces between the lines of iron filings around a magnet? Explain your answer.

5. Is the magnetic pole area in the northern hemisphere an N-pole or an S-pole? Explain.

6. Vertical retort-stand rods in laboratory classrooms are often found to be magnetized, and the polarity of such rods in Canada is opposite to the polarity of those in Australia. Explain this statement.

7. Given two apparently identical bars of steel, one a permanent magnet and the other unmagnetized, and without the help of any other equipment, describe a method for determining which bar is the magnet.

8. Describe what would happen to a magnetic compass and to a dipping needle if each were placed (**a**) at the north pole, and (**b**) at the equator.
9. Using the domain theory, explain the difference between soft iron and steel, and indicate which you would select for use as (**a**) a compass needle, and (**b**) keepers for a pair of bar magnets.
10. How might a wristwatch become magnetized? Why would this cause problems? What does the term ''anti-magnetic'' stamped on the back of a watch indicate?

13.7 Learning Objectives

1. To state the law of magnetic poles.
2. To state the general characteristics of a magnetic force field, and to draw the magnetic field of (**a**) a bar magnet, (**b**) a pair of similar poles close together, and (**c**) a pair of opposite poles close together.
3. To describe the magnetic field of the Earth, and to define ''magnetic north-seeking pole'', ''magnetic declination'', and ''magnetic inclination''.
4. To list three ferromagnetic substances, and to state the conditions under which such a substance may be induced to become magnetized.
5. To describe the major features of the domain theory of magnetism by defining "magnetic dipole", "magnetic domain", "random orientation of domains", and "alignment of domains".
6. To use the domain theory to explain (**a**) demagnetization, (**b**) reverse magnetization, (**c**) breaking a bar magnet, (**d**) magnetic saturation, (**e**) Earth induction, and (**f**) keepers for bar magnets.

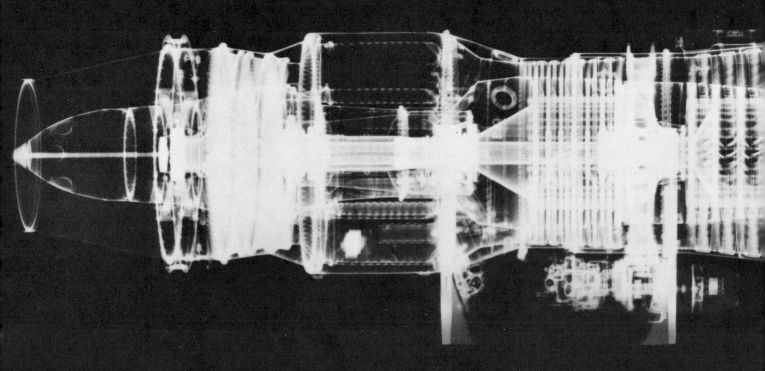

3

Modern Physics:
The Energy of
the Atom

14 Investigating New Rays

In 1808, an English chemist, John Dalton, proposed that matter was composed of tiny particles called atoms. Every pure substance, according to his theory, was made up of a single type of atom, or combination of atoms called a molecule. For over 150 years, atoms were considered to be the smallest particles of matter, and thus indivisible. (Dalton called them the "ultimate" particles of matter.)

In the second half of the 19th century, experiments were carried out which showed that the atom *was* divisible and that particles even more elementary than the atom existed. Many new kinds of particles were discovered, along with new forces that held them together, and powerful new sources of energy were revealed.

14.1 Cathode Rays

The fact that the noisy succession of sparks from an induction coil changes to a quiet, luminous discharge when the surrounding air pressure is reduced was known as early as 1750. But it was not until the middle of the 19th century, with the invention of more efficient vacuum pumps, that scientists were able to investigate this phenomenon more thoroughly.

The earliest investigations were made by Heinrich Geissler in Bonn, Germany. He had invented a new pump that produced extremely low pressures. He was also an expert glass-blower, and by skilfully shaping tubes in a variety of patterns and using different gases and types of glass he produced colourful displays of electric sparks. Geissler's work led to 40 years of intensive investigation, climaxed by the discovery of the electron.

A tube that allows an electric current to pass through a gas at low pressure is called a **gas-discharge tube**. A simple gas-discharge tube is illustrated. The two metal plates marked + and −, sealed in the ends of the tube, are called **electrodes**. The positive electrode is called the **anode** and the negative electrode is called the **cathode**.

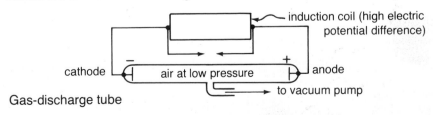

Gas-discharge tube

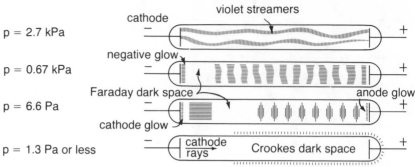

Electric discharge through air at low pressures

The electrodes are connected to a source of high electric potential (usually an induction coil producing more than 10 000 V). The tube is connected to a vacuum pump through a side tube.

Shortly after the pump is turned on, the discharge ceases at the induction coil, and electrodes are joined by one or more violet streamers. As the pressure is further reduced, an intense pink discharge gradually fills the space between the electrodes. This discharge then begins to break up into two parts. A pink glow appears near the anode and a bluish glow near the cathode, separated by a dark, or clear, area called the **Faraday dark space**. As the tube is evacuated still further, the dark space expands and the colour at the electrodes fades until the dark space fills the tube and only a faint green or violet glow surrounds the anode. At this stage the sides of the tube fluoresce, usually in green. The dark space between the electrodes at this stage is called the **Crookes dark space**.

Scientific interest centred on what was happening in the Crookes dark space. Various tubes were constructed and the pressure was reduced until the space between the electrodes was completely occupied by the Crookes dark space.

The early researchers decided that the coloured glow in a gas-discharge tube originated at the cathode. Therefore, they named this discharge the **cathode ray** and called the tube a **cathode ray tube**. Some of the investigations that were done to determine the properties of cathode rays are described next.

Maltese cross Tube

In 1859, Julius Plücker, a German physicist, made a special tube in which the anode was an aluminum Maltese cross. The cross formed a distinct shadow on the end of the tube, indicating that cathode rays travel in a straight line from the cathode to the anode.

The colour of the discharge is orange-red if the tube contains neon gas instead of air. Such tubes are used in advertising signs.

The original Maltese cross tube

Paddle-wheel Discharge Tube

In 1879, the English physicist William Crookes reported the results of his many experiments with cathode rays. In one tube, he had placed a small paddle wheel, free to rotate, between the cathode and the anode. When cathode rays struck the blades of the paddle wheel, the wheel began to rotate as if it had been struck by a beam of tiny particles. This experiment showed that cathode rays might be composed of moving particles.

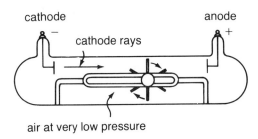

Paddle-wheel discharge tube

Cathode Rays in a Magnetic Field

In another tube, Crookes showed that cathode rays are deflected by a magnetic field. It can be demonstrated that a force acts on moving electric charges in a magnetic field at right angles both to the magnetic field and to the direction of motion of the charge. Crookes found that cathode rays, when passing through a magnetic field, are deflected in exactly the same way (see illustration). On the basis of this experiment, Crookes proposed that cathode rays are a stream of negative particles, moving from the cathode to the anode.

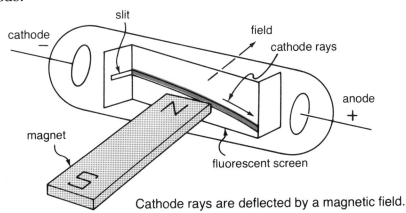

Cathode rays are deflected by a magnetic field.

Cathode Rays and an Electric Field

In 1890, Arthur Schuster, a professor of physics at Manchester University, sent a beam of cathode rays between two oppositely charged plates. The rays were repelled by the negative plate and attracted to the positive plate – another indication that cathode rays might be beams of small, negatively charged particles.

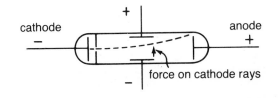

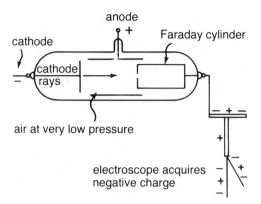

How Perrin demonstrated that cathode rays convey negative charge

J.J. Thomson (1856-1940)

Cathode Rays Carry a Negative Charge

Jean Perrin, a physicist at the University of Paris, designed a tube to test Crookes's hypothesis. In his tube, the anode was a hollow aluminum cylinder, open at both ends. Near the end of the cylinder and insulated from it was a closed cylinder with a small opening at one end, as illustrated. Some cathode rays shot past the anode and into the closed cylinder. A negative charge quickly built up on the anode—indicated by the divergence of the leaves of a metal-leaf electroscope connected to the closed cylinder. The charge on the electroscope was checked in the usual way with a negative ebonite rod. This showed that cathode rays are negatively charged.

J. J. Thomson's Tube

In 1897, J.J. Thomson of Cambridge University repeated many of the earlier experiments and added one of his own—an attempt to measure the mass and charge of the particles in cathode rays.

Thomson's tube contained two charged plates to deflect the cathode rays in one direction. The tube was placed in a magnetic field to deflect the rays in the opposite direction. The electric and magnetic fields were adjusted to balance each other, and the beam of cathode rays travelled straight down the tube. From his measurements, and from the equations for electric and magnetic fields, Thomson was able to calculate the ratio of the mass (m) of one of the particles to its electric charge (e). He found that the ratio m/e was the same no matter what potential difference was used to accelerate the particles, and no matter what type of metal was used as a cathode. This indicated that the particles making up cathode rays are all alike.

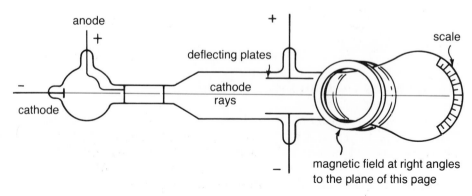

He knew that the ratio m/e for hydrogen ions (charged hydrogen atoms) was a number nearly 2000 times greater than the value for cathode ray particles. Assuming that both kinds of particles had the same charge, the existence of a type of particle with a mass 1/2000 of that of the smallest atom had been established.

Thomson concluded that cathode rays are beams of very light, fast-moving, negatively charged particles. These particles, he predicted, would be found as part of every kind of atom. He called this new elementary particle the **electron**.

Properties of Cathode Rays

- They are produced by the negative electrode, or cathode, in an evacuated tube, and travel towards the anode.
- They travel in straight lines and cast sharp shadows.
- They have energy and can do work.
- They are deflected by electric and magnetic fields and have a negative charge.
- They are beams of tiny, negatively charged particles called electrons.

14.2 Thermionic Effect

The number of electrons flowing through an evacuated tube is limited by the size of the electrodes and the electrical potential difference between them. One day in 1883, Thomas Edison, an American scientist and inventor, was experimenting with one of his incandescent electric filament lamps. Into one bulb he inserted a small metal plate. He found that, if this plate was positive in relation to the filament, a small current flowed between it and the filament. If it was negative, no current flowed. This came to be called the **Edison effect**.

Twenty years later, O. W. Richardson, a physicist at Princeton University, carried out experiments concerning the emission of electrons from heated surfaces. He suggested that the Edison effect occurred because heated surfaces in a vacuum "evaporate" electrons in much the same way that vapour molecules leave a hot liquid. In the Edison effect, these electrons flow from the area surrounding the hot surface to the positive plate, because unlike charges attract. The process whereby electrons are emitted by a hot filament is called **thermionic emission**.

Thomson's m/e apparatus

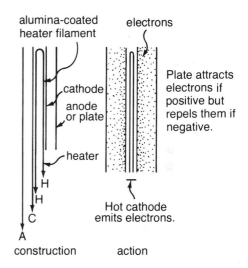

construction   action

Thermionic diode

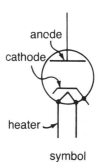

In 1904, J. A. Fleming, applying the work of Edison and Richardson, built the first electron tube, called a **diode** because it consisted of two electrodes. In the tube, a heated cathode was surrounded by a cylindrical anode or **plate**, and the two were enclosed in an evacuated glass tube.

The current in a diode flows in only one direction, from cathode to anode. The diode's first applications were as a detector of radio waves and as a device to convert alternating current into pulsating direct current. By introducing other charged plates and magnetic fields, current could be controlled, amplified, and even shut off completely. Such devices, originally called valves (since they control current), were later named **vacuum tubes**. Many electronic devices were developed, including radio and television receivers, sound amplifiers, rectifiers, radar equipment, and computers—all using vacuum tubes. What was considered a laboratory curiosity at the turn of this century had applications and effects that have changed the way we live and communicate.

14.3 Applications of Cathode Rays

In a typical modern cathode ray tube, a tiny filament heats a cathode that is coated with a mixture of barium oxide and strontium oxide. The electrons that are emitted are accelerated towards a cylindrical anode. Between the cathode and the anode is another electrode with a small hole in its centre. It is called the **control electrode**. By making the control electrode more or less negative, the number of electrons passing through it can be decreased or increased. The electrons next pass through one or more focusing electrodes which concentrate the electrons in a fine beam on a small area of the screen of the tube. This collection of electrodes is called the **electron gun**.

The electron beam is deflected by pairs of magnetic deflection coils. By varying the current in these coils, the electron beam can be directed to any point on the screen of the tube. The back of the screen of the cathode ray tube is covered with a thin coat of phosphors. These give off light when struck by electrons. The colour of light given off depends on the type of phosphor used.

Television

The inside of the screen of a black-and-white television tube is coated with a mixture of phosphors that give off a bluish-white glow.

In most applications where vacuum tubes were originally used, the transistor is now used.

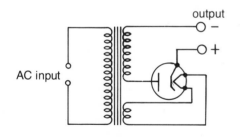

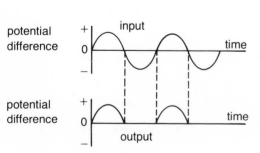

A diode used as a half-wave rectifier

An electronic circuit in the set generates currents at the proper frequency to "scan" the entire screen 30 times /s. While one set of magnetic deflection coils moves the beam back and forth across the screen 525 times, the other set of coils moves the beam down the screen, tracing out the pattern illustrated. (Actually the beam moves down the screen twice to produce one complete picture, the first time scanning every other line, and the second time filling in the missing lines.)

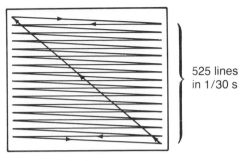

525 lines in 1/30 s

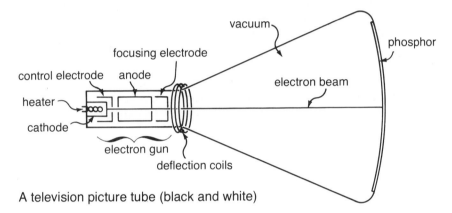

A television picture tube (black and white)

In the North American system, the number of scan lines is 525, but in most of Europe it is 625 and in France it is 819.

As the dot of light created by the electron beam moves, its brightness is controlled by the control electrode. The potential difference on the control electrode is determined by a signal received from the television station the receiver is tuned to.

Every 1/30 s, a complete new picture is scanned out on the screen. Because of the persistence of vision (see Section 25.1), this is a high enough frequency that your eye "sees" a continuously "moving" picture rather than a succession of individual pictures.

In a colour television set, there are three electron guns, one each for red, blue, and green. Each gun produces an electron beam that scans the whole screen. The screen is covered with about 600 000 phosphor bars – 200 000 for each of the three colours. Just behind the screen is a shadow mask, an opaque screen with 200 000 tiny slots in it that are very accurately aligned with the three electron beams and the phosphor bars. When the scanning electron beam from the red electron gun passes through these slots, it hits only the red phosphor bars. The green beam hits only the green bars, and so on (see Section 25.5).

A colour television station must provide enough information to produce a red picture, a green picture, and a blue picture every 1/30 s (and another, separate signal for the sound). Your eye combines the three images to produce a full-colour picture.

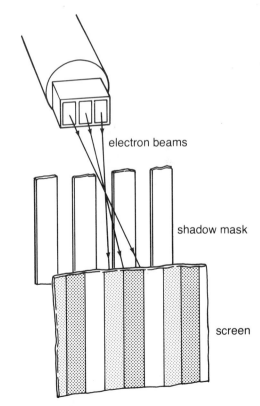

electron beams

shadow mask

screen

Colour television

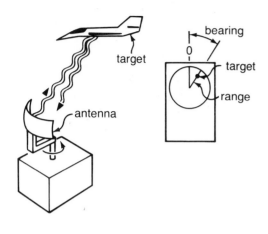

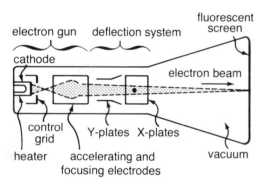

electron gun   deflection system   fluorescent screen

cathode

electron beam

control grid   Y-plates X-plates

heater   accelerating and focusing electrodes   vacuum

Main features of the cathode ray tube used in an oscilloscope

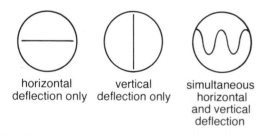

horizontal deflection only

vertical deflection only

simultaneous horizontal and vertical deflection

Radar

"Radar" means radio detection and ranging. In a radar receiver, the electron beam in a cathode ray tube is synchronized with the pulses of microwaves sent out by a rotating radar antenna. When the antenna sends out a pulse, the electron beam is deflected outwards from the centre of the radar screen in a direction corresponding to the direction in which the antenna is pointed. When the pulse reflected from the target is received by the antenna, a short time later, a signal is sent to the control grid of the tube, increasing the strength of the electron beam momentarily and making a bright dot on the screen. The distance of the dot from the centre of the screen corresponds to the distance to the target.

As the antenna turns, emitting pulse after pulse, a picture of everything around the station is created on the screen, as if taken by a camera pointing straight down from high above the station.

Oscilloscopes

Oscilloscopes are used in electronics to make patterns representing electrical signals of varying strength. The signal might be the output from a microphone, pulses in a computer, or signals picked up by a radio or television receiver.

The electron beam is deflected by two sets of charged plates instead of by magnetic fields. A signal generated by the oscilloscope deflects the beam back and forth at a chosen frequency. This makes a horizontal line across the screen. The input signal is applied to the second set of plates to deflect the beam vertically. The combination of horizontal and vertical motion produces a picture of the waveform.

14.4 X-rays

In December 1895, Wilhelm Röntgen, working in Germany, made a remarkable discovery. He noticed that a fluorescent screen placed several metres from an operating cathode ray tube glowed in the dark, even when the tube was covered with black paper. He also noticed that some covered photographic plates left near the tube became fogged. He concluded that some mysterious, invisible radiation was being emitted from places in the cathode ray tube that had been struck by cathode rays, and that the radiation could penetrate substances opaque to visible light. He called the radiation

X-rays, since "x" is commonly used in mathematics as a symbol for an unknown. The radiation was also known as **Röntgen rays**.

In another experiment, Röntgen noted that if he placed his hand between the X-rays and a fluorescent screen, a faint shadow of his hand appeared on the screen. The bones were clearly visible because they were more opaque to X-rays than the surrounding flesh. Substituting covered photographic paper for the fluorescent screen, he created a permanent record – the first X-ray photograph. Röntgen also found that X-rays were not deflected by magnetic or electric fields. On the basis of this evidence, he concluded that they were not particles but electromagnetic radiation of very short wavelength with properties similar to those of light waves. Later experiments showed that X-rays were produced whenever fast-moving electrons were decelerated quickly by an obstacle.

The first cathode ray tubes designed specifically to generate X-rays contained large anodes slanted so that X-rays were emitted in a specific direction. The anode was large so that it could also conduct away the heat produced by the impact of the electrons. Within a few years, these tubes were being used extensively to examine broken bones and gunshot wounds. Unfortunately, the penetrating power and the intensity of X-rays was difficult to control in the early tubes.

Wilhelm Röntgen (1845-1923)

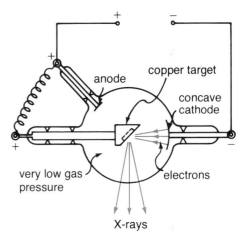

Gas-filled X-ray tube

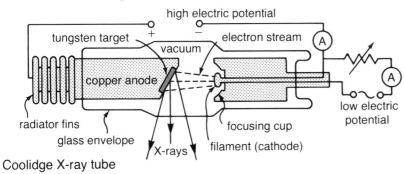

Coolidge X-ray tube

Modern X-ray tubes are based on a design devised by W. D. Coolidge in 1916. By varying the current in the filament, the number of electrons hitting the target, and therefore the intensity of the resulting X-ray, is controlled. By varying the potential difference between the cathode and the anode, the kinetic energy of the electrons striking the target is controlled. The higher the potential difference used, the shorter the wavelength of the X-rays and the greater their penetrating power. Less penetrating X-rays with a longer wavelength are referred to as **soft rays**, while short-wavelength X-rays with high penetrating ability are called **hard rays**.

Molybdenum is used as a target material in most modern X-ray tubes. Also, the target is usually made as a disc that rotates at a high speed when the X-ray machine is operating, producing uniform wear of the target and a longer life for the X-ray tube.

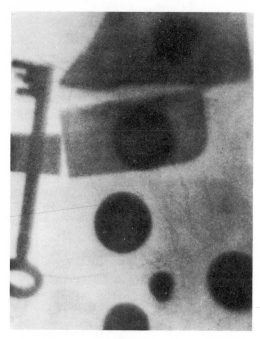

The first X-ray photograph—January 8, 1896

In spite of the dangers, X-ray machines were widely used. By the 1940s nearly every shoe store had a fluoroscope in which you could see the bones of your feet inside your new shoes, ensuring a good fit.

For persons working daily with X-rays, the amount of radiation their bodies receive over a specific time interval (usually a month) is important to their health. A plastic badge containing a photographic plate is worn. Any X-ray (or gamma radiation) they receive exposes the plate. These plates are checked regularly to ensure that the safe level of exposure is not exceeded.

Properties of X-rays

- They are produced by the collision of high-energy electrons with the anode of a cathode ray tube.
- The intensity of X-rays that have passed through an object depends on the object's thickness and density.
- They can expose photographic plates and film and make phosphorescent substances give off light.
- They cannot be deflected by electric or magnetic fields. They have no electric charge.
- They travel at the speed of light.
- They are electromagnetic waves with a very short wavelength—about 1/100 that of visible light.

14.5 Applications of X-rays

In an X-ray photograph, or **radiograph**, the object is placed between the X-ray tube and the photographic film or fluorescent screen (commonly called a **fluoroscope**). The X-rays pass better through some materials than through others. The resulting photographs, produced by the X-rays, are used by doctors and dentists in the diagnosis of various disorders.

X-rays can also be used to kill human cells. Malignant growths, such as cancer cells, can be treated in this way. Unfortunately, many normal cells are also killed in the process. This was not known to the early investigators, and many of them became ill and died as a result of their work with X-rays.

In one tragic case, in 1896, Clarence Daly, Thomas Edison's assistant, was exposed to a large dose of X-rays while helping Edison develop the fluoroscope. Shortly after, Daly's hair fell out and his scalp became inflamed and ulcerated. By 1904 cancer had developed, and he died soon after.

Today, X-rays are used with much more caution. Sensitive photographic materials now permit very short exposure times when X-rays are used for medical and dental purposes. Lead screens, leaded glass, and lead-covered walls protect the X-ray technician, and lead blankets and aprons protect the patient except in the areas being photographed. These precautions are important, because it has also been found that X-rays can affect the genetic make-up of the cell nucleus, without killing the cell. The exposure of sex cells to X-rays can result in birth defects.

In industry, X-rays are often used to examine the interiors of complex equipment, to check for broken parts, bad connections, or poor welding. When sections of a natural gas pipeline are welded together, X-rays are used to check the welds to make sure they are sound and will not fail under pressure.

X-ray photographs have also been used to detect alterations in works of art. This technique depends on the fact that most oil paints contain lead pigments. These pigments absorb more of the X-rays than do other, lighter substances. Thus, changes that have been made in an oil painting can often be detected with the help of X-rays.

14.6 Radioactivity

Fluorescence is produced in some substances when they are exposed to the radiations from cathode ray tubes and X-ray tubes. It is also produced by a number of substances when exposed to sunlight. Early investigators had noted that the reverse is true— some phosphorescent chemicals emit weak X-rays when exposed to sunlight. But which ones?

In 1896, Henri Becquerel, a French physicist, carried out a number of experiments with phosphorescent crystals of different chemical compounds, placing them on top of photographic plates that had been wrapped in black paper, and putting the plates in the sunlight so that the chemicals would fluoresce. He then developed all the photographic plates to see whether there was any sign of X-rays having penetrated the black paper.

On Wednesday, February 26, Becquerel was preparing to perform the investigation with still another compound—this one containing uranium. He had already placed a sample of the compound on a photographic plate when he realized that the weather was too cloudy for the experiment. He placed the uranium compound and the photographic plate in a drawer to wait for better weather. By Sunday the sun had still not appeared. Expecting to find only a feeble image, Becquerel developed the plate he had stored away earlier in the week. To his surprise, it was strongly exposed. His explanation was that uranium compounds emit radiation that can expose photographic plates even when these are not exposed to sunlight. Becquerel had discovered **radioactivity**.

Soon others joined Becquerel in the search for more radioactive substances and for an explanation of the nature of the radiation produced by them.

Antoine Henri Becquerel (1852-1908)

A few months later, Marie Curie, a young chemistry student in Paris, chose the new field of radioactivity for her graduate thesis, a subject that also interested her husband, Pierre, a physicist. In her

Marie Curie in her laboratory

Other radioactive elements discovered in pitchblende were actinium (1899), radon gas (1900), and protactinium (1917).

investigation of uranium compounds, she found that the amount of radiation depended only on the amount of compound present, not on its shape or temperature, or on the other substances present. This was a most important discovery, for it showed that the radioactivity of a substance is determined by something inside its atoms, not by any external factors.

Marie Curie's experiments with uranium compounds led her to examine the ores from which uranium is obtained—pitchblende and chalcolite. To her surprise, she found that the ores were more radioactive than pure uranium. This suggested to her that other, more radioactive substances were present in the ores, and she set out to find them.

She ground up pitchblende 20 kg at a time in a large iron pot, dissolved it, filtered it, crystallized it, collected it, redissolved it—over and over again until she was left with a minute quantity of a new element 300 times more radioactive than uranium. She named it **polonium**, after Poland, where she was born. Then she noticed that the residue from this separation was also highly radioactive.

In December 1898, after working together on the project for six months, Marie and Pierre Curie announced the discovery of another new radioactive element, also found in pitchblende, that was 900 times as radioactive as uranium. They named it **radium**.

In 1903, Becquerel and the Curies were awarded the Nobel Prize for physics jointly for their investigation of radioactivity. In 1911, Marie Curie was awarded a second Nobel Prize for her discovery of radium and polonium. She was the first woman to win a Nobel Prize and the only person ever to win two Nobel Prizes for science.

Radium was soon found to be effective in the treatment of cancer because it killed cancerous cells. Within a few years, hospitals around the world were using radiation therapy. At the same time, the dangers of the radiation were becoming painfully apparent. The hands of Pierre and Marie had been burned by exposure to radioactivity. They both complained of continuous fatigue, and were generally in poor health—the first signs of radiation sickness. Neither would believe that radiation could do any long-term damage. To prove this, in one of his experiments, Pierre strapped a sample of radium to his arm. Within a few hours it produced a large burn. He felt he had proved his point when the burn healed.

We do not know how much effect radiation had had on Pierre Curie, for in 1906 he was killed by a horse-drawn wagon. We do know that when Marie died she showed all the symptoms of radiation sickness, though she had lived for 30 years after her massive exposure. Others were not so fortunate. In the 20 years following Marie's experiments, more than 100 people died from exposure to radioactive radiation.

Both Becquerel and the Curies had noticed that some of the radioactive radiation could be deflected by a magnetic field. Some emitted radiations were deflected in the same way as cathode rays and thus were negative, while others were deflected in the opposite direction and thus were positive. At about the same time, P. Villard discovered a third and more penetrating radiation that was unaffected by magnetic or electric fields.

In 1889, Ernest Rutherford, a physicist from New Zealand working at McGill University in Montreal, took up the study of radioactivity. It was Rutherford who named the three types of radioactive emission: alpha (α) radiation, beta (β) radiation, and gamma (γ) rays.

To investigate the properties of these emissions, Rutherford placed a small quantity of radium in a small lead box that had an opening at the top. After performing a series of experiments, he was able to state some of the properties of radioactive emissions. Further knowledge was gained by others in subsequent experiments. What follows is a summary of all the chief properties of radioactive radiations.

Properties of Radioactive Emissions

Alpha (α) Particles
- They are positively charged particles (actually the nuclei of helium ions).
- They are ejected at a high speed but have a range of only a few centimetres in air.
- They are stopped by an ordinary sheet of thin aluminum foil.

Beta (β) Particles
- They are streams of high-energy electrons.
- They are ejected at various speeds, sometimes approaching the speed of light (3.00×10^8 m/s).
- Some beta particles are able to penetrate several millimetres of aluminum.

Gamma (γ) Rays
- They are electromagnetic radiations with very short wavelengths.
- Their wavelengths and energies can vary.
- High-energy gamma rays can penetrate at least 30 cm of lead or 2 km of air.

Ernest Rutherford (1871-1937) in his laboratory at McGill University

Rutherford studied as a research student at Cambridge University under J.J. Thomson. He received the Nobel Prize for Chemistry in 1908 for his work in radioactivity but he is better known for his model of the atom (see Chapter 15).

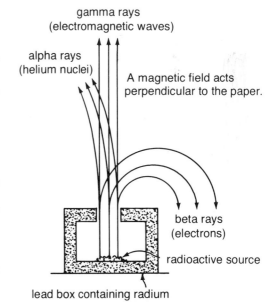

Illustrated is a composite diagram. It is not possible to study all three particles at the same time in the same apparatus.

The original unit for radioactivity was the curie. One curie represents 3.7×10^{10} disintegrations per second.

Units of Radioactivity

The unit used to measure radioactivity is the **becquerel** (Bq), named after the discoverer of radioactivity. The level of radiation is 1 Bq when one disintegration or particle is emitted per second. One gram of radium has a radioactivity of 3.7×10^{10} Bq.

14.7 Detectors of Radioactivity

There are many ways of detecting the radiation from radioactive substances. We already know that such radiation exposes photographic film and makes fluorescent substances glow. There are three other devices that can be used to detect radioactive emissions – the scintillation counter, or spinthariscope, the cloud chamber, and the Geiger-Müller tube.

Crookes Spinthariscope

William Crookes noted that, when an alpha particle strikes a thin layer of zinc sulphide, a flash of light, or **scintillation**, is created at the point of contact. By mounting a screen coated with zinc sulphide at one end of a brass tube and attaching a magnifying glass at the other end, Crookes created an alpha particle detector. He named it the **spinthariscope**. Although this device is not much used today, it was very useful for the purpose of counting alpha particles when the structure of the atom was being investigated, as we will see in the next chapter.

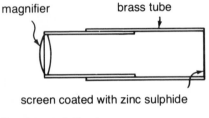

magnifier   brass tube

screen coated with zinc sulphide

Crookes spinthariscope

Cloud Chamber

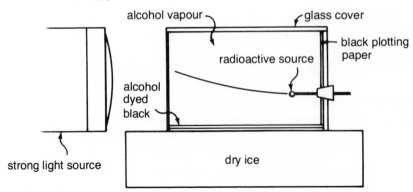

The cloud chamber is a container filled with alcohol vapour or water vapour. As a charged particle travels through the chamber, it knocks electric charges off any water or alcohol molecules it happens to hit. These charged particles attract nearby molecules, forming tiny drops of liquid that are seen as a small vapour trail in the chamber. The appearance of cloud chamber tracks varies according to the particle concerned. Cloud chamber tracks for alpha, beta, and gamma radiations are illustrated. Today, high-energy particles are usually studied in **bubble chambers**. In these chambers the passage of particles leaves a trail of bubbles in liquid hydrogen.

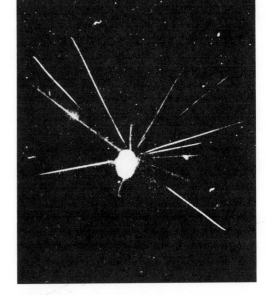

Alpha particle "tracks" in a cloud chamber

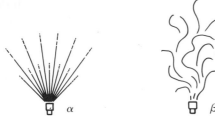

Appearance of cloud chamber tracks

Geiger-Müller Tube

The Geiger-Müller tube consists of a large cylindrical cathode, with a wire down its centre serving as an anode. The tube is filled with argon gas at low pressure and a trace of bromine. When a particle enters the tube through a thin mica window on one end, it ionizes some of the gas in the tube. The charged molecules are then attracted to the central electrode, colliding with other molecules on the way to make more ions and create a pulse of current through the tube. These pulses may be heard as clicks on a small loudspeaker, and may be counted with an electronic counter. Each click indicates the presence of one particle.

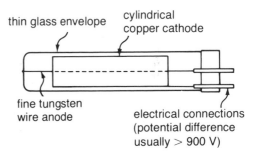

Geiger-Müller tube

14.8 Additional Investigation: Detecting Radiation

The Geiger-Müller tube was developed partly because of Geiger's frustrations when he was using the spinthariscope to detect alpha particles in the course of his investigations of the atom (see Section 15.6).

Problems:
1. How can radiation be detected?
2. What factors influence the detection of radiation?

Materials:
Geiger-Müller tube with ratemeter
radioactive sources (beta and gamma)
strips of thick paper, glass, aluminum, and lead

Procedure
1. Move all radioactive sources several metres away from the tube. Turn on the ratemeter at high amplification. Place the tube in the position it will occupy for the remainder of the investigation, and observe the activity rate, if any. This will provide a measure of the background radiation present near the tube.
2. Move the beta source towards the tube until a full-scale deflection is obtained. Measure the distance to the tube from the source (d). Move the beta source away from the tube in steps of about $\frac{1}{4}d$, and record the activity in your notebook, in a table such as the following one.

Distance	$d =$	$1.25d =$	$1.50d =$	$1.75d =$	$2.00d =$
Rate					

Plot a graph of activity rate versus distance.
3. Move the beta source back to the position of full-scale deflection. Place strips of thick paper, one at a time, between the source and the tube. Record any difference in rate. Repeat this procedure using strips of glass, then aluminum, then lead. Plot graphs of activity rate versus the number of strips of each material used. Put all graphs on the same sheet of graph paper.
4. Repeat the entire experiment using the gamma source.

Questions
1. What factors can influence the measured activity rate of a radioactive source?
2. What could cause the background radiation observed?
3. If the distance of a source from a tube is doubled, what should happen to the measured activity rate? Try to find a relationship between rate and distance from your graphs. (Hint: Plot rate versus $1/d^2$)
4. List in order of effectiveness the materials used to absorb beta radiation. Does this order also hold true for gamma radiation?
5. Which type of radiation is more penetrating? Suggest a reason for your answer.
6. What thickness of each type of material would be needed to shield all radiation from the beta source effectively? Use your graphs to assist your predictions.
7. Answer question 6 for the gamma source.

14.9 Summary

1. Electric currents can flow through gas-discharge tubes, producing a variety of colour effects, provided that the gas pressure is low.
2. Cathode rays consist of tiny, negatively charged particles called electrons moving at a high speed from the cathode of a gas-discharge tube to the anode. They travel in straight lines, have energy, and are deflected by magnetic and electric fields.
3. In the process called thermionic emission, electrons are emitted from a hot surface located within a partial vacuum.
4. In vacuum tubes, electric current can be controlled, rectified, and amplified by the use of additional electrodes.
5. A modern cathode ray tube consists of a heated cathode, a control electrode, an anode, focusing electrodes, deflecting magnetic or electric fields, and a screen coated with phosphor.
6. Cathode ray tubes are used in television receivers, radar equipment, and oscilloscopes.
7. X-rays are produced by the collision of high-energy electrons with an anode.
8. X-rays are electromagnetic radiations with short wavelengths which travel in straight lines at the speed of light, have high penetrating ability, have no charge, expose photographic film, and make fluorescent screens glow.
9. X-rays can be used in medical diagnosis, for the treatment of cancer, and for the detection of defects in manufactured products.
10. X-rays and gamma radiation can kill or change the genetic structure of human cells; they must therefore be used with great caution.
11. Radioactive emissions consist of alpha and beta particles and gamma rays.
12. Alpha particles are positively charged helium ions with relatively low kinetic energies and low penetrating ability. Beta particles are fast-moving electrons with high kinetic energy and high penetrating ability. Gamma radiation is an electromagnetic radiation with a very short wavelength, high energy, and an extremely high penetrating ability.
13. The becquerel (Bq) is the unit of radioactivity, and it represents particle emission at the rate of one particle per second.
14. Radioactivity can be detected by means of photographic plates, fluorescent screens, scintillation counters, cloud chambers, and Geiger-Müller tubes.

The important difference between X-rays and gamma rays is the source of energy. The origin of X-rays is the electron structure of the atom. The nucleus is the origin of gamma radiation.

Properties of the Radiation from Radioactive Substances

Radiation	Relative mass	Charge	Penetrating power	Nature
α	7300	+2	poor	charged helium atoms
β	1	−1	medium	fast electrons
γ	0	0	excellent	electromagnetic waves with a short wavelength

1 g of radium releases about 25 J/h of energy.

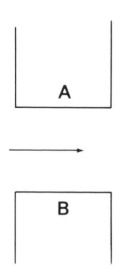

Question 2

14.10 Review

1. Describe the observation that shows each of the following properties of cathode rays.
   (a) They travel from cathode to anode.
   (b) They travel in straight lines.
   (c) They have energy.
   (d) They are negatively charged.

2. The arrow in this diagram represents a stream of electrons moving in the plane of the paper from left to right. How would the electrons be deflected, relative to the paper, in each of the following cases?
   (a) A is negatively charged.
   (b) B is positively charged.
   (c) A is an S-pole and B is an N-pole.

3. When a thin beam of cathode rays is sent through a magnetic field, the beam is deflected to one side but remains a thin beam. What would happen if:
   (a) the beam consisted of electrons, all with the same mass, but with various amounts of charge?
   (b) the beam consisted of electrons, all with the same charge, but with various masses?
   (c) the beam consisted of electrons whose charge was proportional to their mass? (An electron with three times the mass would have three times the charge.)

4. Does Thomson's experiment prove that all electrons have the same mass and the same charge? Explain your answer.

5. Using a diagram of a simple diode, explain how a current flows through the tube.

6. What would be the effect of each of the following on the beam of electrons in a cathode ray tube and on the dot of light on the screen?
   (a) A hotter filament is used.
   (b) The anode voltage is increased.
   (c) The control electrode is made more negative.

7. The cathode ray tube is used in radar. It is also used in sonar, particularly in military ships and submarines. Briefly compare the two applications, stating the similarities and the differences.

8. What properties of X-rays enable them to make X-ray photographs?

9. Explain why it is dangerous to X-ray a human fetus.

10. X-rays can be used to destroy cancer cells. Why are there often side effects such as loss of hair, dizziness, and lack of energy?

11. How might X-rays be used to check welds in a gas pipeline?
12. What is the difference between X-rays and γ-rays?
13. If α-rays and β-rays with the same speed were passed through a magnetic field,
    (a) which particles would have the greater force acting on them?
    (b) which particles would undergo the greater deflection? Explain your answers.
14. Which of the radioactive detectors that have been described could be used in each of the following applications?
    (a) to detect α-particles only
    (b) to detect the presence of gamma radiation
    (c) to determine the direction in which a particle is moving
    (d) to determine the depth of penetration of a radioactive particle
    (e) to detect the collision of one particle with another
15. A radiation reading is 100 000 Bq. Describe this level of radiation in other terms.

14.11 Learning Objectives

1. To describe briefly the changes that occur in a gas-discharge tube connected to an induction coil as the tube is evacuated.
2. To describe briefly experiments that have been done to illustrate that cathode rays travel in straight lines, have mass and energy, are deflected by magnetic fields, and have a negative charge.
3. To state five properties of cathode rays.
4. To explain what is meant by "thermionic emission" and "Edison effect".
5. To describe, using a diagram, how electrons are focused on a screen in a modern cathode ray tube.
6. To explain how the modern cathode ray tube is used in television receivers, radar equipment, and oscilloscopes.
7. To state five properties of X-rays.
8. To describe how X-rays are used to assist in medical diagnosis.
9. To describe an industrial use of X-rays.
10. To state both the beneficial and the harmful effects of X-rays and γ-rays when used on living tissue.

11. To state the three types of emissions from a radioactive source, and to explain three properties of each.
12. To explain the meaning of a radiation reading stated in becquerels.
13. To describe how three different types of radioactivity detectors function.

15 Investigating the Atom

15.1 Early Ideas about the Atom

As early as 400 B.C., the Greek philosopher Democritus proposed that all matter was composed of tiny, indivisible particles called atoms. His theory was based more on philosophical reasoning than on any direct experimental evidence. Experimental evidence of the existence of atoms was not found until much later, early in the 19th century, by an English scientist, John Dalton (1766-1844). Even then, Dalton's atomic theory was based more on its usefulness in explaining observed natural phenomena than on experimental evidence. The evolution of the modern atomic theory from Dalton's theory is an outstanding example of the development of a scientific model (see Section 26.1).

Dalton's Atomic Theory

John Dalton (1766-1844)

Dalton's theory, published in 1810, was the first systematic approach to the development of a model of atomic structure. It made the following basic statements about the structure of matter:
- All matter consists of very small, indivisible, indestructible particles called atoms.
- All atoms of a given element are identical.
- Each element's atomic mass is unique, that is, different from the mass of each other element's atoms.
- Atoms combine together, in simple whole-number ratios, to form compounds.
- Atoms are neither created nor destroyed during a chemical reaction.

Dalton's model of the atom is sometimes called "the billiard-ball model of the atom": the atom has no internal or external features; it exists merely as an indivisible chunk of matter.

The Periodic Table

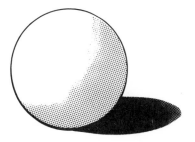

Dalton's billiard-ball atom

Dalton's atomic theory stated that all matter consists of atoms and combinations of atoms, or molecules. In the 60 years that followed, chemists were able to figure out which substances were **elements**, composed of a single kind of atom, and which were

Today, atomic masses are measured in units called "unified atomic mass units" (u) and

$$1 \text{ u} = 1.66043 \times 10^{-27} \text{ kg}$$

The mass of an atom of carbon-12 was chosen arbitrarily as 12 u and the masses of all other atoms are expressed, in unified atomic mass units, relative to carbon-12.

The first 92 elements (with a few exceptions) occur naturally. Some of the 105 elements that are known today have been under observation only for short periods in the laboratory. Artificially created, they existed for only a few micro-seconds and then changed into other substances. Still, scientists were able to recognize properties that make these substances unique. Elements 104 and 105 were unnamed for a long time, but they are now called Kurchatovium and Hahnium, respectively.

The mass of an electron is 9.11×10^{-31} kg.

compounds, composed of molecules. In addition, they were able to figure out the relative masses of the various kinds of atoms. They knew, for example, that the hydrogen atom is the lightest, and assigned it an atomic mass of 1. The carbon atom was found to be 12 times as heavy, giving it an atomic mass of 12.

As early as 1869, a Russian chemist, Dmitri Mendeleev (1834-1907), began searching for some fundamental laws regarding the structure of atoms with similar chemical and physical properties. He arranged the 63 known atoms in ascending order of atomic mass, grouping elements with similar chemical and physical properties in separate vertical columns.

The real genius of Mendeleev's work lies in the fact that his table contained several "holes"—blank spaces where elements appeared to be missing. He reasoned that the spaces represented elements that had not yet been discovered. He even went so far as to predict some of their properties, should they be found. To date, all of the first 105 spaces in this table, called the **Periodic Table of the Elements,** have been filled (see Appendix F).

With a few modifications, Dalton's theory stands unchanged after 150 years. It has been altered and amended, as must all good scientific models, to account for new experimental discoveries. Perhaps the most significant change that it has undergone concerns the divisibility of the atom. Towards the end of the 19th century, scientists using research tools and techniques not available to Dalton made discoveries that could not be explained by the concept of a tiny, solid, indivisible and indestructible atom.

Thomson's Atomic Model

In Chapter 14, you became familiar with the properties of cathode rays. It was Crookes who first deduced that cathode rays consist of negatively charged particles, and his deduction was supported by Arthur Schuster and J. J. Thomson.

In fact, Thomson was able to measure the ratio of mass-to-charge for these particles, using a tube that deflected the beam both electrically and magnetically. He estimated the speed of the particles to be about 3×10^7 m/s and their mass to be about 1/1800th of the mass of a hydrogen ion. He called them electrons. He was able to show that electrons have identical properties regardless of the electrode material or the gas in the discharge tube. As a result, he suspected that they must be a fundamental particle found in all atoms. By investigating the properties of cathode rays, he had made a discovery that would be the starting point for a whole new way of looking at the structure and nature of matter. (See also Section 14.1).

Thomson devised a model of the atom, based on his findings, and it was widely accepted about the turn of the century. In this model, the atom was represented as a sphere of positive charge with negative electrons embedded in it, much like raisins in a bun. Thomson knew that atoms are neutral, so he believed that there were just enough negative electrons in his model to balance the positive charge throughout the remainder of the atom. As we will see, Thomson's model was not able to stand up for long.

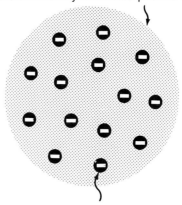

sphere of uniformly distributed positive charge

negatively charged electrons embedded throughout

Thomson's raisin-bun atom

15.2 The Discovery of the Nucleus: Rutherford's Experiment

In 1911, two German physics students, H. Geiger and E. Marsden, working under Ernest Rutherford at the University of Manchester, performed a series of experiments that led to a greater understanding of the internal structure of the atom.

A beam of alpha particles from a radon source was shot at a thin sheet of gold foil, less than 10^{-4} cm thick. When an alpha particle strikes a screen coated with zinc sulphide, a tiny flash of light (called a scintillation) is produced at the point where the alpha particle hits the screen. A zinc sulphide screen and microscope detector were mounted so that they could be moved to any position around the gold foil. (See also Section 14.6).

A device for detecting and measuring radioactive emissions, the Geiger counter, was named after Hans Geiger, whose work led to its development.

Gold foils were used by Rutherford because the gold atom has a relatively heavy nucleus and acts as a good scattering centre for alpha particles. Also, gold can be rolled thin enough that most particles will pass through the foil and be deflected only by a single nucleus, if at all. Even so, the gold foils used in this experiment were about 400 atoms thick.

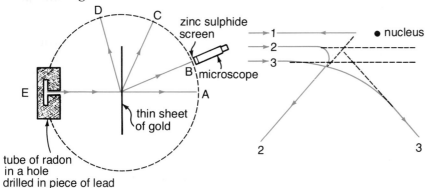

Apparatus used by Geiger and Marsden to measure scattering angles of alpha particles

The paths of three alpha particles as they approach the positive gold nucleus closely enough to be scattered

This is the same electrostatic force that was discussed in Chapter 10. The smaller the distance between the alpha particle and the nucleus, the greater the force of electrostatic repulsion.

If the atom and the nucleus are thought of as spheres whose volume is given by the equation $V = 4/3\pi\,r^3$, then

$$\frac{\text{volume of atom}}{\text{volume of nucleus}} = \frac{4/3\pi(10^{-10})^3}{4/3\pi(10^{-14})^3}$$
$$= \frac{10^{-30}}{10^{-42}}$$
$$= 10^{12}$$

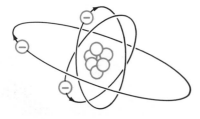

Rutherford's solar-system atom

Some modern theories visualize electrons as cloud-like distributions of negative electric charge, more concentrated in some places than in others.

Geiger and Marsden spent months laboriously recording the numbers of alpha particles that were scattered at each angle by the gold foil. Their results may be summarized as follows:

- Most of the alpha particles were detected at point A, having passed through the gold foil without being noticeably deflected.
- Some alpha particles were detected at points B and C; furthermore, on rare occasions, alpha particles that had been deflected by more than 90° were detected at points D and even E.

In 1911, Ernest Rutherford (1871-1937), director of the laboratory at the University of Manchester and a supervisor of Geiger and Marsden, suggested the following explanation of their results:

- The positive alpha particles were scattered by the force of electric repulsion between themselves and the positive charges within the gold atoms.
- Since few alpha particles were noticeably scattered, the positive charge of the atom must be concentrated within a very small region of space. (Rutherford called this space the **nucleus**.) Only alpha particles that passed very close to the nucleus were scattered.
- The electrons were in orbit in the empty space around the nucleus of the atom, held by the force of electric attraction of the positive nucleus.

This explanation was immediately accepted, and it formed the basis of Rutherford's "nuclear atom" model, sometimes called the solar system atom, with the electrons in orbit around the nucleus, just as the planets are in orbit around the sun. Rutherford's calculations showed that the nucleus has a diameter of about 10^{-14} m compared with an atomic diameter of about 10^{-10} m. Thus, the volume of an atom is about 10^{12} times the volume of its nucleus. Since the remainder of the atom is essentially empty space, it is easy to understand why a large majority of the alpha particles in the Rutherford gold-foil experiment passed through the foil without being scattered by the nucleus.

The actual structure of the nucleus was not immediately apparent to Rutherford. He did know that the hydrogen nucleus has the smallest charge of any known nucleus, and that all the other nuclei have charges that are approximately whole-numbered multiples of this smallest charge. He also realized that the positive charge on the hydrogen nucleus is equal in magnitude to the negative charge on an electron. In 1920, he gave the hydrogen nucleus its name—he called it the **proton**. Other nuclei with greater amounts of positive charge must contain more protons, he said. For example, an oxygen nucleus, with a positive charge eight times that of a hydrogen nucleus, must contain eight protons. By the same reasoning, the oxygen nucleus might be expected to have a mass eight times that of the hydrogen nucleus. However, accurate measurements showed that the mass of the oxygen nucleus is not eight but 16 times the mass of the hydrogen nucleus. Rutherford and his colleagues were, at first, perplexed by this problem, but later they proposed the existence of another particle in the nucleus, a particle with a mass approximately equal to that of a proton but with no electrical charge. These particles were called **neutrons**, and their existence was verified, experimentally, by the English physicist James Chadwick in 1932 (see Section 16.6).

With this new knowledge, it became possible to represent the structure of every known element in terms of the number of protons and neutrons in its nucleus, and the number of electrons in orbit around its nucleus. The number of protons in an atom's nucleus is called the **atomic number**. Since atoms are electrically neutral, and since the amount of positive charge on a proton is equal to the amount of negative charge on an electron, the atomic number is also the number of electrons orbiting the atom's nucleus. The total number of particles in the nucleus (protons and neutrons) is called the **atomic mass number**. Symbolically, then, the structure of any atom may be written as:

$$^{A}_{Z}X$$

where A is the atomic mass number
Z is the atomic number
X is the atomic symbol

Such an atom is composed of Z protons, (A − Z) neutrons, and Z electrons.

15.3 The Bohr Model of the Atom

There was one major problem with Rutherford's "planetary model" of the atom. He reasoned that an atom's electrons must be moving around the nucleus, in orbits, just as the planets move around the sun. If electrons were stationary, they would be attracted towards the positive nucleus, and the atom would collapse. In 1864, James Clerk Maxwell (1831-79) had predicted that whenever an electric charge accelerated (changed its speed and/or its direction) it should give off energy in the form of an electromagnetic wave (Section 26.10). In fact, Heinrich Hertz (1857-94) succeeded in producing and detecting these waves in 1887 (Section 26.11). As a result, electrons in orbit around a nucleus should be giving off energy continuously, as they change direction. As they lose energy, an atom's electrons should quickly

To calculate the approximate density of a nucleus with a mass of 10^{-27} kg and a volume of 10^{-44} m³:

$$D = \frac{M}{V}$$
$$= \frac{10^{-27} \text{ kg}}{10^{-44} \text{ m}^3}$$
$$= 10^{17} \text{ kg/m}^3$$

This is about the same density as some stars.

Niels Bohr (1885-1962)

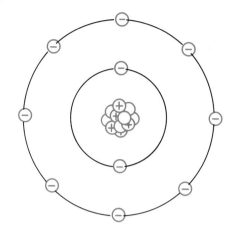

Bohr's atom

The amount of energy required to remove
an electron completely from an atom is
called the ionization energy, E_I. For a
hydrogen atom, this energy is 13.6 eV.

spiral in towards the nucleus, eventually colliding with it and being captured by it. Atoms should spontaneously collapse. Why, then, are they stable — why don't they continuously give off energy and collapse?

In 1913, Niels Bohr (1885-1962), a Danish physicist working in Rutherford's laboratory, became interested in this problem. After extensive research, using hydrogen atoms, he published the following conclusions:

- Within an atom, there are certain **allowed orbits** around the nucleus, in which electrons can move indefinitely without giving off energy.
- Each of these allowed orbits represents a definite amount of electron energy. For an electron to occupy any one of the allowed orbits, it must possess the energy allowed for that orbit.
- The orbit with the least energy is found closest to the nucleus. Each orbit is assigned a **quantum number**, n, where $n = 1, 2, 3\ldots$ (i.e., "$n = 1$" refers to the lowest energy orbit, "$n = 2$" refers to the second lowest energy orbit, etc.)
- Only a specific number of electrons can occupy each of the allowed orbits. Under normal conditions, all of an atom's electrons occupy orbits with the lowest allowed amounts of energy.

Bohr was able to determine both the energy and the radius of the allowed orbits for hydrogen atoms, in terms of the quantum number. He found that:

$$E_n = -\frac{13.6}{n^2} \text{ eV}$$
$$r_n = 5.3 \times 10^{-11} n^2 \text{ m}$$

where E_n is the energy of an electron in the nth allowed orbit, in electronvolts

r_n is the radius of the nth allowed orbit, in metres

NOTE: The energies of electrons within atoms are usually measured in units called **electronvolts** (eV).

1 eV is the energy of an electron accelerated from rest by a potential difference of 1 V.

1 eV = 1.6×10^{-19} J

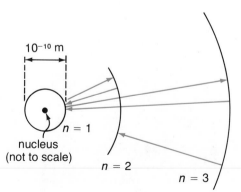

10^{-10} m

nucleus
(not to scale)

$n = 1$

$n = 2$

$n = 3$

The first, second, and third Bohr orbits for the hydrogen atom

Thus, Bohr was able to draw scale diagrams of both the allowed orbits for the hydrogen atom, and also the allowed energy levels for an electron in a hydrogen atom.

As you can see, Bohr assigned an energy value of 0 to an electron that was just able to escape from an atom. All electrons held within an atom's orbits, then, have a negative value of energy. Also, the difference between the energy at one energy level and the energy at the next level decreases as the quantum number increases. In fact, at very large values of n the levels become difficult to distinguish and seem to merge into a continuum. We will study the significance of these levels in Section 15.5.

The Bohr concept of allowed orbits and distinct energy levels for electrons may also be applied to atoms that are more complicated in their structure than the hydrogen atom. Recent theories of atomic structure have almost abandoned any notion of electrons as particles moving around a nucleus in allowed orbits; nevertheless, the Bohr model is still useful in explaining most atomic phenomena and has not been discarded entirely.

Rutherford and Bohr were both aware of Mendeleev's periodic table, but their ideas concerning nuclear structure and electrons in allowed orbits contradicted the order of some elements in the table. The table as we know it today represents the work of H. G. Moseley, a colleague of Rutherford, who arranged the elements in order of the number of protons in their nuclei, rather than their atomic masses. Each successive element in the table has one more proton and one more electron than its predecessor. The number of neutrons in the nucleus increases also, but not in such a regular fashion.

Bohr's theory suggested the existence of allowed orbits for the electrons, each orbit, or **electron shell**, being characterized by a specific amount of electron energy. The number of electrons that can occupy an electron shell with quantum number n was found to be $2n^2$.

As mentioned in Section 15.3, a normal atom's electrons will always be found in the available allowed orbits with the least energy.

The table on page 296 shows the first 18 atoms in the periodic table, with their atomic numbers, atomic masses, and electron orbit structures.

Each atom of a given substance has the same number of protons in its nucleus, but the number of neutrons may vary. Atoms of a substance that have different numbers of neutrons are called different **isotopes** of that substance. Hydrogen, for example, has three isotopes (see diagram on page 296).

Most of the elements in the periodic table have several isotopes, found in nature in varying proportions. In most cases, the average atomic mass of the various isotopes is used in the periodic table. In

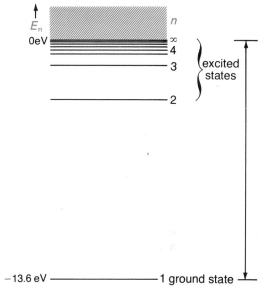

The Bohr energy-level diagram for the hydrogen atom

"Energy level" and "electron shell" are used interchangeably in references to Bohr's allowed orbits for electrons.

After element 18 (argon), the distribution of electrons in shells appears to become quite complicated. Even so, all the electrons in an atom are found in the lowest-energy orbits available to them. If you are interested in this problem, try to find a periodic table that includes electron-shell distributions.

The name "isotope" was coined in 1913 by Frederick Soddy (1877-1956), an English chemist who was associated with Rutherford at McGill University. He was awarded a Nobel Prize for Chemistry in 1921.

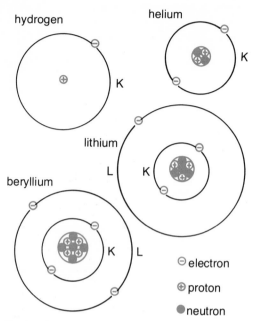

Rutherford-Bohr atom models

the chart on this page, the atomic mass number for each element is that of its most abundant isotope. The known isotopes of all the elements are given in Appendix F.

Sample problem

Determine the number of protons, electrons, and neutrons in the isotope of chlorine that has an atomic mass number of 37, often written as chlorine-37.

From the periodic table, the atomic number of chlorine is 17. Therefore, its chemical designation is

$$^{37}_{17}\text{Cl}$$

And, the number of protons = Z = 17
the number of electrons = Z = 17
the number of neutrons = A − Z
= 37 − 17
= 20

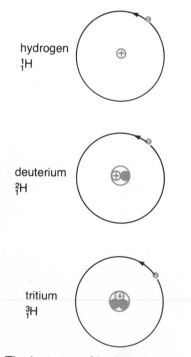

The isotopes of hydrogen

Element	Chemical symbol	Atomic number	Atomic mass number	#p	#n	#e	Distribution of electrons in Bohr orbits					
							K 2	L 8	M 18	N 32	O 50	P 72
hydrogen	H	1	1	1	0	1	1					
helium	He	2	4	2	2	2	2					
lithium	Li	3	7	3	4	3	2	1				
beryllium	Be	4	9	4	5	4	2	2				
boron	B	5	11	5	6	5	2	3				
carbon	C	6	12	6	6	6	2	4				
nitrogen	N	7	14	7	7	7	2	5				
oxygen	O	8	16	8	8	8	2	6				
fluorine	F	9	19	9	10	9	2	7				
neon	Ne	10	20	10	10	10	2	8				
sodium	Na	11	23	11	12	11	2	8	1			
magnesium	Mg	12	24	12	12	12	2	8	2			
aluminum	Al	13	27	13	14	13	2	8	3			
silicon	Si	14	28	14	14	14	2	8	4			
phosphorus	P	15	31	15	16	15	2	8	5			
sulphur	S	16	32	16	16	16	2	8	6			
chlorine	Cl	17	35	17	18	17	2	8	7			
argon	Ar	18	40	18	22	18	2	8	8			

Practice

By referring to the periodic table in Appendix F, write the chemical designation for each of the following isotopes, and state the number of protons, electrons, and neutrons in each.

(**a**) carbon-12
(**b**) copper-65
(**c**) magnesium-25
(**d**) nickel-60
(**e**) uranium-238

15.4 Another Look at the Nature of Light

At about the same time that Rutherford and Bohr were refining their models of atomic structure, other scientists were beginning to take a new interest in the nature of light. You may recall that the phenomena of interference and diffraction can be explained by assuming that light behaves like a wave (Chapter 26). As a result, the wave model of light enjoyed widespread popularity during the 18th and 19th centuries.

Towards the end of the 19th century, the German physicist Max Planck (1858-1947) undertook a study of the radiation emitted by very hot objects. The precise nature of his findings need not concern us, but their general significance is important: the wave theory of light did not fully account for the observed properties of the radiation emitted by hot objects. The wave theory of light, which had been so successful for so long, was seen to have serious deficiencies.

At about the same time, a slightly different and equally puzzling phenomenon was observed by Wilhelm Hallwachs, another German physicist. He noticed that the energy of light can cause electrons to be emitted from atoms near the surface of some materials. Apparently, electrons could gain sufficient energy from light to "escape" from their allowed orbits and become totally free of the atom. This phenomenon is called the **photoelectric effect**, and it may be demonstrated by means of the apparatus shown.

Two startling facts were discovered through the use of this apparatus:

- For low-frequency light (i.e., long wavelengths), no electrons were emitted, regardless of the intensity of the light.
- For frequencies higher than a certain value (i.e., shorter wavelengths) electrons were emitted, even when the weakest intensities of light were used. Also, the number of electrons emitted appeared to depend on the intensity of the light.

Max Planck

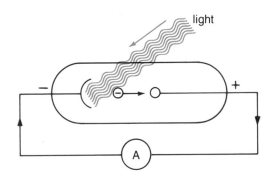

Electrons emitted by the illuminated surface move across the gap in the vacuum tube and form an electric current through the circuit that may be measured with a sensitive ammeter.

If a negatively charged metal-leaf electroscope is connected to a clean sheet of zinc and irradiated with ultraviolet light, electrons emitted from the zinc photoelectrically will cause it to lose its charge.

Einstein devised the equation $E = hf$, where E represents the energy of a photon, f represents its frequency, and h is a proportionality constant that Planck found to have a value of 6.63×10^{-34} J·s.

Planck and his colleagues were quite puzzled at first by this result. Light was believed to be wavelike. Hence, electrons could be expected to be emitted as soon as the light wave had transferred enough energy to any electron to free it from its atom. The amount of energy in a wave depended on its amplitude, so electrons should have been emitted almost immediately when a strong beam was used, and after a short build-up time when a weaker beam was used. Yet it seemed that it was the frequency, not the intensity, of the light that determined whether electrons were emitted from the illuminated surface.

In 1905, the German physicist Albert Einstein (1879-1955) was able to suggest an explanation that was consistent with Planck's other discoveries about the nature of radiation from hot objects. Einstein proposed that light energy was not transferred continuously and evenly, as the energy of a wave would be, but in small packages, or bundles, much like a stream of microscopic bullets. This approach, suggesting that the energy of light comes in small, discrete packages, is called the **quantum theory**, each "package" of energy being called a **quantum**. Einstein coined the term **photons** to describe these tiny particle-like quanta of energy.

To explain the photoelectric effect, Einstein assumed that the energy of a photon depends on the frequency of the light—the higher the frequency, the more energy the photon possesses. As a result, in low-frequency light, even though an immense number of photons may have been striking the illuminated surface, no single photon possessed enough energy to free an electron, so that no electrons were emitted. Higher-frequency light consisted of photons whose energy, if absorbed by an electron, would be sufficient to cause the electron to be emitted.

The most important aspect of Einstein's explanation has to do with the relationship between a photon's energy and the frequency of light.

- **The energy of a photon varies directly with its frequency (the higher the frequency of a photon, the greater its energy).**
- **Each quantity of photon energy corresponds to a specific and unique frequency of light.**

15.5 Atoms and Light

Solids heated to a very high temperature give off light with a wide range of frequencies. Gases at low pressure also give off light when an electric current is passed through them or when they are heated. However, the light emitted by gases is not at all like the light given off by solids. Rather than emitting a continuous range of frequencies, each gas gives off its own distinct set of frequencies. The set of frequencies given off by a substance is called its **emission spectrum**. By observing the emission spectrum of a mixture of gases, it is possible to identify the gases present in the mixture.

The reason why a gas emits only its own special set of frequencies remained a mystery for many years. It took a combination of the Bohr-Rutherford model of the atom and Einstein's and Planck's quantum theory of light to provide the explanation. According to Bohr, atomic electrons can only have certain specific values of energy that correspond to the allowed orbits, or electron shells, that they must occupy within the atom. Under normal conditions, all of an atom's electrons occupy the lowest energy levels available to them, and the atom is in its **ground state**. However, when an electric current is passed through a gas, or it is heated, some electrons can absorb energy and jump up into higher-energy levels. When such a transition occurs, the atom is said to be in an **excited state**, since it possesses more energy than it does when it is in the ground state. This type of transition may be depicted on an energy-level diagram, as shown on the next page.

An electron in an excited state is unstable, since there is a vacant, lower-energy level available to it. After a very short time (about 10^{-9} s) in the excited state, the electron will spontaneously jump down to one of the lower-energy levels, and will release its excess energy in the form of a photon of light. This transition may also be depicted on an energy-level diagram.

The energy of the emitted photon will be equal to the difference between the higher−and lower−energy levels, as follows:

$$E_{\text{photon}} = E_{\text{higher}} - E_{\text{lower}}$$

This difference in energy would result in the production of a photon with a specific frequency.

The spectrum of frequencies emitted by an atom represents all of the possible transitions for that atom between the excited states and the ground state. For example, a hydrogen atom, with one electron, is in its ground state when this electron is in the K-shell (n = 1). If the electron absorbs energy and jumps into any other shell,

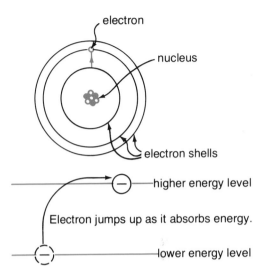

An electron absorbs energy when it jumps to a higher energy level.

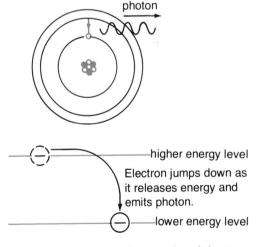

An electron emits a photon when it jumps to a lower energy level.

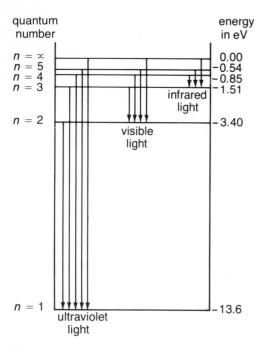

quantum
number

energy
in eV

$n = \infty$ ——— 0.00
$n = 5$ ——— −0.54
$n = 4$ ——— −0.85
$n = 3$ ——— −1.51

infrared
light

$n = 2$ ——— −3.40

visible
light

$n = 1$ ——— −13.6

ultraviolet
light

Energy-level diagram for hydrogen

then it must de-excite by a series of downward transitions until it is
once again in the K-shell. Each of these downward transitions
results in the emission of a photon; this is illustrated by the
energy-level diagram for hydrogen. Each arrow on the diagram
represents a possible downward electron jump producing a
photon with a definite frequency.

The emission spectrum for hydrogen (see the colour plate in
Chapter 25) shows the many colours of light whose photons have
frequencies in the visible range, corresponding to downward transitions to the $n = 2$ energy level. Transitions to a lower energy level
can occur in one step or in a series of steps.

Lasers

Ever since Planck and Einstein first proposed the quantum theory,
physicists have been intrigued with the idea of producing an
intense beam of visible light photons powerful enough to burn
holes through solids in milliseconds. The idea was pursued seri-
ously in industrial research laboratories in the United States,
Japan, Russia, and England during the late 1950s. The breakthrough came on July 7, 1960, when Dr. Theodore Maiman, a
research physicist at Hughes Aircraft Company in California, built
the world's first laser. Within months, the scientific community
began to work feverishly on the development of this new technology. By 1965, most of the key concepts in laser technology had
been discovered, and the emphasis of research turned to applications of the new phenomenon.

Laser is an acronym for light amplification by the stimulated
emission of radiation. Some substances or combinations of substances have excited states that are **metastable**; that is, electrons
can jump up into these excited energy levels and stay there for a
short time without jumping immediately back down into available
lower-energy levels. Ruby crystals, calcium fluoride crystals,
carbon dioxide gas, and a mixture of helium gas and neon gas are
examples of substances with metastable excited states.

When many atoms or molecules are in a metastable condition
(called a **population inversion**), the excited electrons may be
stimulated to jump down to a lower level by the presence of
another photon whose energy is exactly equal to the energy of the
photon created by the downward transition.

An amplification of the light intensity is produced, because the
emitted photon is created "in phase" with the stimulating photon,
so that they interfere constructively to produce a maximum inten-

sity. Each of the two photons can then stimulate the emission of yet another photon, and a chain reaction occurs. The final result is a beam of photons, all with the same energy (frequency and wavelength) and all travelling in phase, producing a fine but very intense beam of light.

Lasers are used extensively today in communications, navigation, medicine, industry, and scientific research. A laser beam can make precise measurements to an accuracy of millionths of a centimetre–about 1/250th the diameter of a human hair. A laser rangefinder (Section 21.2) has been used to measure the distance between the Earth and the moon to within 15 cm, and to map the contours of the bottoms and rims of the moon's craters. The applications of laser technology to medicine are multiplying rapidly. They range from the "welding" of a detached retina painlessly in 10^{-3} s to the treatment of certain types of skin malignancies. In industry, lasers are being used to weld dissimilar materials together, with temperatures in excess of 18 000°C, and to cut and shape tough and brittle metals instantly. In quality control applications, they are used to check the size, shape, and texture of manufactured parts with extreme precision.

15.6 Summary

1. John Dalton proposed that matter consists of tiny indivisible particles, called atoms. Atoms of a given element are identical, and atoms of different elements have different masses. Dalton pictured the atom as a solid chunk of matter, with no internal or external features.
2. Mendeleev arranged all known elements into the periodic table, in order of increasing atomic mass, grouping atoms with similar chemical properties into vertical columns.
3. In Thomson's model, the atom was thought of as a uniform sphere of positive charge, with negative electrons distributed through it, much like raisins in a bun.
4. Ernest Rutherford, using data from the scattering of alpha particles by a thin gold foil, proposed a model of the atom in which most of the mass is concentrated in a very small central region called the nucleus. The remainder of the atom is empty space, except for the negative electrons that are in orbit around the nucleus.
5. Bohr proposed the existence of certain "allowed orbits" in which electrons can move without radiating energy in the

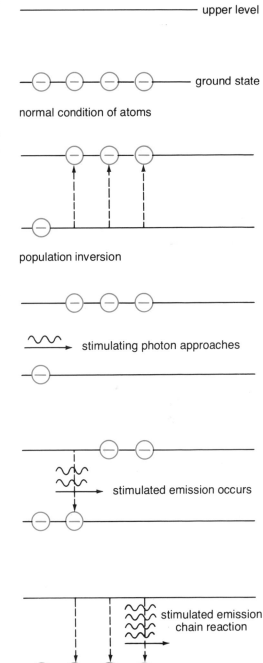

Steps in the action of a laser

form of electromagnetic waves. Each orbit has a specific amount of electron energy, and is assigned a quantum number $n = 1, 2, 3 \ldots$ The orbit closest to the nucleus contains electrons with the least energy.

6. For a hydrogen atom, the energy and radius of the nth orbit are

$$E_n = -\frac{13.6}{n^2} \text{ eV}$$

and $$r_n = n^2 \times 5.3 \times 10^{-11} \text{ m}$$

7. Moseley reordered Mendeleev's periodic table by arranging the elements according to the number of protons in the nucleus.

$$^A_Z X$$

where X is the atomic symbol
Z is the atomic number
A is the atomic mass number

also Z = number of protons in the nucleus
Z = number of orbiting electrons
A = number of particles (protons + neutrons) in the nucleus

8. Light energy comes in small packages, called quanta, or photons, and the energy of a photon varies directly with its frequency: the higher the frequency of a photon, the greater its energy.

9. Electrons within atoms can absorb energy and jump from their ground state into higher-energy, excited states. After a very short time, an electron will jump down to a lower available energy level, giving off its excess energy by creating a photon. All of the different photons given off by the atoms of a substance form that substance's emission spectrum.

10. Substances with metastable excited states can become lasers. A photon with just the right amount of energy can stimulate an electron in a metastable state to jump down and create an identical photon in phase with the stimulating photon. This process repeats itself, in a chain reaction, to produce a very intense beam of in-phase light.

15.7 Review

1. By giving a brief description of each of their models of the atom, show how the model was changed during the time of Dalton, Thomson, Rutherford, and Bohr.

2. What was the major difference between Mendeleev's periodic table and Moseley's?

3. (a) In the Rutherford gold foil experiment, what type of force causes alpha particles to be scattered by a gold nucleus?

(b) Why are some alpha particles scattered at greater angles than others? What is the largest possible scattering angle for an alpha particle?

(c) What type of "hit" between an alpha particle and a gold nucleus would cause the alpha particle to be scattered the maximum amount?

4. (a) Distinguish between the atomic number and the atomic mass number of an element.

(b) What is meant by the term "isotopes of an element"? What do the isotopes of an element have in common, and how do they differ?

(c) Write the proper chemical designation for each of the following isotopes and indicate the number of protons, electrons, and neutrons in each atom.

(i)   tritium   (iv) polonium-210
(ii) carbon-14   (v) lead-207
(iii) lithium-7

5. (a) What defect was there, according to Maxwell's laws of electromagnetism, in Rutherford's model of the atom, with electrons moving in orbits around the nucleus?

(b) Describe Bohr's assumption, about the nature of electrons within atoms, that solved this apparent problem.

6. (a) Using the equations from Section 15.3, calculate the radius and energy of the first five allowed orbits for the hydrogen atom.

(b) What is the difference in energy between an electron in the L-shell and an electron in the K-shell of a hydrogen atom?

(c) What is the ionization energy for hydrogen; that is, how much energy is required to completely remove an electron from the atom? Hint: as an electron occupies an orbit with a higher quantum number, it is closer to being removed from the atom.

7. An electron in a hydrogen atom absorbs energy and jumps up into the N-shell ($n = 4$). Draw an energy-level diagram showing the electron in this excited state, and indicate on the diagram all of the various ways it could return to the ground state. State the number of different photons emitted during each of the possible downward transitions.

8. (a) What is a photon?

(b) How did Einstein's and Planck's concept of light differ from the accepted theory at the turn of the twentieth century?

(c) What does the energy of a photon depend on?

9. Arrange the following electromagnetic radiations in order of increasing photon energy (refer to chart in Section 26.11):

radio waves, infrared light, microwaves, visible light, gamma rays, ultraviolet light, X-rays.

10. (a) What is the "emission spectrum" of a substance?
    (b) Describe the way in which a substance such as mercury vapour, with an electric current passing through it, can give off light.

15.8 Learning Objectives

1. To state the main ideas in Dalton's atomic theory, and to describe Dalton's model of the atom.
2. To describe the basis upon which Mendeleev arranged all known elements into his periodic table.
3. To describe the features of Thomson's model of the atom.
4. To describe the work of Geiger and Marsden, and to state the results of the gold-foil experiment.
5. To describe the features of Rutherford's model of the atom.
6. To explain the problem associated with the idea of orbiting electrons in the Rutherford model, based on Maxwell's laws of electromagnetism.
7. To describe Bohr's solution to this problem, and to describe Bohr's model of the atom, defining allowed orbit, quantum number, electron shell, ground state, and excited state.
8. To state the equations giving the energies and radii of the allowed orbits for the hydrogen atom.
9. To describe the changes made in Mendeleev's periodic table by Moseley, based on the Bohr-Rutherford model of the atom.
10. To write the proper chemical representation for each of the first 18 elements, and, for each, to state the number of protons and neutrons in the nucleus, and the number of electrons in each electron shell.
11. To define isotopes, and give examples from the first 18 elements in the periodic table.
12. Given the symbolic representation of any atom, to state the number of protons, electrons, and neutrons it contains.
13. To describe the way in which atoms absorb energy and then re-emit this energy in the form of light; also, to describe what an emission spectrum consists of.
14. To state what "laser" stands for, and to describe how certain substances emit laser light; also, to describe the special features of the light emitted by a laser, and to state several uses of this light.

16 Investigating the Nucleus

16.1 What's in the Nucleus?

In Chapter 15, we learned through Rutherford's alpha particle scattering experiment that the positively charged nucleus has a diameter of approximately 10^{-14} m and occupies only a tiny fraction of the volume of an atom. Nevertheless, the nucleus contains nearly all the mass of the atom. These discoveries raise a number of questions. What is the internal structure of the nucleus? Is it one large mass or is it made up of a number of particles? How can the properties of so small an object be investigated?

The origin of the alpha and beta particles emitted by a radioactive substance puzzled scientists for many years. Finally, they concluded that these emissions must come from the atomic nucleus. Thus, the study of radioactivity became the key to an understanding of the structure of the nucleus, and this is where we will begin our study of nuclear physics.

16.2 Natural Transmutations

One discovery that was made by scientists working with radioactive elements was that helium gas was usually present, either enclosed in the element or as a product of radioactivity. Rutherford proposed that the alpha particle was a helium atom with its orbiting electrons removed. In other words, it was a helium nucleus.

To test this hypothesis, Rutherford devised an experiment in 1909 with the help of a student, T.D. Royds. Alpha particles from radioactive radon were passed through an inner thin-walled glass tube, as illustrated. The particles entered the evacuated outer chamber but were stopped by the thicker glass in the outer tube, trapped like mice in Rutherford's "mouse trap". The apparatus was left for a week and then, by means of mercury, the gas that had collected in the outer chamber was compressed into the upper part of the tube and an electric spark was passed through it. When the resulting emission spectrum (see Sections 15.5 and 25.5) was analysed, helium gas was detected, proving that the trapped alpha particles were helium nuclei, as Rutherford had hypothesized. Even more important, the experiment showed that the radon nucleus had spontaneously split, throwing off a small fragment (an alpha particle) and leaving behind a larger fragment—a different

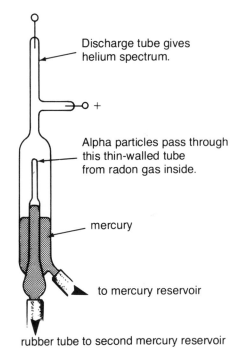

Discharge tube gives helium spectrum.

+

Alpha particles pass through this thin-walled tube from radon gas inside.

mercury

to mercury reservoir

rubber tube to second mercury reservoir

The apparatus Rutherford and Royds used to demonstrate that alpha particles are helium nuclei

nucleus with different chemical properties (polonium).

$$\text{radon} \longrightarrow \text{polonium} + \text{helium}$$

The natural change of radon into polonium is an example of a **transmutation** – the process of changing one element into another. If a transmutation is accompanied by the emission of an alpha particle, it is called **alpha decay**. If a beta particle is emitted, it is called **beta decay**. The word "decay" is used because an atom with a large mass is changing, or decaying, into particles with smaller masses.

Alpha Decay

The alpha decay of radon will serve to illustrate the general properties of alpha decay. The equation for the alpha decay of radon is stated as follows:

$$^{222}_{86}\text{Rn} \longrightarrow {}^{218}_{84}\text{Po} + {}^{4}_{2}\text{He}$$
$$(\alpha \text{ particle})$$

The alpha particle is represented as ${}^{4}_{2}\text{He}$ since it is a helium nucleus. Note that the atomic number of the radon nucleus decreases by two, since two protons are lost, and that the mass number decreases by four, since two neutrons as well as the two protons are lost. The arrow in a nuclear equation indicates the direction of the reaction and also may be thought of as an equal sign. The sum of the atomic numbers on the right side equals the atomic number on the left side, and the sum of the mass numbers on the right equals the mass number on the left.

In general, for alpha decay:

$$^{A}_{Z}\textbf{X} \longrightarrow {}^{A-4}_{Z-2}\textbf{Y} + {}^{4}_{2}\textbf{He}$$

| parent nucleus | $\longrightarrow$ | daughter nucleus | $+$ | α particle (helium nucleus) |

Beta Decay

When a beta particle is emitted by a radioactive element, the atomic number of the nucleus increases by one, but the mass number remains the same. For example, in the beta decay of sodium-24,

$$^{24}_{11}\text{Na} \longrightarrow {}^{24}_{12}\text{Mg} + {}^{0}_{-1}\text{e}$$

Beta particles are electrons with a high speed and are represented as $_{-1}^{0}e$, since they have a charge of -1 but negligible mass (when compared with the nucleus).

This reaction appears to be impossible. After all, the electron is negative. How can it be emitted from a positively charged nucleus? The explanation lies in the fact that a neutron breaks up into a proton, an electron (beta particle), and a third mysterious, massless particle called an anti-neutrino. The production of a proton, which remains in the nucleus, accounts for the fact that the atomic number increases by one though the mass number remains constant. (The total number of particles in the nucleus remains the same.)

In general, for beta decay:

$$_{Z}^{A}X \longrightarrow \ _{Z+1}^{A}Y \ + \ _{-1}^{0}e$$

$$\underset{\text{nucleus}}{\text{parent}} \longrightarrow \underset{\text{nucleus}}{\text{daughter}} + \underset{\text{(electron)}}{\beta \text{ particle}}$$

Gamma Radiation

Usually accompanying alpha and beta decay is gamma radiation, which consists of photons, not particles, that have no mass or electric charge (see Section 15.4). Gamma rays, by themselves, produce no changes in the atomic number or the atomic mass of the nucleus. Gamma rays are represented by the symbol $_{0}^{0}\gamma$.

$$_{Z}^{A}X \longrightarrow \ _{Z}^{A}X \ + \ _{0}^{0}\gamma$$

Alpha decay and beta decay may be illustrated by a series of naturally occurring transmutations called the uranium-lead **decay series**. The nuclear equations for the first five of these transmutations are:

α-decay	$_{92}^{238}U$	$\longrightarrow$	$_{90}^{234}Th$	$+$	$_{2}^{4}He$	$+$	$_{0}^{0}\gamma$
β-decay	$_{90}^{234}Th$	$\longrightarrow$	$_{91}^{234}Pa$	$+$	$_{-1}^{0}e$	$+$	$_{0}^{0}\gamma$
β-decay	$_{91}^{234}Pa$	$\longrightarrow$	$_{92}^{234}U$	$+$	$_{-1}^{0}e$	$+$	$_{0}^{0}\gamma$
α-decay	$_{92}^{234}U$	$\longrightarrow$	$_{90}^{230}Th$	$+$	$_{2}^{4}He$	$+$	$_{0}^{0}\gamma$
α-decay	$_{90}^{230}Th$	$\longrightarrow$	$_{88}^{226}Ra$	$+$	$_{2}^{4}He$	$+$	$_{0}^{0}\gamma$

The gamma ray symbol has been written into each of these equations as a reminder that gamma radiation often accompanies alpha decay and beta decay. It is usually omitted, the primary concern being the particles created in the transmutation.

Decay series may also be shown by a graph of atomic number versus mass number, as illustrated.

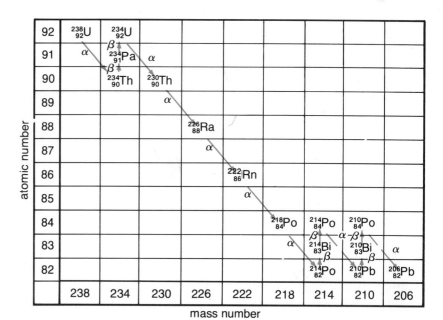

The decay chart for uranium-238

Sample problem

Give the value of x and y in each of the following equations.
(a) $^{212}_{82}\text{Pb} \longrightarrow {}^{212}_{x}\text{Bi} + {}^{0}_{-1}\text{e}$
(b) $^{210}_{84}\text{Po} \longrightarrow {}^{y}_{x}\text{Pb} + {}^{4}_{2}\text{He}$
(c) $^{227}_{89}\text{Ac} \longrightarrow {}^{227}_{90}\text{Th} + \text{x}$

(a) x = 83 (atomic numbers on right must add algebraically to 82)
(b) x = 82, y = 206 (mass numbers on right must add up to 210, atomic numbers must add up to 84)
(c) x = $^{0}_{-1}\text{e}$ (for atomic numbers on right to add up to 89 and mass numbers to 227, the unknown particle must be a β particle)

Practice

Give the value of x and y in each of the following equations.

(a) $^{212}_{x}\text{Pb} \longrightarrow ^{212}_{83}\text{Bi} + \text{y}$ $(x = 82, y = ^{0}_{-1}e)$

(b) $^{214}_{83}\text{Bi} \longrightarrow ^{x}_{y}\text{Po} + ^{0}_{-1}e$ $(x = 214, y = 84)$

(c) $^{x}_{y}\text{Ra} \longrightarrow ^{222}_{86}\text{Rn} + ^{4}_{2}\text{He}$ $(x = 226, y = 88)$

(d) $^{215}_{84}\text{Po} \longrightarrow ^{211}_{82}\text{Pb} + \text{x}$ $(x = ^{4}_{2}\text{He})$

(e) $^{3}_{1}\text{H} \longrightarrow \text{x} + ^{0}_{0}\gamma$ $(x = ^{3}_{1}\text{H})$

16.3 Decay Rate and Half-life

As we have just seen, **radioisotopes** (radioactive isotopes) disintegrate spontaneously into atoms with smaller masses. These disintegrations are unaffected by changes in temperature or pressure or by the other factors that normally affect the rate of chemical reactions. The rate at which a radioisotope of a given substance disintegrates is unique to that substance and is completely independent of external forces.

The rate of decay is measured by a scale of time called the **half-life**. A half-life is the time required for one-half of the atoms in any sample of a radioisotope to decay. For example, thorium-234 has a half-life of 24 d. This means that if we start with a 100 g sample of thorium-234, after 24 d 50 g will have changed into other atoms and 50 g of thorium-234 will remain. After another 24 d, one-half of what remained will disintegrate, leaving 25 g of thorium-234, and so on.

The term "half-life" was first used by Rutherford.

$^{234}_{90}$Th has a half-life of 24 days.

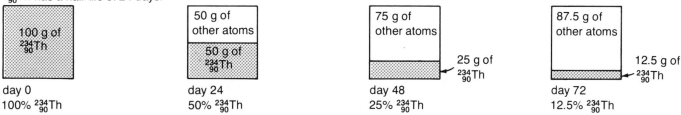

| day 0 | day 24 | day 48 | day 72 |
| 100% $^{234}_{90}$Th | 50% $^{234}_{90}$Th | 25% $^{234}_{90}$Th | 12.5% $^{234}_{90}$Th |

Decay of thorium

The half-lives of radioisotopes vary from element to element. Some elements have very short half-lives, such as radon-26 (4 d) and polonium-214 (10^{-4} s). Others have very long half-lives, such as strontium-90 (10^{5} years), plutonium-239 (2.44×10^{4} years), and uranium-238 (4.6×10^{9} years).

The level of radioactivity emitted by an isotope may be measured by means of a device such as a Geiger counter. The reading will be in becquerels (Bq), the unit of radioactivity equivalent to one emission per second.

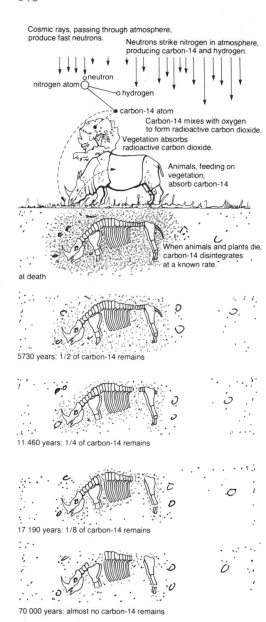

Cosmic rays, passing through atmosphere, produce fast neutrons.

Neutrons strike nitrogen in atmosphere, producing carbon-14 and hydrogen.

nitrogen atom   neutron

hydrogen

carbon-14 atom

Carbon-14 mixes with oxygen to form radioactive carbon dioxide.

Vegetation absorbs radioactive carbon dioxide.

Animals, feeding on vegetation, absorb carbon-14

When animals and plants die, carbon-14 disintegrates at a known rate.

at death

5730 years: 1/2 of carbon-14 remains

11 460 years: 1/4 of carbon-14 remains

17 190 years: 1/8 of carbon-14 remains

70 000 years: almost no carbon-14 remains

Radiocarbon dating is possible because plant and animal life absorb radioactive carbon-14. When an organism dies, this carbon-14 begins disintegrating at a rate determined by the carbon-14 half-life of 5730 years. At any stage, the amount of carbon-14 that is left in a specimen indicates its age.

The level of radioactivity emitted by a sample of a substance is proportional to the mass of the sample. A 100 g sample of thorium-234 will have twice the radioactivity of a 50 g sample, four times that of a 25 g sample, and so on. Thus the graph of radioactivity versus time is similar to the graph of the percentage of the sample present versus the time elapsed. If the half-life of a radioisotope is known, the age of a sample of it may be determined. Knowledge of the decay rate of certain isotopes has important applications in archaeology and geology.

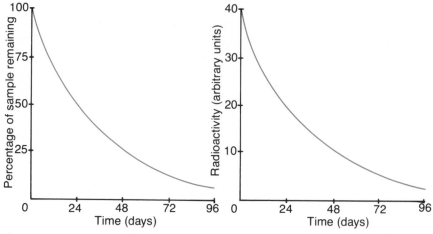

Decay curves for thorium

16.4 Radioactive Dating

Carbon has two isotopes – carbon-12 (non-radioactive) and carbon-14 (radioactive). Carbon-14 is created in the upper atmosphere as a result of the collision of high-energy particles, coming from the sun, with air molecules. The resulting interactions change nitrogen atoms into the radioisotope carbon-14.

Both carbon isotopes can combine chemically with oxygen to form carbon dioxide gas. Carbon dioxide is taken in by green plants and eventually, via the food chain, both carbon-12 and carbon-14 are found in all living things. Once a living thing dies, the carbon-14 in it begins to decay, and is not replaced. The amount of carbon-12 remains constant.

The half-life of carbon-14 is known to be 5730 ± 30 years. If a 1 g sample of a living tree produces a radioactivity reading of 0.30 Bq, then a 1 g sample of a piece of wood with a radioactivity reading of 0.15 Bq must be from a tree that died approximately 5700 years ago. Carbon dating can be used to estimate the age of archaeological samples up to 50 000 years old.

Another use of radioactive dating is in geology. Uranium-238, with a half-life of 4.6×10^9 years, disintegrates to lead-206. By determining the ratio of the two atoms present in a uranium sample, the age of the sample can be estimated. For instance, if a sample is half uranium-238 and half lead-206, then it is approximately 4.6×10^9 years old.

The oldest rocks on Earth, discovered in Tanzania, have been found to be 3.6×10^9 years old. Rock formations in the Sudbury region of Ontario have been calculated to be almost as old. Recent radioactive dating of meteor fragments and Apollo 11 moon samples gives estimates of 4.5×10^9 years. Measurements such as these provide an approximation of the age of the Earth, since the radioisotopes of uranium were probably created when the Earth was formed by the solidification of the large mass of gas that was the source of our sun and its planets.

16.5 Artificial Transmutation

Transmutation, the process by which one element is changed into another, was the alchemists' dream. The first artificial transmutation occurred when Rutherford and his colleagues investigated the effect of "firing" alpha particles into various gases.

Rutherford used an evacuated metal tube containing a radioactive alpha particle source and a zinc sulphide screen, as illustrated.

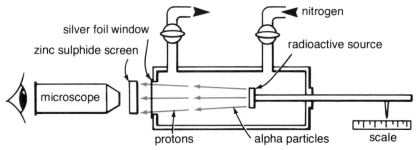

Rutherford's experiment to show that alpha-particle bombardment can disintegrate nitrogen nuclei

Any particles that passed through the silver foil window and struck the zinc sulphide screen gave off scintillations (flashes of light), which were observed through the microscope. Rutherford increased the distance of the source of alpha particles from the screen, until the scintillations stopped, indicating that the particles did not have enough energy to reach the screen. When he intro-

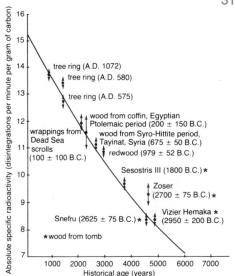

The graph shows samples from objects of known age, dated by the carbon-14 method. The curve is based on an assay of modern wood and laboratory measurement of the half-life of carbon-14. The individual points show the specific radioactivities of the various samples, from which their ages were estimated.

Dating process	Material tested	Potential range: years	Half-life: years
carbon-14	wood charcoal shell	70 000	5 730
protactinium-231	deep sea sediment	120 000	32 000
thorium-230	deep sea sediment coral shell	400 000	75 000
uranium-234	coral	1 000 000	250 000
chlorine-36	igneous and volcanic rocks	500 000	300 000
beryllium-10	deep sea sediment	800 000	2 500 000
helium-4	coral shell	—	4.5 billion
potassium-40 argon-40	volcanic ash lava	—	1.3 billion

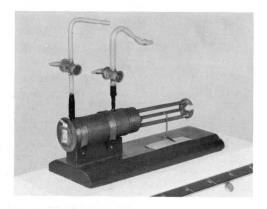

Rutherford's apparatus

duced nitrogen gas into the tube, scintillations again appeared on the screen. The particles hitting the screen must have been protons that had been knocked out of the nitrogen nuclei by alpha particles, causing the nitrogen nuclei to become oxygen nuclei. The nuclear reaction is written as follows:

$$^{14}_{7}\text{N} + ^{4}_{2}\text{He} \longrightarrow ^{17}_{8}\text{O} + ^{1}_{1}\text{H}$$
$$(\alpha \text{ particle}) \qquad \qquad (\text{proton})$$

This was an exciting discovery. For the first time one substance had been changed to another artificially. Rutherford and his colleague, James Chadwick, succeeded in producing other transmutations, and they discovered that, aside from the new element, something of even greater value was produced—energy. The collision of the alpha particle with a nucleus released part of the energy stored in the nucleus.

Many more studies were made using alpha-particle sources, but their scope was limited by the low energy of the alpha particles and the inability to control the particles adequately.

In 1932, in Cambridge, J.D. Cockcroft and E.T.S. Walton produced nuclear disintegrations by means of artificially accelerated protons, using the apparatus shown. Transformers were used to produce a 400 000 V potential difference to accelerate the protons to extremely high speeds (800 km/s). When a proton struck the lithium plate, its kinetic energy was given up to a lithium nucleus, causing this nucleus to disintegrate into two helium nuclei. This nuclear reaction is represented as follows:

$$^{7}_{3}\text{Li} + ^{1}_{1}\text{H} \longrightarrow ^{4}_{2}\text{He} + ^{4}_{2}\text{He} + \text{energy}$$
$$(\text{proton}) \quad (\text{alpha} \qquad (\text{alpha}$$
$$\text{particle}) \quad \text{particle})$$

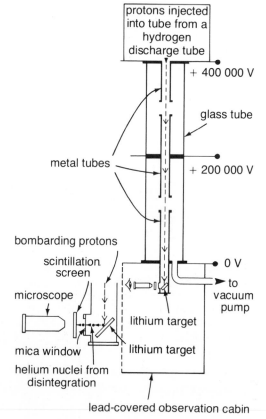

The Cockcroft-Walton proton accelerator

In the United States, E.O. Lawrence, R.J. Van de Graaf, and others developed devices to accelerate charged particles. Some of these devices are illustrated. Although modern **accelerators** are much more complex and powerful than those of Rutherford's day, the basic method of obtaining information about the nature of nuclei remains the same—observation of the collision between a projectile and a target nucleus. In the collision the original particles may be scattered with or without the production of radiation, and new products may be formed. The radiations and products are then studied by means of a variety of detection systems, including the cloud chamber and the mass spectrometer.

High-energy accelerators, sometimes called "atom smashers", are usually rated in terms of the energy of the accelerated particles, measured in electronvolts (see Section 15.3). The electronvolt is so small that the units used are the kiloelectronvolt (keV), the megaelectronvolt (MeV), and the gigaelectronvolt (GeV).

These high-energy accelerators give us the ability to probe the nucleus and discover the fundamental components of matter.

E.O. Lawrence's cyclotron

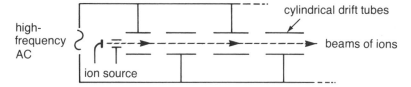

In the linear accelerator, the voltages of the drift tubes are successively increased as the charged particles pass through them.

Stanford linear accelerator

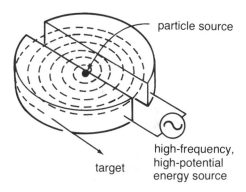

In the cyclotron, a field between two hollow semicircles accelerates the particles, which are kept in an outward spiral by a magnetic field perpendicular to their motion.

Stanford linear accelerator (inside)

16.6 Chadwick's Discovery of the Neutron

The neutron is a basic particle in the nucleus of all atoms, except the hydrogen atom (see Chapter 15). Its existence had been predicted earlier by Rutherford and others, but it was James Chadwick (1891-1974) who proved that it existed. In 1930, the German physicists W. Bothe and H. Becker had found that beryllium, when bombarded with alpha particles, produced high-energy emissions that penetrated several centimetres of lead but had no detectable charge. Frédéric Joliot-Curie (1900-58) and his wife Irène (1897-1956), working in France, found that these emissions caused protons to be emitted from compounds containing hydrogen, such as paraffin. In England, in 1933, Chadwick set up an experiment to identify the unknown emissions. In his apparatus, alpha particles struck a beryllium target, producing the emissions, which in turn struck a paraffin block, causing protons to be emitted into an ionization chamber.

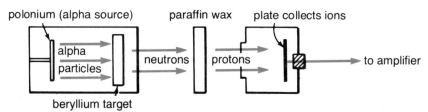

The apparatus Chadwick used to discover the neutron

Using the ionization chamber, Chadwick calculated the energy of the individual protons. Recognizing that this energy had come from the collision between the unknown particles and the protons, and that energy was conserved in the collision, he calculated the mass of an unknown particle. Its mass was virtually the same as that of the proton. It was, indeed, the neutron whose existence Rutherford had predicted 13 years earlier.

16.7 Neutron Transmutation

The discovery of the neutron and the techniques necessary to isolate neutrons provided physicists with another important tool. Up to that point, the particles used in research into the structure of the nucleus had been the proton and the alpha particle. Both of these particles have positive charges, making it possible for them

Frédéric Joliot-Curie took his wife's name when they were married. Irène was the daughter of Marie Curie. The Joliot-Curies were awarded the Nobel Prize for Chemistry in 1935.

James Chadwick (1891-1974), an English physicist, won the Nobel Prize for Physics in 1935 for his discovery of the neutron.

to be accelerated to a high value of kinetic energy, in strong magnetic and electric fields.

The nuclei of all atoms are also positive. Thus, alpha particles and protons are repelled when they encounter a nucleus. Since the neutron is uncharged, it can approach the nucleus very closely, unaffected by its positive charge. A neutron is represented as ^1_0n.

One of the first recorded neutron transmutations was that of lithium-6 into tritium and an alpha particle.

$$^6_3Li + \,^1_0n \longrightarrow \,^3_1H + \,^4_2He$$
$$\text{(neutron)} \quad \text{(tritium)} \quad \text{(helium nucleus)}$$

Uranium is the heaviest naturally occurring element. If it is bombarded with neutrons, even heavier elements are created. These elements do not occur naturally. The first element to be identified in this way was neptunium, named after the planet Neptune. It decays quickly to form another new element called plutonium, named after the planet Pluto. The nuclear reactions are as follows:

$$^{238}_{92}U + \,^1_0n \longrightarrow \,^{239}_{92}U$$
$$^{239}_{92}U \longrightarrow \,^{239}_{93}Np + \,^0_{-1}e \quad (\beta \text{ decay})$$

Neptunium decays to form plutonium.

$$^{239}_{93}Np \longrightarrow \,^{239}_{94}Pu + \,^0_{-1}e \quad (\beta \text{ decay})$$

Other elements have been produced, all radioactive, extending the periodic table to 105. These man-made elements are referred to as the **transuranic elements** and they include neptunium, plutonium, mendelevium, curium, berkelium, californium, einsteinium, nobelium, and lawrencium. Note that most of the elements are named after the scientists and the research institutions that were involved in particle physics.

16.8 Writing Nuclear Reactions

In the equations we use to describe nuclear reactions, the sums of the mass numbers on each side are equal and so are the sums of the atomic numbers. Applying this rule to alpha decay, we note (Section 16.2) that the mass numbers of polonium and helium, 218 and 4, add up to the mass number of the radon, 222. Similarly, the atomic numbers of polonium and helium, 84 and 2, add up to that of radon, 86.

$$^{222}_{86}Rn \longrightarrow \,^{218}_{84}Po + \,^4_2He$$

When a deuterium nucleus collides with a magnesium nucleus, the two join momentarily but then quickly disintegrate into an

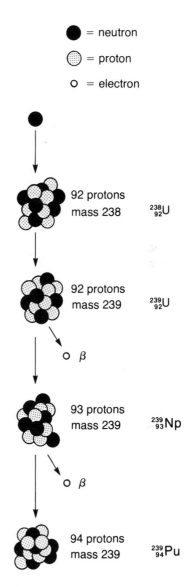

● = neutron

◉ = proton

○ = electron

92 protons
mass 238 $^{238}_{92}U$

92 protons
mass 239 $^{239}_{92}U$

○ β

93 protons
mass 239 $^{239}_{93}Np$

○ β

94 protons
mass 239 $^{239}_{94}Pu$

A neutron enters the nucleus of $^{238}_{92}U$, which then becomes $^{239}_{92}U$. This nucleus is unstable. It converts a neutron to a proton and an electron (β), ejects the electron, and becomes neptunium, $^{239}_{93}Np$. The neptunium soon emits an electron and becomes plutonium, $^{239}_{94}Pu$, with a half-life of 24 400 years.

alpha particle and a sodium nucleus. This nuclear reaction is written as:

$$^{26}_{12}\text{Mg} + \ ^{2}_{1}\text{H} \longrightarrow \ ^{4}_{2}\text{He} + \ ^{24}_{11}\text{Na}$$

Note that the sum of the mass numbers on the right (4 + 24) equals the sum of those on the left (26 + 2) and that the sum of the atomic numbers on the right (2 + 11) equals the sum of those on the left (12 + 1).

Sample problems

1. Write in the missing atomic numbers and mass numbers.
   (a) $^{27}_{13}\text{Al} + \ ^{4}_{2}\text{He} \longrightarrow \ ^{?}_{?}\text{P}$
   (b) $^{1}_{0}\text{n} + \ ^{238}_{92}\text{U} \longrightarrow \ ^{?}_{?}\text{Np} + \ ^{0}_{-1}\text{e}$

   In part (a), the mass numbers add up to 31 (27 + 4) and the atomic numbers add up to 15 (13 + 2). Thus, the isotope is $^{34}_{15}\text{P}$. In part (b), the mass numbers of the isotopes on the left side of the equation add up to 239 and the atomic numbers of the isotopes add up to 92. Thus, the isotope of neptunium has a mass number of 239 and an atomic number of 93 (the sum of 93 and −1 is 92). The answer is expressed as $^{239}_{93}\text{Np}$.

2. Identify the unknown isotope in each of these nuclear reactions.
   (a) $^{1}_{0}\text{n} + \ ^{14}_{7}\text{N} \longrightarrow \ ^{14}_{6}\text{C} + ?$
   (b) $? \longrightarrow \ ^{208}_{82}\text{Pb} + \ ^{4}_{2}\text{He}$

   In part (a), the atomic number and mass number of the unknown isotope are both 1. Therefore it is the isotope of hydrogen, $^{1}_{1}\text{H}$. In part (b), the mass number of the unknown isotope is 212 and the atomic number is 84. Referring to appendix F, we find that the element with an atomic number of 84 is polonium. Thus, the unknown isotope is $^{212}_{84}\text{Po}$.

Practice

(a) $^{239}_{93}\text{Np} \longrightarrow \ ^{?}_{?}\text{Pu} + \ ^{0}_{-1}\text{e}$ $(^{239}_{94}\text{Pu})$

(b) $^{15}_{7}\text{N} + \ ^{1}_{1}\text{H} \longrightarrow \ ^{12}_{6}\text{C} + ?$ $(^{4}_{2}\text{He})$

(c) $^{2}_{1}\text{H} + \ ^{2}_{1}\text{H} \longrightarrow \ ^{?}_{?}\text{He} + \ ^{1}_{0}\text{n}$ $(^{3}_{2}\text{He})$

(d) $^{1}_{0}\text{n} + \ ^{19}_{9}\text{F} \longrightarrow \ ^{?}_{?}\text{Ne} + \ ^{0}_{-1}\text{e}$ $(^{20}_{10}\text{Ne})$

(e) $^{9}_{4}\text{Be} + \ ^{4}_{2}\text{He} \longrightarrow \ ? + \ ^{1}_{0}\text{n}$ $(^{12}_{6}\text{C})$

(f) $^{212}_{83}\text{Bi} \longrightarrow \ ? + \ ^{0}_{-1}\text{e}$ $(^{212}_{84}\text{Po})$

(g) $^{14}_{7}\text{N} + \ ^{4}_{2}\text{He} \longrightarrow \ ? + \ ^{4}_{2}\text{He} + \ ^{1}_{1}\text{H}$ $(^{13}_{6}\text{C})$

16.9 Uses for Artificial Radioisotopes

The nuclear structure of lighter elements can be changed by neutron bombardment. This is accomplished by placing the element near a source of high-energy neutrons, usually a nuclear reactor (Section 17.3). Many of the new isotopes produced are radioactive and have a wide variety of practical applications.

The radioisotope sodium-24 has a half-life of only 15 h and is soluble in blood. Small quantities of sodium-24 are injected into the human body in blood-circulation studies. The radiation emitted by the sodium permits doctors to study its progress through the circulatory system. Other substances can be made radioactive by neutron bombardment and then used to study certain organs of the body, where they concentrate. Radioactive iodine, for example, concentrates in the thyroid gland. Small quantities of a radioactive substance can be added to machinery parts, e.g., gears, and the rate of wear then calculated by measuring the radioactivity of the lubricating oil (which contains the worn gear metal). Isotopes used in these ways are referred to as **tracers**.

Cobalt, when bombarded by neutrons in a nuclear reactor, is transmuted into a radioactive isotope of cobalt called cobalt-60, as follows:

$$^{59}_{27}\text{Co} + ^{1}_{0}\text{n} \qquad ^{60}_{27}\text{Co}$$

Cobalt-60 decays, emitting beta particles and high-energy gamma radiation. This gamma radiation is much more powerful than the highest-energy X-rays. X-rays can control cancer by killing cancerous cells. Cobalt-60 radiation serves the same purpose, and uses much simpler equipment. The Cobalt-60 apparatus, developed by Atomic Energy of Canada Limited and sold throughout the world, is commonly referred to as the "cobalt bomb".

In gamma-ray emitters, the radioactive source is usually enclosed in a lead container constructed with a lead window. When the window is opened, the gamma radiation is emitted. When it is closed, the radiation stops. Industrial uses include the detection of defects in metal castings or pipelines, and the measuring of the thickness of paper in paper mills or the thickness of hot steel in a rolling mill.

16.10 Summary

1. An alpha particle is a helium atom with its orbiting electrons missing.

Radiograph — fern

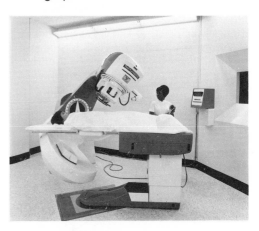

"Cobalt bomb" being used to treat cancer

See pages 268-69 for a radiograph of a jet turbine created by a gamma-ray emitter.

Sub-atomic particles: quarks
A few decades ago, the atom was thought to be merely a nucleus, composed of protons and neutrons, and orbited by varying numbers of electrons. Now, hundreds of other particles have been counted, among them "quarks". Physicists hope that the theory of quarks will help to explain the very large number of particles. Most of them now believe that the quark is the fundamental building block of the nucleus.

Quarks have a property called "colour" that enables them to bind strongly with other quarks to form new particles. "Flavour" is the sum total of the quark's other properties, which include electrical charge and, in some cases, "charm". Charm is the property that lends greater mass and a shorter life to some quarks. A quark, if found by itself instead of bound to other quarks (some scientists say this is impossible), could be a key to a better understanding of the forces that hold the universe together. Today we can list four basic forces: gravity, electromagnetism, and two nuclear forces, one strong (colour) and one weak (flavour). Could these all be expressions of the same universal force? Some scientists believe they are on the track of the ultimate truth in their pursuit of the quark.
(Adapted from *National Geographic*)

2. Transmutation is the process by which one element is changed into another. If an alpha particle or a beta particle is emitted in the transmutation, this is called a decay.
3. In alpha decay, the atomic number of the parent nucleus decreases by two and the mass number decreases by four.
4. In beta decay, the atomic number of the parent nucleus increases by one and the mass number remains the same. A beta particle is an electron.
5. Gamma radiation always accompanies alpha and beta decay. Gamma radiation by itself produces no change in the atomic number or mass number of the parent.
6. In a nuclear equation, the sums of the mass numbers on each side of the equation are equal, as are the sums of the atomic numbers.
7. A half-life is the time required for one-half of the atoms in a sample of a radioactive isotope to decay into new atoms.
8. If the half-life of a radioactive isotope and the level of radioactivity are known, the age of the material can be determined.
9. Rutherford produced the first artificial transmutation, changing nitrogen into oxygen by alpha particle bombardment.
10. Particle accelerators are used to investigate the nucleus by bombarding nuclei with high-energy positive particles and analysing the particles of the resulting collision.
11. The neutron, discovered by Chadwick, has no charge and its mass is almost the same as that of a proton.
12. The bombarding of heavy nuclei with neutrons can produce elements that do not occur naturally.
13. Radioactive isotopes produced by neutron bombardment have many practical uses in industry and medicine.

16.11 Review

1. Describe the change that occurs in the nucleus of a radioactive isotope when it undergoes transmutation by emitting (a) an alpha particle and (b) a beta particle. Write an equation, using symbols, giving an example of each type of decay.
2. In each of the following equations either alpha decay or beta decay occurs. Determine the nature of the emitted particle in each case.

(a) $^{222}_{86}Rn \longrightarrow ^{218}_{84}Po + ?$ (c) $^{35}_{17}Cl \longrightarrow ^{35}_{18}Ar + ?$

(b) $^{238}_{92}U \longrightarrow ^{234}_{90}Th + ?$ (d) $^{226}_{88}Ra \longrightarrow ^{222}_{86}Rn + ?$

(e) $^{141}_{57}La \longrightarrow {}^{141}_{58}Ce + ?$ **(g)** $^{212}_{82}Pb \longrightarrow {}^{212}_{83}Bi + ?$

(f) $^{141}_{56}Ba \longrightarrow {}^{141}_{57}La + ?$ **(h)** $^{215}_{84}Po \longrightarrow {}^{211}_{82}Pb + ?$

3. Radium-226 decays to polonium-84 as follows:

$$^{226}_{88}Ra \xrightarrow{\text{(a)}} {}^{222}_{86}Rn \xrightarrow{\text{(b)}} {}^{218}_{84}Po \xrightarrow{\text{(c)}} {}^{214}_{82}Pb \xrightarrow{\text{(d)}} {}^{214}_{83}Bi \xrightarrow{\text{(e)}} {}^{214}_{84}Po$$

What kind of particle is emitted in each of the transmutations, labelled (a) to (e)?

4. Indicate which of the following transmutations contain errors and in each case state why.

(a) $^{141}_{58}Ce \longrightarrow {}^{141}_{59}Pr + {}^{0}_{-1}e$ **(d)** $^{16}_{8}O + {}^{1}_{1}H \longrightarrow {}^{19}_{9}F$

(b) $^{27}_{13}Al + {}^{2}_{1}H \longrightarrow {}^{27}_{14}Si$ ✗ **(e)** $^{226}_{88}Ra \longrightarrow {}^{230}_{90}Th + {}^{4}_{2}He$

(c) $^{107}_{47}Ag + {}^{1}_{0}n \longrightarrow {}^{108}_{47}Ag$

5. Determine the missing atomic numbers and/or mass numbers in each of the following nuclear transmutations.

(a) $^{141}_{58}Ce \longrightarrow {}^{?}_{59}Pr + {}^{0}_{-1}e$ **(e)** $^{?}_{?}Pb \longrightarrow {}^{212}_{83}Bi + {}^{0}_{-1}e$

(b) $^{214}_{82}Pb \longrightarrow {}^{?}_{83}Bi + {}^{0}_{-1}e$ **(f)** $^{238}_{92}U \longrightarrow {}^{?}_{?}Th + {}^{4}_{2}He$

(c) $^{238}_{92}U \longrightarrow {}^{?}_{90}Th + {}^{4}_{2}He$ **(g)** $^{227}_{89}Ac \longrightarrow {}^{?}_{?}Th + {}^{0}_{-1}e$

✗**(d)** $^{203}_{84}Po \longrightarrow {}^{207}_{?}Pb + {}^{4}_{2}He$ **(h)** $^{116}_{49}In \longrightarrow {}^{?}_{?}In + {}^{0}_{0}\delta$

6. The half-life of a certain radioactive isotope is 20 h. How much of an original 320 g sample will remain the same radioactive isotope after (a) 40 h? (b) 80 h? (c) 5 d?

7. Which of these two would you expect to have the higher level of radioactivity: 10 g of a radioactive isotope with a short half-life, or 10 g of another radioactive isotope with a long half-life? Explain your reasoning.

8. Strontium-82 has a half-life of 25.0 d. If you begin with a sample having a mass of 140 g, in how many days will you have only 17.5 g of strontium-82 left?

9. The average natural radioactivity of 1 m³ of radon gas is 10 emissions per second, or 10 Bq. If the half-life of radon gas is 4 d, how long will it take for a 1 m³ sample of radon gas to reach an average radioactivity of 2.5 Bq?

10. Charcoal taken from the ruins of an early Viking settlement near St. Anthony, Newfoundland, is being used to carbon-date the settlement. A reading of 14 emissions/min·g⁻¹ is recorded. Using the graph on page 311, determine the approximate age of the settlement.

11. The accuracy of the carbon-14 method of dating has come under question in recent years. It has been found that cosmic radiation levels at the Earth's surface have not been constant but have varied because of shifts in the position of the Earth's

Photograph showing the transmutation of nitrogen

(a) $^{27}_{13}\text{Al} + ^{4}_{2}\text{He} \longrightarrow ? + ^{1}_{1}\text{H}$

(b) $^{12}_{6}\text{C} + ^{2}_{1}\text{H} \longrightarrow ^{1}_{1}\text{H} + ?$

(c) $^{9}_{4}\text{Be} + ^{1}_{1}\text{H} \longrightarrow ? + ^{2}_{1}\text{H}$

(d) $^{14}_{7}\text{N} + ^{1}_{0}\text{n} \longrightarrow ^{14}_{6}\text{C} + ?$

(e) $^{1}_{1}\text{H} + ^{1}_{0}\text{n} \longrightarrow ?$

(f) $^{23}_{11}\text{Na} + ^{2}_{1}\text{H} \longrightarrow ^{1}_{1}\text{H} + ?$

(g) $^{14}_{7}\text{N} + ^{4}_{2}\text{He} \longrightarrow ? + ^{1}_{1}\text{H}$

magnetic field. Why would these changes affect the accuracy of carbon-14 dating?

12. At the left are some equations of artificial transmutations produced by particle bombardment. The particles produced are protons, deuterium nuclei, or neutrons. Using the periodic table (Appendix F), if necessary, determine the other product in each case.

13. A radioactive source and a Geiger counter to measure the level of radioactivity are located on opposite sides of a moving sheet of hot steel. How is the level of radioactivity at the detector affected by variations in the thickness of the steel?

14. How does the gamma radiation from a "cobalt bomb" assist in the treatment of cancer? Why do some side effects, such as a temporary loss of hair, usually accompany such treatment?

16.12 Learning Objectives

1. Given the atomic number, the mass number of the nucleus, and the type of decay occurring, to write the equation describing the transmutation.

2. Given a nuclear equation, to determine the missing atomic numbers and/or mass numbers.

3. Given the period of time during which a radioactive sample has been decaying and its half-life, to determine what proportion of the original still remains in the sample.

4. Given the levels of radioactivity before and after a decay has occurred and the half-life, to determine the approximate age of the sample.

5. To describe, briefly, the principle and the use of particle accelerators in nuclear research.

6. To describe why a neutron can more easily collide with a nucleus than a proton or an alpha particle with the same energy.

7. To describe how radioactive isotopes can be used in medicine and in industry.

17 Nuclear Energy

17.1 Mass-Energy Relationships in Nuclear Reactions

When a transmutation occurs, the total atomic number and the total atomic mass number of all the particles involved in the reaction do not change. It appears that both mass and electric charge are conserved. There is another aspect of a nuclear reaction that we have not yet considered—that of the conservation of energy.

In all chemical reactions, energy is either liberated or absorbed. For example, the burning of gasoline liberates energy, and the separation of water into hydrogen and oxygen by electrolysis absorbs energy. Nuclear reactions can also liberate or absorb energy, but we are primarily interested in those that liberate energy, because when that happens the quantity liberated can be enormous. So much energy can be released, in fact, that the Law of Conservation of Energy appears to be violated. Where does all this extra energy come from?

In 1905, Albert Einstein published his **Theory of Relativity.** In this important document, he suggested that mass is another form of energy—that a decrease in mass of one object might show up as an increase in the energy of another object. His equation relating energy and mass was:

$$E = mc^2$$

where E is the energy liberated, in joules
m is the mass that disappears, in kilograms
c is the speed of light, in metres per second

Albert Einstein (1879-1955)

In 1932 Cockcroft and Walton, using their accelerator (see Section **16.5**), bombarded lithium with protons, creating two alpha particles for each proton.

$$^1_1H + ^7_3Li \longrightarrow ^4_2He + ^4_2He$$

The mass of the two alpha particles was found to be slightly less than the mass of the proton and the lithium nucleus together. It was found that the kinetic energy of the two alpha particles far exceeded the initial kinetic energy of the proton. Careful calculations showed that the extra energy possessed by the alpha particles exactly equalled the loss in mass, in accordance with Einstein's equation. The Law of Conservation of Energy, as it had been known

Law of Conservation of Energy—see Section 8.7.

Nuclear energy is actually nuclear *potential* energy, since it is energy stored up in the nucleus.

before Einstein, had been violated: energy appeared to have been created. In fact, energy had not been created, but mass had been converted into energy.

Since 1932, hundreds of similar nuclear experiments have been devised to check Einstein's mass-energy relationship, and in each case it was found to be valid. The energy, because it usually originates in the conversion of nuclear mass into energy, is called **nuclear energy**. To provide some concept of the magnitude of the energy involved, we can calculate the amount of energy liberated when 1.0 kg of mass is completely transformed into energy.

$$E = mc^2$$
$$= (1.0 \text{ kg}) (3.0 \times 10^8 \text{ m/s})^2$$
$$= 9.0 \times 10^{16} \text{ J}$$

Nuclear fission and **nuclear fusion** are two types of nuclear reactions in which the amount of energy released is very large. The nature of these reactions and how they can be utilized for the benefit of mankind are the topics of this chapter.

Sample problem

A nuclear reaction produces 9.0×10^{11} J of heat energy because of the conversion of mass into energy. What mass was converted?

$$E = mc^2$$
$$m = \frac{E}{c^2}$$
$$= \frac{9.0 \times 10^{11} \text{ J}}{(3.0 \times 10^8 \text{ m/s})^2}$$
$$= 1.0 \times 10^{-5} \text{ kg, or } 10 \text{ mg}$$

Practice
1. The loss in mass in a fission reaction is 0.010 g. How much energy will have been produced?   (9.0×10^{11} J)
2. Two hundred atoms of uranium-235 split. If each atom releases 3.2×10^{-8} J when fission occurs, what nuclear mass was converted into energy?   (7.1×10^{-23} kg)

17.2 Nuclear Fission

Otto Hahn (1879-1968), a German physical chemist, received the Nobel Prize for Chemistry in 1944 for the discovery of fission. In his later years he actively opposed the use of nuclear weapons.

With the help of the mass-energy relationship and the earlier measurements of atomic mass, it was determined that, if heavier atoms such as those of uranium were split into lighter atoms, nuclear energy would be released. This splitting or **fission** of the heavy nucleus cannot be done with a charged particle such as an alpha particle, which would be repelled by the high positive charge on the nucleus of the heavier atom. It was Chadwick's discovery of the neutron that made fission possible, since a neutron, with no electric charge, can approach a positive nucleus more closely, in a collision, than a positive proton or alpha particle can.

In 1934, Enrico Fermi, an Italian doing research in Germany, was attempting to produce transuranic elements, using neutron bombardment. It is probable that he achieved the first fission reaction but was not aware of having done so because he could not separate, and thus identify, the fission products. By 1939, two German chemists, Otto Hahn and Fritz Strassmann, managed to separate the products of fission chemically, and they discovered that a uranium nucleus had been split into two pieces—a barium nucleus and a krypton nucleus.

$$^{235}_{92}U + ^{1}_{0}n \longrightarrow ^{144}_{56}Ba + ^{90}_{36}Kr + 2\,^{1}_{0}n + energy$$

A week later, two Austrian physicists working in Denmark, Lise Meitner and Otto Frisch, obtained a similar result. Frisch coined the expression "nuclear fission", having noted that the process is similar to what occurs when a living cell divides into two equal parts, in the biological process called fission. The importance of fission is that it is accompanied by the release of approximately 10 times as much energy as occurs in a normal nuclear disintegration and more than a million times as much as occurs in any chemical reaction.

Subsequent research showed not only that a large amount of energy was released but also that two or three neutrons were emitted. These neutrons can cause fission in another uranium nucleus they might happen to collide with. When fission occurs in a second uranium nucleus, it too will emit two or three neutrons and release energy. As this process continues, more and more uranium nuclei undergo fission, releasing larger and larger numbers of neutrons as well as large amounts of energy. This is called a neutron **chain reaction.**

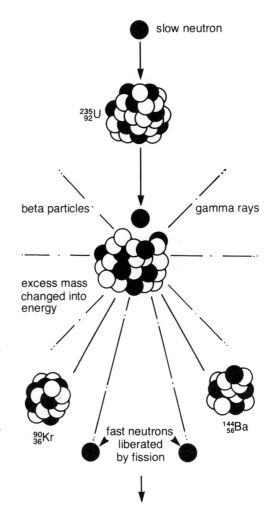

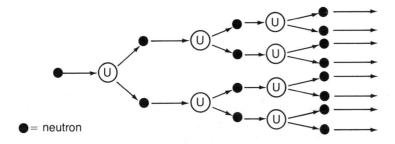

● = neutron

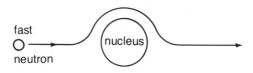

The neutrons are slowed down from approximately 4×10^6 m/s to 2×10^3 m/s.

The first nuclear reactors were called "piles" because they consisted of piles of graphite blocks. The use of this term helped to disguise the reactors' true nature during the Second World War.

Natural uranium is composed of 99.3% uranium-238, 0.7% uranium-235, and traces of uranium-234. Uranium-235 is the only fissionable isotope of uranium. Since the nucleus is very small in comparison with the atom, the chance of a neutron colliding with a uranium-235 nucleus is very small. To increase the likelihood of this happening, the number of uranium-235 atoms must be increased. The process of increasing the proportion of uranium-235 isotopes in natural uranium is called **enrichment**.

If too few of the uranium-235 isotopes are present, neutrons will escape from the surface of the mass and hence will not collide with other nuclei. Also, some of the neutrons will be absorbed by impurities. To sustain a chain reaction, the amount of uranium-235 must be increased until the number of neutrons produced exceeds the number lost from the surface and to impurities. This amount of uranium-235 is called the **critical mass**. When a critical mass is present, the chain reaction proceeds without any outside assistance, and we say that the fissionable material has "gone critical".

The probability of a collision between a neutron and a uranium-235 nucleus is also increased if the ejected neutrons are slowed down. Fast-moving neutrons tend to be deflected around nuclei, in much the same way that waves are diffracted around a small obstacle. The substances used to slow down the neutrons are called **moderators**. Atoms with low atomic mass such as graphite, ordinary water, heavy water, and beryllium are excellent moderators since they slow neutrons down without absorbing them.

The rate of a chain reaction is controlled by inserting substances that absorb neutrons, such as boron or cadmium, into the enriched uranium. These substances are made into **control rods**. The chain reaction is controlled by varying the amount of control substance present (by moving the rods in and out). If enough neutrons are absorbed by the rods, the reaction will stop altogether.

In a **nuclear bomb**, there are no control rods and the chain reaction continues unchecked. In a fraction of a second, enormous amounts of energy, fast-moving neutrons, and gamma radiation are released. The same energy that is wasted in the exploding of a nuclear bomb can be controlled and transformed into useful heat energy. This is accomplished by means of a device known as a **nuclear reactor**.

17.3 The First Reactor and the First Atomic Bombs

The concept of a controlled nuclear reaction was known both in Germany and in the United States by 1939, but the first nuclear reactor was not built until 1942. Albert Einstein, Enrico Fermi, Leo Szilard, and many other prominent European physicists moved to the United States because of the political climate in Europe in the 1930s and the disruptions of World War II. Through the influence of Einstein and others on President Roosevelt, financial assistance was given to nuclear research programs. The vast financial and physical resources of North America and the talent of European, American, British, and Canadian scientists was harnessed under a very secret program, code-named the Manhattan Project.

Fermi was one of the leaders in this project. He and his team constructed the first reactor in a squash court at the University of Chicago, in December 1942. It had taken three years of concentrated effort to obtain the necessary quantity of uranium-235. The reactor consisted of a pile of graphite blocks which acted as a moderator. Lumps of uranium were inserted into holes in the graphite. To control the reaction, neutron-absorbing cadmium strips were inserted into the pile.

The neutron and radiation levels were monitored as the reactor was constructed of layer upon layer of graphite. When the 57th layer was added, the neutron intensity level increased dramatically. The first chain reaction was occurring. Quickly, cadmium strips were inserted into the pile, to shut down the reaction before heat and radiation could reach dangerous levels. The theory originating with the work of Einstein in 1905 had been verified, experimently, on a large scale!

The Manhattan Project continued. The chain reaction had been achieved, and its destructive use to help defeat Germany and Japan was of immediate importance. In a large plant at Oak Ridge, Tennessee, sufficient quantities of uranium were enriched for two nuclear bombs (commonly called atomic bombs); and enough fissionable plutonium-239 for a third bomb was extracted from nuclear reactors similar to the one designed by Fermi. One of the uranium-235 bombs was tested successfully in the desert in New Mexico on July 16, 1945. The other uranium bomb and the plutonium bomb were dropped on Hiroshima on August 6, and on Nagasaki on August 8, respectively. Thousands of people were killed and the two cities were levelled by the combination of heat, shock waves, gamma radiation, and high-energy neutrons. Many

The first graphite reactor

Enrico Fermi (1901-54) — second from the right

The ruins of Hiroshima — 1946

The chain reaction was first conceived in 1934 by Leo Szilard (1898-1964), a Hungarian-American physicist. Szilard, when he realized that the atomic bomb was to be used on the Japanese, proposed that it should be tested before an international audience so that the Japanese would recognize its power and (he predicted) surrender.

who survived were to die later of cancer caused by exposure to gamma radiation. The nuclear explosions in the summer of 1945 inaugurated a new era in the story of mankind.

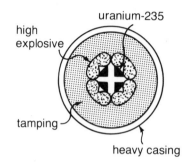

A cross section of a nuclear fission bomb. When the pieces of $^{235}_{92}U$ are forced together by the explosive charges, they have a mass exceeding the critical mass and are said to be "supercritical". Failure of one explosive charge will disable the bomb, since it can no longer sustain a chain reaction.

17.4 Using the Energy from Nuclear Fission

Several designs for nuclear power reactors have been successfully developed. All have three basic components: uranium as fuel, a moderator to slow down the neutrons, and neutron-absorbing control rods.

The variations in design are associated with the different types of moderators and fuels used. Most United States reactors use ordinary water as the moderator; British reactors use graphite, and Canadian reactors use heavy water. Canadian reactors are fuelled with natural uranium oxide, which is relatively inexpensive, whereas most other reactors use expensive enriched uranium. The Canadian reactor, using heavy water (D_2O) as the moderator and natural uranium as the fuel is known as the CANDU (Canadian Deuterium Uranium) reactor.

Research reactors are similar in structure to power reactors, except that they do not generate large quantities of heat. They are used as sources of neutrons for bombardment experiments and for making artificial radioactive isotopes.

CANDU Nuclear Power Reactor

In the Canadian reactor, neutrons emitted in the fission reaction are slowed down by heavy water, which also acts as a coolant, carrying the heat energy produced in the nuclear reaction from the uranium rods to the turbines, to produce electric power (see illustration). The heat is produced by the fast-moving fission products, which agitate the atoms, heating them up. The heavy water is kept under high pressure to prevent it from boiling.

The use of heavy water as the moderator makes the CANDU

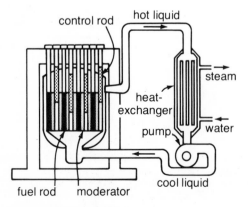

The basic parts of a fission nuclear reactor

reactor one of the safest. If excessive heat builds up in the reactor, the heavy water can be drained out. Then, deprived of a moderator, the nuclear reaction stops. The CANDU reactor can be constructed on a much larger scale than most reactors of United States or British design. Another important advantage of the CANDU reactor is that it can be refuelled without being shut down, which contributes to the efficient use of the fuel.

The nuclear power station at Pickering, Ontario.

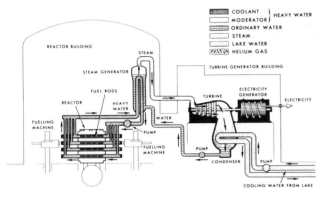

Heavy water passing over hot fuel bundles transfers heat to a steam generator, which turns ordinary water into steam. The steam is fed to a turbine which drives an electricity generator.

Pressured Water Reactor

The United States has developed a reactor that uses ordinary water as a combined moderator and coolant. Because ordinary water absorbs many more neutrons than heavy water, this type of reactor must be fuelled with enriched uranium, which costs more than natural uranium. The hot moderator-coolant is pumped to a boiler where the heat is used to convert ordinary water into steam, which in turn drives a turbine. Another version, the boiling water reactor, permits the water to boil inside the reactor to produce steam, which is fed directly to the turbine.

The Gas-cooled Reactor

Britain has developed a reactor that uses graphite as a moderator and carbon dioxide or helium gas, under pressure, as a coolant. The hot gas is passed to a boiler, where steam is created to drive a turbine.

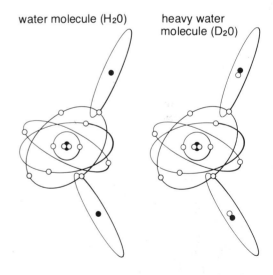

Ordinary, or "light", water molecules consist of an oxygen atom and two hydrogen atoms. In heavy water molecules, the central oxygen atom is linked to two deuterium atoms. The proportion of heavy water found in ordinary water is one part in 7000. It is very expensive to separate the two.

$^{239}_{94}$Pu is produced by neutron bombardment. See Section 16.7.

The Fast Breeder Reactor

"Fast" refers to the speed of the neutrons in the reactor. Each time a neutron causes an atom to split, two or three neutrons are ejected. Only one is required to continue the chain reaction. In this type of reactor, the surplus neutrons are absorbed by fertile atoms, such as uranium-238, which are held in a blanket surrounding the core of uranium-235. The atoms in the blanket are changed into fissionable atoms such as plutonium-239 and uranium-233.

The reactor is designed in such a way that the quantity of fissionable by-products "manufactured" exceeds the quantity of uranium-235 used as fuel. The fissionable by-products can themselves be used as fuel in the same reactor. So the fast breeder reactor "breeds" more fuel than it uses, and could therefore be used to extend the usefulness of nuclear fuel. "Conventional" reactors use only about 1% of the uranium mined to produce power. With fast breeder reactors, about 50% of the uranium could be used. Unfortunately fast breeder reactors are technically complex and elaborate measures are required to separate the fissionable products from the other atoms. Their most serious disadvantage is that they produce quantities of fissionable products such as plutonium—substances that are deadly radioactive poisons and can be used to make atomic bombs. For these reasons funds for the research and development of breeder reactors have been restricted.

17.5 By-products of Nuclear Power

The by-products of nuclear reactions may be categorized as: **low-level radioactive wastes**, **high-level radioactive wastes**, and **thermal discharges**.

Low-level Radioactive Wastes

A small amount of low-level radioactive material may be released in the form of fission products and activation products. **Fission products** are the lighter atoms, such as krypton-85, that are produced in the fission process. These substances are formed inside the fuel bundles, but they could escape from the reactor through small defects in the fuel coverings. **Activation products** result from neutrons in the reactor bombarding materials such as air, coolant metal in the plumbing system, and suspended particles in the coolant. An example is tritium, which is produced in all reactors containing water. In CANDU reactors, tritium is produced in large quantities through neutrons captured by the deuterium in the heavy-water moderator (see illustration).

Elaborate precautions are necessary for detecting and containing any radiation leak in a nuclear power plant. The whole plant is wired with detectors, and workers are checked daily for excessive levels of radiation. Despite all precautions, there is a slight increase in the annual radiation count in the area of a nuclear power station.

Most solid and liquid low-level wastes are disposed of by being buried in soil beds that are able to trap radioactive components and prevent them from being carried into nearby rivers and streams. These disposal sites must be carefully monitored and perpetually reserved for the burial of low-level radioactive wastes.

Low-level wastes can become concentrated in the food chain, as illustrated on page 330. They must be respected and controlled because they are potentially harmful to all living things.

High-level Radioactive Wastes

Most of these wastes come from the fission process. When the uranium-235 is fissioned, producing radioactive barium and krypton, the neutrons that are emitted transform the uranium-238, which is also present in the fuel rod, into radioactive plutonium, americium, and other products. Most of these products have long half-lives. They are known as high-level wastes because, gram for gram, they emit radiations with an intensity many billion times greater than the radiation of natural uranium oxide. The "spent" fuel rods are stored temporarily (that is for a few years) under 4.0 m of water in tanks, usually inside the plants where they were used.

A large nuclear power station, such as the one at Pickering, near Toronto, produces about 40 bundles of "spent" fuel a day, each weighing 20 kg. By the year 2000, it is estimated, Canada will have 130 000 t of spent fuel rods.

High-level wastes contain components that have a wide range of decay periods. Some will decay to 0.1% of their initial level within 300 years. Plutonium, which takes approximately 250 000 years, is lethally radioactive. Even a very small amount, taken into the lungs by a human being, can result in death. So it is imperative that high-level wastes such as plutonium be safely and securely stored.

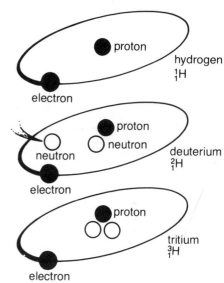

Deuterium nucleus absorbs neutron and becomes tritium.

Transporting spent fuel rods

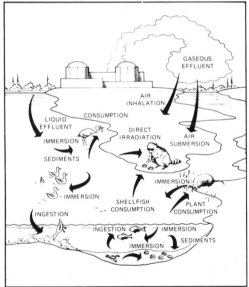

Generalized exposure pathways for organisms other than man

Two methods for the **intermediate storage** (approximately 25 years) of high-level wastes have been proposed in Canada. In one, concrete silos 2.2 m in diameter and 4.2 m high would be constructed above the ground. Each silo would hold 216 bundles, or about 4000 kg, of spent fuel rods. In the other arrangement, "farms" of water-filled pools similar to those at reactor sites would be used. Intermediate storage is required to allow time for the concentration of radioactivity to decrease to levels low enough that **permanent storage** can be effected.

The problem of long-term storage of high-level wastes has yet to be resolved. The fact that the wastes must be stored safely for a period of over 100 000 years makes the solution difficult, to say the least. Suggestions have included: burying the wastes deep in salt mines and burying them in the hard rock of the Canadian Shield.

Canadian reserves of natural uranium will last only 50 to 60 years, but the era of nuclear power would be greatly extended if it were decided to reprocess the spent fuel into even more potent plutonium fuel. Such large-scale reprocessing would entail considerable risks. There would be the possibility of radioactive contamination of the environment, the problem of disposing of the dangerous wastes of reprocessing, and the possibility of theft by terrorists or criminals who could use the plutonium to make bombs.

The extensive use of nuclear fission as a source of electric power may be limited by the hazards this would present, unless management and control procedures are developed that are acceptable to all concerned.

Thermal Discharges

Both fossil fuel (coal, gas, oil) generating plants and nuclear plants require large quantities of cooling water to condense the steam back into water after it has done its job in the turbines. A nuclear plant requires approximately 50% more cooling water than a fossil-fuel plant of similar capacity. Usually, the cooling water is drawn from a river, lake, or ocean. The used warmer water is then discharged back into the same body of water. If the capacity of the available body of water is inadequate, the water must be cooled in a specially built tower or pond and used over and over again.

In large bodies of cold water such as Lake Huron and Lake Ontario, the effects of discharging hot water are minimal, though it does cause some changes in the distribution of species and populations of fish, algae, and bottom-living organisms. In smaller bodies of water such as rivers, drastic biological changes can occur, including the excessive formation of algae and the depletion of oxygen in the water.

In an energy-short world, new ways are being investigated for using the waste hot water. It could provide heating for industries and homes near nuclear power plants, it could be distributed through pipes in the soil to increase crop yields, or it could be used to heat greenhouses.

17.6 Nuclear Fusion

Fusion is the process by which light elements combine to produce heavier ones. Nuclei must be joined together, but all nuclei have positive charges and thus repel each other. For nuclei to fuse, they must be brought so close together that the stronger nuclear forces of attraction can overcome the electric repulsion. This can only occur when the two nuclei are no more than approximately 10^{-15} m apart.

Atoms move faster when heated. If light atoms, such as deuterium and hydrogen atoms, are heated enough, their speeds will be great enough that fusion can occur when they collide. This reaction is the primary source of the world's energy. It has been taking place on the sun for at least 5.0×10^9 years. At 1 000 000°C, 1 g of deuterium can undergo fusion and release enough energy to supply the electrical needs of an average North American home for nearly 40 years.

A typical fusion reaction is:
$$^2_1H + {}^2_1H \longrightarrow {}^3_2He + {}^1_0n + energy$$
This and three other possible fusion reactions are illustrated.

Accurate calculations of atomic mass have shown that the mass of the products is less than the mass of the reactants. Just as in the fission reaction, it is the amount of the loss in mass that is converted into energy.

The advantages of fusion power are that the fuel is cheap and easy to obtain (probably deuterium from water), and the by-products are harmless (primarily helium and a few neutrons). With these advantages, fusion power would seem to be the answer to the world's energy needs. However, man-made fusion has so far been accomplished only in the hydrogen bomb. In this application, a fission bomb provides the temperatures that it takes to accomplish fusion. Various methods have been used in the attempt to create the necessary high temperatures and to use the energy constructively. In one such method, hydrogen atoms are first

The first hydrogen bomb was exploded in 1952. It was devised by Edward Teller (born 1908), an American physicist. Many famous scientists refused to participate in the project because of the destructive power of nuclear weapons.

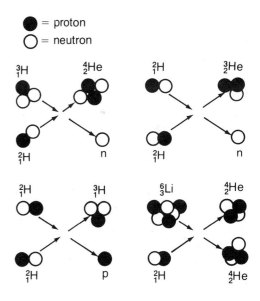

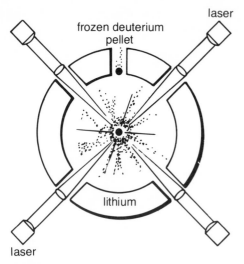

A proposed method of achieving fusion, by firing a frozen deuterium pellet into an evacuated reaction chamber. At the centre of the chamber, the pellet undergoes violent compression from lasers, causing the production of heat and neutrons. A blanket of lithium surrounds the chamber, recovers the heat, and breeds tritium.

ionized, to rid them of their electrons, and then compressed by strong electrical and magnetic fields to raise their temperature to the point at which fusion can occur. Several such methods have produced fusion reactions, but only for a fraction of a second.

Another technique involves the use of high-temperature lasers focused on tiny pellets of frozen deuterium. To be useful as a source of energy, the fusion process must liberate more energy than it consumes. The break-even point has not yet been achieved, and past experience with fission reactors suggests that fusion power will not be commercially viable before the end of the century.

17.7 Nuclear Energy – an Answer or a Challenge?

Our principal sources of electrical energy in Canada, now and in the immediate future, are hydro-electric stations and thermal stations using fossil fuels or uranium. Conservation measures and supplementary sources of energy, such as solar energy, will probably affect the demand for electric power, but we will continue to rely heavily on the sources we are using now.

In the next decades the percentage of energy supplied by water power will decline and the percentage contributed by nuclear reactors will increase. In the more distant future, a new generation of nuclear reactors may be developed that will exploit the plutonium in the "waste" products of today's reactors. The exploitation of the fusion reaction is almost as elusive as it was 10 years ago, and most knowledgeable scientists and engineers say that it could be another 20 years before a commercially viable system is developed. So it appears that we must tolerate the presence of nuclear power stations in our society, at least for the next few decades.

When the word "nuclear" is used many people think of bombs, usually because they do not understand the difference between a controlled and an uncontrolled neutron chain reaction. Ignorance has bred fear. Knowledge should breed respect and concern. The background knowledge you now have should enable you to contribute, as a responsible citizen, to the resolution of some of the issues society must face in the next decades.

Among the issues that affect the future of nuclear power are the disposal of radioactive wastes, the siting of nuclear power plants, the sale of nuclear power plants to other countries, and the processing of high-level wastes. These issues are the concern of all citizens, and should not be left to business and government experts. Whenever the products of science and technology affect the well-being of future generations and the quality of life on this planet, it is time for citizens to get involved.

17.8 Summary

1. In some nuclear reactions, large quantities of energy are liberated since a small part of the nuclear mass of the reactants has been converted into energy according to the equation $E = mc^2$.
2. In nuclear fission, a heavier element splits into lighter elements, accompanied by a release of energy.
3. Transuranic elements are elements that do not occur naturally but are produced by the nuclear bombardment of heavy elements.
4. In a chain reaction, each fission is responsible for producing, on the average, one other fission, and the reaction can only continue as long as a sufficient quantity of fissionable material, called the critical mass, is present.
5. The chain reaction of uranium-235 in a reactor can only continue as long as the speed of the neutrons is slowed down by a moderator.
6. A chain reaction is controlled by the insertion among the fissionable materials of substances that absorb neutrons.
7. Fission bombs utilize enriched uranium or plutonium for the chain reaction.
8. The three primary components of every nuclear reactor are a fissionable fuel, a moderator, and control rods.
9. The heat produced by the fission reaction in a nuclear power reactor is converted into electric power by means of steam turbines.
10. The CANDU nuclear power reactor uses natural uranium as a fuel and heavy water as a moderator. Other nuclear reactors use enriched uranium as a fuel and graphite as a moderator.
11. The heat energy from the core of a nuclear reactor is usually transmitted by heavy water, ordinary water, or a gas.
12. Breeder reactors are constructed so that they produce more fissionable material than they use as fuel.
13. The by-products of nuclear power reactors include low-level and high-level radioactive wastes and heat.
14. Radioactive wastes tend to concentrate in the food chain and thus can be dangerous to all living things.

A Forecast of the Distribution of Ontario Hydro's Annual Energy Production (percentages)

	Coal	Oil	Gas	Nuclear	Water	Purchases	Total
1975	24	1	6	13	39	17	100
1980	34	6	3	28	26	3	100
1985	27	5	2	47	19	0	100
1990	24	3	2	58	13	0	100
1995	21	2	1	66	10	0	100

15. Nuclear fusion is the process by which light elements combine to produce heavier ones as the nuclei join together, at high temperatures.

17.9 Review

1. Each of the following represents the loss in mass produced by a fission reaction. In each case, calculate the energy released by the conversion of mass into energy.
   (a) 2.0 kg (b) 40 g (c) 0.1 mg
2. Predict the loss in mass that will occur in each case, when the following quantities of energy are given off because of the conversion of mass into energy in nuclear reactions.
   (a) 9.0×10^{16} J (b) 4.5×10^{14} J (c) 1.8×10^{11} J
3. The energy output of the sun is approximately 4.0×10^{26} J/s. If all this energy results from mass-energy conversion in the fusion process, calculate the rate at which the sun is losing mass.
4. The energy released by the fission of one atom of uranium-235 is 3.2×10^{-8} J. The energy released by the atomic bomb dropped at Hiroshima was estimated to be the equivalent of 18 140 t of dynamite or 8.0×10^{13} J.
   (a) How many atoms of uranium-235 underwent fission?
   (b) What mass of uranium-235 was converted into energy?
5. (a) What are two important isotopes of uranium?
   (b) One is fissionable and the other produces a transuranic element. Explain.
6. Nuclear bombs are defused by making it impossible for the pieces of fissionable material to come together to form a critical mass. Why does this make the chain reaction impossible?
7. What factors must be considered when siting a nuclear power reactor?
8. Why is the CANDU reactor considered to be
   (a) safer than other types of nuclear power reactors?
   (b) cheaper to operate than other types?
9. Why does the burying of radioactive wastes deep in the ground protect this generation of human beings? Discuss why this may or may not be a satisfactory long-term solution.
10. Until recently, radioactive wastes were encased in concrete and dumped in the ocean. Explain why this method of disposal was discontinued.

11. In the late 1950s two United States bombers collided over southern Spain and the material from their nuclear devices was distributed in the ocean and on the nearby beaches. Why were large quantities of the sand and earth trucked away before the area was considered safe?

12. Explain why the "wastes" of nuclear power reactors can be used for non-peaceful purposes.

13. Why does fusion require such a high temperature before it can begin?

14. When a fission bomb explodes, radioactive isotopes are produced on the Earth and in the atmosphere. A fusion reaction in a hydrogen bomb produces no radioactive isotopes. Why is there still radioactive "fall-out"?

15. Astro-physicists speculate that stars are created when vast clouds of hydrogen come together because of mutual gravitational attraction, collapsing into denser and denser mass. Eventually fusion begins. Why?

Numerical Answers to Review Questions
1. (a) 1.8×10^{17} J (b) 3.6×10^{15} J (c) 9.0×10^{9} J
2. (a) 1.0 kg (b) 5.0×10^{-3} kg (c) 2.0×10^{-6} kg
3. 4.4×10^{9} kg/s
4. (a) 2.5×10^{21} (b) 8.9×10^{-4} kg

17.10 Learning Objectives

1. To describe, briefly, why large quantities of energy are released in some nuclear reactions.

2. Given either the apparent loss of mass or the energy released in a nuclear reaction, to calculate the other.

3. To distinguish between fission and fusion, and to give an example of each.

4. To describe, using a diagram, what is meant by a chain reaction.

5. To describe why a critical mass must be present if a chain reaction is to occur.

6. To describe why the products of a nuclear explosion have both short-term and long-term effects.

7. To state the function and operation of the fuel rods, moderator, and control rods in a nuclear reactor.

8. To describe, briefly, how low-level radioactive wastes become concentrated in the food chain.

9. To state why high-level wastes such as plutonium are of serious concern.

10. To describe why nuclear fusion is considered by some to be an answer to the world's energy problems, and to state why its development will probably be slow.

4

Waves: The
Energy of Sound
and Light

18 The Properties and Behaviour of Waves

18.1 What Are Waves

Energy can be transmitted from one place to another by a moving object, such as a baseball when thrown by a pitcher to a catcher. The kinetic energy given to the ball by the pitcher is transferred to the catcher. But this is not the only way to effect a transfer of energy. It can be brought about without any movement of matter from source to receiver—by means of a wave.

Imagine a cold winter morning. A car slides into the back of a line of cars that are stopped at an intersection. In the collisions that result, energy is passed down the line, from one car to the next. Such a travelling disturbance is called a wave.

When you push, pull, or shake a rope, you send waves down its length. When you shake a spiral "slinky" spring, your energy is transferred from coil to coil down the spring.

A water wave can travel hundreds of kilometres over the ocean, but the water just moves up and down as the wave passes. Energy is transferred from one water molecule to the next by the forces that hold the molecules together.

A **wave**, then, is a transfer of energy, in the form of a disturbance, usually through a material substance, or medium.

We live surrounded by waves. Some are visible, others are not. Water waves and the waves in a rope or spring we can see. Sound waves and radio waves we cannot. By observing the visible waves in ropes, springs, and water you can discover some characteristics that all waves, including invisible ones, have in common.

18.2 Vibrations

All waves are caused by a vibrating object, and to understand them we must understand the properties of vibrating objects. Most waves come from objects that are vibrating so rapidly that they are difficult to observe. For the purpose of observing the properties of vibrating objects, a slowly moving device such as a swinging pendulum is ideal.

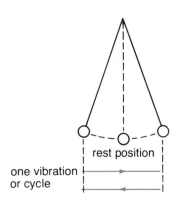

one vibration
or cycle

rest position

$$\frac{1}{s} = s^{-1} = 1 \text{ Hz}$$

Some of the terms and concepts that were discussed in Section 1.2 are needed again here:

When an object has a repeating pattern of motions—as a pendulum does—we use the term **cycle** to describe one complete pattern.

The time required for one cycle is called the **period** (T).

The number of cycles (c) per second is called the **frequency** (f), which is measured in **hertz** (Hz).

$$1 \text{ Hz} = 1 \text{ c/s}$$

Frequency and period are reciprocals.

$$T = \frac{1}{f} \qquad\qquad f = \frac{1}{T}$$

Sample problems

1. A pendulum on a clock makes 240 complete cycles in 60 s. What are its period and its frequency?

$$\text{period} = \frac{\text{time required}}{\text{number of cycles}}$$
$$T = \frac{60 \text{ s}}{240}$$
$$= 0.25 \text{ s}$$
$$\text{frequency} = \frac{\text{number of cycles}}{\text{time required}}$$
$$f = \frac{240}{60 \text{ s}}$$
$$= 4.0 \text{ Hz}$$

The unit for frequency is named after the German scientist Heinrich Rudolph Hertz (1857-94). See Section 26.11.

2. What is the period of a pendulum that has a frequency of 10 Hz?

$$T = \frac{1}{f}$$
$$= \frac{1}{10 \text{ Hz}}$$
$$= 0.10 \text{ s}$$

Practice
1. A child on a swing completes 20 cycles in 25 s. Calculate the frequency and the period of the swing.   (0.80 Hz, 1.3 s)
2. A metronome clicks 80 times in 20 s. What are its frequency and its period?   (4.0 Hz, 0.25 s)
3. A stroboscope is flashing so that the time interval between flashes is 1/80 s. Calculate the frequency of the strobe light's flashes.   (80 Hz)
4. Calculate the frequency and the period of a tuning fork that vibrates 24 000 times in 1.00 min.   (400 Hz, 2.50×10^{-3} s)

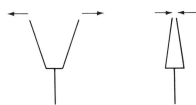

rest position

A = amplitude

Displacement is used here because it is a distance with a direction relative to the rest position, that is, a vector quantity. See Section 3.1.

As a pendulum swings, it repeats the same motion in the same time intervals. We say that it makes a **periodic motion**. Observing successive swings, we find that the distances reached by the pendulum on either side of the rest position are almost equal. The distance from rest to maximum displacement is called the **amplitude**.

Two identical pendulums are said to be vibrating **in phase** if, at any given moment, they have the same displacement from the rest position and are moving in the same direction.

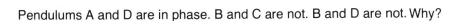

Pendulums A and D are in phase. B and C are not. B and D are not. Why?

The tines of a tuning fork do not vibrate in phase. When one tine moves to the right, the other moves to the left. The tines are said to be **out of phase**.

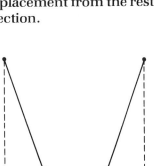

18.3 Transverse Pulses and Waves

If you hold a piece of rope with your hand, and move your hand up and down, a wave will travel along the rope, away from you. Your hand, then, is the vibrating source of energy, and the rope is the material medium through which the energy is transferred. By moving your hand through one-half of a cycle, as illustrated, you can create what is called a **pulse**.

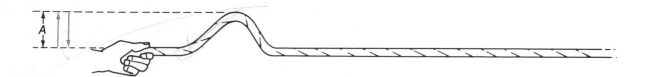

Pulses in a rope usually move too quickly to be properly observed, so we use a device in which the speed of the pulse is relatively low, such as a spiral spring.

Investigation: Pulses in a Spiral Spring

Problem:
How do pulses travel in a spiral spring?

Materials:
spiral spring

Procedure
1. With the help of your partner, stretch the spring to a length of approximately 5 m on a smooth, clean floor. Your partner should hold one end of the spring rigid throughout this investigation.
2. Create a pulse at your end of the spring by moving your hand quickly from the rest position to one side and back to the rest position, at right angles to the length of the spring.
3. Describe the motion you observe of a point in the middle of the spring as the pulse passes.
4. Move your hand in such a way as to generate a pulse with a large

amplitude. What do you observe concerning the amplitude and the speed of the pulse this time, as it moves along the spring?

5. Generate two pulses, one right after the other. Does the distance between them change as they move along the spring? What does this tell you about the speed of the pulses? Generate two more pulses, close together and one distinctly larger than the other. Does the size of the pulse affect its speed?

6. Stretch the spring further. What effect does the resulting increase in the tension of the spring have on the speed of the pulse?

7. During the investigation, the pulses you generated at the free end of the spring were "reflected" from the fixed end. Compare the reflected pulses with the original pulses.

Questions

1. Describe what happens at a given point on the spring as the pulse passes.
2. Does the amplitude of the pulse change as the pulse moves from one end of the spring to the other?
3. Does the speed of the pulse vary as the pulse moves along the spring?
4. Is the speed of the pulse affected by changes in the amplitude?
5. Is the speed of the pulse affected by changes in the tension of the spring?
6. What change occurred in a pulse as it was reflected from the fixed end of the spring?

In this investigation, each coil of the spring moved at right angles to the direction in which the pulse was moving. This kind of motion is called a **transverse pulse**. We call the pulse in one direction, relative to the rest position, a **crest**, and the pulse in the other direction, a **trough**. A crest is sometimes referred to as a **positive pulse** and a trough as a **negative pulse**.

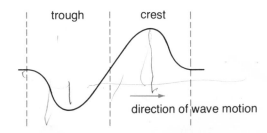

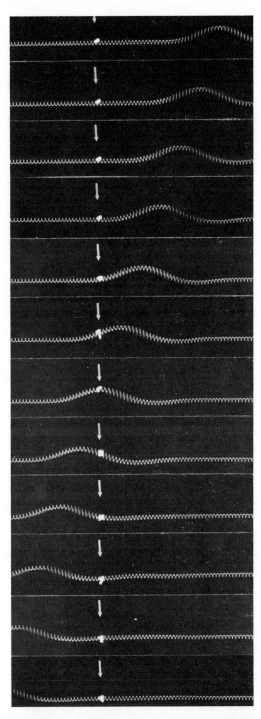

A crest moves through a spring from right to left.

A series of crests and troughs at right angles to the direction of motion is called a **transverse wave**.

As the investigation showed, the speed of the transverse wave in a spring is constant. It changes only when the tension in the spring is changed. This is a characteristic of all waves—their speed remains constant, as long as the material medium through which they are travelling remains unchanged.

In transverse waves, the lengths of the successive crests and troughs are equal. The distance from the mid point of one crest to the mid point of the next, or from the mid point of one trough to the mid point of the next, is called the **wavelength**, which is represented by the Greek letter λ (lambda).

Note, in the illustration below, that some of the pairs of particles on the wave are in phase, that is, they are moving in the same direction and are the same distance from the rest position. As can be seen, the distance between successive particles in phase is also one wavelength (λ).

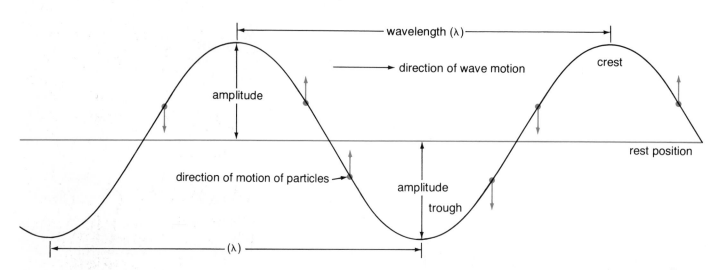

Each particle in the wave illustrated moves up and down with a frequency and a period that are exactly the same as those of the source of the wave.

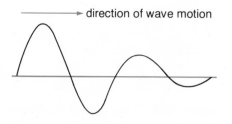

Most waves lose energy in the medium, resulting in a decrease in amplitude.

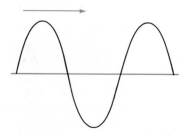

Ideal wave – no decrease in amplitude

As a wave travels along a spring, its amplitude usually decreases, some of its energy being lost to friction. If there was a complete transfer of energy, there would be no decrease in amplitude, and, hence, the wave would be what is called an **ideal wave**. To make analysis easier, we will as a rule be assuming that the waves we are examining are ideal waves.

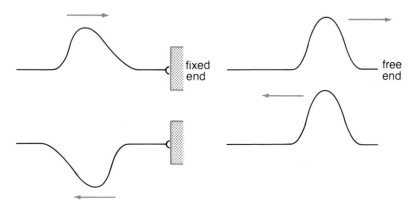

Pulses reflected from the fixed end of the spring in the investigation were inverted. A crest was reflected as a trough and a trough was reflected as a crest. Pulses may also be reflected from the end of a spring that is free to move. There is no inversion in the case of reflection from a free end. Crests are reflected as crests and troughs as troughs.

18.4 Waves in Two Dimensions

Waves in a stretched spring or in a rope illustrate some of the basic concepts of wave motion in one dimension. The behaviour of waves in two dimensions may be studied by observing water waves in a ripple tank.

The ripple tank is a shallow, glass-bottomed tank on legs. Water is put in the tank to a depth of 2-3 cm. Light from a source above the tank passes through the water and illuminates a screen on the table below. The light is converged by wave crests and diverged by wave troughs, as illustrated, creating bright and dark areas on the screen. The distance between successive bright areas caused by crests will be one wavelength (λ). Circular waves may be generated on the surface of the water by a point source, such as a finger or a drop of water from an eye-dropper. Straight waves may be produced by moving a dowel in the water.

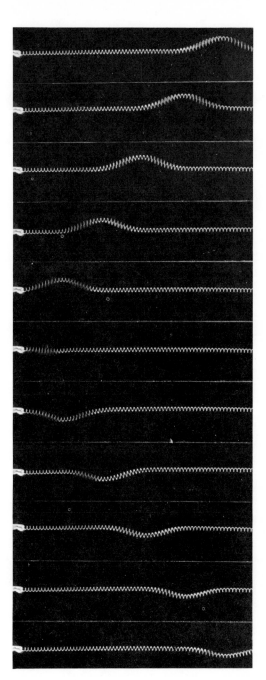

A crest is reflected as a trough.

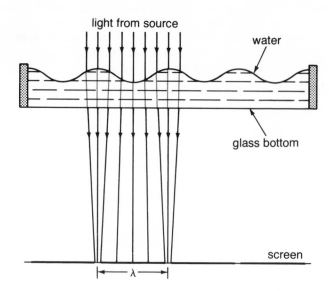

Bright lines occur on the screen where light rays converge.

Investigation: Water Waves—Transmission and Speed

Problem:
How are circular and straight waves transmitted?

Materials:
ripple tank
light source
wooden or metal dowel
screen
dampers

Procedure
1. Put water in the tank to a depth of approximately 1 cm. Level the tank, to ensure that the depth of the water is uniform. (If necessary, place screen dampers at the perimeter of the tank to reduce reflection.)
2. Touch the surface of the water lightly at the centre of the tank with your finger. What is the shape of the wave produced by such a point source? Make a sketch showing the wave and the source of the wave.
3. On your sketch, at four equally spaced points on the crest of the wave, draw arrows indicating the direction of wave motion.

How can you tell, by the shape of the wave, that its speed is the same in all directions?

4. Generate a straight wave with the dowel by rocking it back and forth across the surface. Does the wave remain straight as it travels across the tank? Does its speed change? In what direction does the wave move, relative to its crest? Draw a straight wave, showing the direction of its motion.

5. Generate continuous straight waves by rocking the dowel back and forth steadily. What happens to the wavelength if you reduce the frequency? Does the speed change? What do you predict will be the effect on the wavelength and on the speed of the waves if the frequency is increased?

6. Prop up the tank so that the water on one side is only 1 mm deep. Send straight waves from the deep end to the shallow end. In what way do the speed and the wavelength change as the waves move to the shallow end? Make a sketch illustrating any changes in wavelength.

Questions

1. What is the direction of the wave motion relative to the crest of a wave?
2. How does a decrease in the frequency of the source affect the wavelength of the waves? How is the wavelength affected if the frequency increases?
3. How is the speed of a wave affected by a change in frequency?
4. If the depth of the water decreases, what happens to the speed and the wavelength of a wave?

Circular waves can also be generated by means of drops of water from an eyedropper or from the edge of a wet ruler.

Periodic circular waves

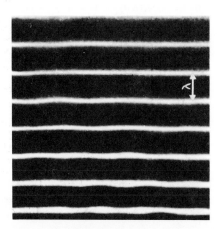

Periodic straight waves

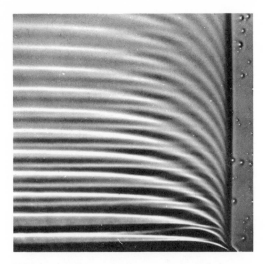

Waves entering shallow water, at the
right, decrease in speed and wavelength.

Waves coming from a point source are circular, whereas waves
from a linear source are straight. As a series of waves moves away
from its source, the spacing between successive crests and troughs
remains the same as long as the speed does not change. In other
words, the wavelength does not change as long as the speed
remains constant. When the speed decreases, as it does in shallow
water, the wavelength also decreases.

When the frequency of a source is increased, the distance
between successive crests becomes smaller. In other words, waves
with a higher frequency have a shorter wavelength.

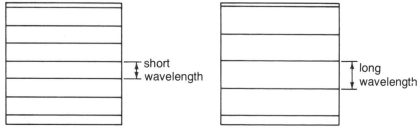

High-frequency waves   Low-frequency waves

Although the wavelength and the speed of a wave may change as
the wave moves through a medium, the frequency will not change.
The frequency can be changed only at the source, and not by the
medium.

The shape of a continuous crest or trough is called a **wavefront**.
To determine the direction of motion, or transmission, of a
wavefront, draw an arrow at right angles to the wavefront, as
illustrated.

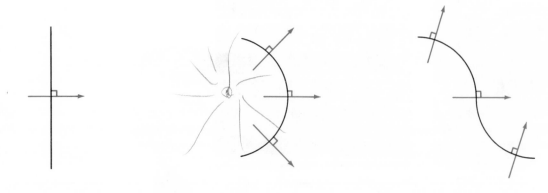

Straight wavefront   Circular wavefront

18.5 The Universal Wave Equation

The investigations in Sections 18.3 and 18.4 showed that the speed of a wave remains constant unless the medium changes. This behaviour is characteristic of all waves. But wavelength depends upon frequency as well as speed in a given medium. What we are considering here is the relationship between the frequency, the wavelength, and the speed of a wave.

When a wave is generated in a spring or a rope, in the time required for one complete vibration of the source, that is, the period (T), the wave travels a distance of one wavelength.

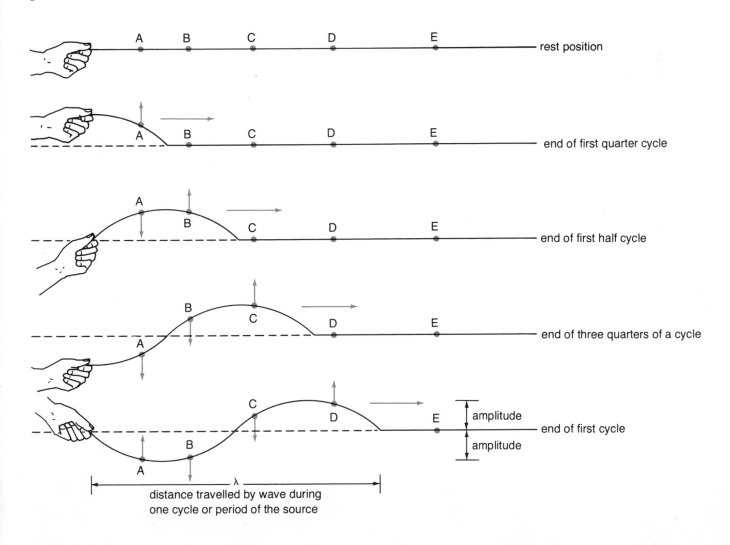

Since $v = \dfrac{\triangle d}{\triangle t}$

and $\triangle d = \lambda$ and $\triangle t = T$

$\therefore v = \dfrac{\lambda}{T}$ or $v = \left(\dfrac{1}{T}\right)(\lambda)$

but $f = \dfrac{1}{T}$ (Section 18.2)

$$v = f\lambda$$

This equation is called the **Universal Wave Equation** because it applies to all waves, visible and invisible.

Sample problems

1. The wavelength of a water wave is 0.05 m. If the frequency of the wave is 4.0 Hz, what is its speed?

   $v = f\lambda$
   $\quad = (4.0 \text{ Hz})(0.05 \text{ m})$
   $\quad = 0.20 \text{ m/s}$

2. A wave travels along a spring at a speed of 1.7 m/s. If the frequency of the source of the wave is 7.5 Hz, what is the wavelength of the wave?

   $v = f\lambda$
   or $\lambda = \dfrac{v}{f}$
   $\quad = \dfrac{1.7 \text{ m/s}}{7.5 \text{ Hz}}$
   $\quad = 0.23 \text{ m}$

Practice

1. A source with a frequency of 30 Hz produces waves that have a wavelength of 2.0 cm. What is the speed of the waves? (60 cm/s)

2. A wave in a rope travels at a speed of 2.5 m/s. The frequency of the wave is 2.0 Hz. Calculate the wavelength of the wave. (1.3 m)

3. Waves travel along a wire at a speed of 10 m/s. Find the frequency and the period of the source if the wavelength is 0.10 m. (1.0×10^2 Hz, 0.010 s)

4. A sound wave travels at 350 m/s. What is the wavelength of a sound with a frequency of 1.4×10^3 Hz? (0.25 m)

18.6 Reflection of Water Waves

Waves in a coiled spring or a rope are reflected from a fixed end (Section 18.3). Ocean waves crashing onto a rocky cliff are reflected away from the cliff. Sound waves reflected from a concrete wall are heard as echoes. Radio waves from a communications satellite are reflected to the focal point of a parabolic antenna on Earth. Laws govern the way in which waves, both visible and invisible, are reflected. The next investigation concerns one of the laws that govern the reflection of waves.

Investigation: Water Waves—Reflection

Problem:
How are straight waves reflected from straight barriers and circular barriers?

Materials:
ripple tank
wooden dowel
wax blocks
rubber hose

Procedure
1. Put water in the tank to a depth of approximately 0.5 cm.
2. Form a straight barrier on one side of the tank, using the wax blocks sitting on edge on the bottom. Send straight waves towards the barrier so that their wavefronts are parallel to the barrier. How does the direction of transmission of the incoming, or incident, wavefronts compare with that of the reflected wavefronts? Does the speed or the wavelength of the waves change after they have been reflected? Make a diagram illustrating your observations.
3. Now arrange the barrier so that the waves strike it at an angle. How does the angle between incident wavefronts and the barrier compare with the angle between reflected wavefronts and the barrier? To help you judge the angles, align rulers or other straight objects with the wavefront images on the screen below. Make a diagram showing incident wavefronts and reflected wavefronts and their directions of transmission.
4. Place some rubber tubing in the tank, allowing it to fill with water. Bend the tubing into the approximate shape of a

Adding a drop of liquid detergent to the water breaks down the surface tension in the water, making the shadows created by the barriers more distinct.

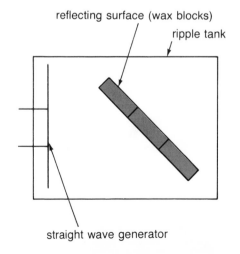

reflecting surface (wax blocks)

ripple tank

straight wave generator

parabola. With the dowel, generate straight waves towards the open side of the parabola. Observe how the wavefronts move before and after they strike the curved barrier. Record your observations in a sketch. Using your finger as a point source, generate circular waves that are reflected from the parabolic barrier as straight waves.

Questions

1. When a straight wave strikes a barrier so that its wavefront is parallel to the barrier, in what direction is the wave reflected?
2. When an incident wavefront strikes a barrier at an angle (that is, obliquely), how do the angles between the barrier and the incident and reflected wavefronts compare?
3. How are straight waves reflected by a parabolic reflector?

When waves run into a straight barrier, as illustrated, they are reflected back along their original path.

If a wave hits a straight barrier obliquely, the wavefront is also reflected at an angle to the barrier. The angles formed by the incident wavefront and the barrier and by the reflected wavefront and the barrier are equal. These angles are called the **angle of incidence** and the **angle of reflection**, respectively.

Obliquely—"slanting, declining from the vertical or horizontal"

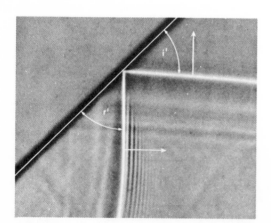

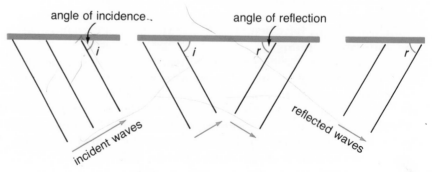

In neither case does the reflection produce any change in the wavelength or in the speed of the wave.

Sometimes we refer to **wave rays** instead of to wavefronts, in describing the behaviour of waves. Wave rays are simply straight lines perpendicular to wavefronts indicating the direction of transmission.

When describing the reflection of waves, using wave rays, the angles of incidence and reflection are measured relative to a straight line perpendicular to the barrier, called the **normal**. This line is constructed at the point where the incident wave ray strikes the reflecting surface. As may be seen from the geometrical analysis illustrated, the angle of incidence has the same value whether wavefronts or wave rays are used to measure it. In both cases the angle of incidence equals the angle of reflection. This is one of the laws of reflection.

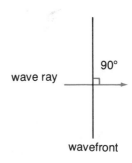

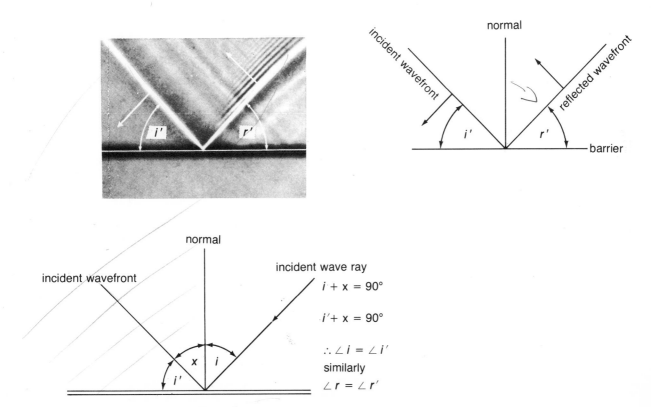

In the investigation, straight waves were reflected by a parabolic reflector to one point, called the **focal point**. This could have been predicted by means of the laws of reflection and wave rays.

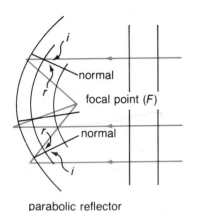

parabolic reflector

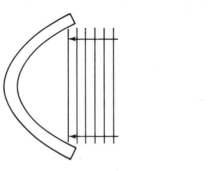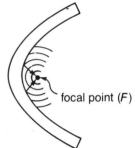

18.7 Diffraction of Water Waves

Many city waterfronts are protected by breakwaters—concrete obstacles that reflect the wave energy away from the shoreline, protecting the beach and harbour. In the breakwater there are openings to permit boats to enter. Some of the energy being transmitted by the waves passes through these openings to the region behind the breakwater. The bending of the waves that occurs as they pass through such small openings is called **diffraction**.

How a wave is diffracted and the properties of the wave and of the barrier that affect diffraction are examined in the next investigation.

Investigation: Water Waves—Diffraction

Problem:
What factors affect the diffraction of a wave?

Materials:
ripple tank
wooden dowel
wax blocks

Procedure
1. Put water in the tank to a depth of 1 cm.
2. Place a wax block at the centre of the wave tank, with a bevelled

end about 10 cm away from the dowel. Line up the other wax blocks so that they prevent waves from passing by the other end of the first wax block.

3. Generate periodic waves with a long wavelength and observe how the wavefronts pass by the bevelled end of the block. Record your observations in a sketch showing a series of wavefronts on both sides of the block.

4. Slowly increase the frequency of the waves. What change in wavelength occurs? Is the amount of diffraction greater or smaller than before? Make a sketch to illustrate your answer.

5. Using two pieces of bevelled wax, create a barrier about 10 cm from the dowel, with an opening of approximately 4 cm. Generate waves with a long wavelength, observing the amount of bending that occurs. Increase the frequency gradually. Was the amount of diffraction greater or smaller than before? Record your observations in the form of sketches.

6. While your partner generates waves with a constant frequency, slowly decrease the size of the opening by moving one of the blocks. How does the size of the opening affect the diffraction?

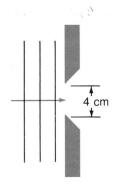

4 cm

Questions

1. What kind of wavelengths are diffracted more—long ones or short ones?
2. What is the relationship between the size of the opening and the amount of diffraction?
3. Describe two conditions for maximum diffraction through an opening in a barrier.

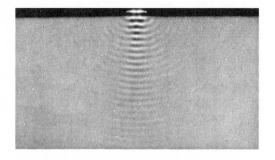

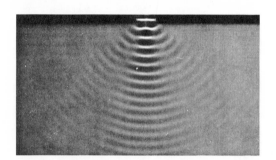

As the size of the opening decreases, the amount of diffraction increases.

Water waves are diffracted when they pass by the edge of a barrier or through a small opening in a barrier. How much they are diffracted depends mainly on their wavelength. Shorter wavelengths are diffracted slightly. Longer wavelengths are diffracted to a greater extent.

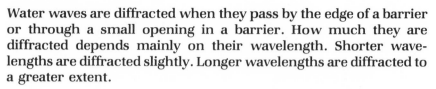

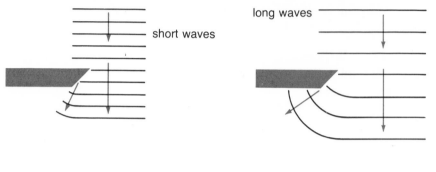

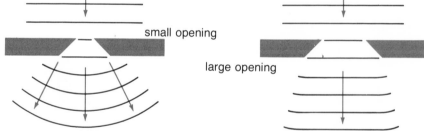

As a general rule, diffraction is increased when the size of an opening is decreased. If the wavelength remains constant, diffraction becomes more apparent when the opening is decreased to approximately the same dimension as the wavelength.

18.8 Refraction of Water Waves

When the depth of the water in a ripple tank was decreased (Section 18.4), the speed and the wavelength of the waves also decreased. What about the direction in which the waves are moving: is it affected by changes in the speed? That is the topic of the next investigation. We will create two depths of water in the same ripple tank by supporting a glass plate above the bottom of the tank.

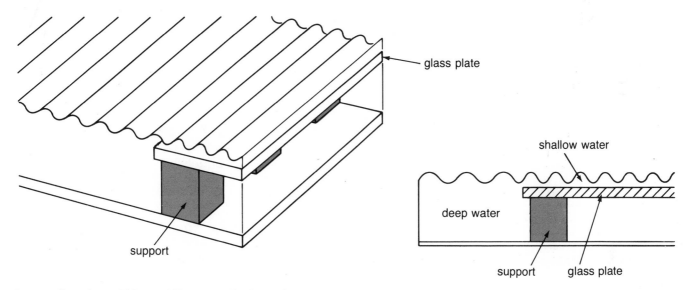

Investigation: Water Waves – Refraction

Problem:
How do the wavelength and the direction of transmission of a wave change when its speed changes?

Materials:
ripple tank
straight wave generator
glass plate
glass plate supports (if necessary)

Procedure
1. Support a glass plate on the spacers so that it is approximately 1.5 cm above the bottom of the tank and about 15 cm from the wave generator. Its longest edge should be parallel to the generator.
2. Put enough water in the tank to cover the glass plate to a depth of about 1 mm. Adjust the height of the wave generator so that the bottom of the vibrator is just below the surface of the water.
3. Adjust the generator so that it produces waves with a long wavelength. As the waves pass from the deeper water to the shallower water, what changes occur in their speed and their wavelength? Draw a diagram to show clearly what happens to the wavelength.
4. Set the glass plate at an angle of approximately 45° to the incoming waves. Note any changes that occur in the direction of

It is sometimes easier to fill the tank until the glass plate is covered and then siphon off the water until only a thin film (1 mm) remains over the glass.

motion of the waves. Does the wavelength change? Is any part of the wave reflected? Draw a diagram showing all of the waves and the directions of transmission of these waves in the deep and shallow water.

Questions

1. What changes occurred in the wavelength of the waves and in their speed when they entered the shallower water?
2. What changes in direction occurred when waves entered shallow water, straight on and obliquely?
3. What changes in the wavelength, speed, and direction do you predict will occur when waves pass obliquely from shallow water to deep water? Draw a sketch illustrating your prediction. Test your prediction in the ripple tank.

When waves enter shallow water they slow down. At the same time their wavelength decreases, as illustrated.

The waves travelling in deep water have a speed that is expressed by the equation $v_1 = f_1\lambda_1$ (the Universal Wave Equation). Similarly, $v_2 = f_2\lambda_2$, for waves in shallow water. But the frequency of a water wave is determined by the wave generator, and does not change when the speed changes. Thus $f_1 = f_2$.

If we divide the first equation by the second equation, we get

$$\frac{v_1}{v_2} = \frac{f_1\lambda_1}{f_2\lambda_2}$$

But $f_1 = f_2$

$$\frac{v_1}{v_2} = \frac{\lambda_1}{\lambda_2}$$

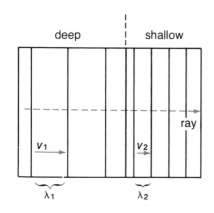

Water wave passing from deep to shallow water

Sample problem

Water waves have a wavelength of 2.0 cm in the deep section of a tank and 1.5 cm in the shallow section. If the speed of the waves in the shallow water is 12 cm/s, what is their speed in deep water?

$$\frac{v_1}{v_2} = \frac{\lambda_1}{\lambda_2}$$

$$v_1 = \left(\frac{\lambda_1}{\lambda_2}\right)(v_2)$$

$$= \left(\frac{2.0 \text{ cm}}{1.5 \text{ cm}}\right)(12 \text{ cm/s})$$

$$= 16 \text{ cm/s}$$

Practice

1. The speed and the wavelength of water waves in deep water are 15.0 cm/s and 2.2 cm, respectively. If the speed in shallow water is 10.0 cm/s, what is the wavelength? (1.5 cm)
2. Waves travel 0.75 times as fast in shallow water as they do in deep water. What will be the wavelength of the waves in deep water, if their wavelength is 2.0 cm in shallow water? (2.7 cm)

When waves travel from deep water to shallow water in such a way that they cross the boundary between the two depths straight on, no bending occurs.

On the other hand, if a water wave travels obliquely from one depth to another, its direction changes. This phenomenon is called **refraction**.

We usually refer to wave rays when describing refraction. In Section 18.6, dealing with the reflection of waves, it was explained that the normal is a line drawn at right angles to the boundary at the point where the incident wave ray strikes the boundary. The angle formed by the incident wave ray and the normal is called the angle of incidence (i). The angle formed by the refracted wave ray and the normal is called the **angle of refraction** (R).

When a wave travels obliquely into a medium in which its speed decreases, the refracted wave ray is bent (refracted) towards the normal. If the wave travels obliquely into a medium in which its speed increases, the refracted wave ray is bent away from the normal.

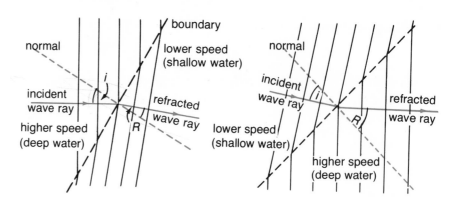

When water waves travel obliquely into a slower medium, the wave ray bends towards the normal, whereas if the medium is a faster one the wave ray bends away from the normal.

When refraction occurs, some of the wave energy is usually reflected as well as refracted. In a ripple tank, this behaviour is only apparent at large angles of incidence.

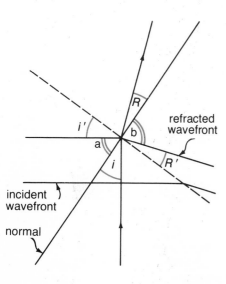

$$i + a = 90° \qquad R + b = 90°$$
$$i' + a = 90° \qquad R' + b = 90°$$
$$\therefore i = i' \qquad \therefore R = R'$$

18.9 Interference of Waves

Waves travelling out from a source usually encounter other waves, which may be from another source or may be reflected waves that originated from the same source. For example, a water wave crashing into a concrete wall is reflected back into succeeding waves.

Wave **interference** occurs when two or more waves act simultaneously on the same particles of the medium. Up to this point, we have been dealing with one wave at a time. What happens when two waves meet? Do they bounce off each other? Do they cancel each other out? What effect does wave interference have on the particles in a medium? By studying wave interference in a simple rope or spring and in a ripple tank we can observe some of the fundamental properties of wave interference, properties that are useful in the study of sound and light.

Investigation: Interference in a One-dimensional Medium

Problem:
How is a one-dimensional medium affected by two pulses passing through it simultaneously?

Materials:
spiral spring with tabs or a length of rubber tubing (or a Bell wave machine)

Procedure
1. Stretch the spiral spring or the rubber tubing between yourself and your partner. (Omit, if using the Bell wave machine.)
2. Simultaneously, generate positive pulses from both ends of the medium. Are the two pulses reflected off each other or do they pass through each other unaffected? Check your answer by simultaneously generating a positive pulse from one end and a negative pulse from the other.
3. Noting a specific point near the middle of the medium, simultaneously generate positive pulses from both ends. How is the point affected when the two pulses act on it at the same time? What do you predict would happen if two negative pulses were used? Check your prediction.
4. Simultaneously generate a positive pulse from one end and a negative pulse from the other. How are certain points, located

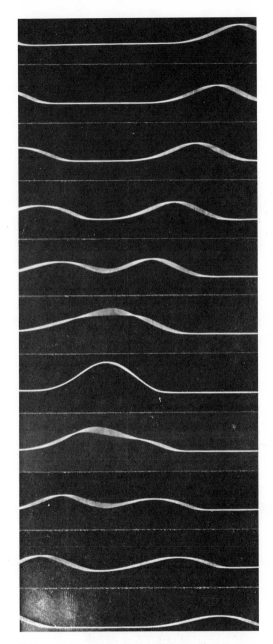

Two crests moving in opposite directions in a rope interfere in the sixth, seventh, and eighth frames.

A positive pulse = a crest. A negative pulse = a trough. See Section 18.3.

near the middle of the medium, affected when these two pulses act on them at the same time?

Questions

1. How is a pulse affected when it passes through another pulse?
2. When two positive or two negative pulses act on the same particles at the same time, is the resultant displacement greater or smaller than it would be in the case of a single pulse acting alone?
3. When a positive and a negative pulse act simultaneously on a particle in a medium, is the resultant displacement greater or smaller than it would be in the case of either of the pulses acting alone?

As we have seen, after interference each pulse appears to be the same as it was before. This behaviour is common to all types of waves: they pass through each other unaffected. What happens, then, to certain particles in a medium when both waves act on them at the same time? The resultant displacement of a given particle is equal to the sum of the displacements that would have been produced by the two waves acting independently. This is called the **Principle of Superposition**. Note that the individual displacements may be positive (+) or negative (−). A plus or a minus sign must be included in each calculation of the resultant displacement.

In the example illustrated, pulses A and B are interfering, each making its own contribution to the resultant displacement of the particles in a medium. For example, point P in No. 3 is moved upwards 8 mm by pulse A and up another 4 mm by pulse B for a total displacement of + 12 mm. Other particles are moved varying distances from the rest position, each displacement being determined by the sum of the contributions of the two pulses. The solid lines represent the resultant displacement of all the particles at a given instant. The dotted lines represent the individual displacements of pulses A and B and are not seen when interference occurs. Only the resultant displacement is seen (solid line).

When pulses A and C interfere, pulse A displaces the particles upwards whereas pulse C displaces them downwards. Particle P is moved up 11 mm by pulse A and down 5 mm by pulse C, giving it a resultant displacement at one instant of + 6 mm. The solid line indicates where other particles would be displaced by the interference of the two waves. Note that, in the areas of the medium where interference does not occur, the position of the

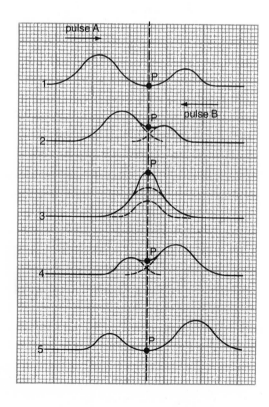

particles in the medium (representated by the solid line) is that created by each individual wave.

When two or more waves interfere to produce a resultant displacement greater than the displacement that would be caused by either wave, by itself, we call it **constructive interference**. When the resultant displacement is smaller than the displacement that would be caused by one wave, by itself, we call it **destructive interference**.

The Principle of Superposition may be used to find the resultant displacement of any medium when two or more waves of different wavelengths interfere. In every case, the resultant is determined by an algebraic summing of all the individual wave displacements. These displacements may be added together electronically and the resultant displacement displayed on an oscilloscope, as illustrated. Once again, the resultant wave is the only one seen, not the individual interfering waves.

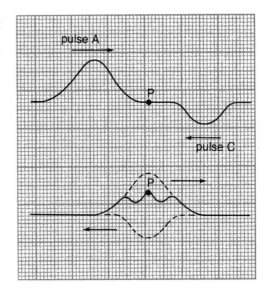

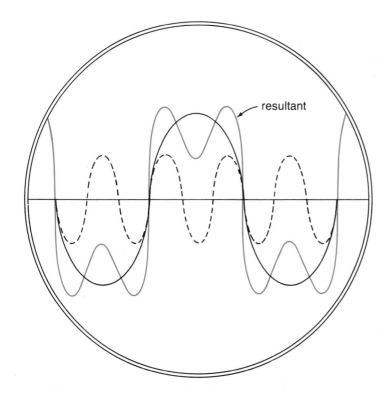

Resultant displacement displayed on an oscilloscope

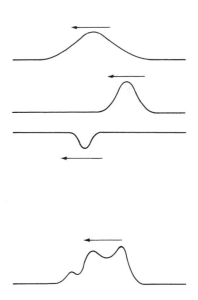

Three pulses and the resultant displacement that is produced by superposing them

18.10 Standing Waves – a Special Case of Interference

The amplitude and the wavelength of interfering waves are often different. But, if conditions are controlled so that the waves have the same amplitude and wavelength, the resultant interference pattern is both unique and interesting. Such an interference pattern remains nearly stationary and thus is referred to as a **standing wave interference pattern**.

In most cases of interference, the resultant displacement remains for only an instant, as you discovered in the last investigation. This makes analysis of interference difficult.

Since standing wave interference remains relatively stationary, it is much easier to analyse, and so is a useful tool in the study of waves. Later, its importance in the study of sound-wave interference will be noted.

Investigation: Standing Waves in a One-dimensional Medium

Problem:
How are standing waves produced in a one-dimensional medium?

Materials:
a spiral spring or a length of rubber tubing (or a Bell wave machine)

Procedure
1. Simultaneously generate a series of waves of equal frequency and amplitude from each end of the medium (spring or tubing). Adjust the frequency until the medium maintains a fixed pattern. Compare the displacement of some particles in the medium with that of other particles. Draw a sketch illustrating the resultant displacement of the medium.
2. Change the frequency of the waves. How is the pattern affected when the frequency is increased? Decreased?
3. Fix one end of the medium rigidly. Generate a series of waves towards the fixed end. What is the effect on the medium when the incident waves interfere with the reflected waves? How is the pattern affected by changes in the frequency of the source? What is the resultant displacement, at all times, of the end of the medium (where the wave is reflected)?

Questions

1. On your sketch of a standing wave interference pattern (step 1), indicate the points of constructive interference and destructive interference.
2. For complete destructive interference, what must be true of the wavelengths and amplitudes of the two waves?
3. Why is it easier to produce standing waves by the use of reflection than by means of two vibrating sources acting on the same medium?
4. Why is it easier to measure the wavelength of a wave using the standing wave interference pattern than it is to measure it directly?

When positive and negative pulses of equal magnitude interfere, there is a point that remains at rest throughout the interference of the pulses. This point is called a **node**, or **nodal point**.

When waves with identical wavelengths and amplitudes interfere, a stationary interference pattern called a "standing wave" is produced. In the next diagram, two identical waves, A and B, are interfering. The resultant displacement caused by their interference produces areas of constructive and destructive interference. Note that the nodes are equidistant and that their spacing is equal to one-half of the wavelength of the interfering waves. Midway between the nodes are areas where double crests and double troughs occur. These areas are called **loops.**

Standing waves may be produced by means of a single source. Reflected waves, for instance, will interfere with incident waves, producing standing waves. Since the incident waves and the reflected waves have the same source, they have the same frequency, wavelength, and amplitude. The distance between nodal points may be altered by changing the frequency of the source. However, for a given length of rope or of any other medium, only certain wavelengths are capable of maintaining the standing wave interference pattern.

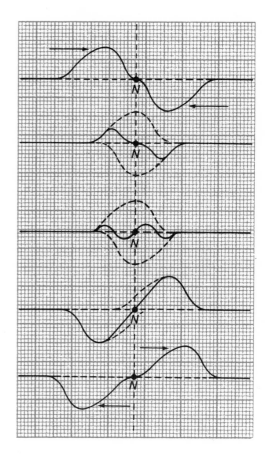

N = nodal point

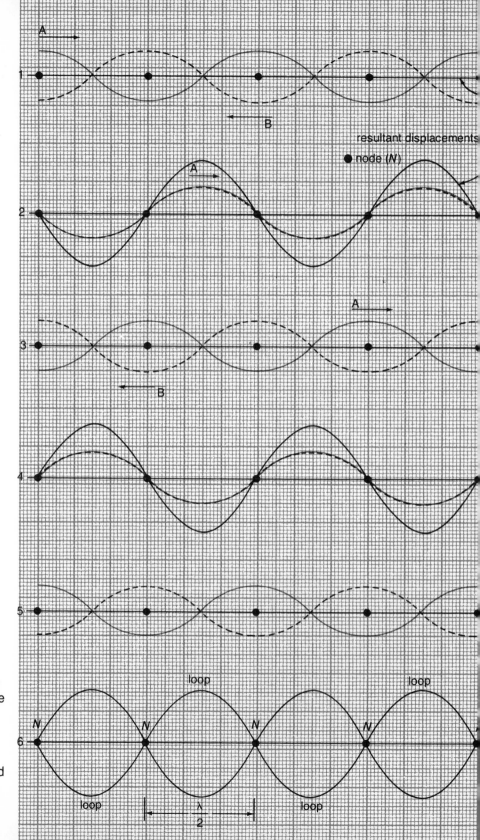

Diagrams 1, 3, and 5 show the two identical waves interfering so that destructive interference occurs at every point in the medium. Thus, the resultant displacement line is horizontal.
Diagrams 2 and 4 show the two waves interfering in such a way that there are areas of constructive interference and areas of destructive interference.
Diagram 6 shows the resulting "standing wave interference pattern" created as the waves continually pass through one another, creating stationary regions of constructive interference and nodal points. Diagram 6 is a summary of the motions of the medium that are illustrated in diagrams 1 to 5.

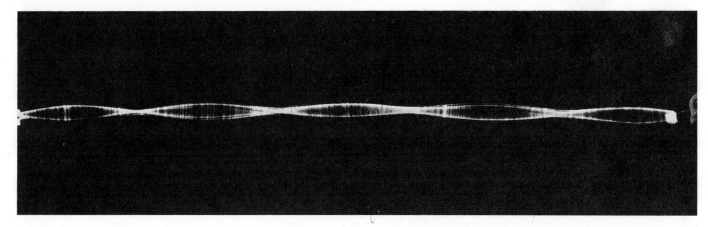

Standing waves in a vibrating string

Sample problem

The distance between two successive nodes in a vibrating string is 10 cm. If the frequency of the source is 43 Hz, what is the wavelength of the waves? What is their velocity?

The distance between successive nodes is $\frac{1}{2}\lambda$.

Therefore the wavelength is 2(10 cm) = 20 cm.

$v = f\lambda$
$\quad = (43 \text{ Hz}) (20 \text{ cm})$
$\quad = 860 \text{ cm/s or } 8.6 \times 10^2 \text{ cm/s}$

Practice

1. A standing wave interference pattern is produced in a rope by a vibrator with a frequency of 28 Hz. If the wavelength of the waves is 30 cm, what is the distance between successive nodes?
(15 cm)
2. The distance between the second and fifth nodes in a standing wave is 60 cm. What is the wavelength of the waves? What is the speed of the waves, if the source has a frequency of 20 Hz?
(40 cm, 8.0 m/s)

18.11 Interference of Water Waves

In a one-dimensional medium, such as a spring, constructive or destructive interference may occur, sometimes producing fixed patterns of interference (Sections 18.9 and 18.10). What patterns of interference occur between two waves interfering in a two-dimensional medium—the ripple tank?

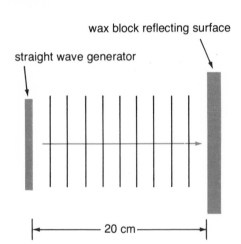

straight wave generator

wax block reflecting surface

|← 20 cm →|

In the ripple tank, crests produce bright areas and troughs produce dark areas, when illuminated from above.
Undisturbed or flat water (nodal areas) appears semi-bright or grey.

Investigation: Interference of Water Waves in a Ripple Tank

Problem:
What patterns of interference are produced by identical water waves in a ripple tank?

Materials:
ripple tank
wax blocks
wave generator
straight wave source
two point sources

Procedure
1. Set up the ripple tank and put water in it to a depth of 1 cm.
2. Make a wave with one finger and then start a second wave some distance away. Observe the two waves. Repeat the procedure for various points in the tank. Do the two waves affect each other? Are they changed as a result of interference?
3. With the wax blocks, create a straight reflecting barrier approximately 20 cm from the straight wave generator and parallel to it.
4. Adjust the frequency of the wave generator so that a standing wave pattern is produced. Record your observations in a sketch, labelling one wavelength.
5. Increase the frequency of the source. What change occurs in the interference pattern?
6. Remove the wax blocks and the straight wave source and attach the point sources to the generator so that they are approximately 5 cm apart. Make sure that the two sources are in phase.
7. Adjust the generator to a frequency of approximately 10 Hz. Make a sketch of the interference pattern.
8. Increase the frequency of the generator gradually. Sketch the pattern at one higher frequency.

Questions
1. When two waves pass through each other, is either of them permanently changed? Was this true for one-dimensional interference?
2. What happened to the standing wave interference pattern when the frequency was increased? Why?
3. Describe in words the interference pattern between two point sources in phase.

In the last investigation, when straight waves were reflected by the straight barrier, the reflected waves interfered with the incident waves. Since the reflected waves and the incident waves had the same wavelength and amplitude, a standing wave interference pattern resulted. The straight nodal lines appeared as stationary, grey, equally spaced areas when illuminated from above.

Between the nodal lines were loops that appeared as alternating bright (double crests) and dark (double troughs) lines of constructive interference.

A nodal line is a line joining a series of nodal points.

The two vibrating point sources were attached to the same generator and thus had identical wavelengths and amplitudes. Also, they were in phase. As successive crests and troughs travelled out from each source they interfered, sometimes crest on crest, sometimes trough on trough, and sometimes crest on trough. Thus, areas of constructive and destructive interference were produced. These areas moved out from the source in symmetrical patterns, producing nodal lines and areas of constructive interference, as illustrated.

Although the nodal lines appear to be straight when they move away from the sources, they are actually curved lines in a mathematical shape called a hyperbola. When the frequency of the sources is increased, the wavelength decreases, bringing the nodal lines closer together and increasing their number.

This **two-point-source interference pattern** is of great importance in the study of the interference of sound waves and light waves.

Having discovered many of the properties of waves, we can apply this knowledge in an investigation of the properties of sound, another wave phenomenon.

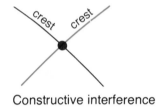

Constructive interference

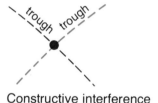

Constructive interference

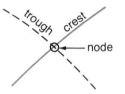

Destructive interference

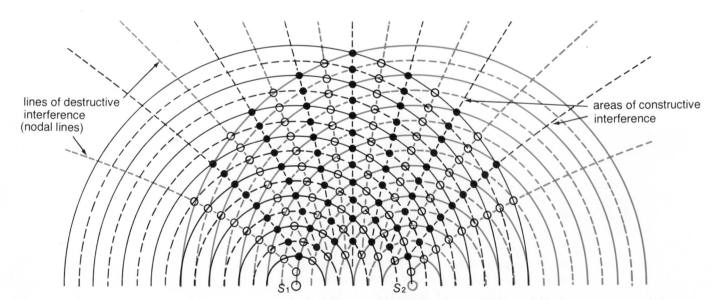

The interference pattern between two identical point sources (S₁ and S₂), vibrating in phase, is a symmetrical pattern of nodal lines and areas of constructive interference in the shape of hyperbolae.

18.12 Summary

1. A wave is a transfer of energy through a medium in the form of a disturbance. All waves originate from a vibrating source.
2. Frequency is the number of cycles per second. One cycle in one second is defined as one hertz (Hz).
3. The period is the time required for one cycle, and the unit in which the period is expressed is usually the second.
4. The frequency (f) and the period (T) are related by these equations:

$$f = \frac{1}{T} \quad \text{or} \quad T = \frac{1}{f}$$

5. Particles or objects are said to be vibrating in phase if they have the same frequency, have the same displacement from their rest positions, and are moving in the same direction. If any one of these conditions is absent, the vibrating particles or objects are not in phase.
6. In a transverse wave, the particles of the medium move at right angles to the direction of the wave motion.
7. The speed of a wave is unaffected by changes in the frequency or amplitude of the vibrating source.
8. One wavelength is the distance between the mid points of successive crests or troughs.
9. If the frequency of a wave increases, the wavelength decreases, provided that the medium does not change.
10. One vibration of the source produces one complete wavelength.
11. The frequency and the period of a wave are the same as those of the source, and they are not affected by changes in the speed of the wave.
12. An equation governing all waves is: $v = f\lambda$. It is called the Universal Wave Equation.
13. Pulses reflected from a rigid obstacle (or a fixed end) are inverted. Pulses reflected from a free end are not changed.
14. A wave ray is a straight line drawn at right angles to the wavefront, indicating the direction of the wave motion.
15. When waves are reflected from a solid obstacle, the angle of incidence is always equal to the angle of reflection. This is one of the laws of reflection and it holds for both curved and flat reflecting surfaces.

16. Waves bend, in a phenomenon called diffraction, when they pass edges and go through small openings. Waves with longer wavelengths are diffracted more than waves with shorter wavelengths.

17. When waves enter a medium in which their speed is reduced, their wavelengths decrease. If their speed is increased, their wavelengths increase. An equation relating velocity to wavelength is:

$$\frac{v_1}{v_2} = \frac{\lambda_1}{\lambda_2}$$

18. Refraction is the change that occurs in the direction of motion of a wave when it passes obliquely into a medium that causes it to change speed.

19. When a wave encounters a new medium
    (a) obliquely, and the speed decreases, the wave ray is refracted towards the normal.
    (b) obliquely, and the speed increases, the wave ray is refracted away from the normal.
    (c) straight on, that is, in such a way that the wave ray forms a 90° angle with the boundary, there is no refraction.

20. Waves can pass through each other in a medium without affecting one another. Only the medium is affected, momentarily.

21. The resultant displacement of a particle is the algebraic sum of the individual displacements contributed by each wave. This is called the Principle of Superposition.

22. If the resultant displacement is greater than that caused by either wave, alone, constructive interference is occurring. If it is less, destructive interference is occurring.

23. For total destructive interference to occur, with a resultant displacement of zero, the waves interfering must have identical frequencies, wavelengths, and amplitudes.

24. Nodal points, or nodes, are points in a medium that are continuously at rest, that is, the resultant displacement of the particles at these points is always zero. Points in a medium at which constructive interference always occurs are called loops.

25. A stationary interference pattern of successive nodes and loops in a medium is called a standing wave interference pattern.

26. The distance between successive nodes or loops in a standing wave interference pattern is one-half the wavelength of the interfering waves.

27. The interference pattern between two identical point sources, vibrating in phase, is a symmetrical pattern of alternating nodal lines and areas of constructive interference loops in the shape of hyperbolae.

18.13 Review

1. A pendulum swings back and forth 20 times in 15 s. Calculate its period and its frequency.
2. A swimmer notices that 30 waves strike a breakwater in 1.00 min. What is the period of the waves in seconds?
3. Determine the frequency in each of the following.
   (a) a basketball player who scores 36 points in 24 min
   (b) a roadrunner who escapes from a coyote 27 times in a 9 min cartoon
   (c) a fan that turns 170 times in 15.0 s
4. Determine the period of each of the following.
   (a) the pulse from a human heartbeat that is heard 30 times in 12 s
   (b) a tuning fork that vibrates 2048 times in 8.0 s
   (c) the moon, which travels around the Earth six times in 163.8 d
5. Calculate the frequency of each of the following periods.
   (a) 5.0 s
   (b) 0.01 s
   (c) 2.5×10^{-2} s
   (d) 0.80 s
   (e) 6.0 s
   (f) 0.40 min
6. Calculate the period of each of the following frequencies.
   (a) 10 Hz
   (b) 0.25 Hz
   (c) 500 kHz
   (d) 0.10 Hz
   (e) 2.5 Hz
   (f) 3.5 Hz
7. The horizontal distance between the end points in the swing of a pendulum is 8.0 cm. What is the amplitude?
8. The tine of a tuning fork, when struck, has an amplitude of 0.13 cm. If the frequency of the fork is 200 Hz, what total distance will the tine travel in 1.00 min?

9. The diagram shows the profile of waves in a ripple tank.

direction of wave motion

A   C

undisturbed
water

(a) By measuring, find the wavelength and the amplitude of the waves.
(b) If crest A takes 2.0 s to move to where crest C is now,
    (i)   What is the speed of the waves?
    (ii)   What is the frequency of the waves?
    (iii) What is the frequency of the source?

10. The wavelength of a water wave is 8.0 m and its speed is 2.0 m/s. How many waves will pass a fixed point in the water in 1.0 min?

11.

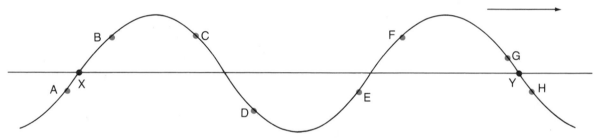

Examine this diagram of a wave and
(a) list all pairs of points that are in phase.
(b) determine the wavelength, in centimetres, by measurement.
(c) determine the speed of the waves, if they take 0.50 s to travel from X to Y.

12. Water waves with a wavelength of 6.0 m approach a lighthouse at 5.6 m/s.
(a) What is the frequency of the waves?
(b) What is their period?

13. 5.0 Hz waves move along a rope with a wavelength of 40 cm. What is their speed?

14. The distance between successive crests in a series of water waves is 5.0 m, and the crests travel 8.6 m in 5.0 s. Calculate the frequency of a block of wood bobbing up and down in the water.

15. The wavelength of a water wave is 3.7 m and its period is 1.5 s. Calculate
    (a) the speed of the wave.
    (b) the time required for the wave to travel 100 m.
    (c) the distance travelled by the wave in 1.00 min.
16. A water wave travels 60 cm in 2.0 s. If the wavelength is 5.0 cm, what is the frequency of the wave?
17. A boat at anchor is rocked by waves whose crests are 30 m apart and whose speed is 8.0 m/s. What is the interval of time between crests striking the boat?
18. What is the speed of a sound wave with a wavelength of 3.4 m and a frequency of 100 Hz?
19. The period of a sound wave emitted by a vibrating guitar string is 3.0×10^{-3} s. If the speed of the sound wave is 360 m/s, what is its wavelength?
20. A television station broadcasts with a frequency of 90 MHz. If the speed of the electromagnetic waves emitted by the station tower is 3.0×10^8 m/s, what is the wavelength of the waves?
21. The frequency assigned to an FM (frequency modulation) station is 102 MHz. What is the wavelength of the waves if they travel at 3.0×10^8 m/s?
22. Bats emit ultrasonic sound to help them locate obstacles. The waves have a frequency of 5.5×10^4 Hz. If they travel at 350 m/s, what is their wavelength?
23. When a stone is dropped into water, the resulting ripples spread farther and farther out, getting smaller and smaller in amplitude until they disappear. Why does the amplitude eventually decrease to zero?

24. Transfer each of the following diagrams into your notebook by tracing. Complete the diagrams, showing the location of the waves a few seconds later. Indicate on each diagram the direction(s) of transmission.

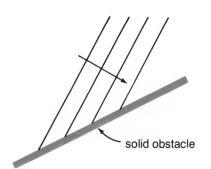

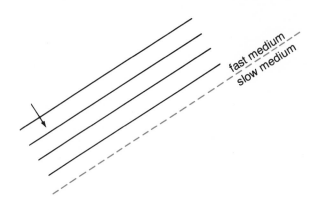

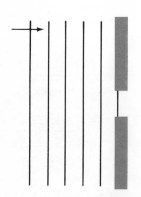

solid obstacle

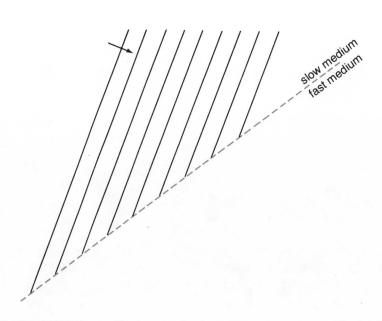

25. In this diagram, QRS is a straight wave, and the wave rays indicate the direction of its motion towards a refracting surface, AB. Copy the diagram into your notebook and draw the wavefront $Q_1 R_1 S_1$ when it has reached R_2 and R_3. Label the corresponding wavefronts at these points $Q_2 R_2 S_2$ and $Q_3 R_3 S_3$.

26. The speed of water waves is 30 cm/s in deep water and 15 cm/s in shallow water. If the wavelength in deep water is 1.0 cm, what is the wavelength in shallow water?

27. The velocity of sound waves in cold air is 320 m/s, and in warm air it is 384 m/s. If the wavelength of the sound waves was 3.0 m in cold air, what would it be in warm air?

28. As water waves approach a beach, their wavelengths become shorter. Why?

29. What happens when two billiard balls, rolling towards one another, collide head on? How does this differ from two waves or pulses that collide head on?

30. Trace the pulses illustrated into your notebook, and determine the resultant displacement of the particles of the medium at each instant, using the Principle of Superposition.

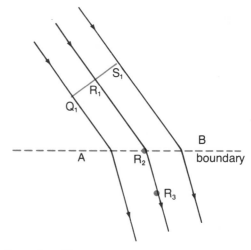

Question 25

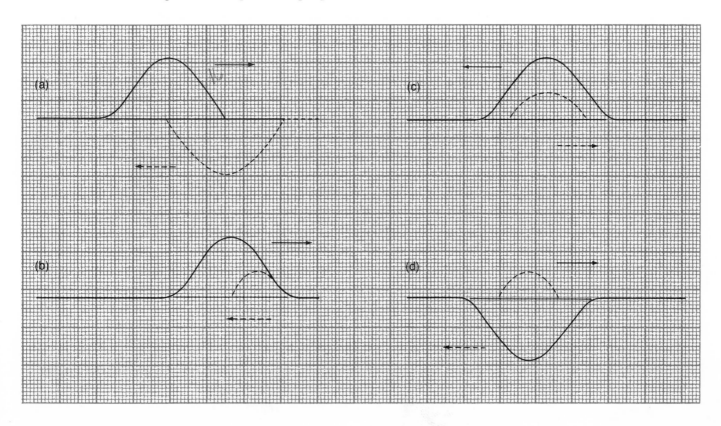

31. Trace the waves illustrated into your notebook and determine their resultant displacement.

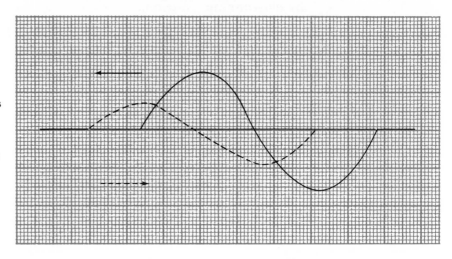

32.

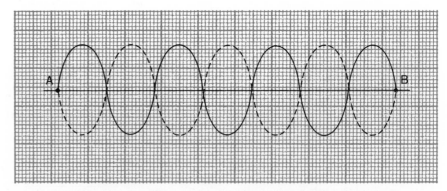

Using measurements taken directly from this diagram of a standing wave pattern, determine each of the following.

(a) the wavelength of the waves
(b) the speed of the waves, if they move between points A and B in 3.0 s
(c) the frequency of the waves

33. Calculate the wavelength if the distance between adjacent nodes in a vibrating medium is

(a) 1.5 m   (b) 4.0 cm   (c) 48 mm

34. The distance between adjacent nodes in the standing wave pattern in a piece of string is 25.0 cm.
    (a) What is the wavelength of the wave in the string?
    (b) If the frequency of the vibration is 200 Hz, calculate the velocity of the wave.
35. Standing waves are produced in a string by sources at each end with a frequency of 10.0 Hz. The distance between the third node and the sixth node is 54 cm.
    (a) What is the wavelength of the interfering waves?
    (b) What is their speed?
36. Standing waves are produced in a string by two waves travelling in opposite directions at 6.0 m/s. The distance between the second node and the sixth node is 80 cm. Determine the wavelength and the frequency of the original waves.
37. In the middle of a page in your notebook, mark two points 4.0 cm apart. Using a compass, draw in circular wavefronts originating at the points with 2.0 cm wavelengths. Use solid lines for crests and dotted lines for troughs. Mark all the nodes and points of maximum constructive interference.

18.14 Learning Objectives

1. Given the time required for a definite number of vibrations, to determine the frequency and period of the vibrating object.
2. Given either the frequency or the period of a vibrating object, to determine the other.
3. To distinguish between objects vibrating in phase and out of phase.
4. Given any two of frequency (or period), speed, and wavelength, to determine the third using the Universal Wave Equation.
5. To predict how a given pulse will be reflected by the fixed end or the free end of a piece of rope or a spring.
6. Given a sketch of a straight wave and a circular wave, to draw in wave rays.
7. To draw a diagram showing the reflection of a straight wave striking a straight obstacle, both at an oblique angle and straight on.
8. To use the Laws of Reflection to predict how a wave ray will be reflected from a straight obstacle and a curved obstacle.

9. To draw a diagram showing how straight waves with short and long wavelengths are diffracted by an edge of an obstacle and by a small opening in an obstacle.

10. Using both wavefronts and wave rays, to draw diagrams illustrating how straight waves behave when they encounter a slower medium and a faster medium, either straight on or obliquely.

11. To use the relationship $\dfrac{v_1}{v_2} = \dfrac{\lambda_1}{\lambda_2}$ to determine the wavelength or the speed in a new medium.

12. To determine the resultant displacement of two or more waves acting on the same particles in a medium, using the Principle of Superposition.

13. To locate on a diagram the parts of a standing wave, and to determine the wavelength of the interfering waves.

14. Given any two of the frequency, the speed, and the dimensions of a standing wave pattern, to determine the third.

15. To draw a diagram showing the interference pattern between two point sources in phase, and to locate both the nodal lines and the lines of maximum constructive interference.

19 The Production and Properties of Sound Waves

19.1 What Is Sound?

From our earliest years we are accustomed to a great variety of sounds: our mother's voice, a telephone ringing, a kitten purring, a piano being played, the blaring of a rock band, a siren, a jet engine roaring, a rifle shot. Some of these sounds are pleasant to the ear and some are not. They are all called **sounds** because they stimulate the auditory nerve in the human ear.

In the 18th century, the philosophers and scientists debated the question, ''If a tree falls in the forest and no one is there to hear it, will there be sound?''

''Of course there will,'' said the scientists, ''because the crash of the tree is a vibrating source that sends out sound waves through the ground and the air.'' To them, sound was the motion of the particles in a medium, caused by a vibrating object.

''Of course not,'' said the philosophers, ''because no observer is present.'' To them, sound was a personal sensation, existing only in the mind of the observer.

This debate could never be resolved, because one group was defining sound objectively, in terms of its cause, and the other was defining it subjectively, in terms of its effects on the human ear and brain. In physics, we study the transmission of sound objectively, leaving the subjective interpretation of the effects of sound waves on the human ear and brain to the philosophers.

Every sound wave originates from a vibrating source. The average human is responsive to frequencies of between 20 Hz and 20 000 Hz (see table). Frequencies of less than 20 Hz are referred to as **infrasonic** and those of more than 20 000 Hz are called **ultrasonic**.

Subjectively—"dependent on an individual's point of view"
Objectively—"dependent on external evidence and not on thoughts or feelings"

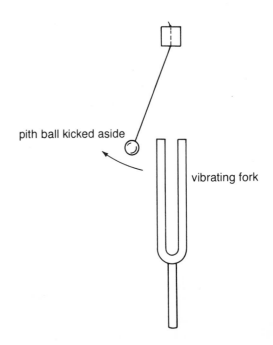

pith ball kicked aside

vibrating fork

Frequencies of Commonly Heard Sounds

Source	Frequency (Hz)	Source	Frequency (Hz)
Lowest piano note	27.50	Middle C of piano	261.63
Male speaking voice (average)	120	A above middle C	440.00
Female speaking voice (average)	250	Highest piano note	4186.01

Range of transmitted sound

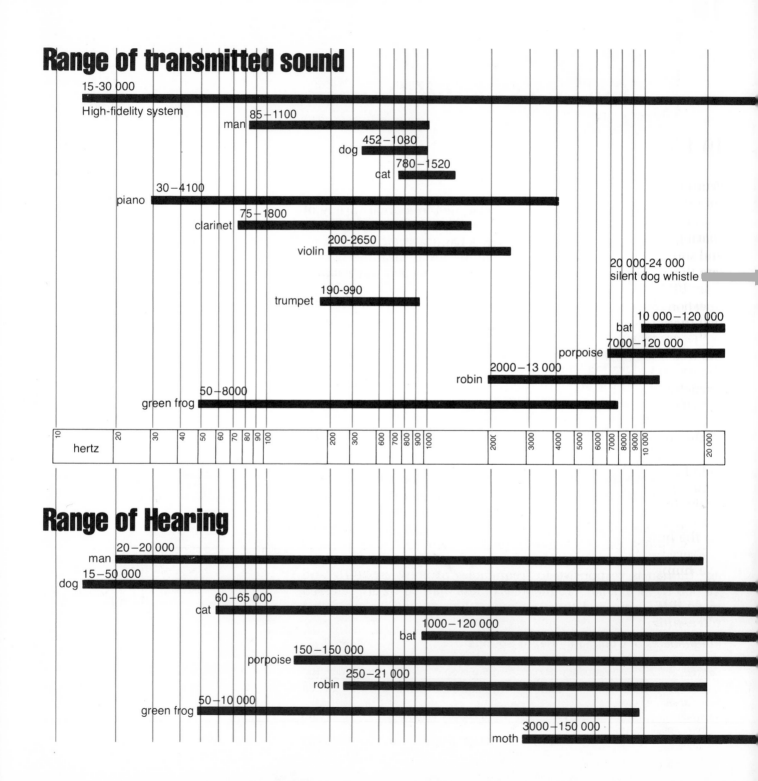

15-30 000	High-fidelity system
85−1100	man
452−1080	dog
780−1520	cat
30−4100	piano
75−1800	clarinet
200-2650	violin
20 000-24 000	silent dog whistle
190-990	trumpet
10 000−120 000	bat
7000−120 000	porpoise
2000−13 000	robin
50−8000	green frog

hertz: 10 20 30 40 50 60 70 80 90 100 200 300 600 700 800 900 1000 2000 3000 4000 5000 6000 7000 8000 9000 10 000 20 000

Range of Hearing

20−20 000	man
15−50 000	dog
60−65 000	cat
1000−120 000	bat
150−150 000	porpoise
250−21 000	robin
50−10 000	green frog
3000−150 000	moth

19.2 The Speed of Sound Waves

In 1654, Otto von Guericke, the inventor of the air pump, discovered that the intensity of the sound from a mechanical bell inside a jar decreased steadily as the air was removed from the jar. Today this effect is demonstrated by means of an electric bell in a bell jar from which air is drawn out by a vacuum pump.

Von Guericke learned from another experiment that the sound of a ringing bell could be transmitted clearly through water. In his experiment, fish were attracted by the sound of a bell in the water. An underwater swimmer sometimes hears an approaching motorboat before a swimmer on the surface does. Most of us have experienced vibrations in the ground from a passing truck or train. If you put your ear against a steel fence, you can hear the sound of a stone being tapped against it a considerable distance away.

These examples all point to the conclusion that sound needs a material medium for its transmission. It will not travel through a vacuum.

In the case of sound travelling along a metal fence, you may hear the same sound twice – first through the fence, then through the air. You hear it first through the fence because sound travels approximately 15 times faster in steel than it does in air. Experiments in water indicate that sound travels four times faster in water than in air.

How fast does sound travel in air? The speed of sound in air was first accurately measured in 1738 by members of the French Academy. Cannons were set up on two hills approximately 29 km apart. By measuring the time interval between the flash of a cannon and the "boom", the speed of sound was calculated. Two cannons were used, and they were fired alternately, to minimize errors due to the wind and to delayed reactions in the observers.

Accurate measurements of the speed of sound in air have been made at various temperatures and air pressures. At normal atmospheric pressure and at 0°C, it is 332 m/s. If the air pressure remains constant, the speed of sound increases as the temperature increases. It has been found that the speed of sound in air changes by 0.6 m/s for each degree Celsius.

**Speed of sound in air = (332 + 0.6 T) m/s
(at normal atmospheric pressure)**

---

where T represents the temperature in °C and the speed is in metres per second

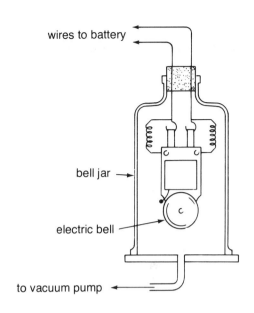

The speed of light was assumed to be great enough that the flash was seen instantaneously.

Speed of Sound in Various Media

Substance	Speed at 0°C (m/s)
carbon dioxide	258
oxygen	317
air	332
cork	500
lead	1200
alcohol	1241
hydrogen gas	1270
sea water*	1440-1500
fresh water	1500
pine wood	3320
copper	3560
marble	3810
maple wood	4110
steel	5050
aluminum	5104
earth	7000-13 000

*varies with depth, temperature, and salinity

Sample problem

What is the speed of sound at (a) 20°C and (b) −20°C?

(a) $v = (332 + 0.6\,T)$ m/s
= 332 + 0.6 (20)
= 332 + 12
= 344 m/s

(b) $v = (332 + 0.6\,T)$ m/s
= 332 + 0.6 (−20)
= 332 − 12
= 320 m/s

Practice

1. What is the speed of sound in air when the temperature is (a) −10°C, (b) 24°C, and (c) 35°C?
(326 m/s, 346 m/s, 353 m/s)
2. How much time is required for sound to travel 1.4 km through air if the temperature is 30°C? (4.0 s)

The speed of sound varies in different materials. In general, it is greater in solids and liquids than in gases, but there are some exceptions (see chart). For example, in lead and hydrogen sound has similar speeds at the same temperature. Some substances, such as earth and sea water, display a range of speeds for sound because other physical factors, and not just temperature, can affect the speed.

19.3 Mach Number

High speeds for supersonic aircraft, such as the Concorde, are given in terms of **Mach number** rather than kilometres per hour. The Mach number is the ratio of the speed of an object to the speed of sound.

$$\text{Mach number} = \frac{\text{speed of object}}{\text{speed of sound}}$$

The speed of sound at sea level and 0°C is 332 m/s, or approximately 1200 km/h. At an altitude of 10 km, it is approximately 1060 km/h. An aircraft flying at an altitude of 10 km with a speed of 1800 km/h has a Mach number of $\frac{1800 \text{ km/h}}{1060 \text{ km/h}}$ or 1.7

Practice

1. What is the Mach number of an aircraft travelling at sea level at 0°C with a speed of (**a**) 1440 km/h, and (**b**) 900 km/h?
   (**1.2; 0.75**)

2. A military interceptor airplane can fly at Mach 2.0. What is its speed in kilometres per hour at sea level, and at 0°C?
   (**2400 km/h**)

19.4 The Transmission of Sound Waves

In Chapter 18, we investigated waves travelling along a spiral spring. These waves were called transverse waves because the particles in the spring vibrated at right angles to the direction of the motion of the waves. In the next investigation, we will examine another type of wave, the longitudinal wave.

Investigation: Longitudinal Waves

Problem:
How is a longitudinal wave transmitted through a spiral spring?

Materials:
spiral spring
masking tape

Procedure

1. With the help of your partner, stretch the spring out to a length of approximately 3.0 m on a smooth, clean floor.
2. Attach masking-tape tabs at six equally spaced points along the spring.
3. At one end of the spring, compress approximately 10 coils between your fingers.
4. Release the compressed coils and observe the motion of the masking-tape tabs as the pulse travels along the spring. Repeat this procedure a number of times, until the motion of the tabs is easily observed.
5. Place your hand in the coils at one end of the spring, and move your hand forward quickly. Note the motion of the tabs. Now, move your hand back quickly, and again note the motion of the tabs.
6. Move your hand back and forth quickly at a uniform frequency. Watch the series of pulses as it travels down the coil. Note the motion of the tabs.

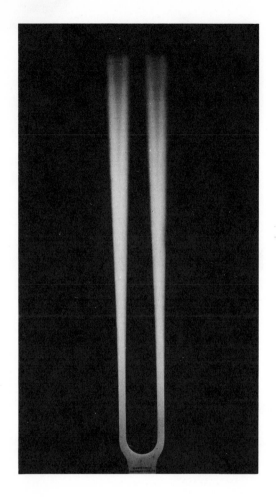

Questions

1. Describe how each section of the spring moved, relative to the direction of motion of the pulse along the spring.
2. What happened to the coils in the spring when your hand moved forward? (This is called a "compression".)
3. What happened to the spaces between the coils when your hand moved back? (This is called a "rarefaction".)
4. When you moved your hand back and forth at a uniform frequency, how did the spaces between successive compressions compare?
5. How many complete vibrations of your hand were required to produce one compression and one rarefaction?

The waves in this investigation differ from the transverse waves described in Chapter 18, in that the coils vibrate parallel to the direction of the motion of the waves, and not at right angles to it. Such waves are called **longitudinal waves**. Sound travels as a longitudinal wave, and it consists of a series of compressions and rarefactions.

When a tuning fork is struck, it vibrates with its tines out of phase (see photograph). As each tine moves out, it pushes air molecules out until they bump against their neighbours. This creates a steadily moving area of collision, called a **compression**. When the tine moves back it creates a region of emptiness, a **rarefaction**, into which the displaced air molecules rebound. This follows the compression outwards. As the tines move back and forth, rarefactions and compressions follow one another as the sound waves travel through the air away from the tuning fork (see illustration). The particles of air only vibrate. They do not move from the source to the receiver.

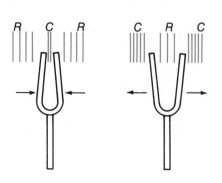

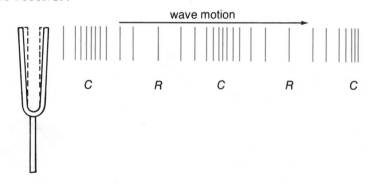

The diagram shows the propagation of sound waves in one direction only. Actually, the sound waves go out in all directions, as do any waves from a vibrating point source.

In transverse waves, one **wavelength** is the distance between the mid points of successive crests or successive troughs (Section 18.3). In longitudinal waves, one wavelength is the distance between the mid points of successive compressions or rarefactions. The maximum displacement of the particles from the rest position is the **amplitude** of the sound wave, and the Universal Wave Equation ($v = f\lambda$) may be used, since it applies to all waves (see illustration).

In sound waves, a compression is an area of higher than normal air pressure and a rarefaction is an area of lower than normal air pressure. The graph illustrates these variations in pressure as a sound wave moves away from its source. Longitudinal waves are difficult to represent visually, and it is more helpful, at times, to use a graph of pressure variations.

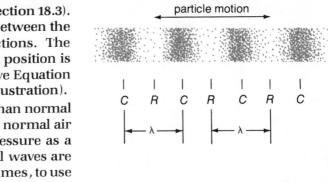

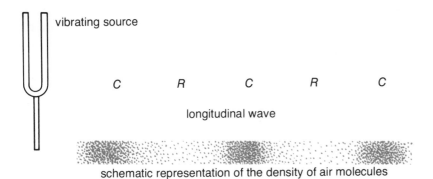

schematic representation of the density of air molecules

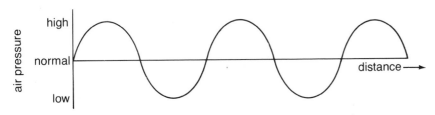

Sample problem

The sound from a trumpet travels at a speed of 350 m/s in air. If the frequency of the note played is 300 Hz, what is the wavelength of the sound wave?

$$\lambda = \frac{v}{f}$$
$$= \frac{350 \text{ m/s}}{300 \text{ Hz}}$$
$$= 1.17 \text{ m}$$

Alexander Graham Bell

The "bel" is too large a unit to be used for most sounds. So the decibel (dB) is usually used.

Practice

1. An organ pipe emits a note of 50 Hz. If the speed of sound in air is 350 m/s, what is the wavelength of the sound wave?
(**7.0 m**)

2. If a 260 Hz sound from a tuning fork has a wavelength of 1.30 m, at what speed does the sound travel? (**338 m/s**)

3. A sound wave with a wavelength of 10 m travels at 350 m/s. What is its frequency? (**35 Hz**)

19.5 The Intensity of Sound

Frequency, wavelength, and speed are all quantities of sound that can be measured accurately.

Sound intensity, or loudness, is more difficult to measure because the amount of energy involved is small in comparison with other forms of energy and because the potential range of sound intensity is great.

The heat energy equivalent of the sound energy emitted over a 90 min period by a crowd of 50 000 at a football game is only enough to heat one cup of coffee! A stereo amplifier with a maximum power output of 30 W/channel has an actual sound output of less than 10 W – more than enough to fill an auditorium with sound.

Sounds audible to humans can vary in intensity from the quietest whisper to a level that is painful to the ear – a difference of a factor of 10^{13}. The unit used to measure the intensity of sound is the **decibel** (dB), named after the inventor of the telephone. On the decibel scale, 0 dB is fixed near the threshhold of hearing, at a value of 0.000 000 000 001 W/m^2 (10^{-12} W/m^2). The scale is not linear, with uniform gradations. A sound 10 times louder than 0 dB is 10 dB, a sound 100 times louder than 0 dB is 20 dB, a sound 1000 times more intense than 0 dB is 30 dB, and so on. The level of sound that is painful to the human ear (130 dB) is 10^{13} times more intense than the level at the threshold of hearing. The sound intensity levels for common sources are listed in a chart.

Sound Intensity Levels for Various Sources

Source	Intensity (dB)	Intensity (W/m^2)
threshold of hearing	0	10^{-12}
normal breathing	10	10^{-11}
average whisper at 2 m	20	10^{-10}
empty theatre	30	10^{-9}
residential area at night	40	10^{-8}
quiet restaurant	50	10^{-7}
two-person conversation	60	10^{-6}
busy street traffic	70	10^{-5}
vacuum cleaner	80	10^{-4}
at the foot of Niagara Falls loud hi-fi in average room passing subway train	90	10^{-3}
maximum level in concert hall − 13th row	100	10^{-2}
pneumatic chisel	110	10^{-1}
maximum level of some rock groups propeller plane taking off	120	1
threshold of pain	130	10
military jet taking off	140	10^2
wind tunnel	150	10^3
space rocket instant perforation of the eardrum	160	10^4

The sound intensity levels of some rock bands exceed 110 dB.

The intensity of a sound received by the human ear depends on the power of the source and the distance between the source and the person. Like water waves, sound waves moving out from a point source spread their wave energy over an increasing area. Thus, the intensity of a sound decreases as the wave moves from the source to the receiver. The reading on the decibel scale also decreases as the distance increases. For example, a reading of 100 dB at 1 m becomes 60 dB at 100 m.

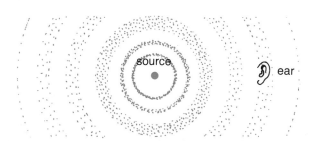

As a sound wave moves out from a source, its energy is spread more and more thinly.

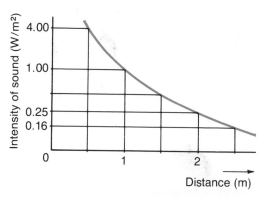

Graph of sound intensity versus distance

19.6 The Human Ear

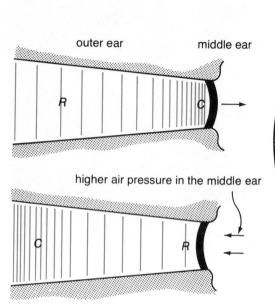

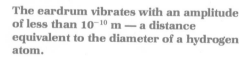

higher air pressure in the middle ear

The eardrum vibrates with an amplitude of less than 10^{-10} m — a distance equivalent to the diameter of a hydrogen atom.

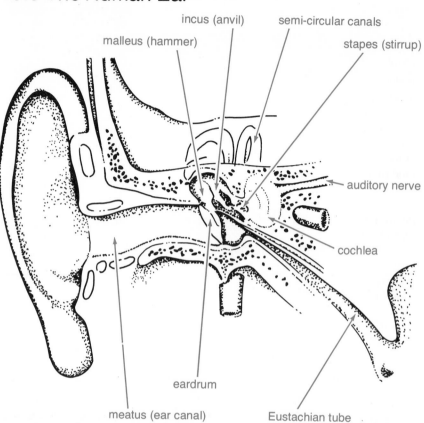

A rarefaction is actually an area of reduced atmospheric pressure. Thus, when a rarefaction approaches the external side of the eardrum, the higher atmospheric pressure in the middle ear causes the eardrum to move out.

The human ear consists of three sections: the outer ear, the middle ear, and the inner ear. The outer ear consists of the external ear flap and a cylindrical canal (the meatus). The function of these two parts is to help the hearer identify the direction of the sound and to direct the sound to the eardrum. The **ear canal** is about 2 cm long, and so the eardrum is protected from direct injury. Although the hearing range of a healthy young adult is approximately 16 to 20 000 Hz, the structure of the ear canal amplifies frequencies between 2000 and 5500 Hz by a factor of nearly 10, emphasizing these frequencies.

The ear canal ends at the **eardrum**, which is constructed of a very tough, tightly stretched membrane less than 0.1 mm thick. The eardrum is forced into vibration by successive compressions and rarefactions coming down the ear canal. Compressions force the eardrum in and rarefactions cause it to move out, and the resultant vibration has the same frequency as the source of the sound waves.

Attached to the inside of the eardrum are three small interlocking bones: the **hammer** (malleus), the **anvil** (incus), and the **stirrup** (stapes). These bones constitute the middle ear and transmit the vibrations of the eardrum to the inner ear, mechanically amplifying them by a factor of three. The cavity containing the middle ear is filled with air and is connected to the mouth by the **Eustachian tube**. This tube is normally closed but it opens during swallowing or yawning, equalizing the air pressure in the middle ear. If the Eustachian tube becomes blocked, because of a cold, for example, pressure equalization cannot take place, and the result is pressure in the middle ear which can be quite painful and can affect hearing.

The stirrup transmits the eardrum vibrations to the threshold of the inner ear. The vibrations set up pressure waves in the fluid that fills the inner ear's cochlea. The **cochlea** is a snail-shaped organ approximately 3.0 cm long, divided into two equal sections by a partition for most of its length. Waves are transmitted down one side of the cochlea, around the end of the partition, and back almost to the point of origin. As these waves move, they cause approximately 23 000 microscopic hairs to vibrate. Each hair is connected to a cell that converts the mechanical motion of the hair into an electrical signal, which is in turn transmitted to the brain by the auditory nerve. How these codified electrical signals are interpreted by the brain is a wondrous thing we know very little about.

In addition to the cochlea, the inner ear contains three hard, fluid-filled loops, called the semi-circular canals, which are situated more or less at right angles to each other. These act as miniature accelerometers, transmitting to the brain electrical signals necessary for balance.

Loud sounds do not as a rule harm the eardrum, although an exploding firecracker may cause it to burst. Such damage can be repaired, but permanent damage may be inflicted by intense sounds on the microscopic, hairlike cells in the inner ear. A particularly loud sound may rip away these delicate cells. A single blast of 150 dB or more can cause permanent damage to the ear, and levels of more than 90 dB over a prolonged period can produce the same effect. Persons employed in noisy places usually wear ear protectors as a precaution against this danger. Many cases of premature deafness are caused by prolonged exposure to loud sounds. Examples include rock musicians, skeet shooters, factory workers, miners, construction workers, and young people listening to music at high levels.

The graph shows that all human beings suffer some loss of hearing as they grow older. The loss is significantly higher for those living in an industrial setting – whether or not they are employed in

High sound levels near jet engines make the use of ear-protection devices imperative.

Tests carried out on Mabaan tribesmen in remote Sudanese villages in 1962 showed that the normal deterioration of their hearing was considerably less than the average American's and strikingly less than that of noise-exposed North American industrial workers.

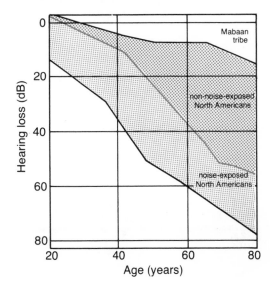

noisy occupations. Our increasingly noisy environment has penalties beyond mere annoyance, which emphasize the need for sound-pollution legislation.

19.7 Reflection of Sound Waves

Sound waves radiating out from a source are reflected when they strike a rigid obstacle, the angle of reflection being equal to the angle of incidence. This can be demonstrated using two cardboard tubes inclined to one another and directed towards a flat surface, such as a blackboard or wall. A ticking watch placed near the end of one tube can be heard clearly by an ear at the end of the other tube only if the tubes are arranged so that the angle of incidence and the angle of reflection are equal.

At the Ontario Science Centre, sound waves reflected from a curved reflector similar to this one, located 50 m away, may be clearly heard.

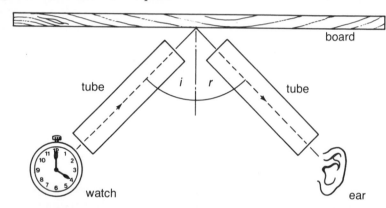

Sound waves conform to the Laws of Reflection. A good demonstration of this may be observed at the Ontario Science Centre in Toronto. Two large metal concave reflectors are located at opposite ends of a large room. A person standing at the focus of one reflector can talk in a normal voice and be heard clearly by a person standing at the focus of the other reflector, which is 50 m away. Outdoor stages are usually designed to reflect the sound of a band or orchestra to the audience. The performers are located in the focal plane of a hard concave reflector, which is often called a band shell because it looks like a large sea shell. The Hollywood Bowl in California and the Band Shell at the Canadian National Exhibition in Toronto are two examples. Sometimes it is necessary to reflect sound from the ceiling of a concert hall. Large, convex, acrylic discs were installed in the Forum at Ontario Place in Toronto and suspended from the ceiling of the Royal Albert Hall in London, England, to improve the acoustical properties of these buildings.

Curved reflectors suspended above the stage at the Ontario Place Forum in Toronto direct sound waves towards the audience.

A microphone at the focal point of a concave reflector, called a **parabolic microphone**, is sometimes used to pick up remote sounds at a sports event or to record bird calls.

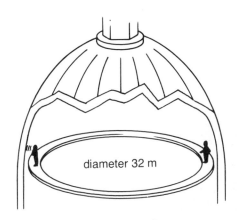

In the dome of St. Paul's Cathedral, London, whispers can be heard clearly 32 m away.

Stereo parabolic microphones in use on a movie set

Echoes are produced when sound is reflected by a hard surface, such as a wall or cliff. The echo can be heard by the human ear only if the time interval between the original sound and the reflected sound is greater than 0.1 s. For practical purposes, the distance between the observer and the reflecting surface must be greater than 17 m.

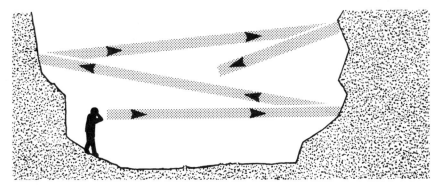

As the sound is reflected back and forth, the caller hears the echo of his call. The diagram shows only some of the sound waves. Actually, the waves are reflected all around the canyon, and only some of them return to the caller, making the echo less intense than the original call.

Investigation: Speed of Sound—Echo Method

Problem:

What is the speed of sound, as determined by the echo method?

Materials:

2 wooden blocks
stopwatch

Procedure

1. Locate a high wall with clear space at least 100 m deep in front of it.
2. Clap two boards together and listen for the echo. Repeat until you have determined the approximate time interval between the original sound and the echo.
3. Now clap the two boards together, adjusting the rate of the striking so that each clap is made simultaneously with the arrival of the echo from the previous clap.
4. When you have achieved the correct timing, have your partner record, with the stopwatch, the number of seconds required for 20 or more clap intervals. (Remember to start counting with zero!)
5. Determine the average interval between claps. This interval is equal to the time taken for the sound to travel twice the distance between you and the wall.
6. Measure the distance to the wall in metres and the temperature of the air.
7. Calculate the speed of sound in air.

Questions

1. How does your value for the speed of sound in air compare with the accepted value? What was your percentage error?
2. Knowing the speed of sound, how might you determine the distance between your point of observation and a granite cliff some distance away?

The **echo-sounder** is a device that uses the principles of sound reflection to measure the depth of the sea. A so-called "transducer" is placed in the bottom of a ship. It converts electrical energy into sound energy and sends out a series of equally spaced sound pulses with a frequency of approximately 30 kHz. The pulses are reflected from the sea bed back up to the ship where they are received by an underwater microphone, called a "hydrophone". The time interval between the emission of the signal and the reception of the echo is measured by a computer which then calculates the depth of the water and records it on a moving chart.

Similar equipment is used by fishermen to locate schools of fish. More sophisticated equipment of the same type is used by the armed forces to locate submarines. All such devices are called **sonar** (sound navigation and ranging) devices. Ultrasonic sonar devices are also used to detect flaws in railway tracks and pipelines, to determine the fat/lean ratio in live cattle and pigs, to diagnose brain damage, to detect breast cancer, and to monitor the growth of a human fetus in the womb.

A similar technique is used in **radar** (radio detection and ranging). A rotating transmitter sends out a series of high-frequency radio pulses that are reflected back as echoes from an object such as an airplane or a coastal cliff. The time interval between transmission of the signal and reception of the echo depends on the object's distance from the transmitter. The results are usually displayed on a cathode ray tube. It is important to note that radar employs very short radio waves, not sound waves.

This recorder is capable of recording a single fish at over 100 fathoms.

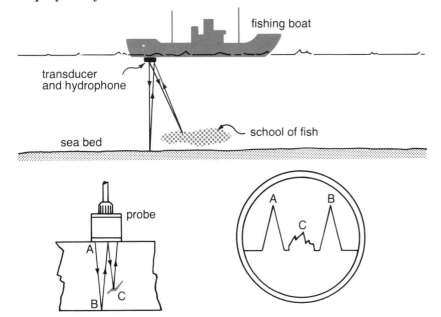

Echoes can be used to detect flaws in a metal casting.

A=pulse sent out by transducer
B=pulse reflected from bottom of metal
C=pulse reflected by a flaw in the metal

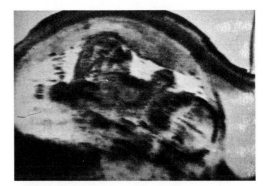

Sonar photograph of a human fetus in the womb.

Sample problems

1. In an experiment to determine the speed of sound by the echo method, two students find that 20 claps of the board require 10 s. If the distance to the wall is 86 m, what is the speed of sound in air?

$$\text{Period} = \frac{\text{time}}{\text{number of claps}}$$
$$= \frac{10 \text{ s}}{20}$$
$$= 0.50 \text{ s}$$

Distance sound travelled = 2(86 m) = 172 m

$$v = \frac{\triangle d}{\triangle t}$$
$$= \frac{172 \text{ m}}{0.50 \text{ s}}$$
$$= 3.4 \times 10^2 \text{ m/s}$$

2. A boy yells towards a cliff and hears his echo 2.00 s later. If the speed of sound is 340 m/s, how far away is the cliff?

$$\triangle d = v \triangle t$$
$$= (340 \text{ m/s}) (2.00 \text{ s})$$
$$= 680 \text{ m}$$

Distance to the cliff
$$= {}^1/_2(680) = 340 \text{ m}$$

Practice

1. A student stands 90 m from the foot of a cliff, claps his hands, and hears the echo 0.50 s later. Calculate the speed of sound in air.   (3.6×10^2 m/s)
2. A sonar device is used in a lake, and the interval between the production of a sound and the reception of the echo is found to be 0.40 s. The speed of sound in water is 1500 m/s. What is the depth of the water?   (3.0×10^2 m)

19.8 Acoustics in Buildings

When the reflecting surface is less than 17 m away, the echo follows so closely behind the original sound that the original sound appears to be prolonged (Section 19.7). This effect is called **reverberation.** Reverberations are particularly noticeable in large, empty buildings such as cathedrals and concert halls, but they also occur when we shout in a road underpass or sing in the shower. A certain amount of reverberation may enhance the quality of sound. Excessive reverberation in a concert hall is undesirable because it interferes with the original sound, making speech and music indistinct.

The acoustics of a concert hall are the most important concern of the architect, and the most important property of a concert hall is its **reverberation time.** This is defined as the time required for sound of a standard intensity to die away and become inaudible. The reverberation time depends on the materials used on the walls, the height of the ceiling, the length of the hall, the type of music being played, and the presence or absence of an audience. In some halls, such as the Royal Festival Hall in London, England, the seats are designed so that when they are unoccupied they will absorb the same amount of sound as a seated person. Well-designed halls for orchestral concerts tend to have a reverberation time of between 1 s and 2 s, and halls that are best for choral music have a reverberation time of 2 s to 5 s. Comparative absorption values of various construction materials are given in a chart. Notice that the absorption of sound by a given material varies with the frequency. By the careful choice of materials, a room can be made acoustically "dead", with a reverberation time near zero. Such rooms are called **anechoic** and they are used for studying the performance of sound devices such as telephones, microphones, and loudspeakers.

The Vancouver Symphony Orchestra performing in the 2788-seat Orpheum, Canada's largest concert hall

The ceiling design and suspended reflectors are two notable features of the plan for Toronto's New Massey Hall.

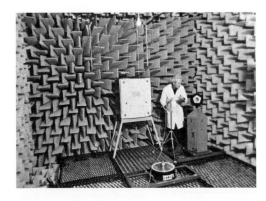

Telephone equipment being tested in an anechoic chamber

Sound Absorption Coefficients for Various Substances

Substance	Frequency 512 Hz	Frequency 2048 Hz
cement	*0.025	0.035
brick	0.03	0.049
wood (pine)	0.06	0.10
carpet	0.02	0.27
fibre glass	0.99	0.86
acoustic tile	0.97	0.68
theatre seats	1.6 – 3.0	–
seated audience	3.0 – 4.3	3.5 – 6.0

*To simplify the chart, units have not been supplied. Substances with larger coefficients have better sound absorption qualities.

19.9 Diffraction and Refraction of Sound Waves

A teacher in the hall can hear the sounds of the classroom through an open door, even though the students are out of sight and separated by a wall. Sounds travelling through an open window are easily heard outside, and even around the corner of a building. The ''sound around the corner'' effect is so familiar to us that we don't give it a second thought. Sound waves can travel around corners because of diffraction. In Section 18.7, it was demonstrated that water waves with relatively long wavelengths are diffracted around an obstacle or through an opening more than water waves with short wavelengths. Sound waves have relatively long wavelengths and thus are easily diffracted.

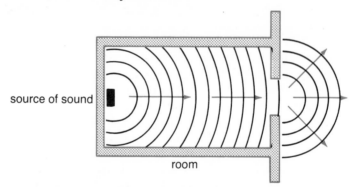

Sound waves are diffracted as they pass through a doorway from one room into the next.

The speed with which a sound travels through air can be affected by the temperature of the air (Section 19.2). Sound waves travel faster in warm air than they do in cold air. If they move from air at one temperature to air at a different temperature, at an angle, they are refracted, as illustrated.

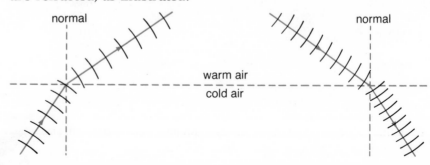

On a warm day, sound waves tend to be refracted away from an observer, which decreases the intensity of the sound heard by the observer. On the other hand, at night, the cooler air near the surface of the Earth tends to refract sound waves towards the surface and so they travel a greater distance. This is particularly true on flat ground or on water. Watch what you say outdoors at night—you may be surprised how far your voice carries!

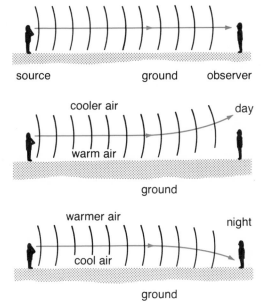

19.10 Summary

1. The frequency limits of sound, for a normal human ear, are usually 20 Hz to 20 000 Hz.
2. Sound requires a material medium for its transmission.
3. The speed of sound waves in a medium is determined by the type of medium and the temperature of the medium.
4. Mach number is the ratio of the speed of an object to the speed of sound.
5. Sound travels as a longitudinal wave.
6. In a longitudinal wave, the particles in the medium vibrate parallel to the direction in which the wave is moving.
7. A longitudinal wave consists of alternate compressions and rarefactions.
8. One wavelength, in a longitudinal wave, is the distance between the mid points of successive compressions or rarefactions.
9. Sound intensity is measured in decibels (dB) or watts per square metre (W/m^2) and 0 dB = 10^{-12} W/m^2.
10. The intensity of sound depends on the power of the source and the distance between the source and the receiver.
11. The human ear transforms sound waves into electrical impulses, which are transmitted to the brain for interpretation.
12. Hearing loss increases with age, and is accelerated by prolonged exposure to high-intensity sound.
13. Sound waves obey the Laws of Reflection.
14. Echoes may be used to determine the speed of sound in air and to locate objects in the same medium as the echo.
15. The types and locations of sound reflectors in a building determine its acoustical properties, including its reverberation time.
16. Sound waves are diffracted around corners and through small openings.

17. Sound waves are refracted because temperature variations in the air change the speed of sound.

19.11 Review

1. What is the speed of sound in air at each of the following temperatures? **(a)** 0°C **(b)** 10°C **(c)** 15°C **(d)** 20°C **(e)** 25°C **(f)** −20°C **(g)** −30°C

2. How long does it take sound to travel 20 km at 15°C?

3. A fan at a baseball game is 100 m from home plate. If the speed of sound is 350 m/s, how long after the batter actually hits the ball does the fan hear the crack? Assume that there is no wind.

4. A lightning flash is seen 10.0 s before the rumble of the thunder is heard. Find the distance to the lightning flash if the temperature is 20°C.

5. A man sets his watch at noon by the sound of a factory whistle 4.8 km away. If the temperature of the air is 20°C, how many seconds slow will his watch be?

6. 6.0 s after a man sees the flash of a distant cannon, he hears the sound of the firing. How far away is the cannon, assuming there is no wind and that the temperature is 25°C?

7. A ship sends a sound signal simultaneously through the air and through the salt water to another ship 1000 m away. Using 336 m/s as the speed of sound in air and 1450 m/s as the speed of sound in salt water, calculate the time interval between the arrival of the two sounds at the second ship.

8. You are standing on a straight road and see lightning strike the ground ahead of you. 3.0 s later you hear the thunderclap. If the speed of sound is 330 m/s, how far will you have to walk to reach the point where the lightning struck?

9. Marchers in a parade sometimes find it difficult to keep in step with the band, if it is some distance from them. Explain why.

10. A violin string is vibrating at a frequency of 440 Hz. How many vibrations does it make while its sound travels 664 m through air at a temperature of 0°C?

11. What is the Mach number of a plane travelling at each of the following speeds at sea level in air with a temperature of 12°C? **(a)** 1020 m/s **(b)** 170 m/s **(c)** 1836 km/h **(d)** 3040 km/h

12. A pulse is a wave of short duration. How could the driver of a diesel locomotive demonstrate a pulse in a train of freight cars?

13. How could you demonstrate a pulse, given six billiard balls and a flat billiard table?

14. The tine of a vibrating tuning fork passes through its central position 600 times in 1.0 s. How many of each of the following has the prong made?
(a) complete cycles
(b) complete waves
(c) compressions
(d) rarefactions

15. Calculate the frequency of a sound wave if its speed and wavelength are
(a) 340 m/s and 1.13 m
(b) 348 m/s and 69.5 cm
(c) 344 m/s and 0.11 cm

16. Calculate the speed of a sound wave in air if its frequency and wavelengths are
(a) 384 Hz and 90.0 cm
(b) 256 Hz and 1.32 m
(c) 1.50 kHz and 23.3 cm

17. Find the wavelengths corresponding to each of the following frequencies, assuming that the speed of sound is 342 m/s.
(a) 20 Hz (b) 500 Hz (c) 2.0×10^4 Hz.

18. What is the wavelength in metres of sound waves with a frequency of 8000 Hz in (a) air (b) water (c) steel? (Use the values given in the table on page 382.)

19. The power of the sound emitted from an average conversation between two people is 10^{-6} W. How many two-people conversations would it take to keep a 60 W bulb glowing, assuming that all the sound energy could be converted into electrical energy?

20. A student standing 99 m from a wall claps his hands and hears the echo 0.60 s later. Calculate the speed of sound in air.

21. A ship is travelling in a fog parallel to a dangerous, cliff-lined shore. The boat whistle is sounded and its echo is heard clearly 11.0 s later. If the air temperature is 10°C, how far is the ship from the cliff?

22. 3.5 s after a man makes a sound, the echo returns from a nearby wall. How far is the man from the wall, assuming that the speed of sound is 350 m/s?

23. A ship is 2030 m from an above-water reflecting surface. The temperature of the air and water is 0°C.
(a) What is the time interval between the production of a sound wave and the reception of its echo, in air?

Numerical Answers to Review Questions

1. (a) 332 m/s (b) 338 m/s (c) 341 m/s (d) 344 m/s (e) 347 m/s (f) 320 m/s (g) 314 m/s
2. 59 s
3. 0.286 s
4. 3.44×10^3 m
5. 14 s
6. 2.1×10^3 m
7. 2.29 s
8. 9.9×10^2 m
10. 880
11. (a) 3.01 (b) 0.501 (c) 1.50 (d) 2.49
14. (a) 300 (b) 300 (c) 300 (d) 300
15. (a) 301 Hz (b) 501 Hz (c) 3.1×10^5 Hz
16. (a) 346 m/s (b) 338 m/s (c) 350 m/s
17. (a) 17 m (b) 0.684 m (c) 1.7×10^{-2} m
18. (a) 4.15×10^{-2} m (b) 0.188 m (c) 0.631 m
19. 6×10^7
20. 3.3×10^2 m/s
21. 1.86×10^3 m
22. 6.1×10^2 m
23. (a) 12.2 (b) 2.71 s
25. 3.3×10^3 m
27. (a) 400 Hz, 3.75 m (b) 400 Hz, 0.830 m
29. 6.6 s
30. (a) 338 m/s (b) 329 m/s (c) 4 m/s

(b) What would the interval be if the reflecting surface was under fresh water?

24. How are sound waves used to map the bottoms of lakes and oceans?

25. An armed forces ship patrolling the ocean receives its own sound signals back, by underwater reflection, 4.5 s after emitting them. How far away is the reflecting surface, in metres?

26. How does a stethoscope transfer sounds from a patient's body to a doctor's ears?

27. A vibrating 400 Hz tuning fork is placed in pure distilled water.
    (a) What are the frequency and the wavelength (in metres) of the sound waves produced within the water at 0°C?
    (b) What would be the frequency and the wavelength in the adjacent air, if the sound waves moved from the water into the air at 0°C?

28. Lightning can produce a sharp crack of thunder or a long rumble lasting a number of seconds, depending on the position of the observer in relation to the lightning discharge. The lightning could strike towards the observer or along a path parallel to the observer. Using your knowledge of sound waves, explain why such variations in the sound of thunder occur.

29. A man drops a stone into a mine shaft 180 m deep. If the temperature is 20°C, how much time will elapse between the moment when the stone is dropped and the moment when the sound of the stone hitting the bottom of the mine shaft is heard?

30. Two observers, A and B, are located 1 km apart. Each has a gun and a stopwatch and a wind is blowing directly from A to B. When the gun is fired by A, B hears the sound 2.96 s later. When the gun is fired by B, the sound is heard by A 3.04 s later. Calculate **(a)** the speed of sound travelling from A to B, **(b)** the speed of sound travelling from B to A, and **(c)** the speed of the wind.

19.12 Learning Objectives

1. To distinguish between audible sound, infrasonic sound, and ultrasonic sound.
2. Given the speed of sound in air at 0°C, to determine the speed at a given temperature.
3. Given any two of Mach number, speed of sound, and speed of an object, to determine the third.
4. To compare the characteristics of a longitudinal wave and a transverse wave.
5. Given any two of the speed of sound, the frequency (or period), and the wavelength, to determine the third, using the Universal Wave Equation.
6. To state four sample readings of sound intensity on the dB scale, including the threshold of hearing and the threshold of pain.
7. To describe, briefly, the principle parts of the outer ear, the middle ear, and the inner ear.
8. To explain why prolonged, high-intensity sound can cause premature loss of hearing.
9. To distinguish between echoes and reverberations.
10. To describe a method for determining the speed of sound in air, using the echo method.
11. Given any two of the speed of sound, the distance to a reflecting surface, and the time interval between the occurrence of a sound and the reception of its echo, to calculate the third.
12. To describe why reverberation time is important to the design of a concert hall.
13. To describe why sound waves are diffracted and refracted in air.

20 Interference in Sound Waves

It is quite common for two or more sound waves to travel through a medium at the same time. When two or more sound waves act on the same air molecules, at the same time, interference occurs. In Chapter 18, the interference of transverse water waves was examined. It was found that water waves can interfere constructively or destructively.

Sound energy, travelling as a wave, should exhibit many of the properties of wave interference previously discussed. In this chapter we will investigate interference in sound waves and use this knowledge to examine some of its applications.

20.1 Interference of Identical Sound Waves

In Section 18.11, we examined the interference of two water waves, originating from two point sources in a ripple tank. Since the water waves were identical, a stationary interference pattern was produced consisting of a symmetrical pattern of alternating nodal lines and regions of constructive interference. In the next investigation we will examine the interference created by sound waves originating from two identical sources.

Investigation: Interference in Sound Waves from a Tuning Fork and Two Loudspeakers

Problem:
What is the interference pattern produced in the region surrounding a tuning fork and in the region between two identical loudspeakers?

Materials:
tuning fork
rubber hammer
audio signal generator
audio amplifier
two identical loudspeakers

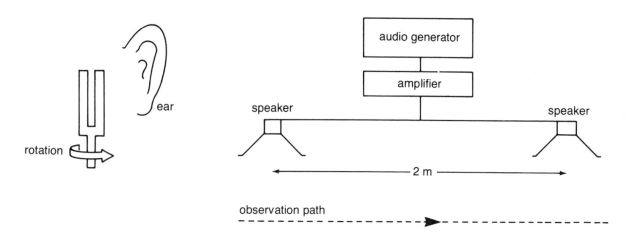

Procedure

1. Strike the tuning fork sharply with the rubber hammer.
2. Place the vibrating tuning fork near your ear.
3. Rotate the tuning fork slowly, through one complete rotation, and note any variations in the intensity of the sound.
4. Ask your partner to note the positions of the tuning fork when the intensity of the sound is at its lowest and its highest levels.

(Steps 5 to 8 are usually done as a class investigation.)

5. Set up the amplifier, generator, and speakers as illustrated, with the speakers approximately 2.0 m apart and raised about 1.0 m from the floor.
6. Adjust the frequency of the generator to approximately 500 Hz.
7. Walk along a path parallel to the plane of the speakers, and note any changes in the intensity of the sound.
8. Repeat this procedure for a higher frequency, e.g., 1200 Hz.

Questions

1. What changes in intensity did you notice when the tuning fork was turned through one rotation?
2. In what specific areas, near the tines, was the sound intensity the greatest and the least?
3. What changes in intensity occurred when you walked from one speaker to the other?
4. What changes in the intensity pattern occurred when the speakers were adjusted to emit a sound of higher frequency?
5. What conditions of interference must have been necessary to produce the maximum intensity and the minimum intensity?

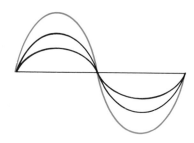

Constructive interference of sound waves

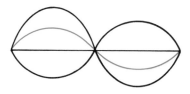

Sound is diminished

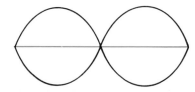

Total destructive interference of sound waves

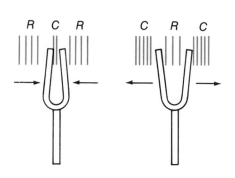

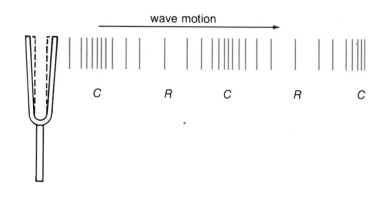

When a tuning fork vibrates, the tines are out of phase (Sections 18.2 and 19.4). A rarefaction is produced in the space between the tines and at the same time a compression is produced on the outer side of each tine. When the tines vibrate, a series of compressions and rarefactions is emitted from the outer sides of the tines and from the space between them, as illustrated. Since the tines are out of phase, the compressions and rarefactions interfere destructively, producing nodal lines that radiate out from the corners of the tines. In the area between the corners of the tines no interference occurs and a normal sound wave emanates from the tines. When the tuning fork is rotated near the ear, the relative sound intensity alternates between loud (normal sound intensity) and soft (destructive interference).

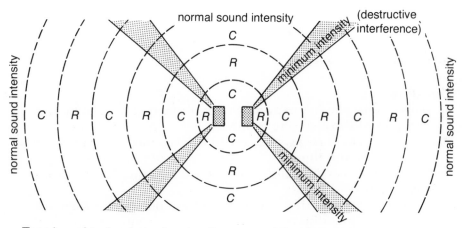

Top view of tuning fork, showing the areas of the destructive interference of sound waves

The interference pattern between the two loudspeakers is similar to the pattern that is observed in water waves, between two point sources. Areas of constructive and destructive interference are located symmetrically about the mid point of the pattern, midway between the speakers. If the loudspeakers are in phase, there is an area of constructive interference (maximum sound intensity) at the mid point. When the frequency is increased, the wavelength decreases. This produces more areas of destructive and constructive interference, as illustrated, but the symmetry of the interference pattern does not change. It is difficult to produce areas of total destructive interference, because sound waves are reflected from the walls and from other surfaces in the room.

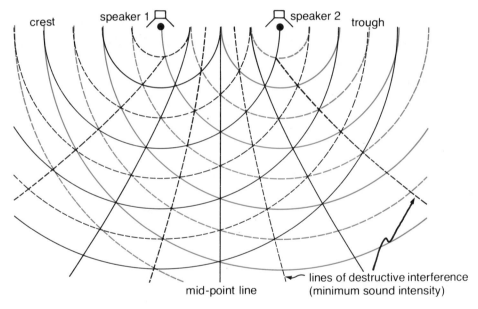

Interference in sound waves from a single source may be demonstrated with an apparatus called a **Herschel tube**. Sound waves from a source such as a tuning fork enter the tube, as illustrated, and split, travelling along two separate paths. If the paths are of the same length, the waves will meet on the other side in phase; that is, compression will meet compression, rarefaction will meet rarefaction, and the intensity will be at a maximum. If, on the other hand, the tube on one side is longer, the waves on that side will have to travel farther. At some point, compressions will emerge with rarefactions, and interfere destructively to produce a minimum sound intensity. Further extension of the tube on one side will reveal other positions in which destructive interference will occur.

William Herschel (1738-1822), a British astronomer, discovered the planet Uranus (in 1781) and the existence of double stars. He constructed the best telescopes of his day.

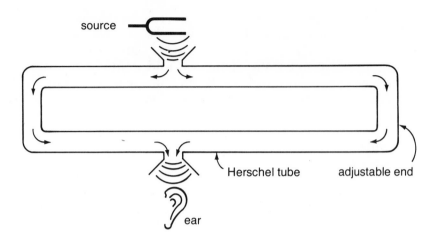

Constructive interference will occur when the path difference is λ, 2λ, 3λ, etc.

In a large auditorium, sound waves are reflected by the walls and ceilings, producing reverberations (Section 19.7). The sound waves can also interfere with one another. In some areas, the audience will receive sound from more than one direction, resulting in interference that may decrease the intensity of the sound in those areas and produce "dead" spots in the auditorium.

20.2 Beat Frequency

We have been examining the interference of sound waves with identical frequencies and wavelengths. Now we will consider the interference of sound waves with slightly different frequencies and wavelengths. If a tuning fork that has one tine "loaded" with plasticine is struck at the same time as an "unloaded" but otherwise identical tuning fork, the resulting sound will alternate between loud and soft, indicating alternating constructive and destructive interference. Such periodic changes in sound intensity are called **beats**.

The next diagram shows two sources with slightly different frequencies. Thus, the wavelengths are not equal and the distances between successive compressions and rarefactions are dissimilar. At certain points, a compression from one source coincides with a rarefaction from the other, producing destructive interference and minimum sound intensity. When compression and compression coincide, constructive interference results, and maximum sound intensity occurs. The number of maximum intensity points that occur per second is called the **beat frequency**.

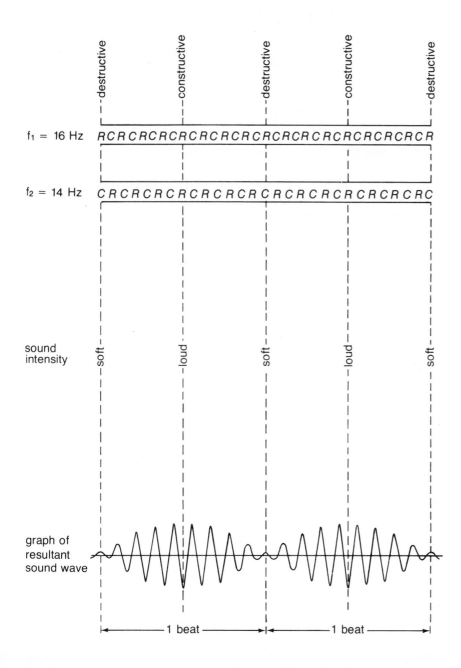

The diagram shows two beats being produced in 1 s. In other words, the beat frequency is two beats per second. The two sources have a frequency difference of 2 Hz. Thus, the difference in frequency between the two sources is equal to the beat frequency. For example, if a tuning fork of 436 Hz is sounded with a 440 Hz tuning fork, the beat frequency will be 4 Hz.

$$\text{Beat frequency} = |f_1 - f_2|$$

where f_1 and f_2 are the frequencies of the two sources

If the two sources have the same frequency (that is, if $f_1 = f_2$), no beats are heard. A piano-tuner makes use of this fact. He plays a note and at the same time sets in vibration a tuning fork or pitch pipe. If there are beats, the two frequencies are dissimilar and the tension in the piano string must be adjusted. Initially, the piano-tuner may have no idea whether the string's frequency is too high or too low. But he knows that the frequency of the beats will change when he adjusts the tension. If the frequency of the beats decreases when he tightens a string, he keeps on tightening it until no beats are audible. Then, the two vibrating sources have the same frequency and the string is "tuned". Once he has tuned seven notes using beat frequency, the piano-tuner adjusts all the other strings by tuning in perfect octaves and using his own sense of pitch.

If the tension of the string increases, the frequency increases. If the tension decreases, the frequency decreases. See Section 20.3.

Sample problem

A tuning fork with a frequency of 256 Hz is sounded, together with a note played on a piano. Nine beats are heard in 3 s. What is the frequency of the piano note?

$$\text{Beat frequency} = \frac{9 \text{ beats}}{3 \text{ s}} = 3 \text{ Hz}$$

$$\text{Beat frequency} = |f_1 - f_2|$$
$$3 = |256 - f_2|$$
$$f_2 = 253 \text{ Hz or } 259 \text{ Hz}$$

Note that there are two possible answers. Without more information, there is no way of knowing which is correct.

Practice
1. A tuning fork with a frequency of 400 Hz is struck with a second fork and 20 beats are counted in 5.0 s. What are the possible

frequencies of the second fork?   (396 Hz, 404 Hz)
2. A third fork with a frequency of 410 Hz is struck with the second fork in question 1, and 18 beats are counted in 3.0 s. What is the frequency of the second fork?   (404 Hz)

20.3 Vibrating Strings

Each string on a guitar has a separate, distinct frequency when set in vibration. The strings are tuned by turning pegs. This alters the tension, changing the frequency, or pitch. It is possible to have two strings of the same length and with the same tension, but with different frequencies, because the frequency is also affected by the diameter of the string and the material it is made of, which may be gut, steel, or aluminum. The pitch of a guitar string may, of course, also be altered by changing the effective length of the string. When you press a string against the neck of a guitar, the effective part of the string is shortened and the frequency thus increased. The pitch, or frequency, of a vibrating string, then, is determined by four factors—its length, its tension, its diameter, and the density of the material it is made of.

The mathematical relationships are as follows:

- **The frequency increases when the length decreases; if the length is halved the frequency is doubled. (Frequency varies inversely with length.)**
- **The frequency increases when the tension increases; if the tension increases by a factor of four, the frequency doubles. (Frequency varies directly as the square root of the tension.)**
- **The frequency increases when the diameter decreases; if the diameter is halved, the frequency doubles. (Frequency varies inversely with the diameter.)**
- **The frequency increases when the density decreases; if the density decreases to one-quarter of its former value, the frequency doubles. (Frequency varies inversely as the square root of the density.)**

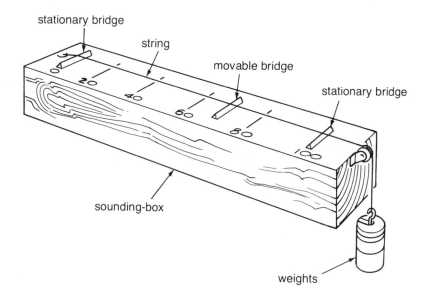

A sonometer can be used to investigate the relationship between the frequency of a stretched string and the tension of the string.

20.4 Modes of Vibration–Quality of Sound

In Section 18.10 we studied the interference of a standing wave pattern in a rope fixed at one end. A series of equally spaced loops (areas of constructive interference) and nodes (points of destructive interference) were formed as the waves interfered after being reflected from the fixed end. Note that, at the fixed end, a node always occurs–never a loop.

The frequencies produced by the fundamental and overtone modes of vibration are sometimes called "harmonics".
The harmonics are numbered as follows:
1st harmonic: the fundamental frequency
2nd harmonic: 1st overtone
3rd harmonic: 2nd overtone
(etc.)

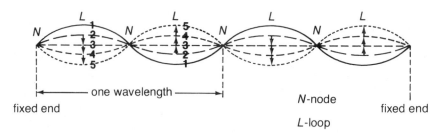

Motion of string in which there is a stationary wave

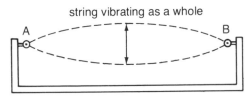

A string vibrating in its fundamental mode

In a vibrating string stretched between two fixed points, nodes occur at both ends. Different frequencies may result, depending on how many loops and nodes are produced. In its simplest mode of vibration, the **fundamental mode**, the string vibrates in one segment, producing its lowest frequency or pitch, called the **fundamental frequency**, f_0. If the string vibrates in more than one segment, the resulting modes of vibration are called **overtones**. Since the string can only vibrate in certain patterns, always with nodes at each end, the frequencies of the overtones are simple (whole numbered) multiples of the fundamental frequency, called **harmonics**, such as $2f_0$, $3f_0$, $4f_0$, and so on.

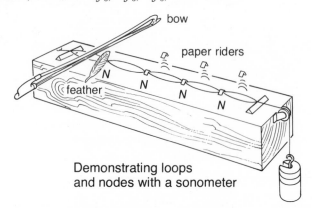

Demonstrating loops and nodes with a sonometer

This can be demonstrated with a sonometer. In this device, the string is touched at its exact centre with a feather, or lightly with a finger, and simultaneously stroked with a bow at the point midway between the centre and the bridge. The string is able to vibrate in only two segments, producing the first overtone, which has twice the frequency of the fundamental. By adjusting the position of the feather, or bow, the string can be made to vibrate in three or more segments, which produces frequencies that are simple multiples of the fundamental frequency, as illustrated.

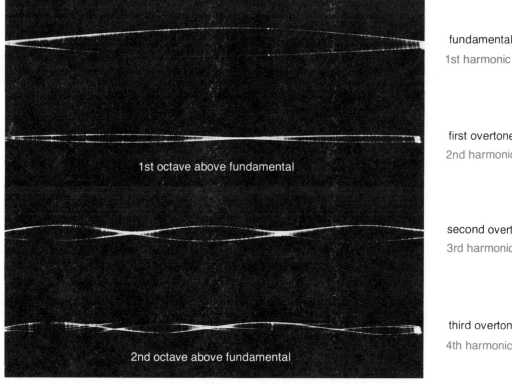

fundamental (f)
1st harmonic

1st octave above fundamental

first overtone ($2f$)
2nd harmonic

second overtone ($3f$)
3rd harmonic

third overtone ($4f$)
4th harmonic

2nd octave above fundamental

The strings of violins and other stringed instruments vibrate in a complex mixture of overtones superimposed on the fundamental. Very few vibrating sources can produce a note free of overtones. An exception is the tuning fork, but even it has overtones when first struck. These disappear quickly, and because of this the tuning fork is a valuable instrument in the study of sound.

The **quality** of a musical note depends on the number and relative intensity of the overtones it produces, along with the fundamental. It is the element of quality that enables us to distinguish

violin

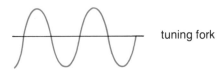
clarinet

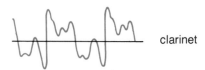
tuning fork

organ pipe

Oscilloscope tracings

between notes of the same frequency and intensity coming from different sources. We are able to distinguish easily between middle C on the piano, on the violin, and in the human voice.

The oscilloscope is an instrument used in the study of sound waves emitted from different sources. A tuning fork, struck lightly, produces a wave pattern that is symmetrical, because the fundamental is the only frequency present. If the tuning fork is struck sharply, it will produce overtones as well, and these will interfere with the fundamental, producing the pattern illustrated.

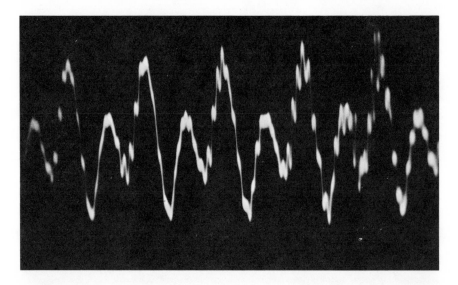

Oscilloscope patterns show that the resultant wave, for a given frequency, is unique for each instrument. The fundamental frequency sets the pitch of a musical note, but in some cases the overtones may be more intense than the fundamental. The overtone frequency structures for various instruments are given in a diagram.

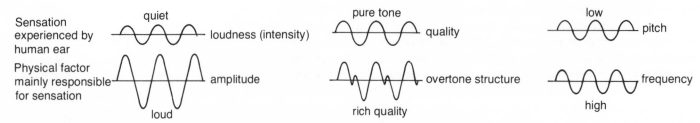

Oscilloscope patterns can be used to illustrate the three characteristics of musical sounds.

20.5 Mechanical Resonance

Every object has a natural frequency at which it will vibrate. To keep a child moving in a swing, we must push the child with the same frequency as the natural frequency of the swing. We use a similar technique to "rock" a car stuck in the snow. When a large truck passes your house, you may notice that the windows rattle.

These are all examples of a phenomenon called **resonance**, which is the response of an object that is free to vibrate to a periodic force with the same frequency as the natural frequency of the object. We call such resonance **mechanical** because there is physical contact between the periodic force and the vibrating object. It can be demonstrated with a series of pendulums suspended from a stretched string (see diagram).

When A is set in vibration, E begins to vibrate but B, C, and D do not. When B is set in vibration, D begins to vibrate in sympathy but A, C, and E remain still. The pairs A and E, and B and D, each have the same lengths and thus have the same natural frequencies. They are connected to the same support, so the energy of B (for example) is transferred along the supporting string to D, causing the latter to vibrate. This occurs only if D is free to vibrate. The periodic vibratory force exerted by one of the pendulums moves through the supporting string to all the other pendulums, but only the other one with the same natural frequency begins to vibrate in resonance.

Mechanical resonance must be taken into account in the designing of bridges, airplane propellers, helicopter rotor blades, turbines for steam generators and jet engines, plumbing systems, and many other types of equipment. A dangerous resonant condition may result if this is not done. The Tacoma suspension bridge in Washington state collapsed in 1941 when wind caused the bridge to vibrate. In 1841, a troop of British soldiers marched in step across a bridge and the tramping feet created a periodic force that set the bridge in resonant vibration and the bridge collapsed.

Suspension systems for cars with radial tires must be designed so that the motion in the tires does not set up a resonant vibration in the suspension. Helicopter blades, propellers, and turbines must be expertly designed and balanced. If they are not, they may produce a resonant vibration when rotated at a certain speed, and the equipment to which they are attached may be destroyed.

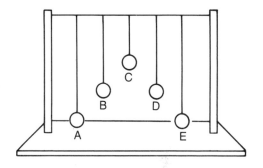

The Tacoma bridge vibrated in an overtone mode of three segments.

As a result of the collapse, British army regulations were changed, requiring soldiers to break step when crossing a bridge.

20.6 Resonance in Air Columns

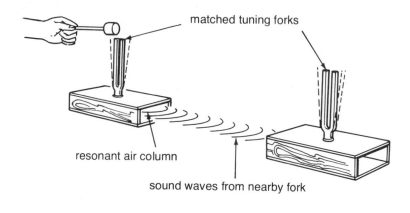

matched tuning forks

resonant air column

sound waves from nearby fork

Sound waves from one source can cause an identical source to vibrate in resonance. Suppose that two tuning forks of identical frequency mounted on wooden boxes of identical length and open at one end are placed about 1 m apart. When the first fork is struck and then silenced, a sound of the same frequency comes from the second fork even though it was not struck. Resonance has occurred because the forks have the same natural frequency. Energy has been transferred from one fork to the other by sound waves.

But, why is the wooden box attached to the tuning fork? Why is it open at one end and why is the resonance box designed to be of a specific length? This is the topic of the next investigation.

Investigation: Resonance in Closed Air Columns

A closed air column is an enclosed air space open at one end and closed at the other.

Problem:
What lengths of a closed air column will resonate in response to a tuning fork of known frequency?

Materials:
80 cm of plastic pipe
large graduated cylinder
512 Hz and 1024 Hz tuning forks
metre stick
thermometer

Procedure

1. Place the plastic pipe in the graduated cylinder, as illustrated. Fill the graduated cylinder with water, as close to the top as possible.
2. Sound the tuning fork and hold it over the mouth of the plastic pipe. Have your partner move the pipe slowly out of the water, and listen for the first resonant point. At points of resonance the intensity of the sound originating from the tuning fork will increase dramatically. Ignore points of slightly increased intensity that are not of the same frequency as the tuning fork.
3. Using the metre stick, measure the length of the air column for the first point. Record your measurements in a chart, as illustrated.

If there is a meniscus, take all measurements from its mid point.

Resonance point	Fork No. 1 f_1 = 512 Hz		Fork No. 2 f_2 = 1024 Hz	
	length in centimetres	length in wavelengths	length in centimetres	length in wavelengths
First				
Second				
Third				

4. Continue to raise the pipe, finding and measuring other resonant points.
5. Repeat the procedure with a tuning fork of higher frequency.
6. Record the air temperature in the room.

Questions

1. What is the speed of sound at the air temperature you recorded?
2. What is the wavelength of the sound wave emitted by each tuning fork used in the investigation?
3. What is the relationship between the length of the closed air column for the first resonant point you encountered and the wavelength of the tuning fork, for each fork?
4. What is the relationship between the length of the closed air column for the second resonant point you encountered and the wavelength of the tuning fork, for each fork?
5. As a general rule, what are the resonant lengths, expressed in wavelengths, for a closed air column?

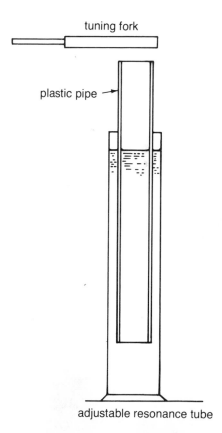

tuning fork

plastic pipe →

adjustable resonance tube

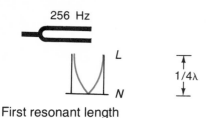

First resonant length

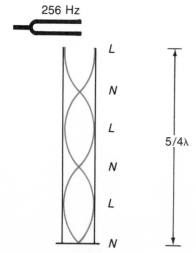

Second resonant length

Third resonant length

Resonant lengths of a closed air column
for a given frequency

When a vibrating tuning fork was held over the closed air column, the intensity of sound varied as the length of the column was altered, and for each fork it was at a peak at certain lengths. In examining this behaviour of the motion of the sound waves in a **closed air column**, we must recall our investigation of standing waves (Section 18.10).

When a series of transverse waves was sent down a rope or spring towards a fixed end, it was reflected back, interfering with the incident waves. A node was always formed at the fixed end where the reflection occurred.

In the previous investigation, longitudinal sound waves were emitted by a tuning fork, and some of them travelled down the closed air column. The surface of the water reflected the sound waves back, in the same way that the waves in a rope were reflection from the fixed end (Section 18.10). A node was thus formed at the bottom of the column, and, since the air was free to move at the top of the tube, a loop formed there.

When the resonance first occurs, the column is $1/4\lambda$ in length, since a single loop and node are formed. The next possible lengths with a node at one end and a loop at the other are $3/4\lambda$, $5/4\lambda$, and so on. Thus, the **resonant lengths** in a closed air column occur at $1/4\lambda$, $3/4\lambda$, $5/4\lambda$, $7/4\lambda$, and so on. The resonant length of the wooden box that is open at one end and attached to a tuning fork is $1/4\lambda$. For a 256 Hz tuning fork, $1/4\lambda$ would be approximately 34 cm at room temperature (20°C).

Sample problem

The first resonant length of a closed air column occurs when the length is 18 cm. (a) What is the wavelength of the sound? (b) If the frequency of the source is 512 Hz, what is the speed of sound?

(a)   first resonant length = $1/4\lambda$
  $1/4\lambda$ = 18 cm
      λ = 72 cm
        = 0.72 m
(b) $v = f\lambda$
        = (512 Hz) (0.72 m)
        = 3.7×10^2 m/s

Practice

1. The first resonant length of a closed air column occurs when the length is 30 cm. What will the second and third resonant lengths be?
(90 cm, 150 cm)

2. The third resonant length of a closed air column is 75 cm. Determine the first and second resonant lengths.

(15 cm, 45 cm)

3. What is the shortest air column, closed at one end, that will resonate at a frequency of 440 Hz, when the speed of sound is 352 m/s? (20.0 cm)

Resonance may also be produced in **open air columns** or pipes. If a standing wave interference pattern is created by reflection at a free end, a loop occurs at the free end. Since an open pipe is open at both ends, loops are formed at both ends. The first length at which resonance occurs is $\frac{1}{2}\lambda$. Succeeding resonant lengths will occur at λ, $\frac{3}{2}\lambda$, 2λ, and so on, as illustrated.

Sample problem

An organ pipe, open at both ends, produces a musical note at its first resonant length.
(a) What is the wavelength of the note produced?
(b) What is the frequency of the pipe, if the speed of sound in air is 346 m/s?

(a) First resonant length $= \dfrac{1}{2}\lambda$

$$= 3.6 \text{ m}$$
$$\lambda = 7.2 \text{ m}$$

(b) $f = \dfrac{v}{\lambda}$

$$= \dfrac{346 \text{ m/s}}{7.2 \text{ m}}$$
$$= 48 \text{ Hz}$$

Practice
1. The second resonant length of an air column that is open at both ends is 48 cm. Determine the first and third resonant lengths. (24 cm, 72 cm)
2. An organ pipe, open at both ends, resonates at its first resonant length with a frequency of 128 Hz. What is the length of the pipe if the speed of sound is 346 m/s? (1.35 m)

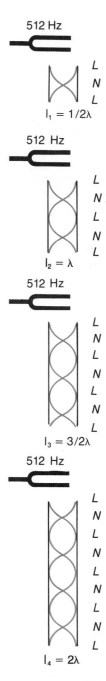

Resonant lengths of an open air column with a sound of given frequency

20.7 Music and Musical Instruments

The mouth, the pharynx, and the larynx together constitute the vocal tract, which is a resonant chamber. The resonant frequencies are determined by the position of the articulators — the lips, the jaw, the tongue — and by the length of the vocal tract, which can be adjusted by the protrusion of the lips or the lowering of the larynx.

A musical note originates from a source vibrating in a uniform manner with one or more constant frequencies. **Music** is a combination of musical notes. (**Noise** is a combination of sounds characterized by vibrations that are constantly changing in frequency.)

Some combinations of musical notes of specific frequencies are pleasing to the ear. This effect is called **consonance**. Other combinations have a harsh effect that is called **dissonance**. The frequencies that are used for musical scales were chosen on the basis of experience and mathematical theory to provide the greatest possible number of pleasing combinations. The conventional musical scale and its frequencies are given in a diagram.

The eight-note scale illustrated is known as the **diatonic major scale**. There are various ways of representing it on paper. In scientific terms, the diatonic scale sets middle C at a frequency of 256 Hz and high C at 512 Hz. Most tuning forks used in the laboratory are pitched to the scientific scale and thus are unsuitable for tuning musical instruments. To standardize musical pitch between instruments, a necessity in an orchestra or when playing in an ensemble, it has been agreed that the standard musical pitch will be based on the frequency 440 Hz (A). This is the note that is sounded by an oboist when the members of an orchestra are ready to tune their instruments in preparation for a performance.

When the base of a vibrating tuning fork is placed on a wooden table, the sound becomes louder and richer. The vibrating fork causes the wood to vibrate, giving the sound a greater intensity, and, since the wood produces overtones as well as the fundamental frequency of the fork, the quality of the sound is enhanced. Most stringed instruments, including the violin, illustrate the same principle.

The four strings of a violin are of equal length. They may be set in vibration by a bow, or plucked with a finger. Each string, besides vibrating along its whole length (producing the fundamental frequency), also vibrates in segments (producing an overtone frequency structure unique to the violin). This vibratory energy is transferred through the bridge that supports the strings to the post inside the violin. This sets the whole belly of the violin in motion, and the entire case together with the air it encloses vibrates in sympathy with the strings. Although some of the sound emitted by the violin comes directly from the strings, most of the sound waves originate from the body of the violin or from the air inside it. The quality of sound produced by violins varies greatly, being affected

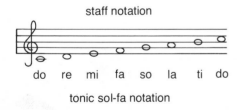

keyboard scale (musical)

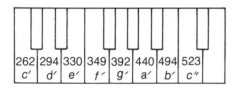

staff notation

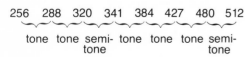

tonic sol-fa notation

frequencies (scientific) intervals

256	288	320	341	384	427	480	512
	tone	tone	semi-tone	tone	tone	tone	semi-tone

by the type of wood, the structure of the body, and even the quality of the varnish and glue.

All wind instruments use resonating air columns to produce their sounds. The origin of the sound may be air vibrating over an opening (organ, flute), or vibrating lips on a brass instrument (trumpet, trombone), or a vibrating reed (oboe, clarinet, organ). The resonating air column may be closed or open. Some columns are of fixed length, their resonant frequency being altered by the opening or closing of holes in the column (clarinet, recorder). Some instruments are played by altering the length of the air column (trumpet, trombone).

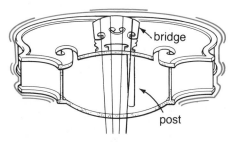

The vibrations of the strings are transmitted through the bridge and post and diffused throughout the violin. All surfaces and the air enclosed in the body of the violin vibrate, sending out separate sound waves that mingle with the original sounds from the strings.

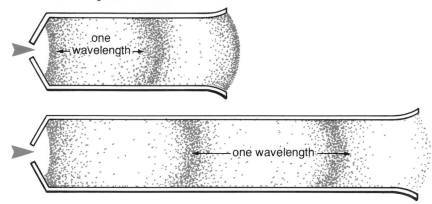

Changing the length of a pipe alters the frequency of the emitted sound waves. The two pipes have the same number of waves. But since the lower one is twice as long its waves are twice as far apart, and so their frequency is one-half that of the shorter pipe's waves.

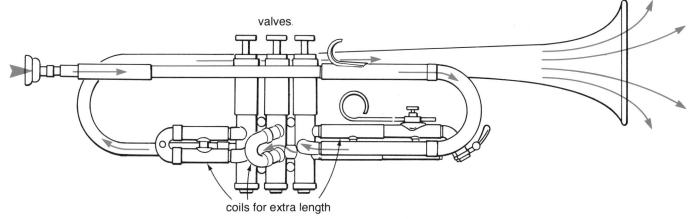

In a trumpet, the length of the air column is altered by opening and closing valves. The sound is not affected by the trumpet's shape. The tubing is coiled only for compactness.

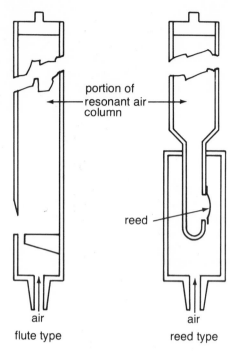

portion of
resonant air
column

reed

air   air

flute type   reed type

Organ pipes

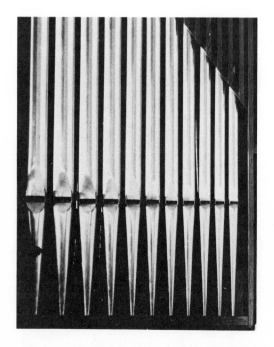

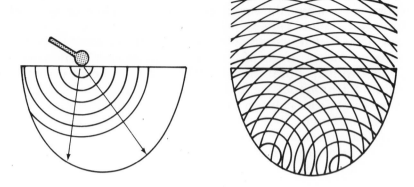

A sound produced at the head of a kettle drum is reflected from a multitude of points on the inner surface of the metal "kettle". The reflection from only two points is shown. Note that all the sound is emitted from the top. Interference of the reflected waves creates the drum's rich boom.

20.8 Sonic Booms

A static, or stationary, source radiates sound waves in concentric spheres. An airplane radiates spheres of sound waves from successive positions. Sphere 1 (in the diagram) was produced by a subsonic airplane at position 1, sphere 2 at position 2, and so on. Note that because the aircraft was moving, the wavefronts were farther apart behind it than they were in front of it.

When an airplane is flying at the speed of sound, the wavefronts in front of it pile up, producing an area of very dense air, or intense compression, called a **sound barrier**. Unless the aircraft has been designed to "cut" through this giant compression, it will be buffeted disastrously. In present-day supersonic aircraft, such as the Concorde, only slight vibration is noticed when the sound barrier is crossed.

At supersonic speeds, the spheres of sound waves are left behind the aircraft. These interfere with each other constructively, producing large compressions and rarefactions along the sides of an imaginary double cone extending behind the airplane from the front and the rear. This intense acoustic pressure wave sweeps along the ground in a swath whose width is approximately five times the altitude of the aircraft and is usually referred to as a **sonic boom**. The sonic boom is heard as two sharp cracks, like thunder or a muffled explosion.

For an airplane flying faster than the speed of sound at a height of 12 km, the sonic boom is produced for 30 km on either side of the flight path. Unless it comes from a supersonic aircraft at a low altitude, the sonic pressure wave is not strong enough to cause any damage on the ground, though the sudden noise may startle or frighten human beings and animals.

Most ecosystems, it is believed, can tolerate random sonic booms. Recurring booms over a long period, on the other hand, might upset them. Supersonic commercial aircraft, as a result, are restricted by many countries to subsonic speeds except over water.

The first supersonic flight was achieved on October 14, 1947, in California, by a Bell XS-1 rocket plane.

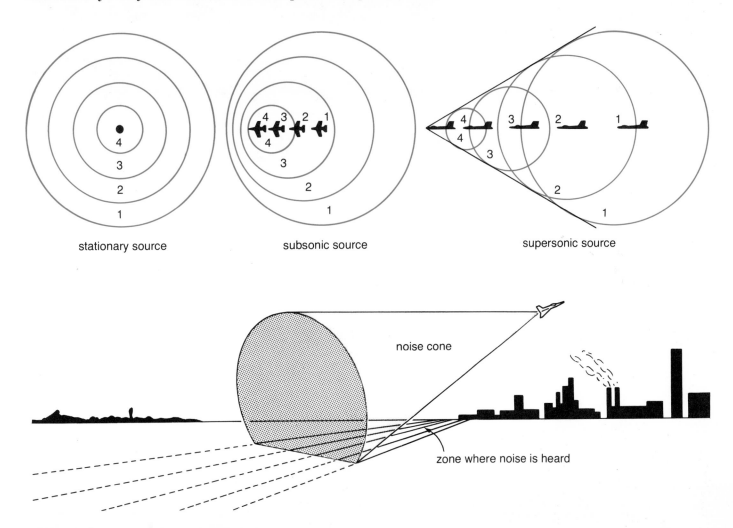

stationary source   subsonic source   supersonic source

noise cone

zone where noise is heard

Noise produced by a supersonic aircraft

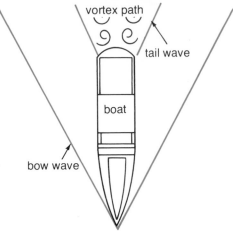

A motor boat moving through the water creates a pattern similar in shape to that of a sonic boom.

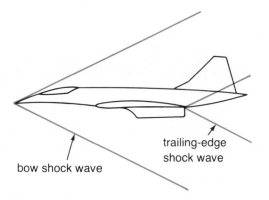

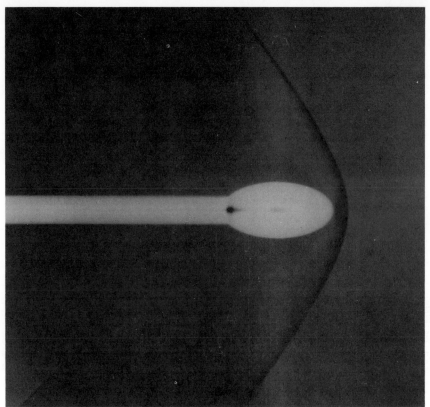

An object being tested in a wind tunnel with an air velocity of Mach 1.38.

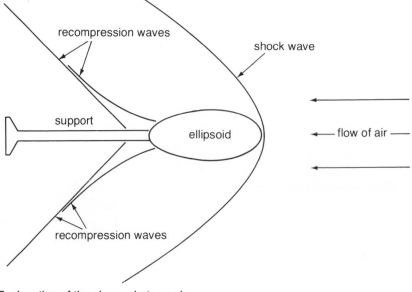

Explanation of the above photograph

20.9 Doppler Effect

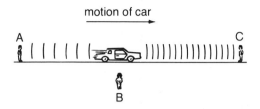

motion of car

Most of us have heard what is called the Doppler Effect at one time or another. As a fast-moving object such as a racing car or train passes by, a change in pitch, or frequency, is apparent. This effect is named after C. J. Doppler (1803-53), an Austrian physicist who was the first to explain the phenomenon.

The wavefronts in front of a moving car are relatively close together and those behind it relatively far apart. Observer C (in the diagram) will receive a larger number of compressions and rare-factions per second than observer A. Thus the pitch of the car's horn will seem relatively high to observer C and relatively low to observer A. For observer B, the pitch will rise when the car approaches him and drop as it moves away. For the driver, the pitch will not change.

The general principle of the Doppler Effect is that, when a source generating waves approaches an observer the frequency of the source apparently increases, and when the source moves away from the observer the frequency apparently decreases.

Although this phenomenon was first explained in relation to sound waves, it may be observed in any moving object that emits waves. The change in frequency and resulting change in wavelength is called the Doppler Shift. The Doppler Shift can be used to determine the speed of a star relative to the Earth.

Short-range radar devices, such as those used by the police, work on the Doppler Shift principle to determine the speed of a car. Radar waves from a transmitter in the police car are reflected by an approaching car and arrive back at a radar receiver in the police car with a slightly higher frequency. The original waves and the reflected waves are very close together in frequency and beats are produced when the two are combined. The number of beats per second is directly related to the speed of the approaching car. This beat frequency is electronically translated into kilometres per hour and displayed on a meter or paper chart in the police car.

20.10 Summary

1. The pattern of interference between two identical sound sources is similar to that produced in a ripple tank by two identical water-wave sources.
2. Beat frequency is the difference between the frequencies of two sources.

$$\text{Beat frequency} = |f_1 - f_2|$$

3. The frequency of a vibrating string is determined by its length, tension, diameter, and density.

4. A string may vibrate along its whole length in a single segment or in segments that are simple (whole-number) fractions of its length.

5. When an object vibrates in its simplest or fundamental mode of vibration it produces its lowest possible frequency, which is called the natural or fundamental frequency.

6. Frequencies of overtone modes are simple (whole-number) multiples of the fundamental frequency.

7. Mechanical resonance occurs when an object that is free to vibrate is acted on by a periodic force that has the same frequency as the object's natural frequency.

8. Resonance occurs in closed air columns whose lengths are $1/4\lambda$, $3/4\lambda$, $5/4\lambda$, and so on, of the original sound wave.

9. The resonant lengths of open air columns are $1/2\lambda$, λ, $3/2\lambda$, 2λ, and so on, of the original sound wave.

10. Music consists of notes with constant frequencies. Noise is sound with a constantly changing frequency.

11. Most musical instruments consist of a vibrating source and a structure to enhance the sound through mechanical and acoustical resonance.

12. A sonic boom is caused by the constructive interference of the sound waves that have been emitted behind an object that is exceeding the speed of sound.

13. The pitch of the sound emitted from an object approaching an observer appears to increase, and when the object is leaving the observer the pitch appears to decrease. This phenomenon is called the Doppler Effect.

20.11 Review

1. Using *one* loudspeaker and a flat wall, you can get effects similar to those you might expect to obtain with *two* loudspeakers. Explain.

2. You sound two tuning forks together. One has a frequency of 300 Hz, the other a frequency of 302 Hz. What do you hear?

3. A tuning fork with a frequency of 256 Hz is sounded at the same time as a second fork. 20 beats are heard in 4 s. What are the possible frequencies of the second fork?

4. Two sources with frequencies of 300 Hz and 308 Hz are sounded together. How many beats are heard in 4.0 s?

5. Two tuning forks are sounded together, producing three beats

per second. If the first fork has a frequency of 300 Hz, what are the possible frequencies of the other fork?

6. Plasticine (which lowers the pitch) is added to one tine of the tuning fork of unknown frequency referred to in question 5. The number of beats decreases to one. What was the frequency of the unknown fork before plasticine was added to one of its tines? What are the possible new frequencies of the fork with plasticine?

7. Two nearly identical forks, one of which has a frequency of 384 Hz, produce seven beats per second when they vibrate at the same time. A small clamp is placed on the 384 Hz fork and then only five beats per second are heard. What is the frequency of the other fork?

8. A 400.0 Hz string produces 10 beats in 4.0 s, when sounded at the same time as a tuning fork. When a little plasticine is placed on one tine of the tuning fork, the number of beats increases. What was the frequency of the fork before plasticine was added to it?

9. A string 1.0 m long vibrates at the rate of 180 Hz. What will its frequency be if it is shortened to 50 cm? 60 cm? 25 cm?

10. A vibrating string has a frequency of 200 Hz. What will its frequency be if (a) its length is decreased to $1/4$ of its original length, or (b) its tension is quadrupled?

11. A string of given length and diameter and density is under a tension of 100 N and produces a sound of 200 Hz. How many vibrations per second will be produced if the tension is changed to (a) 900 N, (b) 25 N, and (c) 200 N?

12. A string 1.0 m long produces a sound of 480 Hz. How many vibrations per second will be produced by segments of this string (a) 33.3 cm long, (b) 25 cm long, (c) 50 cm long, and (d) 10 cm long?

13. If the fundamental frequency produced by a guitar string is 400 Hz, what is the frequency of the second overtone?

14. What is the beat frequency produced by the first overtones of two strings whose fundamental frequencies are 280 Hz and 282 Hz?

15. When a heavy truck passes your house, certain dishes rattle. Explain.

16. When your car moves at a certain speed, there is an annoying rattle. If you speed up or slow down slightly, the rattle disappears. Explain.

17. If you press the loud pedal on a piano and sing, a sound usually comes from the piano. Explain this phenomenon. Why might more than one piano string respond?

Numerical Answers to Review Questions
2. 2 Hz
3. 251 Hz or 261 Hz
4. 32
5. 297 Hz or 303 Hz
6. 303 Hz; 299 Hz or 301 Hz
7. 377 Hz
8. 397.5 Hz
9. 360 Hz, 300 Hz, 720 Hz
10. (a) 800 Hz (b) 400 Hz
11. (a) 600 Hz (b) 100 Hz (c) 283 Hz
12. (a) 1440 Hz (b) 1920 Hz (c) 960 Hz (d) 4800 Hz
13. 1200 Hz
14. 4 Hz
20. 108 cm, 346 m/s
21. (a) 143 Hz (b) 430 Hz (c) 717 Hz
22. (a) 120 cm (b) 289 Hz
23. (a) 1.0 m (b) 3.4×10^2 Hz
24. (a) 28.3 cm, 85.0 cm, 142 cm (b) 56.5 cm, 113 cm, 170 cm
25. (a) 92.0 cm, 120 cm, 152 cm (b) 371 Hz, 284 Hz, 224 Hz
26. 20 cm, 1.7×10^3 Hz
27. 338 m/s
29. 0.312 m

18. Singers are reputed to be able to shatter delicate wine glasses by singing high, loud notes. Explain.

19. How do you account for the noise you hear when you place a large sea shell to your ear?

20. A tuning fork causes resonance in a closed pipe similar to the one used in the investigation in Section 20.6. The difference between the length of the closed tube for the first resonance and the length for the second resonance is 54.0 cm. If the frequency of the fork is 320 Hz, what are the wavelength and speed of the sound waves?

21. A closed air column is 60.0 cm long. Calculate the frequency of forks that will cause resonance at (**a**) the first resonant length, (**b**) the second resonant length, and (**c**) the third resonant length (speed of sound = 344 m/s).

22. A closed tube 30.0 cm long resonates at its shortest resonant length with a tuning fork in a room where the air temperature is 25°C. Calculate:
    (**a**) the wavelength of the sound waves
    (**b**) the frequency of the waves produced by the fork

23. A pipe that is closed at one end can be made to resonate by a tuning fork at a length of 0.25 m. The next resonant length is 0.75 m. If the speed of sound is 338 m/s, calculate:
    (**a**) the wavelength of the sound emitted by the tuning fork
    (**b**) the frequency of the fork

24. A 300 Hz tuning fork is used to produce acoustical resonance in two air columns. Calculate, in centimetres, the first, second, and third resonant lengths of:
    (**a**) closed air column
    (**b**) open air column   (speed of sound = 340 m/s)

25. Organ pipes, open at one end, resonate best when their length is $\frac{1}{4}$ λ. Three pipes have lengths of 23.0 cm, 30.0 cm, and 38.0 cm.
    (**a**) Find the wavelength of the sound emitted by each pipe.
    (**b**) Find the frequency of each pipe, if the speed of sound is 341 m/s.

26. A signalling whistle measures 5.0 cm from its opening to its closed end. Find the wavelength of the sound emitted and the frequency of the whistle if the speed of sound is 344 m/s.

27. The first resonant length of an open air column in resonance with a 512 Hz fork is 33.0 cm. Find the speed of sound.

28. When you fill a "pop" bottle with water, you hear a rise in the pitch of the sound as it fills up. Explain.

29. What is the length of an open air column that resonates at its first resonant length with a frequency of 560 Hz (speed of

sound $=$ 350 m/s)?

30. If a pipe organ is tuned at 25°C, will its pitch be higher or lower at 15°C? Explain your answer.
31. Explain why sonic booms from high-flying aircraft are weaker than booms from low-flying aircraft.
32. The whistle of a diesel locomotive is sounded at a fixed frequency and with constant loudness, or intensity.
    (a) Compare the frequency and loudness of the sound heard by two observers, one 50 m away, and the other 1.0 km away.
    (b) The first observer drives his car towards the whistle at a high speed. What changes in frequency and loudness will he notice?
33. You are travelling in a car near a speeding train. The train whistle blows, but you fail to hear the Doppler Effect. What conditions might prevent you from hearing it?

20.12 Learning Objectives

1. To describe, using a diagram, the areas of destructive interference surrounding either a tuning fork or two identical loudspeakers emitting identical sound waves.
2. Given any two of beat frequency, the frequency of a source, and the frequency of another source, to determine the third.
3. To predict changes in the frequency of a vibrating string resulting from changes in: length, tension, diameter, and density.
4. To describe, using a diagram, the possible modes of vibration of a stretched string.
5. Given the fundamental frequency of a stretched string, to state the possible overtone frequencies.
6. Given an example of mechanical resonance, to explain how it occurs.
7. Given the resonant length of a closed air column, to determine the wavelength of the source of the sound that is creating the resonance.
8. Given any three of frequency, wavelength, resonant length of a closed air column, and the speed of sound, to determine the fourth.
9. To distinguish between music and noise.
10. To explain, using a diagram, how areas of constructive interference are formed in a cone-shaped region behind an object that is exceeding the speed of sound.
11. To explain, using a diagram, how the Doppler Effect is produced by the sound waves emitted by a moving object.

21 Light Rays and Reflection

21.1 What Is Light?

We are all familiar with light—or think we are. Our eyes respond to the light we receive from the objects all around us. We see the sun, the moon, the stars, the sky. We see the blue water, the brown earth, the green plants, and the red rose. But what is light—this mysterious phenomenon of infinitely varied colour that moves at incredible speed from its source to our eye?

The study of light must have begun before the dawn of history, but the earliest surviving records are from the ancient Greeks. Pythagoras (6th century B.C.) and his followers theorized that light was made up of a stream of particles emitted from a source of light. Aristotle (4th century B.C.) disagreed. He believed that light moved as a wave, like ripples on the water. This debate continued down through the centuries. In the 17th century, Isaac Newton (1642-1727) postulated that light moves as a stream of particles, while Christiaan Huygens (1629-95) and others supported the wave theory of light and provided experimental evidence for their belief.

In the early part of the 20th century, it was shown that both theories have some validity. But, before examining the evidence, we must grasp the fundamental properties of light, including those that have to do with its transmission, reflection, refraction, and dispersion. Then, using our knowledge of waves, we can examine the question of what light is. Finally, we will use our answer to that question to investigate some of the special properties of light.

21.2 The Speed of Light

When we turn on an electric light bulb, the light moves almost instantaneously from the bulb to our eye. We can see that light travels at a very high speed, but exactly what is its speed?

Galileo (1564-1642) made the first serious attempt to measure the speed of light. He had an assistant stand on a hilltop about a kilometre away with instructions to flash his lantern when he saw the flash of Galileo's lantern. By timing the interval between the first flash and the returning flash he hoped to measure the speed of light. This experiment failed because the reaction time of the experimenters was much longer than the time the light took to make the round trip.

Galileo Galilei, an Italian scientist, studied falling bodies, the strength of materials, astronomy, thermometry, time measurement, and basic mechanics. He was brought before the Inquisition for his support of the Copernican Theory of the solar system.

The planet Jupiter has 12 moons, four of which are easily seen with a simple telescope. All the moons move relatively quickly around Jupiter. One of them makes one revolution every 42.5 h. A Danish astronomer, Olaus Römer (1644-1710), was the first to measure the period of that moon. He also made the interesting discovery that, each time the moon was eclipsed behind Jupiter, the duration of the eclipse changed. When the Earth was in position B (see illustration), the eclipse ended 1320 s later than when it was in position A. He concluded, rightly, that the extra time was required because the light had to travel the extra distance of the diameter of the Earth's orbit (A→B). Huygens used Römer's 10 years of accurate observations to calculate the speed of light, as follows:

The planet Jupiter

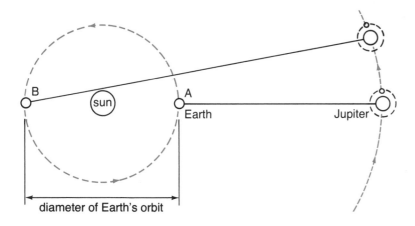

diameter of Earth's orbit

$$AB = 3.0 \times 10^{11} \text{ m}$$
$$\triangle t = 22 \text{ min}$$
$$= 1320 \text{ s}$$

$$v = \frac{\triangle d}{\triangle t}$$
$$= \frac{3.00 \times 10^{11} \text{ m}}{1320 \text{ s}}$$
$$= 2.3 \times 10^{8} \text{ m/s}$$

Modern telescopes and accurate timers have enabled scientists to determine that the time difference is 1000 s; nevertheless, Huygens' calculation was astonishingly accurate considering the equipment he had.

The value Römer and Huygens gave for the speed of light was so great that their fellow scientists rejected it at first. The work of these two scientists was not accepted until after they were both dead.

In 1933 Michelson remeasured the speed
of light with a long evacuated tube in
which light rays were repeatedly reflected
a distance of over 16 km. He died before
the final results were calculated.

In 1905, Albert Michelson (1852-1931), an American scientist, made very accurate measurements of the speed of light. His work was recognized in 1907 by the Swedish Academy, which awarded him the Nobel Prize for Physics.

Michelson's method involved an ingenious arrangement of mirrors (see diagram). Light from a very bright source was reflected from surface A, on an eight-sided, rotatable mirror, to a mirror located about 35 km away. The distant mirror reflected the light back to surface G where it was observed in a telescope. The octagonal mirror was rotated and there were only certain positions in which it reflected light that could be seen in the telescope. These positions occurred every one-eighth of a rotation. For this to happen, the octagonal mirror had to rotate very quickly—approximately 32 000 times/min. The period of rotation of the mirror was accurately determined and the time for the light to make the round trip measured. The speed of light could then be calculated, using this time and the distance travelled by the light on its round trip.

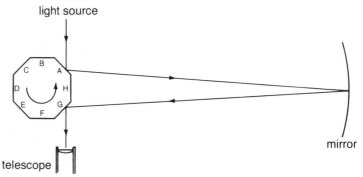

More accurate measurements have been made with lasers. The speed of light in a vacuum has been found to be $2.997\ 925 \times 10^8$ m/s. In air it is only about $0.000\ 87 \times 10^8$ m/s less than that. For most purposes, we will use the value 3.00×10^8 m/s for the speed of light in air or in a vacuum.

The speed of light is constant in a given medium, and we are so confident of its steady value that we can use it to determine large distances very accurately. When the astronauts were on the moon on July 20, 1969, they set up a reflector to reflect laser light back to the Earth. The time required for laser light to travel to the moon and back could then be measured accurately, and the distance between the Earth and the moon calculated much more precisely than ever before. Similar techniques have been used to record earth movement in the San Andreas fault in California, in an attempt to predict earthquakes.

21.3 The Transmission of Light

When the sun's light falls on a solid obstacle, a shadow is produced on the ground. The sharp edges of the shadow remind us that light travels in straight lines. This property of light is called **linear propagation**. This is a fairly obvious property, because we would be unable to line up the sights in a rifle or thread a needle if this were not so. Later, we will see that the rule has some exceptions, which occur when light passes through very small openings and past very small obstacles, but for most purposes we may assume that light travels in straight lines.

Sometimes, if there is dust in the air, we see "rays" of sunlight streaming into the room, or at sunset we may see the sun's rays breaking through the clouds. In everyday language, "ray" means a narrow stream of light energy, but in physics we give it a more precise meaning. A **ray**, in physics, is the path taken by light energy, and it is usually represented by a solid line with an arrow indicating the direction of travel of the light energy. A **beam** of light is a stream of light rays and it is represented by a number of rays. The rays may be converging, diverging, or parallel.

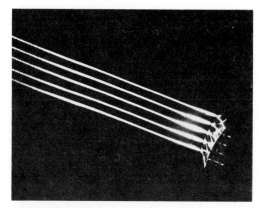

Parallel beam

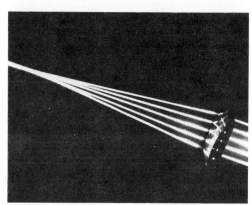

Converging beam

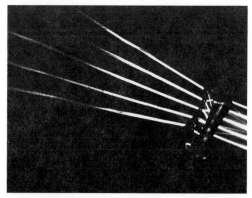

Diverging beam

21.4 The Pinhole Camera

This device was originally called a "camera obscura" when it was invented in the 16th century. It consists of a light-proof box with a pinhole in one end and a screen of frosted glass or tracing paper at the other end. An image is formed on the screen by light travelling in straight lines from an object to the screen. It is easier to see the image on the screen if external light is excluded by shielding the outside of the box with a dark cloth or other covering.

Some early small cameras (1835-39)

Investigation: Images in a Pinhole Camera

Problem:
How is an image formed in a simple camera?

Materials:
simple pinhole camera (no lens)
lighted object such as light bulb or lighted candle

Procedure
1. Point your camera at the lighted source. This is the object.

2. Look at the image in your camera. Is it larger or smaller than the object? Is it erect or inverted, in comparison with the object? This aspect of an image is called its **attitude**.
3. Move the camera closer to the lighted object. Does the size of the image or its attitude change?

Questions
1. From what part of the object does the light at the top of the image originate? From what parts of the object does the light at the middle and bottom of the image originate?
2. If you increase the distance of the camera from the object, what effect does this have on the size and attitude of the image? What is the effect of decreasing the distance?
3. Is the image's attitude erect or inverted throughout the experiment?
4. What property of light, related to transmission, is demonstrated in the simple camera?

Since light travels in straight lines, the rays of light from various parts of the object travel in straight lines through the pinhole and together form an inverted image on the screen. The image is usually smaller than the object. If a line is drawn through the pinhole and perpendicular to both the image and the object, it can be shown by similar triangles that

$$\frac{\text{height of image}}{\text{height of object}} = \frac{\text{distance of image from pinhole}}{\text{distance of object from pinhole}}$$

$$\frac{h_i}{h_o} = \frac{d_i}{d_o}$$

This is called the **magnification equation.** The ratios $\frac{h_i}{h_o}$ and $\frac{d_i}{d_o}$ are called the magnification. For the magnification to be large, the object must be closer to the pinhole than the screen is. In most cases, the reverse is true and the image is smaller than the object.

An image formed on a screen is called a **real image**. An image that is not formed on a screen is called a **virtual image**. The image formed in a pinhole camera is a real one.

In physics, the **characteristics of an image** are stated in terms of its attitude (erect or inverted), its size (larger, smaller, or the same size in comparison with the object), and its type (real or virtual). Thus, from our investigation, we may note that the charac-

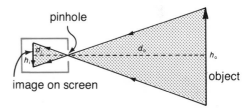

The formation of an image in a pinhole camera

teristics of the image formed in a pinhole camera are that it is inverted, smaller, and real.

If the screen is replaced by a photographic plate, or film, pictures of stationary objects may be taken, provided that a long time exposure is used. Today, all photographs are taken with lens cameras. These admit more light than pinhole cameras, making shorter exposure times possible.

Sample problem

Calculate the size of the image of a tree that is 8.0 m high and 80 m from a pinhole camera that is 20 cm long.

$$\frac{h_i}{h_o} = \frac{d_i}{d_o}$$

$$\frac{h_i}{8.0 \text{ m}} = \frac{20 \text{ cm}}{80 \text{ m}}$$

$$h_i = \left(\frac{0.20 \text{ m}}{80 \text{ m}}\right)(8.0 \text{ m})$$

$$= 0.020 \text{ m or } 2.0 \text{ cm}$$

Practice
1. Calculate the distance from the pinhole to an object that is 3.5 m high, and whose image is 10 cm high in a pinhole camera 20 cm long.   (7.0 m)
2. Calculate the height of a building 300 m away from the pinhole that produces an image 3.0 cm high in a pinhole camera 5.0 cm long. $(1.8 \times 10^2 \text{ m})$

21.5 Laws of Reflection

Light travels in a straight line until it strikes an object. If the object is **opaque**, like a piece of wood, the transmission is interrupted. If the object is **transparent**, like a piece of glass, light passes through.

Mirrors and highly polished opaque surfaces reflect light in predictable ways, and in the next investigation we will examine the laws that govern the reflection of light. The terms used by physicists when describing the reflection of light are as follows:

- The ray approaching the mirror is called the **incident ray**.
- The ray reflected by the mirror is called the **reflected ray**.
- The point where the incident ray strikes the mirror is called the **point of incidence**.
- The construction line drawn at right angles to the mirror at the point of incidence is called the **normal**.
- The angle between the incident ray and the normal is called the **angle of incidence**.
- The angle between the reflected ray and the normal is called the **angle of reflection**.

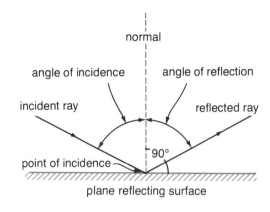

Investigation: Reflection in a Plane Mirror

Problem:
What laws govern the reflection of light in a plane mirror?

Materials:
ray box (single slit)
plane mirror
mirror stand

Procedure
1. Draw a diagram in your notebook like the one at the right, but larger.
2. Place the mirror on the line marked ''plane mirror'' so that the back of the mirror is on the line.
3. Direct single light rays, one at a time, along each line.
4. Draw in the reflected ray accurately, in each case.
5. Construct a normal at each point of incidence.
6. Measure the angles of incidence and reflection in each case, recording the values in a simple chart.

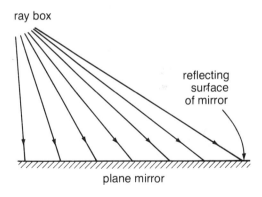

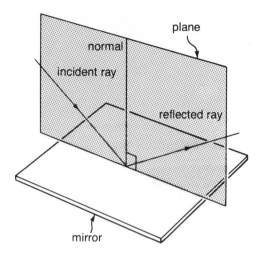

plane

normal

incident ray

reflected ray

mirror

Questions

1. What is the relationship between the angle of incidence and the angle of reflection in each case?
2. At what angle of incidence do the incident ray and reflected ray travel along the same path?
3. If the angle of incidence is doubled, what happens to the angle of reflection? Why?

The angle of incidence equals the angle of reflection for any ray directed towards a plane mirror. This is true even when a ray strikes a plane mirror straight on, since the value of both angles is zero, and it holds without exception for all reflecting surfaces. Therefore, we can use the term ''law'' when describing this relationship between the angle of incidence and the angle of reflection. Also, the incident ray, the normal and the reflected ray all lie in the same plane. This is another **law of reflection**.

A Summary of the Laws of Reflection

- **The angle of incidence is equal to the angle of reflection.**
- **The incident ray, the reflected ray, and the normal all lie in the same plane.**

21.6 Images in a Plane Mirror

When you look into a plane mirror, your image appears to be located somewhere behind the mirror. But where? To find its position it is necessary to consider how the eye sees light rays coming from an object.

Although a lighted object gives off light in all directions, your eye only sees the particular diverging cone of rays that is coming towards it. If you go to the other side of the object, a different cone of rays will enter your eye.

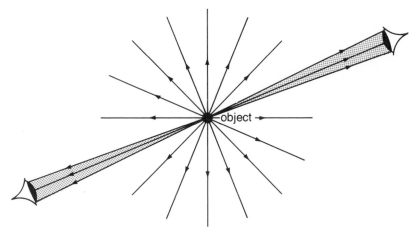

Although an object gives off light in all directions, the eye sees only a diverging cone of rays.

When you see an object in a plane mirror, the cone of rays is reflected by the mirror, as illustrated. Your eye cannot see that the light has been reflected and assumes that, since light travels in straight lines, the origin of the cone of light rays is behind the mirror.

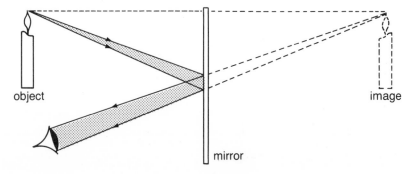

In the next investigation, we will create cones of rays with the ray box, and, by extending the diverging cones of rays behind the mirror, we will locate the image.

Investigation: Locating Images in a Plane Mirror

Problem:
What is the location of the image in a plane mirror?

Materials:
ray box (single slit)
plane mirror

Procedure

1. In your notebook draw a point object and mirror, as illustrated, but on a larger scale.
2. Draw in two cones of rays, so that they strike the mirror.
3. With the ray box, shine a ray of light down the outside of each cone. Draw in the reflected ray in each case.
4. Look into the mirror in such a way that you can see the light originating from the ray box. Where does the light appear to come from?
5. Using a piece of white paper as a screen, try to locate the image behind the mirror.
6. Look into the mirror. What are the attitude, the size, and the type of the image in the mirror?
7. Raise your right hand in front of the mirror. Which hand does the image in the mirror appear to be – the right or the left?
8. Tilt the mirror at an angle to the printing on this page. How does the image of the printing differ from the actual printing?
9. On your diagram, extend all the reflected rays behind the mirror until they meet. Use dotted lines.
10. Label the point of intersection of the extended rays. This is the location of the image.
11. Join the object and image with a dotted line.
12. Measure the angle this dotted line makes with the mirror.
13. Measure the distances along the dotted line, between the object and the mirror, and between the image and the mirror.

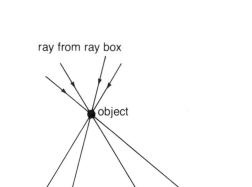
ray from ray box

object

plane mirror

Questions

1. In a plane mirror, where is the image?
2. Since the image cannot be put on a screen, what type of image is it that is formed by a plane mirror?
3. What are the three characteristics of an image in a plane mirror?
4. Although the image in a plane mirror is not inverted vertically, relative to the object, it has been changed. How?
5. You are given the position of an object relative to a plane mirror. List the steps you would follow to locate the image behind the mirror.

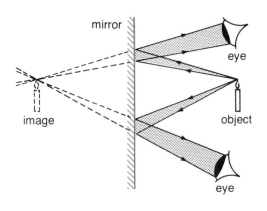

A plane mirror forms an image in this way.

We are familiar with the image in a plane mirror from our everyday experience with mirrors. When you look into a mirror, you see an image of your face, without any magnification, apparently located behind the mirror. If you move towards the mirror, your image will move closer to the mirror, so that the image is always the same distance from the mirror as the object. Unlike the image formed in the pinhole camera, which was formed on a screen and said to be real, the image we see in a plane mirror cannot be formed on a screen and is therefore described as virtual. The image in a plane mirror is produced at the point where the reflected rays, extended behind the mirror, appear to intersect.

When you look in a mirror and raise your right hand, the image appears to be a left hand coming up to meet your right hand. When printing is viewed in a plane mirror, the letters are reversed horizontally but not vertically. This is called **lateral inversion**.

9 The Properties and Behaviour of Waves

9.1 What Are Waves?

Energy can be transmitted from one place to another by a moving object, such as a baseball when thrown by a pitcher to a catcher. The kinetic energy given to the ball by the pitcher is transferred to the catcher. But this is not the only way to effect a transfer of energy. It can be brought about without any movement

In summary, the characteristics of an image in a plane mirror are:
- It is the same size as the object.
- It is vertically erect.
- It is virtual.

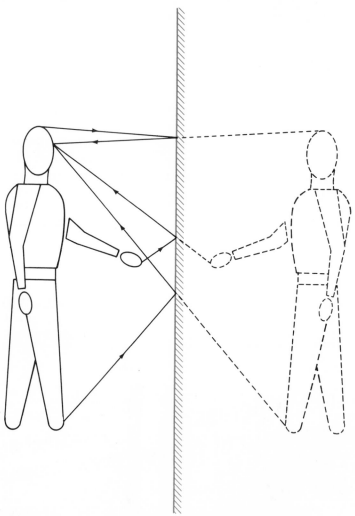

An image in a plane mirror is the same size as the object.

Also, the image is laterally inverted and located at the same perpendicular distance behind the mirror as the object is in front of it.

Sample problem

Given an object located in front of a plane mirror, locate the image and show how the eye "sees" it.

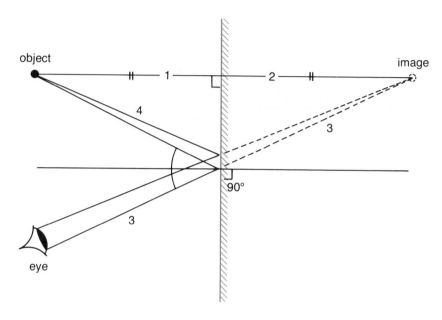

(Each step is indicated by number on the diagram.)
1. Draw a perpendicular from the object to the mirror.
2. Extend this line an equal distance behind the mirror to locate the image.
3. The eye considers that the light originates from a point source image behind the mirror. The light rays from a point source travel out in all directions, and they include a cone of rays travelling towards the eye.
4. Rays actually originate from the object, as illustrated. Note that the angle of incidence equals the angle of reflection.

Practice

1. A point object is located a perpendicular distance of 3.0 cm from a plane mirror.
   (a) Using a full-scale diagram, locate the virtual image.
   (b) Place an eye 2.0 cm to the left of the object. Using a ray diagram, show how the eye "sees" the image.
2. Trace this diagram into your notebook, and locate the image in the mirror.

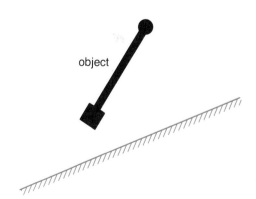

Practice 2

21.7 Applications for Plane Mirrors

1. Plane Mirrors in Cameras

Plane mirrors are used in the viewfinders of many cameras. In simple cameras, they make it possible to view the scene from above the camera. In the single lens reflex (SLR) camera illustrated, the mirror is right behind the lens through which the picture is taken. It is hinged, and when the shutter is released, it flips out of the way to let the light strike the film. It automatically returns to its original position when the picture has been taken. The mirror that is used in this type of camera is called a **front surface mirror**, so called because the reflecting material (usually silver or aluminum) is located on the front of the glass, not on the back as is usual with mirrors. Care must be taken when cleaning or handling this type of mirror because of the danger of damaging it by scratching.

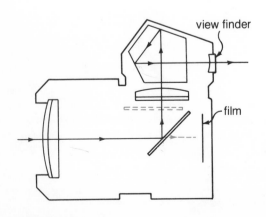

view finder

film

2. The Periscope

A simple periscope consists of two plane mirrors facing each other, mounted at an angle of 45° to the horizontal and vertical planes. Because the light is reflected by two surfaces, the lateral inversion created by the first mirror is reversed by the second mirror, and the scene appears normal.

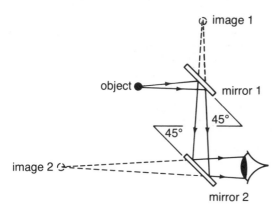

Regular reflection is also known as specular reflection.

3. Diffuse Reflection

Mirrors, stainless steel, and sheets of glass are highly polished flat surfaces, unlike the surfaces of most objects, which are found to be highly irregular when viewed under a microscope. White paper and a painted ceiling are two good examples of irregular surfaces. When a parallel beam of light falls on such a surface, the individual rays have different angles of incidence, and are therefore reflected in different directions, rather than parallel to each other. This type of reflection is called **diffuse reflection**.

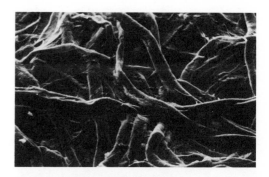

Newsprint magnified 700 times

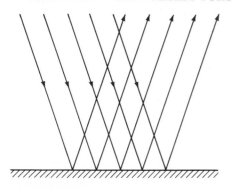

Regular reflection

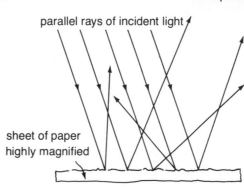

Diffuse reflection

4. Images Formed by Two Mirrors at Right Angles

When two mirrors are mounted at right angles, not only are the two expected virtual images formed, but an extra image is produced as well. The light that enters the eye has been reflected twice, producing three images, as illustrated. Geometrically, the object and the three images lie at the corners of a rectangle whose centre is at the intersection of the mirrors. If the angle between the mirrors is less than 90°, even more images are produced. Try it!

The number of images (N) formed by two mirrors is predicted by the equation:

$$N = \frac{360}{\theta} - 1,$$ **where θ represents the angle between the mirrors. In the case of parallel mirrors, $\theta = 0$ and thus N approaches infinity.**

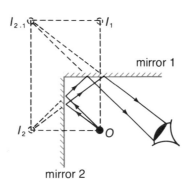

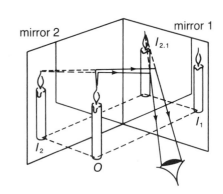

5. Reflection in Parallel Mirrors

Many images are formed by an object placed between two parallel mirrors. This effect is often seen in a barbershop or hairdressing salon where mirrors have been mounted on opposite walls.

The images are located on a straight line that passes through the object and is perpendicular to the mirrors. Each image appearing in one mirror acts as a virtual object that produces another image in the other mirror. Thus, a series of virtual images is produced behind each mirror (see diagram). Since some of the light energy is absorbed by the mirrors at each reflection, the more distant images are fainter.

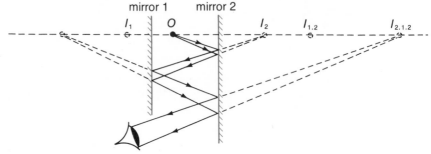

6. The Kaleidoscope

A children's kaleidoscope consists of two long, narrow mirrors mounted along a tube at 60° angles to each other. At the bottom of the tube is a frosted glass plate that admits light. Small pieces of brightly coloured glass are placed between the mirrors. They act as objects which, because of multiple reflections, produce five images. The five images and the objects together form a symmetrical pattern in six sections. The number of different patterns is unlimited, since the pieces of glass are randomly rearranged as the tube is rotated.

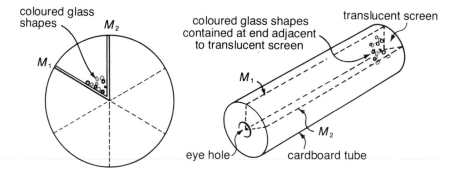

7. Arcade Shooting Gallery

Most shooting galleries use a large mirror placed so as to reflect a picture mounted horizontally below. This gives the impression of a long rifle range. The rifles usually shoot "light bullets", which are detected by light-sensitive targets. When light from a rifle strikes a target, a hit is recorded.

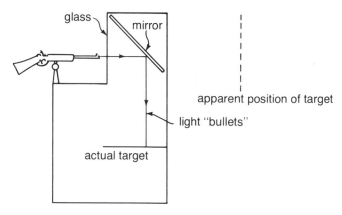

8. Theatrical Effects

A large sheet of plate glass can act as a mirror and at the same time allow objects on the stage behind it to be seen. An actor dressed as a ghost stands off stage. The area around him is painted and draped in a dull black, so that when a strong light is directed on him his virtual image in the plate glass reflects this light towards the audience, creating a virtual image of the actor. This illusion is complete when the objects behind the glass are seen at the same time, making the ghost appear to be transparent. The effect of a headless ghost may be created by covering the head of the actor in a black drape. Similar effects are used by magicians and illusionists.

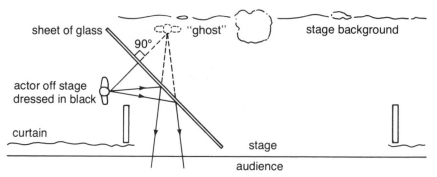

9. Instruments

When a plane mirror is rotated by 10°, the angle of incidence increases by 10°. By the laws of reflection, the angle of reflection also increases by 10°. This means that a light ray is deflected by a total of 20°, which is twice the angle by which the mirror was rotated. Thus, a small rotation in a mirror causes a large movement in the reflected ray. This principle is used to magnify small movements of the hands of such devices as electrical meters.

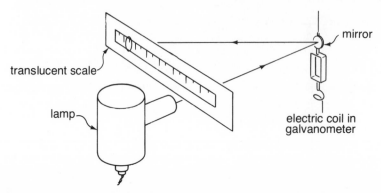

10. See-through Mirrors

Most mirrors are made of a flat piece of glass on which a thin layer of a reflective material such as silver or aluminum has been deposited. Usually this layer is placed on the back of the glass that is to be a mirror and covered with an opaque, protective coating. The reflective layer is easily scratched and, in the case of silver, could be tarnished by certain gases in the atmosphere.

In "see-through" mirrors the protective coating is transparent and the reflective layer is so thin that some light passes through the glass. This allows an observer behind the mirror (and preferably in a darkened area) to see what is happening on the other side without being seen himself. Some sunglasses are constructed on the same principle.

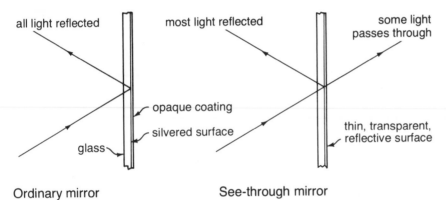

Ordinary mirror

See-through mirror

21.8 Summary

1. The speed of light in a vacuum is constant and has the value of 3.00×10^8 m/s.
2. Since, in most applications, light travels in straight lines, rays are used to represent the transmission of light from a source.
3. A real image is one that can be formed on a screen.
4. A virtual image cannot be formed on a screen and is created by the apparent intersection of reflected light rays, when they are extended backwards, behind the reflecting surface.
5. The characteristics of an image are its size, its attitude, and its type.
6. The characteristics of an image formed in a simple pinhole camera are: it is smaller than the object, it is inverted, and it is real.

7. A normal is a construction line drawn at right angles to a surface at a point of incidence.
8. The Laws of Reflection are: (1) the incident ray, the reflected ray, and the normal are all located in the same plane, and (2) the angle of incidence equals the angle of reflection.
9. The characteristics of the image in a plane mirror are: it is the same size as the object, it is erect, and it is virtual. Such an image is located at the same perpendicular distance behind the mirror as the object is in front of it, and it is laterally inverted.
10. Parallel rays of light are reflected parallel to one another in regular reflection and non-parallel to one another in diffuse reflection.
11. Light reflected by two or more mirrors produces multiple images.

21.9 Review

1. Huygens calculated that the radius of the Earth's solar orbit was 1.5×10^8 km and that the time required for light to travel across a distance equal to the Earth's diameter of orbit was 1320 s. How did he calculate the speed of light?
2. In communicating with an automatic space station, radio signals travelling at the speed of light must travel a distance of 8.7×10^9 m each way. How long does it take for a radio signal to travel to the station and back?
3. The average distance from the sun to the Earth is 1.5×10^8 km. How long (in minutes) does it take for sunlight to reach the Earth?
4. A radar pulse travelling at the speed of light is sent to the moon, and after being reflected returns to the Earth. If the elapsed time is 2.5 s, how far (in metres) is the moon from the radar transmitter?
5. A light-year is the distance light travels in one year. How far (in metres) does light travel in one year?
6. How much time would be required for a spaceship travelling at 3.0×10^5 m/s (1/1000 the speed of light) to reach the closest known star, Proxima Centauri, 4.3 light-years away? How long would it take for the spaceship that went to the moon (maximum speed 10 km/s)?
7. Periodically, a star explodes. If an explosion took place on a star 10 light-years away, when would the astronomers on Earth see it?
8. A pinhole camera 20.0 cm long is used to photograph a student 175 cm high. If the image is 10.0 cm high, how far from

The distances of outer space are so great that they are usually not expressed in metric units, but rather in one of these units:

astronomical unit (AU) = 1.50×10^{11} m

light-year (ly) = 9.46×10^{15} m

parsec (pc) = 3.09×10^{16} m

the camera is the student?

9. A pinhole camera 25 cm long is used to photograph a building 10 m high located 30 m from the camera. Calculate the height of the image on the film.

10. What is the angle of incidence when there is an angle of 60° between the incident rays and the reflected rays?

11. The Laws of Reflection apply not only to light but also in mechanics. Transfer the diagram to your notebook and show how to aim billiard ball A (with no spin) so that it will hit ball C without hitting ball B.

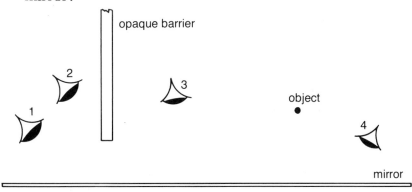

12. In this diagram, which eye(s) would see the image in the mirror?

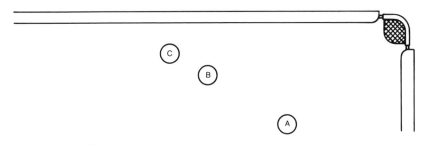

13. A ray of light falls on a plane mirror. The mirror is turned through 5°. The reflected ray is found to have moved by 10°. Explain.

14. An object 4 cm high is located 15 cm in front of a plane mirror. What are the characteristics and the location of the image?

15. A student stands 3.0 m in front of a plane mirror.
   (a) How far behind the mirror is his virtual image?
   (b) If he steps forward 1.0 m, what distance will separate him from his virtual image?

Numerical Answers to Review Questions

2. 58 s
3. 8.3 min
4. 3.8×10^8 m
5. 9.46×10^{15} m
6. 1.4×10^{11} s or 4.3×10^3 years; 1.3×10^5 years
7. 10 years later
8. 350 cm
9. 8.3 cm
10. 30°
15. (a) 3.0 m (b) 4.0 m
16. 6.0 m
18. (a) 0.75 m or half her height (b) 0.75 m
19. (a) 1.0 m/s (b) 2.0 m/s (c) 1.0 m/s
20. 04 00, 04 30, and 18 00

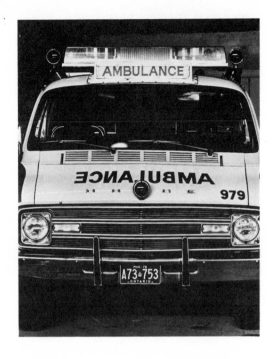

16. A student sitting in an optician's chair views a chart located 1.0 m behind his head by facing a mirror 2.5 m away from him. How far from him does the chart appear to be?

17. You can look into a mirror 10 cm wide and see reflected in the mirror the entire width of the room, which may be 5 m wide. Explain how this is possible.

18. A girl is 1.5 m tall and stands 2.4 m in front of a vertical mirror. For the mirror to be of minimum length, the light reflected from the girl's shoes should be reflected to the girl's eyes from the bottom of the mirror. If the girl sees her entire body, determine:
    (a) the minimum size of the mirror
    (b) the distance from the bottom of the mirror to the floor

19. A student walks towards a plane mirror at 1.0 m/s.
    (a) With what speed does his image approach the mirror?
    (b) With what relative speed do the student and his image approach each other?
    (c) If the student stands still and the mirror is moved towards him at 1.0 m/s, with what speed does the image move relative to the mirror?

20. A clock without numbers, seen in a plane mirror at various times, appears to indicate the following times: 08 00, 07 30, and 18 00. What is the actual time in each case?

21. Some advertising on the front of trucks and buses is printed with the letters reversed. This makes it difficult to read, which would normally be bad advertising. Why is this done?

22. Sometimes it is necessary to read printing on the back of an immovable object, using a mirror. What could you add to make the printing "read" easily?

23. If you were to cut a lobster down the middle, you would find an eye on each side, a claw on each side, an antenna on each side, and so on. Each side would seem to be almost exactly like the other. In fact, they are not. If you were to fold the two parts together, the right claw would meet the left claw, not a right claw. What type of image is the right half of the lobster, compared with the left half of the lobster? This phenomenon is called **plane symmetry**. List five other examples of plane symmetry found in nature.

24. A friend sits on a small table. You say, "The table is bending with your weight". Your friend disagrees. The bending is too slight to see, but you could prove that it did bend, with the help of a small mirror, a ray box, and the white ceiling over your friend's head. Draw a sketch showing how you would place the light and the mirror relative to the table and the ceiling.

25. Explain why interior decorators sometimes use mirrors in small rooms.
26. Why is it easier to read a book printed on porous, matt-finish paper than one printed on shiny, smooth paper, under a bright light?
27. Trace the diagram into your notebook.
    (a) Indicate the location of four of the virtual images formed by the two mirrors.
    (b) With ray diagrams, show how the eye ''sees'' each of the multiple images.

21.10 Learning Objectives

1. Given any two of the speed of light, distance, and time, to determine the third.
2. To describe, using a ray diagram, how an image is formed in a simple camera.
3. To distinguish between the terms ''size'', ''attitude'', and ''type'', and to apply these terms to the image formed in a pinhole camera.
4. To state the Laws of Reflection, and to apply these in a ray diagram involving plane reflecting surfaces.
5. Given the position of an object relative to a plane mirror, to locate the position of the image by means of a ray diagram.
6. To state five unique characteristics and properties of the images formed in a plane mirror.
7. To illustrate by means of a diagram at least two uses of a plane mirror.
8. To distinguish between regular reflection and diffuse reflection, by means of a ray diagram.
9. To determine, by means of a ray diagram, the location of the images formed by two mirrors that are at right angles to each other.
10. To determine, by means of a diagram, the location of the images formed by two mirrors that are parallel to each other.

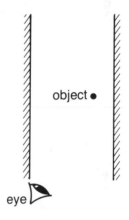

22 Curved Mirrors

22.1 Curved Reflectors

If you have ever been in the fun-house at an amusement park, you have seen your image distorted by a curved mirror. Similar distortions occur when you look into the bowl of a shiny spoon or at the chromed surfaces of an automobile. The images you see look peculiar because of the curved shape of the reflecting surfaces. They are created by light rays obeying the same laws of reflection that were discussed in Chapter 21.

A curved mirror may be thought of as a section of a hollow sphere. If the inside of the sphere is polished to reflect light, the resulting mirror has a **concave** shape and makes parallel light rays converge on each other. The shiny outside of a similar section has a **convex** surface that makes parallel light rays diverge. Hence the terms **converging mirror** and **diverging mirror**.

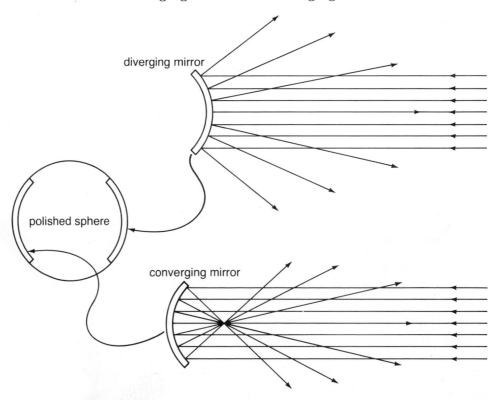

The centre of a curved reflecting surface is called the **centre of curvature** (*C*) and the **radius of curvature** is any straight line drawn from the centre of curvature to the curved surface. The geometric centre of a curved mirror is called the **vertex** (*V*) and the straight line passing through *V* and *C* is called the **principal axis**.

Most of the mirrors used are sections of spheres, shaped like the watch glass used in chemistry. Because ray diagrams are difficult to draw in three dimensions, we will illustrate curved mirrors in two dimensions.

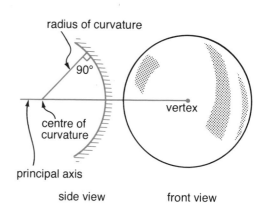

22.2 Reflection in a Converging Mirror

If a group of rays parallel to the principal axis strikes a converging mirror, the rays are all reflected to the same point on the principal axis, called the **principal focus** (*F*). Converging mirrors with a large radius of curvature and a relatively small surface area have their principal focus half-way between the vertex and the centre of curvature. The distance along the principal axis between the principal focus and the vertex is called the **focal length** (*f*).

If several groups of parallel rays are reflected by a converging mirror, each group converges at a point, and each such point is a focus. When all the foci, including the principal focus, are joined, they form the **focal plane** which is a straight line perpendicular to the principal axis. Thus, if a converging mirror is pointed at a distant object, the rays coming from many different points on the object and reaching the mirror at slightly different angles all converge at points along the focal plane, producing a real image there.

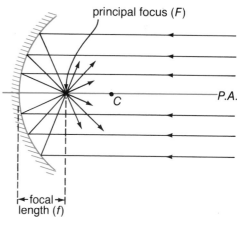

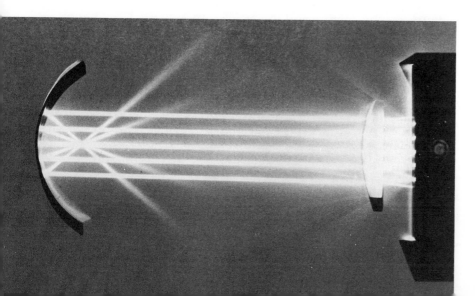

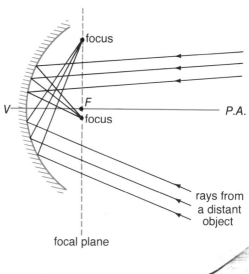

For a mirror with a large radius of curvature, the centre of curvature is two focal lengths from the vertex of the mirror along the principal axis. This is true of all converging mirrors used in this book.

Investigation: Images in a Converging Mirror

Problems:
1. What is the focal length of a converging mirror?
2. What are the characteristics and locations of the images formed by an object located at various positions in front of a converging mirror?

Materials:
light source (candle, small electric bulb)
optical bench
converging mirror
white paper screen

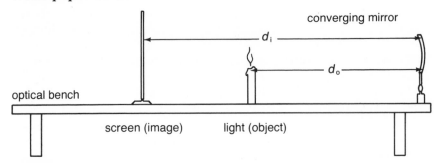

Procedure
1. Hold the mirror in the darkest part of the room and point it at a distant object, such as a window frame or a house near the school.
2. Move the cardboard screen back and forth until the image of the object is clearly focused on the screen. Measure the distance between the mirror and the screen. This is the focal length of the mirror.
3. Using your measured value for the focal length, calculate the distances from the mirror of objects at the following object distances: $2.5f$, $2f$, $1.5f$, f, $0.5f$. Record your observations in your notebook in a suitable chart.

Object distance: the distance from the vertex to the object
Image distance: the distance from the vertex to the image

	Object distance (d_o)	Image distance (d_i)	Characteristics		
Observation			size	attitude	type
1.	$2.5f =$ __				
2.	$2f =$ __				
3.	$1.5f =$ __				
4.	$f =$				

4. Place the mirror at one end of the optical bench. It makes it easier to measure the distance of objects and images if the mirror is placed at the zero end of the scale.
5. Mark on the bench with chalk or masking tape the object positions calculated in step 3.
6. Place the object at $2.5\,f$. Move the screen back and forth until the image is clearly in focus on the screen. Some adjustment of the mirror may be necessary. Record the image distance and the characteristics of the image.
7. Repeat step 6 for the other object distances. If an image is virtual, you should not record its distance.

If the image cannot be placed on a screen, it may be a virtual image. Look into the converging mirror, remembering where the images in plane mirrors are located.

Questions

1. What is the focal length of your converging mirror?
2. As the object is moved closer to the mirror, what regular changes occur in the size of the image, the distance of the image, and the attitude of the image?
3. At what image distance was it difficult, if not impossible, to locate a clearly focused image?
4. Where would you place an object, relative to the principal focus, in order to form a real image? A virtual image?

The characteristics of an image formed in a converging mirror depend on the position of the object. When the object is located beyond the principal focus, the image is inverted and real. When the object distance is less than the focal length, the image is erect and virtual. The image is smaller than the object when the object is beyond the centre of curvature, and it becomes progressively larger as the object is brought closer to the centre of curvature. At the centre of curvature, the image and the object are approximately equal in size. Between the centre of curvature and the principal focus, as well as between the principal focus and the vertex, the image is larger than the object. Thus, a converging mirror can magnify an object.

This property of converging mirrors is used, for example, in shaving mirrors, which have fairly large focal lengths, placing the user's face (the object) inside the focal point. Thus, the image is magnified, erect, and virtual. As the mirror is moved away from the face, the image becomes progressively larger and more distorted until, at the principal focus, no clear image can be seen. Beyond the principal focus, the image is inverted by the mirror. Try it yourself with a converging mirror.

The results that have just been described could have been predicted by means of ray diagrams, as will be explained in the next section.

When the object is inside the focal length, the image is magnified, erect, and virtual.

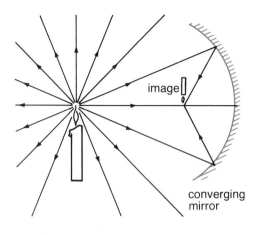

converging
mirror

22.3 Ray Diagrams for Converging Mirrors

Sources of light like the one used in the last investigation emit light in all directions and are called **point sources.** Only some of these rays are reflected from the curved mirror, always, of course, according to the Laws of Reflection. All of the reflected rays would intersect after reflection, forming an image of the light source. To find the location of the image in this way would be a laborious process. Also, only a real image can be located in this way.

To determine the position of an image in a converging mirror it is necessary to use only two rays that intersect. But which two rays? In a converging mirror, any ray parallel to the principal axis is reflected through the principal focus (F). Conversely, any ray through F is reflected parallel to the principal axis. So we select two of the rays radiating out from the tip of the object—the one that passes through F and the one that is parallel to the principal axis.

Sometimes one or the other of the above rays does not hit the mirror. Another ray we can use is the one that goes through the centre of curvature (C) from the tip of the object. Since it moves along a radius of curvature, it hits the mirror with an angle of incidence of 0°. The reflected ray goes back along the same path as the incident ray, since the angle of reflection is 0° (Laws of Reflection).

To locate the image in a converging mirror, then, we may use any two of the rays described in the following rules.

Rules for Rays in a Converging Mirror

1. A ray that is parallel to the principal axis is reflected through the principal focus.
2. A ray that passes through the principal focus is reflected parallel to the principal axis.
3. A ray that passes through the centre of curvature is reflected back along the same path.

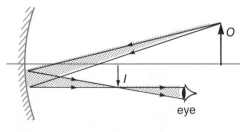

How the eye sees a real image in a converging mirror.

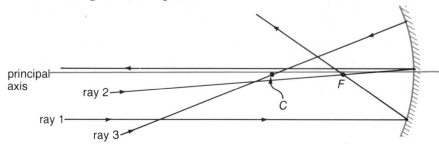

The six diagrams show how the image is located. In each case the object (O) or the image (I) is represented by a vertical arrow. Note that if an object is on the principal axis and is perpendicular to it, the image is also perpendicular to the principal axis and has its base on it. Once the tip of the image is determined, the rest of the image is drawn in by dropping a perpendicular to the principal axis. Note also that only two rays are required to locate the tip of an image. The choice of rays is optional, but it is sometimes dictated by the location of the object. In diagram 2, for example, a ray through C does not hit the mirror.

Real images are formed in diagrams 1, 2, and 3. It is important to note the difference between real and virtual images. A real image can be focused on a screen, but a virtual image cannot (Chapter 21). In ray diagrams, the tip of a real image is formed by the actual intersection of reflected rays, drawn as solid lines. The tip of a virtual image is located at the apparent intersection of reflected rays, when extended behind the mirror as dotted lines. The use of solid lines for objects, real rays, and real images, and the use of dotted lines for virtual images and construction lines are accepted conventions in ray optics.

In diagram 4, the rays from the tip of the object are reflected parallel to each other. No image is formed because neither the rays nor their extensions on the other side of the mirror intersect. Converging mirrors are used in this way in searchlights and in theatre spotlights, since the reflected rays are all parallel and thus form a concentrated beam of light with little divergence.

In diagram 5, the reflected rays diverge from a point behind the mirror and do not intersect in front of the mirror. The image is located behind the mirror by extending the reflected rays backwards as dotted lines. The image formed is virtual, erect, and larger. This type of image is found in cosmetic and shaving mirrors, which magnify the object—your face.

In diagram 6, the rays are coming from a distant object. They intersect and form a real image on the focal plane of the converging mirror. Similar conditions existed in the last investigation, where the focal length was determined. So, also, is the image of a distant planet formed by a reflecting telescope.

Each of the six ray diagrams predicts the location of the image in a converging mirror for various object distances. Compare these predicted images and their characteristics with the actual observations made in the investigation in Section 22.2.

1. Object between *F* and *C*

The image is:
beyond C, real, inverted, larger than the object.

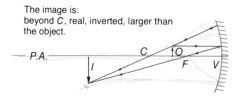

2. Object at *C*

The image is:
at C, real, inverted, the same size as the object.

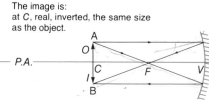

3. Object beyond *C*

The image is:
between C and F, real, inverted, smaller than the object.

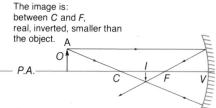

4. Object at *F*

No image is formed.

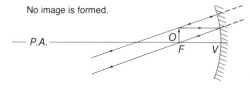

5. Object between *F* and *V*

The image is:
beyond the mirror, virtual, erect, larger than the object.

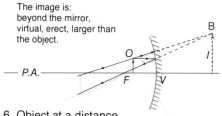

6. Object at a distance

The image is:
at F, real, inverted, smaller than the object.

rays from the same point on a distant object

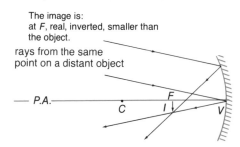

22.4 Images Formed by Diverging Mirrors

In a diverging mirror, the principal focus (*F*) and centre of curvature (*C*) are virtual, since they are located behind the mirror. Rays directed towards the virtual principal focus are reflected parallel to the principal axis, and rays directed parallel to the principal axis are reflected in such a way that, when extended backwards, they go through the virtual principal focus. Rays directed towards the centre of curvature are reflected back along the same path, since they follow a radius of curvature.

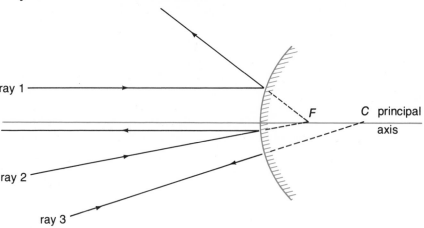

The rules for rays in diverging mirrors are similar to the rules for rays in converging mirrors (Section 22.3). The two sets may be combined to make a set of rules for all curved mirrors, as follows:

Rules for Rays in Curved Mirrors of Both Types

1. A ray that is parallel to the principal axis is reflected through (or as if it had gone through) the principal focus—real or virtual.
2. A ray passing through (or appearing to pass through) the principal focus is reflected parallel to the principal axis.
3. A ray passing through (or appearing to pass through) the centre of curvature is reflected back along the same path.

Unlike the converging mirror, which produces real or virtual images depending on the location of the object, the diverging mirror produces only virtual images. These virtual images are all erect, smaller than the object, and located between the vertex and the principal focus.

How the eye sees a virtual image in a diverging mirror

Image formed by a diverging mirror

Diverging mirrors are useful because they give a wider field of view than plane mirrors of the same size. Unfortunately, all objects are not magnified by the same amount and the image is somewhat distorted. Diverging mirrors are used as rear-view mirrors on trucks and cars and in stores to discourage shoplifting.

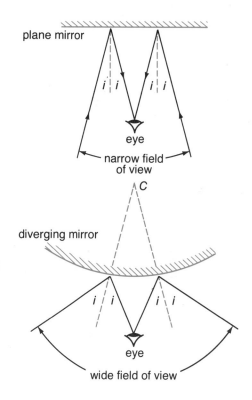

A truck mirror often combines a plane mirror and a diverging mirror.

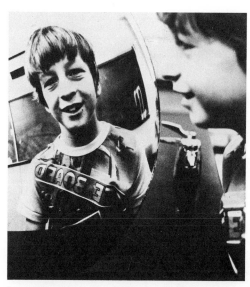

In a diverging mirror the images are all erect, smaller than the object, and virtual.

22.5 Spherical Aberration

In some curved mirrors, rays parallel to the principal axis, which
strike the mirror near the edges, do not intersect at the principal
focus. This defect is called **spherical aberration**. It may be avoided
by designing mirrors in the shape of a parabola rather than a
sphere. Such mirrors, called **parabolic mirrors**, are used where it
is important that all light be reflected to a single focus, for example,
in a solar oven, or that all light reflected from one source be
parallel, for example, in a searchlight or car headlight.

Spherical aberration may occur in both large and small mirrors.
As long as the mirror is small compared with the focal length, the
amount of spherical aberration is negligible.

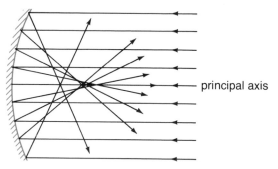

Failure of rays parallel to the principal
axis to meet at a common focus is called
spherical aberration.

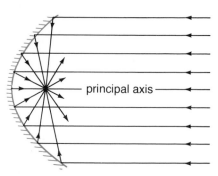

In a parabolic mirror, all rays parallel to
the principal axis are reflected to the
same focus.

Spherical aberration can also be elimi-
nated by using an opaque shield in front
of the mirror, blocking out the rays that
would normally strike the edges of the
mirror.

22.6 Applications of Curved Mirrors

1. Reflecting Telescopes

Parabolic mirrors are used in large telescopes to focus weak light from a distant star or planet onto the focal plane. The larger the diameter of the mirror, the stronger the concentration of light energy at the focus. This makes it possible for an astronomer to see distant stars whose light energy is so low that they cannot be seen without the assistance of a telescope. An eyepiece is used to magnify and focus the image.

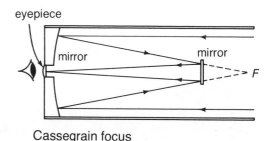

The 5.08 m Hale telescope at the Palomar Observatory in California.

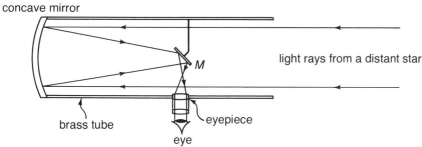

Newtonian focus

The first telescope of this type was made by Isaac Newton in 1668. To make it convenient to see the image, Newton placed a plane mirror at 45° to the axis of the concave mirror, in front of the principal focus. This reflected the rays to one side, and the image could then be viewed through an eyepiece.

Newton's telescope had a mirror with a diameter of approximately 25 mm. Modern telescopes have mirrors with diameters ranging up to 6 m. The reflecting telescope at the David Dunlap Observatory in Richmond Hill, Ontario, once the largest in the world, has a diameter of 1.8 m. The largest reflecting telescope in the world is located on Mount Semirodriki in the Caucasus Mountains of Russia. It has a diameter of 5.99 m and a total mass of 8.6×10^5 kg. The mirrors for large telescopes are made of special glass coated with aluminum. They require a year or more of careful polishing to produce an accurate parabolic surface. The arrangement of the viewing system varies, as illustrated. In the largest telescopes, the astronomer can actually sit at the focal point, suspended above the mirror!

Telescopes of the time had lenses that produced colour distortions. Newton believed that these defects could not be corrected, and he designed the reflecting telescope. See Section 25.5.

Cassegrain focus

Solar furnace used in research

2. Solar Heaters and Furnaces

As sources of non-renewable energy become scarcer, ways of using the sun's energy become more important. A fundamental component of many systems is the concave reflector. The substance to be heated, usually water, is run through a tube at the focal point. The sun's energy is focused on this point, heating the water which is then stored or used to heat a building.

It is difficult to maintain high temperatures (of, say, 6000° C) for any length of time, partially because the container enclosing the furnace will melt or burn. But it is necessary to test some materials, for example, rocket components, at such temperatures. Solar furnaces provide the answer, by concentrating the sun's energy on one point by means of a large concave reflector, thereby producing the high temperatures required. The largest solar furnace is located in the Pyrenees, in southern France. Many large flat mirrors are mounted so that they form a concave reflector. Smaller furnaces, to heat food, have been designed on the same principle.

The largest solar furnace in the world—in southern France

3. Fun-house Mirrors

Amusing effects can be produced by full-length, curved mirrors of both types. As noted in the investigation in Section 22.2, converging mirrors may produce larger or smaller images. The images in diverging mirrors are always smaller. The curved mirrors used in fun-houses are cylindrical, not spherical, and the combinations of converging and diverging mirrors produce amusing distortions.

22.7 Summary

1. The terms used with curved mirrors are: centre of curvature, principal axis, vertex, radius of curvature, principal focus, focal plane, and focal length.
2. All rays parallel to each other and striking a converging mirror are reflected together at a point on the focal plane called the focal point. Rays parallel to the principal axis are reflected through the principal focus.
3. The focal length is the distance between the principal focus and the vertex, measured along the principal axis.
4. Rays from a distant object are considered to be very nearly parallel.
5. For objects located beyond the principal focus, the images in a converging mirror are all inverted and real. For objects located inside the principal focus, the images are all erect and virtual. The images are smaller for objects located beyond the centre of curvature ($2f$) and larger for object distances of less than $2f$.
6. The three rays that may be used in drawing ray diagrams for curved mirrors are: (**a**) a ray parallel to the principal axis, which is reflected through (or as if it had gone through) the principal focus (real or virtual); (**b**) a ray passing through (or appearing to pass through) the principal focus, which is reflected parallel to the principal axis; and (**c**) a ray passing through (or appearing to pass through) the centre of curvature, which is reflected back along the same path.
7. In ray diagrams, solid lines are used for objects and for real rays and images, and dotted lines are used for virtual rays and images, and for construction lines.
8. To locate the tip of an image in a curved mirror, using a ray diagram, at least two rays or their extensions must intersect on one side of the mirror or the other.

9. All the images formed in a diverging mirror are smaller than the object, erect, and virtual. They are all located between the vertex and the principal focus.

10. Spherical aberration occurs in curved mirrors when parallel rays do not all converge on the focal plane. One way to eliminate this is to change the shape of the mirror to a parabola.

11. Some uses of curved mirrors are: reflecting telescopes, solar heaters and furnaces, rear-view mirrors on cars and trucks, mirrors to discourage shoplifting, and fun-house mirrors.

22.8 Review

1. List in your notebook the names of the parts numbered 1 to 5 in this diagram.

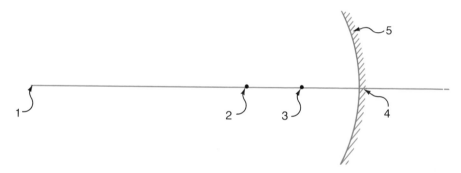

2. In each of these diagrams, an object and its image appear. Copy the diagrams into your notebook. Locate the centre of curvature in each case.

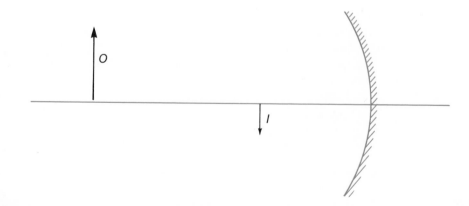

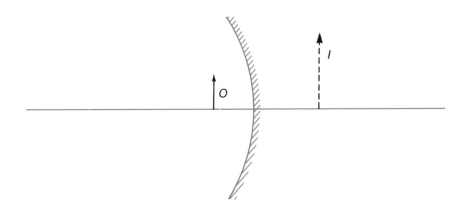

Principle of Reversibility of Light: If a light ray is reversed, it always travels back along its original path.

3. On each of these diagrams, the images formed by curved mirrors are indicated. Copy the diagrams into your notebook and, using ray diagrams, locate the objects.

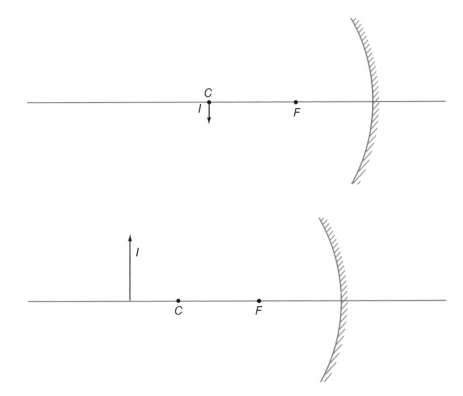

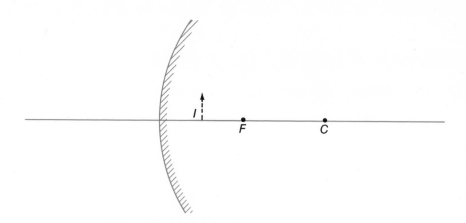

4. You are given a converging mirror, a lighted object, and a white screen. Explain how you would find the centre of curvature.
5. An object and its image, formed by a converging mirror, are indicated on each of these diagrams. Copy the diagrams into your notebook and, using ray diagrams, locate the principal focus of the mirror.

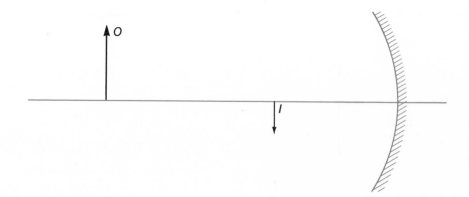

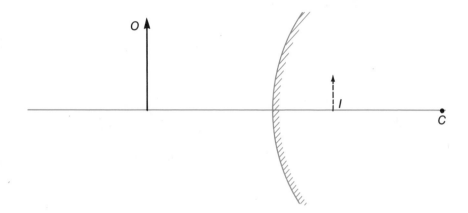

6. A candle 3 cm high is placed 30 cm from a converging mirror with a focal length of 20 cm. By means of a scale ray diagram, locate the image, and determine its height. State the image's characteristics.

7. Use careful scale drawings to locate the images in each of the following cases. State the characteristics of each image.
   (a) A converging mirror has a focal length of 20 cm. An object is placed at (i) 10 cm, (ii) 30 cm, and (iii) 40 cm from the vertex of the mirror.
   (b) A diverging mirror has a focal length of 20 cm. An object is placed (i) 10 cm, and (ii) 30 cm from the vertex of the mirror.

8. Diverging mirrors are often used in stores to discourage shoplifting. Why are they useful in this application?

9. You are given some sheets of polished steel and told to design fun-house mirrors with each of the following groups of characteristics.
   (a) Every dimension of a person standing in front of the mirror is enlarged.
   (b) Every dimension is reduced.
   (c) All vertical dimensions are made larger, while horizontal dimensions remain the same (that is, the person appears taller and thinner).
   (d) The upper features are enlarged vertically and the lower features are reduced vertically, while the horizontal dimensions remain the same (that is, the head appears very long and the legs short).
   With sketches, indicate how you would bend the metal in each case.

22.9 Learning Objectives

1. Given a diagram of a curved mirror, to locate the following: centre of curvature, principal axis, radius of curvature, principal focus, focal plane, and focal length.
2. To describe a method for determining the focal length of a converging mirror, using a distant object.
3. Given the position of the object and the focal length of the mirror, to state the attitude and type of the image formed by a converging mirror and a diverging mirror.
4. Given the position of the object, the focal length, and the centre of curvature of a curved reflector, to locate, on a diagram using at least two rays, the position of the image, and to state the characteristics of the image.
5. To illustrate, using a diagram, the defect called spherical aberration, and to state how it can be corrected.
6. To describe, using a diagram, how a converging reflector is used in any two of the following: a reflecting telescope, a solar oven, a spotlight, and a flashlight.
7. To explain, using a diagram, why a diverging mirror provides a wide field of view.

23 Refraction of Light

23.1 Refraction at Plane Surfaces

A straight stick appears bent when partially immersed in water; the sun appears oval rather than round when it is about to set; a stream may appear to be much shallower than it really is; the pavement shimmers on a hot summer's day. These are some of the effects caused by the **refraction**, or change in direction, of light as it passes from one medium into another.

When light passes from air to glass, it immediately changes direction. Also, at the boundary between the air and the glass, most of the light passes through the glass but some is reflected according to the laws of reflection. This is called **partial reflection and partial refraction**. The diagram illustrates this phenomenon and shows the angles used when describing refraction. The angle of incidence (i in the diagram) is the angle between the incident ray and the normal at the point of incidence. The **angle of refraction** (R) is the angle between the refracted ray and the normal.

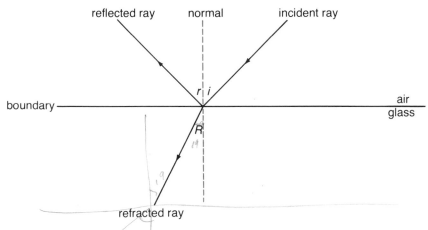

Investigation: Refraction of Light by Glass

Problem:
How is light refracted when it passes from air into glass?

Materials:
ray box (single slit)
semi-circular glass block
polar co-ordinate paper

Plastic blocks are often used, instead of glass blocks, because they do not break easily. Plastic and glass have similar optical properties.

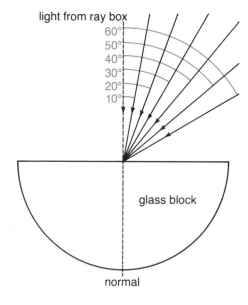

light from ray box

glass block

normal

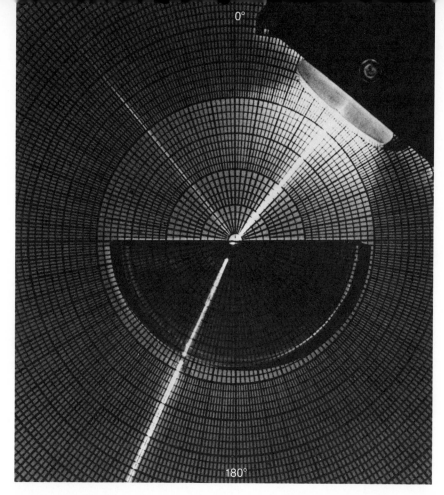

0°

180°

Procedure

1. Place the glass block on the polar co-ordinate paper, as illustrated. Note that the 0°-180° line acts as a normal and passes through the centre of the flat surface.
2. Direct a single ray of light at the flat surface of the glass, along the normal. Measure the angle of refraction, and record it in your notebook in a chart, as illustrated.

Observation	Angle of incidence	Angle of refraction	sin i	sin R	$\dfrac{\sin i}{\sin R}$
1	0°				
2	10°				
3	20°				
4	30°				

3. Repeat the procedure for angles of incidence of 10°, 20°, 30°, 40°, 50°, and 60°, recording your observations in the chart.
4. Using a table of sines or a calculator, determine the values of the sines of the angles of incidence and refraction.
5. Calculate the ratio sin i/sin R for each pair of angles.

Questions
1. When light travels from air into glass with an angle of incidence of 0°, that is, along the normal, what happens to it?
2. When light travels from air to glass at an angle of incidence greater than 0°, how is it bent, in relation to the normal?
3. Where are the incident and refracted rays located, in relation to the normal?
4. How does the angle of refraction compare with the angle of incidence in each case?
5. What do you note about the ratio sin i/sin R for all angles of incidence greater than 0°?
6. If light travels from glass into air, how will it bend in relation to the normal?

23.2 Index of Refraction

The speed and direction of water waves are changed when the waves move from one depth to another (Chapter 18). The speed and direction of light rays also change when they enter a different medium.

With elaborate equipment, it has been determined that the speed of light is less in transparent materials than it is in a vacuum. **Optical density** is the term used to describe the relative speed of light in a given medium. The lower the speed, the greater the optical density. When light travels from air into an optically denser medium, such as glass, it slows down. (Optical density has no relation to the mass, weight, or density of a material.)

Index of refraction is the term used to compare optical densities. The index of refraction (n) is defined as the ratio of the speeds of light in any two media. If the speed of light in a medium is compared with the speed of light in a vacuum, the index of refraction is:

$$n = \frac{v_{\text{vacuum}}}{v_{\text{medium}}}$$

Substance	Index of refraction
vacuum	1.0000
air	1.0003
water	1.33
quartz (fused)	1.46
glass (crown)	1.52
quartz (crystal)	1.54
ruby	1.54
glass (flint)	1.65
zircon	1.92
diamond	2.42

The indices of refraction for various substances are given in a table. The higher the index of a given substance is, the more the light is slowed down when it travels from a vacuum into the substance. Air, with an index of refraction of 1.0003, slows light down very little. Zircon, with an index of 1.92, slows light down considerably more.

Sample problem

If the speed of light in water is 2.25×10^8 m/s, what is the index of refraction of water?

$$n = \frac{v_{air}}{v_{medium}}$$
$$= \frac{3.00 \times 10^8 \text{ m/s}}{2.25 \times 10^8 \text{ m/s}}$$
$$= 1.33$$

Practice
1. What is the index of refraction of a liquid in which the speed of light is 2.50×10^8 m/s?   (1.20)
2. The index of refraction of diamond is 2.42. What is the speed of light in diamond?   (1.24×10^8 m/s)

23.3 Snell's Law

When a ray of light travels from air into glass, it bends towards the normal, except where the ray travels along the normal. This is true for all angles of incidence that are greater than zero. Consequently, the angle of refraction is always less than the angle of incidence. This holds for all cases in which light rays pass from one medium to another that is optically denser.

Although the phenomenon of refraction had been known for centuries, it was not until 1621 that Willebrord Snell (1591-1626), a Dutch mathematician, determined the exact relationship between the angle of incidence and the angle of refraction. This enabled scientists to predict the direction a ray of light would take in various media. **Snell's Law** says:

$$\frac{\sin i}{\sin R} = \text{constant}$$

In the investigation, it was found that the ratio $\sin i / \sin R$ has a constant value of approximately 1.5 for glass, for all angles of incidence except 0°. This is equal to the index of refraction for glass (crown).

The **Snell's Law constant** and the index of refraction (n) are one and the same thing. Consequently, the Snell's Law equation may be rewritten as:

$$\frac{\sin i}{\sin R} = n$$

Sample problems

1. Illustrated is the path of a ray entering a medium (x) of unknown index of refraction. Calculate the index of refraction of medium x.

$$\frac{\sin i}{\sin R} = n$$
$$\frac{\sin 30°}{\sin 24°} = n$$
$$n = \frac{0.500}{0.407}$$
$$= 1.23$$

2. Light travels from air into water ($n_w = 1.33$). If the angle of incidence is 30°, what is the angle of refraction?

$$\frac{\sin i}{\sin R} = n$$
$$\frac{\sin 30°}{\sin R} = 1.33$$
$$\sin R = \frac{\sin 30°}{1.33}$$
$$= \frac{0.500}{1.33}$$
$$= 0.385$$
$$R = 22°$$

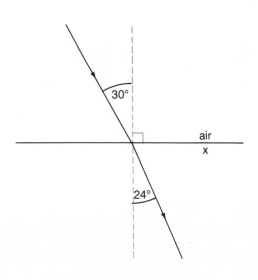

Practice

1. Light passes from air into diamond with an angle of incidence of 60°. What will be the angle of refraction?   (21°)
2. A transparent substance has a refractive index of 1.30. What is the angle of incidence in air when the angle of refraction in the substance is 45°?   (67°)
3. What is the index of refraction of a material if the angle of incidence in air is 50° and the angle of refraction in the material is 40°?   (1.19)

23.4 Refraction of Light Travelling from Glass into Air

We have been considering what happens when light passes from air into glass or some other substance of greater optical density than air. Now we will consider what happens when light moves in the opposite direction, from glass into air. Again we will use a semi-circular glass block. Rays of light are not refracted if the angle of incidence is zero (Section 23.1). Thus, rays that pass through the centre of the curved surface of the glass block will not be refracted, since they are travelling along a radius, striking the curved surface at an angle of incidence of almost 0°.

Investigation: Refraction of Light—Glass into Air

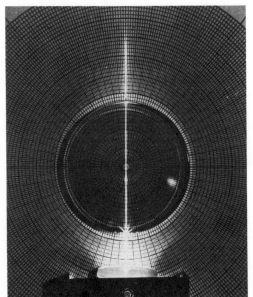

Rays travelling along the diameter of a circular piece of glass are not refracted at either boundary.

Problem:

How is light refracted when it passes from a medium such as glass into a medium that is less dense, such as air?

Materials:

ray box (single slit)
semi-circular glass block
polar co-ordinate paper

0°

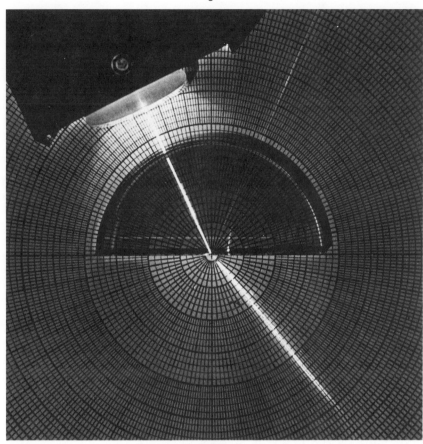

180°

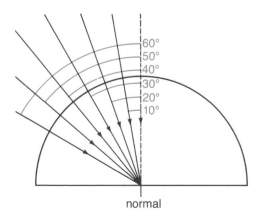

normal

Procedure

1. Place the glass block on the polar co-ordinate paper, as illustrated. Note that the 0°-180° line acts as a normal and that it goes through the centre of the flat surface.
2. Direct a single ray of light at the curved surface of the glass, along the normal. Measure the angle of refraction in air.
3. Repeat the procedure for angles of incidence, in glass, of 10°, 20°, 30°, 40°, 50°, and 60°, recording your observations in a suitable chart (see illustration). Be sure to use the "comments" column for any additional observations.
4. Determine the values of the sines of the angles of incidence and refraction, and calculate the ratio $\sin i/\sin R$ for each pair of angles.

	Angle of incidence	Angle of refraction	$\sin i$	$\sin R$	$\sin i/\sin R$	Comments
1	0°	0°	0	0	undefined	no refraction
2	10°					
3	20°					
4	30°					

Questions

1. How was the light refracted when the angle of incidence was 0°?
2. When light travels from glass to air, at an angle other than 0°, how is it bent in relation to the normal?
3. Which angle is always the greater, the angle of incidence or the angle of refraction?
4. Where are the incident and refracted rays located in relation to the normal?
5. What do you note about the ratio $\sin i/\sin R$ for all angles of incidence greater than 0°?
6. What is the relationship between the index of refraction for light travelling from glass into air and the index of refraction for light travelling from air into glass?
7. What other phenomenon occurs increasingly as the angle of incidence increases?
8. Above 50°, what happens to all the light once it reaches the boundary between the glass and the air?
9. At what angle of incidence is the angle of refraction 90°? Determine the answer experimentally.

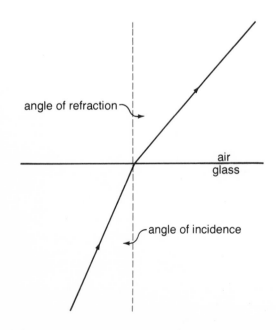

angle of refraction

air
glass

angle of incidence

If we compare this investigation with the investigation in Section 23.1, we notice some similarities and some differences. When light travelled from air into glass or from glass into air with an angle of incidence equal to zero, no refraction occurred. In both cases, incident rays and refracted rays were on opposite sides of the normal, but were in the same plane as the normal. The ratio sin i/sin R was a constant value, although the value was not the same in the two investigations. Furthermore, rays going from air into glass were refracted towards the normal, whereas those going from glass into air were refracted away from the normal.

The Snell's Law equation for light travelling from air into glass is:

$$\frac{\sin i}{\sin R} = n$$

If light travels from glass into air, the angle of incidence will be in the glass and the Snell's Law relation must be altered to:

$$\frac{\sin i}{\sin R} = \frac{1}{n}$$

Thus, if the Snell's Law ratio for air into glass is 1.5, the Snell's Law ratio for glass into air will be $\frac{1}{1.5} = 0.67$. This should be approximately the value determined for the Snell's Law ratio in the previous investigation.

The **Laws of Refraction** may now be summarized:

- **The ratio of the sine of the angle of incidence to the sine of the angle of refraction is a constant (also known as Snell's Law).**
- **The incident ray and the refracted ray are on opposite sides of the normal at the point of incidence, and all three are in the same plane.**

When light travels from one transparent medium into another, some reflection always occurs. This is partial reflection and partial refraction. The degrees of reflection and refraction that occur depend on the angle of incidence and the optical densities of the two media. This will be examined in the next section.

23.5 Total Internal Reflection and the Critical Angle

When light travels from one medium into another that is less dense, for example, from glass into air, some of the light is reflected and some is refracted. As the angle of incidence increases, the intensity of a reflected ray becomes progressively stronger and the intensity of a refracted ray progressively weaker. Also, as the angle of incidence increases, the angle of refraction increases, eventually reaching a maximum of 90°. Beyond this point, refraction ceases and all the incident light is reflected internally. This phenomenon is called **total internal reflection.** It can only occur when light rays travel from one medium to another that is less dense, because the angle of refraction must be greater than the angle of incidence.

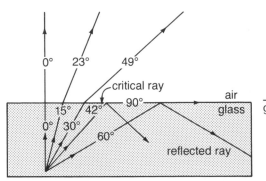

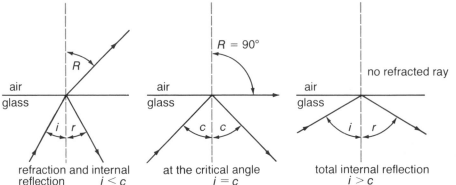

What happens when light rays pass from glass into air.

When the angle of refraction is 90°, the incident ray forms an angle of incidence that has a unique value for each medium. This unique angle of incidence is called the "critical angle of incidence", or simply the **critical angle.** For water, with an index of refraction of 1.33, the critical angle is approximately 49°. For glass ($n_g = 1.5$) the critical angle is 42°. Substances with higher indices of refraction refract the light to a greater degree and thus have lower critical angles. The critical angle for diamond ($n_d = 2.42$), for example, is only 24.5°.

Snell's Law may be used to find the critical angle. For light passing from glass into air, the Snell's Law equation is:

$$\frac{\sin i}{\sin R} = \frac{1}{n_g}$$

At the critical angle, the angle of refraction is 90°. Thus, the sine of the angle of refraction in air is 1.

$$\frac{\sin i_c}{1} = \frac{1}{n_g} \quad \text{or} \quad \sin i_c = \frac{1}{n_g}$$

This relationship can be used for any medium, as follows:

$$\sin i_c = \frac{1}{n_m}$$

where i_c is the critical angle and n_m is the index of refraction of the medium

Sample problem

If the index of refraction for zircon is 1.92, what is the critical angle for zircon?

$$\sin i_c = \frac{1}{n_z}$$
$$= \frac{1}{1.92}$$
$$= 0.521$$
$$= 31.4°$$

Practice
1. What is the critical angle in flint glass when light passes from flint glass into air? (37.3°)
2. If the index of refraction for water is 1.33, what is the critical angle for water? (48.8°)
3. The critical angle for a medium is 40.5°. What is the index of refraction of the medium? (1.54)

23.6 Snell's Law – a General Equation

For convenience when dealing with Snell's Law, we can use subscripts to denote particular angles and substances. For example, the Snell's Law equation for light passing from air into glass may be written as:

$$\frac{\sin \theta_a}{\sin \theta_g} = n_g$$

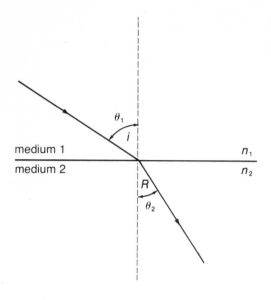

where θ_a is the angle of incidence in air, θ_g is the angle of refraction in glass, and n_g is the index of refraction of glass.

For light travelling from glass into air, the Snell's Law equation may be written as:

$$\frac{\sin \theta_g}{\sin \theta_a} = \frac{1}{n_g}$$

The "1" in the numerator on the right-hand side of the equation is the index of refraction for air ($n_a = 1.00$). Thus, the equation may be rewritten:

$$\frac{\sin \theta_g}{\sin \theta_a} = \frac{n_a}{n_g}$$

$$\text{or } n_a \sin \theta_a = n_g \sin \theta_g$$

This equation may be made more general, as follows:

$$\boldsymbol{n_1 \sin \theta_1 = n_2 \sin \theta_2}$$

The subscripts denote the different media. It is customary to use subscript 1 for the incident medium and subscript 2 for the refracting medium. The general expression of Snell's Law may be used in solving any refraction problem, including the determination of the critical angle.

Sample problems

1. Light travels from crown glass (g) into air (a). The angle of refraction in air is 60°. What is the angle of incidence in glass?

$$n_g \sin \theta_g = n_a \sin \theta_a$$
$$1.52 \sin \theta_g = 1.00 \sin 60$$
$$\sin \theta_g = \frac{1.00 \ (0.866)}{1.52}$$
$$= 0.570$$
$$\theta_g = 34.8°$$

2. Light travels from crown glass (g) into water (w). The angle of incidence in crown glass is 40°. What is the angle of refraction in water?

$$n_g \sin \theta_g = n_w \sin \theta_w$$
$$1.52 \sin 40° = 1.33 \sin \theta_w$$
$$(1.52)(0.643) = 1.33 \sin \theta_w$$
$$\sin \theta_w = \frac{(1.52)(0.643)}{1.33}$$
$$= 0.735$$
$$\theta_w = 47°$$

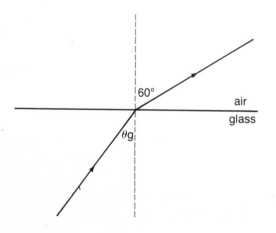

3. What is the critical angle for light passing from crown glass (g) into air (a)?

For total internal reflection to occur, the light must travel from glass into air. Thus, the critical angle is in glass and the angle of refraction, in air, will be 90°.

$$n_g \sin \theta_g = n_a \sin \theta_a$$
$$1.52 \sin \theta_g = 1.00 \sin 90°$$
$$\sin \theta_g = \frac{(1.00)(1.00)}{1.52} = 0.658$$
$$\theta_g = 41°$$

Practice
1. If the index of refraction for diamond is 2.42, what will be the angle of refraction in diamond for an angle of incidence, in water, of 60°? (28°)
2. If the index of refraction for carbon disulphide is 1.65, what is the critical angle for carbon disulphide? (37°)

23.7 Lateral Displacement and Deviation of Light Rays

When a light ray passes from air into glass and then back into air, it is refracted twice. If the two refracting surfaces are parallel, the **emergent ray** is parallel to the incident ray but it is no longer moving in the same path. Such sideways shifting of the path of a ray is called **lateral displacement**. The lateral displacement is greater for thick refracting materials than for thin ones, as illustrated.

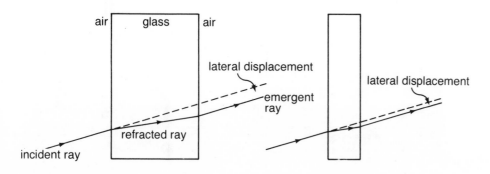

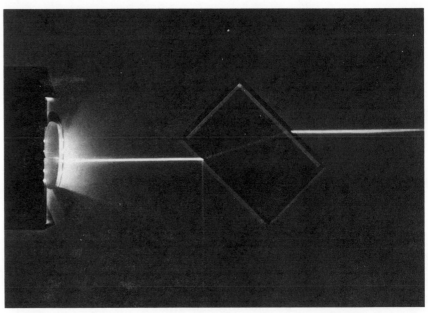

If the surfaces of the refracting material are not parallel—as, for example, in a prism—an emergent ray will take a completely different path. Such a change in the direction of a ray is measured in degrees. The angle between the incident ray and the emergent ray is called the **angle of deviation**.

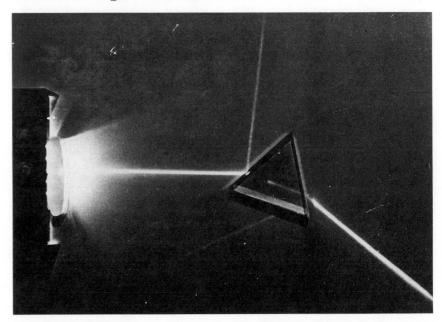

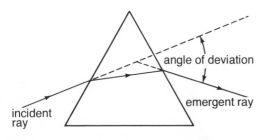

23.8 Some Applications of Refraction

1. Apparent Bending of a Straight Stick in Water

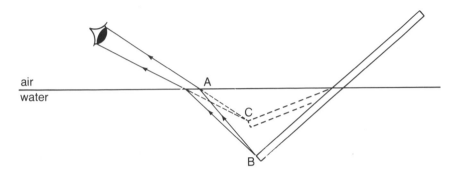

A stick appears bent in water.

Rays of light from the end of the stick, B, pass from water into air, bending away from the normal because they are entering a less dense medium. These rays enter the eye as illustrated, and appear to originate from a point, C, that is higher in the water than B. This is because the eye assumes that the light travelled in a straight line.

The same will be true of light rays coming from other points on the immersed section of the stick and so, viewed from above the surface of the water, the stick will appear to be bent. A similar distortion is produced when you look at stones at the bottom of a shallow stream. The stones appear to be closer to the surface than they really are, a fact that becomes very evident if you try to walk on them!

2. Atmospheric Refraction

The setting sun creates an optical illusion because the light from it is refracted in passing from the vacuum of outer space into the air surrounding the Earth. The density of the air increases as the light gets closer to Earth, so the refraction also increases, resulting in a curved path. To the observer, the sun's light appears to be coming from a higher point in the sky than it really is. In fact, when the observer sees the sun set, the light he sees is coming from below the horizon. The sun has already set!

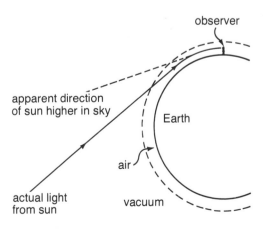

When the sun is very close to the horizon, the light from the lower part of it is refracted more than the light from the upper part. This gives the impression that the sun has a flattened bottom (see photograph). Thus, the sun appears to be oval, rather than round.

The sun and the moon appear larger when they are near the horizon. This illusion is not caused by atmospheric refraction. When the sun or the moon is close to the horizon, we are able to compare it with familiar objects such as trees and buildings, and it appears large in comparison with them. When the sun is high in the sky, there is nothing to compare its size with, and it appears to be smaller than it was near the horizon.

The Earth's atmosphere consists of flowing masses of air of varying density and temperature. Not surprisingly, then, the refractive index varies slightly from one region of the atmosphere

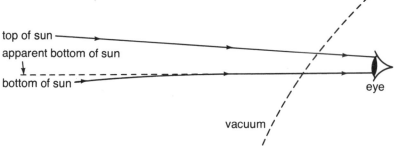

to another. When light from a star enters the atmosphere, it is refracted as it moves from one mass of air to another, and, since the variable masses of air are in motion, the star seems to twinkle.

Astronomers viewing stars must be aware of atmospheric refraction. Sightings near the horizon will be especially inaccurate since the starlight travels through more air.

Most large telescopes are located high on mountains, where there is less of the Earth's atmosphere between them and the stars, and where the air is more uniform in temperature. Many of the distortions of atmospheric refraction are thus avoided. Astronomers find that cold winter nights are usually best for celestial observations. Telescopes have been and will increasingly be placed in orbit above the Earth, to escape the effects of atmospheric refraction.

Shimmering Heat, and Mirages

Warm air has a slightly different index of refraction than cold air. When reflected light passes through a stream of warm air, as it does above a stove or barbecue, it is refracted. This refraction is not uniform because the warm air rises irregularly, in gusts. The light from objects seen through the warm air is distorted by irregular refraction, and the objects appear to shimmer.

The same effect is observed over hot pavement in the summer. A similar phenomenon occurs when gasoline vapour appears to rise from the car while we are filling the tank.

Mirages are most often associated with deserts, but they may occur over any hot, flat surface, such as a road on a summer day. What appears to be a sheet of water sometimes appears on the highway a short distance ahead of us, but we never reach it because it is an optical illusion. We are deceived because we associate reflections from ground level with pools or lakes and make the natural inference that the road is wet.

The word mirage comes from the French verb *se mirer*, to be reflected, and, although most images seen in mirages are similar to images seen in a mirror, reflection plays no part. As the light from the sky nears the Earth's surface, it is progressively refracted by successive layers of warmer air, each with a lower index of refraction. We are conditioned to think of light as always travelling in straight lines and our eye sees a virtual image of the sky in the road.

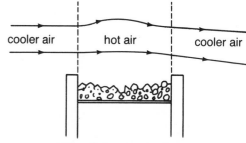

These zebras of the flat, hot Serengetti Plains of Tanzania appear to be beside a large lake—actually, a mirage.

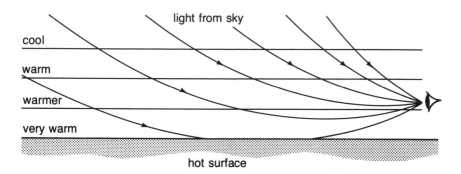

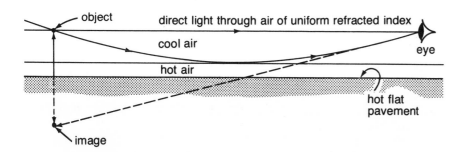

A desert mirage

Sometimes mountains, telegraph poles, and other objects located beyond a hot, flat surface create a mirage.

Total Internal Reflection

The fish's-eye view of the world is distorted both by refraction and by total internal reflection. As the diagram shows, the fish has a full view of everything above the water, but this 180° field of view is squeezed into a cone with an angle of 98° (that is, twice the critical angle). Outside the cone, the light from objects under the water and on the bottom is totally internally reflected at the flat surface and the underside of the surface functions as a mirror. The light from objects directly above the fish is not refracted appreciably, but light coming from the edges of the field of view is severely distorted by refraction. Similar effects are seen by a scuba diver looking up to the surface. Naturally, these effects are only possible when the water is perfectly still.

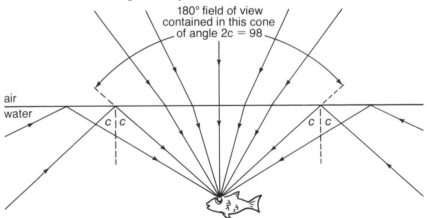

A fish's-eye view of the world above the water.

The life of an ordinary mirror is limited by the fact that the metallic undercoating tends to tarnish in air. Also, only 90 per cent of the light energy is reflected by most metallic reflectors, the other 10 per cent being absorbed by the reflective material. This problem may be remedied by using total internal reflection prisms, which reflect nearly all the light energy and have untarnishable reflective surfaces.

In a submarine periscope, two 45° right-angle glass prisms are mounted as illustrated. Light entering and leaving each prism is not refracted because the angle of incidence is 0°. Light rays striking the hypotenuse side of the prism at an angle of 45° are reflected, because the critical angle for ordinary glass is 42°.

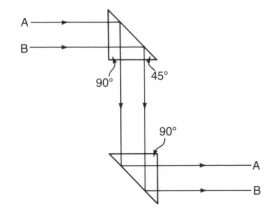

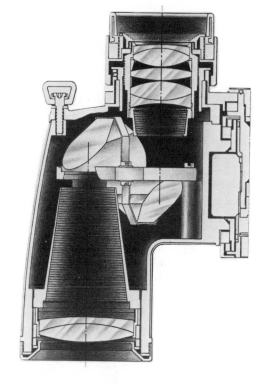

Total reflection prisms are also used in combination with a series of lenses in binoculars, and they are sometimes used in projectors to change the attitude of the image from inverted to erect.

Plane mirrors, made by silvering the back of the glass, can produce extra images because of the reflection from the front surface of the glass and because of internal reflections in the glass. Ordinarily, these extra images are much weaker than the image formed by the silvered surface at the back and go unnoticed. In optical instruments, extra images are a nuisance. For this reason, the plane mirrors in reflex cameras and the curved mirrors in telescopes are silvered on the front surface.

The sparkle of diamonds is partly a result of total internal reflection. Diamonds have a high index of refraction ($n_d = 2.42$) and thus a low critical angle (24.5°). When a ray of light strikes a facet of a diamond at a low angle of incidence, it is either partially or totally internally reflected. Consequently, most of the light that enters a diamond undergoes multiple internal reflection before finally emerging, provided that the surfaces are polished correctly. Careful polishing is even more important than the high optical density of a diamond in producing a glittering display of reflected light. A fortune can rest on the skill of a craftsman as he expertly splits a large diamond into smaller pieces and polishes the surfaces.

Multiple images are formed in a thick glass mirror.

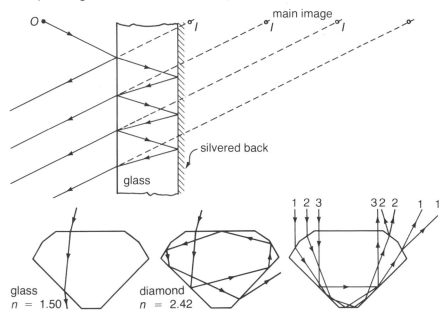

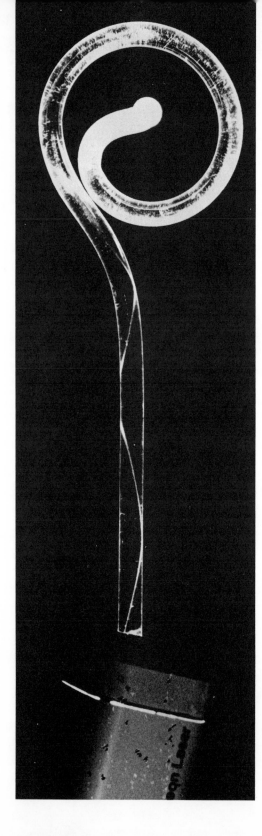

Another application of the phenomenon of total internal reflection is the "light rod", a product of the new technology of **fibre optics**. Light rods are made of a flexible plastic material and are so designed that light undergoes total internal reflection every time it encounters an internal surface. They are used to transmit, over great distances, light carrying information equivalent to thousands of telephone calls.

23.9 Summary

1. The terms used in describing light refraction are: incident ray, angle of incidence, normal, refracted ray, and angle of refraction.
2. When light enters an optically denser medium than air, its speed decreases.
3. The index of refraction is the ratio of the speed of light in air to the speed of light in the medium.

$$n_m = \frac{v_{air}}{v_{medium}}$$

4. The Laws of Refraction are:
   (a) The ratio $\sin i / \sin R$ is a constant for a given medium, for all values of the angle of incidence except $0°$ (Snell's Law).
   (b) The incident ray and the refracted ray are on opposite sides of the normal, and all three are in the same plane.
5. (a) When a ray of light passes from one medium into another, denser, medium, it bends towards the normal ($\angle R < \angle i$).
   (b) When a ray of light passes from one medium into another, less dense, medium, it bends away from the normal ($\angle R > \angle i$).
   (c) When a ray of light passes from one medium into another of different optical density at right angles ($90°$) to the boundary, no refraction occurs ($\angle i = \angle R = 0°$).
6. The conditions for total internal reflection are:
   (a) The ray of light passes from one medium into another that is less dense.
   (b) The angle of incidence exceeds the critical angle.
7. When the angle of incidence is equal to the critical angle, the angle of refraction is $90°$.
8. The general mathematical relationship used with Snell's Law is $n_1 \sin \theta_1 = n_2 \sin \theta_2$, where 1 represents the incident medium and 2 represents the refracting medium.

23.10 Review

1.

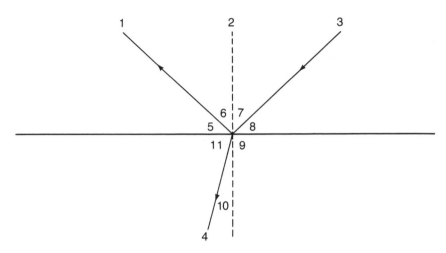

Relate each number in the above diagram to one of the following optical terms: angle of incidence, normal, refracted ray, angle of reflection, incident ray, angle of refraction, reflected ray.

2. Transfer the following diagrams into your notebook. Draw in the general direction of the refracted ray(s) in each case.

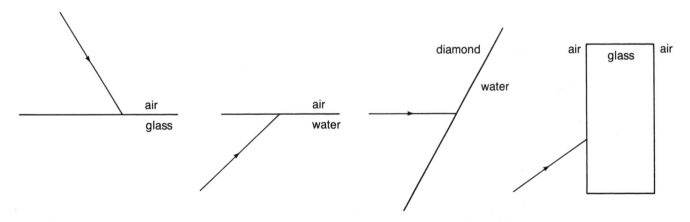

Light rods used for telephone
transmissions

3. Prove geometrically that a ray of light entering a rectangular block of glass always emerges in a direction parallel to the incident ray.

4. Light travels from medium A to medium B. The angle of refraction is less than the angle of incidence.
   (a) Which medium has the higher index of refraction?
   (b) In which medium does the light travel at a lower speed?

5. The speed of light in three different media is as follows:
   (a) 2.25×10^8 m/s (b) 1.24×10^8 m/s (c) 1.95×10^8 m/s
   Determine the index of refraction of each medium, and, using a table of indices of refraction (see Section 23.2), identify the medium in each case.

6. The speed of light in plastic is 2.0×10^8 m/s. What is the refractive index of plastic?

7. Given that the speed of light in air is 3.00×10^8 m/s, find the speed of light in each of the following:
   (a) fused quartz ($n_q = 1.46$) (b) diamond ($n_d = 2.42$)
   (c) flint glass ($n_g = 1.65$) (d) carbon disulphide ($n_{cs} = 1.63$)

8. The index of refraction for blue light in glass is slightly higher than that for red light in glass. What does this indicate about (a) the relative speeds of red light and blue light in glass and (b) the angles of refraction for each colour?

9. The index of refraction of crown glass for violet light is 1.53, and for red light it is 1.51. Assuming that the velocity of light in a vacuum is 3.00×10^8 m/s, what are the speeds of violet light and red light in crown glass?

10. Using the tables in Appendix E, determine the sines of the following angles:
    (a) $30°$ (b) $40°$ (c) $10°$ (d) $60°$ (e) $45°$

11. Using Snell's Law, determine the constant when the angle of incidence and the angle of refraction are:
    (a) $50°$ and $30°$ (b) $30°$ and $18°$ (c) $60°$ and $38°$

12. A ray of light in air strikes a block of quartz at an angle of incidence of $30°$. The angle of refraction is $20°$. What is the index of refraction of the quartz?

13. A ray of light enters water from air at an angle of incidence whose sine is 0.36.
    (a) What is the sine of the angle of refraction?
    (b) What is the angle of refraction?

14. Light travels from air into water. If the angle of refraction is $30°$, what is the angle of incidence?

15. A ray of light passes from air into water ($n_w = 1.33$) at an angle of incidence of $50°$. What is the angle of refraction?

16. One ray of light in air strikes a diamond (n_d = 2.42) and another strikes a piece of fused quartz (n_q = 1.46), in each case at an angle of incidence of 40°. What is the difference between the angles of refraction?

17. A ray of light strikes a block of polyethylene (n_p = 1.50) with angles of incidence of (a) 0° (b) 30° (c) 60°. Determine the angle of refraction in each case.

18. A ray of light passes from water (n_w = 1.33) into carbon disulphide (n_{cs} = 1.63) with an angle of incidence of 30°. What is the angle of refraction in the carbon disulphide?

19. To spear fish, you must aim below the apparent position of the fish. Explain.

20. What is the critical angle for light rays passing from (a) crown glass (n_g = 1.52) into air, and (b) crown glass into water (n_w = 1.33)?

21. In which medium does light travel the faster—one with a critical angle of 27° or one with a critical angle of 32°? Explain.

22. Total internal reflection is easily seen in an aquarium. Where does it occur—at the boundary between the water and the glass or at the boundary between the glass and the air? Explain your answer.

23. (a) What is the index of refraction of a medium if the angle of incidence in air is 63° and the angle of refraction is 30°?
    (b) What is the angle of refraction in a medium if the angle of incidence in air is 48° and the index of refraction of the medium is 1.58?
    (c) What is the angle of incidence in a medium in the case where the angle of refraction in air is 40° and the index of refraction of the medium is 1.58?

24. In each of the following questions, the second medium is air.
    (a) What is the critical angle if the index of refraction for a medium is 1.68?
    (b) What is the index of refraction of a medium if the critical angle is 40°?

25. (a) Is the critical angle for glass with an index of refraction of 1.53 greater or less than that for glass with an index of refraction of 1.60?
    (b) If the medium into which the light is passing is air, what is the critical angle for each type of glass in (a)?

Numerical Answers to Review Questions

5. (a) 1.33 (b) 2.42 (c) 1.54
6. 1.5
7. (a) 2.05 x 10^8 m/s (b) 1.24 x 10^8 m/s
   (c) 1.82 x 10^8 m/s (d) 1.84 x 10^8 m/s
9. 1.96 x 10^8 m/s, 1.99 x 10^8 m/s
10. (a) 0.5000 (b) 0.6428 (c) 0.1736 (d) 0.8660
    (e) 0.7071
11. (a) 1.53 (b) 1.62 (c) 1.41
12. 1.46
13. 0.27, 16°
14. 42°
15. 35°
16. 11°
17. (a) 0° (b) 19° (c) 35°
18. 24°
20. (a) 41.1° (b) 61.1°
23. (a) 1.78 (b) 28° (c) 24°
24. (a) 36.5° (b) 1.56
25. (b) 40.8°, 39.7°

23.11 Learning Objectives

1. To locate, on a diagram, the incident ray, point of incidence, refracted ray, normal, angle of incidence, and angle of refraction.
2. To state the meaning of "index of refraction" in terms of the speed of light and in terms of Snell's Law.
3. To state the Laws of Refraction.
4. To predict the direction in which a ray will be refracted, given the relative optical densities or the indices of refraction.
5. Given any two of the speed of light in air, the speed of light in a medium, and the index of refraction, to determine the third.
6. Given any two of the index of refraction, the angle of incidence, and the angle of refraction, to determine the third.
7. Given any two of the critical angle and the indices of refraction of two media, to determine the third.
8. To describe the conditions under which total internal reflection occurs.
9. To explain, using a diagram, everyday applications of the effects of refraction and total internal reflection.
10. To explain, using a diagram, an application of total internal reflection in an optical device.

24 Lenses and Their Applications

24.1 Lenses

Lenses are not a recent invention. They were used by the Greeks and later, in medieval times, by the Arabs. Lenses of many different types play an important part in our lives. They are used in cameras, telescopes, microscopes, and projectors, and they enable millions of people to read comfortably and to see clearly.

Lenses are of two types: **converging** and **diverging**. Converging lenses bring light rays together. Diverging lenses spread light rays apart. The two are easily distinguished by their shape. Converging lenses are thickest at the centre whereas diverging lenses are thinnest at the centre. Some common types of lenses are illustrated.

Converging lenses are also called convex lenses because of their convex surfaces. Diverging lenses are also called concave lenses because of their concave surfaces.

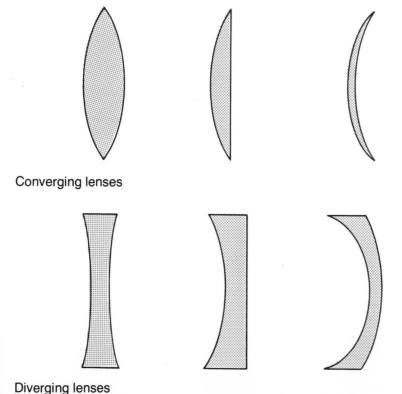

Converging lenses

Diverging lenses

24.2 Refraction in Lenses

When a ray of light travels obliquely from air into glass, it is refracted towards the normal; when it travels obliquely from glass into air, it is refracted away from the normal. In diagram (a) the shape of the glass causes the light to be refracted downwards. In diagram (b) the ray is refracted upwards. If the ray of light strikes the air-glass boundary straight on, no refraction occurs (diagram (c)).

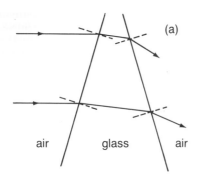

(a)

air   glass   air

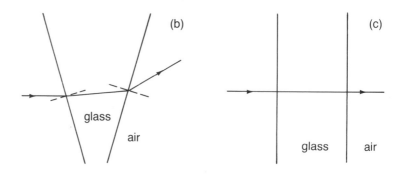

(b)

glass

air

(c)

glass | air

A lens is a circular piece of glass with uniformly curved surfaces that change the direction of light passing through. When a series of rays passes through a lens, each ray is refracted by a different amount, at each surface. Rays striking the lens near the edge are bent the most, because the curvature is greatest there. The least bending occurs at the centre of the lens because the two surfaces are nearly parallel there. Parallel rays striking a converging lens are refracted together. A diverging lens spreads parallel rays out uniformly, as illustrated.

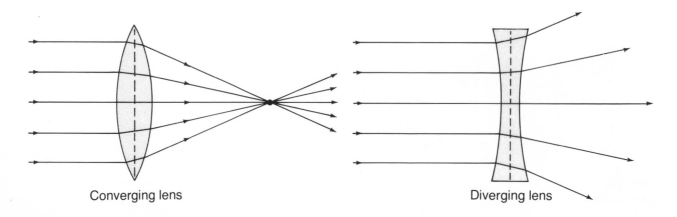

Converging lens   Diverging lens

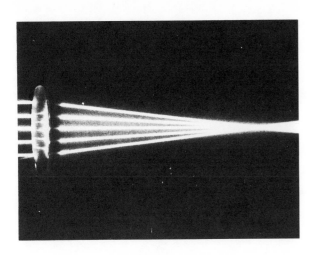
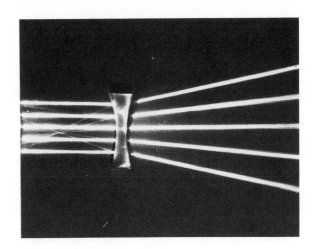

24.3 Images Formed by Converging Lenses

In a converging lens, the geometric centre is called the **optical centre** (O). A line drawn through the optical centre perpendicular to the surfaces of the lens is the **principal axis**. When a group of rays, parallel to the principal axis, is refracted by a converging lens, the rays converge at a point on the principal axis called the **principal focus** (F). The **focal length** (f) is the distance between the principal focus and the optical centre, measured along the principal axis.

Other groups of parallel rays also converge at focal points, but not necessarily on the principal axis. All focal points, including the principal focus, lie on the **focal plane**, which is perpendicular to the principal axis. When a converging lens refracts light from a distant object, the rays arriving at the lens are nearly parallel; thus, a real image is formed on a screen at a distance of one focal length from the lens. We will use this fact in the next investigation to determine the focal length of a lens.

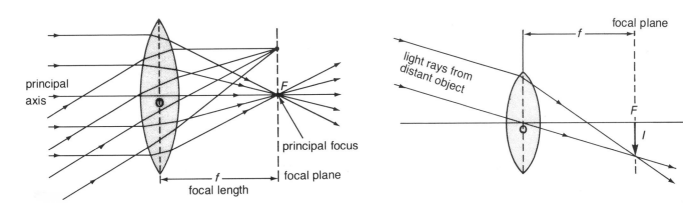

Investigation: The Location and Characteristics of Images Formed by a Converging Lens

Problem:

What are the characteristics and locations of the images formed by an object located at various positions in front of a converging lens?

Materials:

optical bench
converging lens
light source
white paper screen

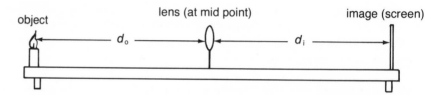

Procedure

1. Hold the lens in a dark part of the room so that light from a distant object passes through it and onto the screen. Move the screen back and forth until the image is clearly focused. Measure the distance between the lens and the screen. This distance is the focal length (f) of the lens.

2. Repeat step 1, this time turning the lens around so that the other side of it faces the screen. Compare the numerical values of the focal length, measured on both sides of the lens.

3. Using the value of the focal length obtained in step 1, calculate the following object distances: 2.5f, 2.0f, 1.5f, f, and 0.5f. Record the information in your notebook in a chart.

Observation	Object distance (d_o)	Image distance (d_i)	Characteristics		
			size	attitude	type
1.	2.5f =				
2.	2f =				
3.	1.5f =				
4.	f				

4. Place the lens in the exact centre of the optical bench.
5. Mark the object distances calculated in step 3 on the optical bench, with chalk or masking tape.
6. Place the object at $2.5\,f$. Move the screen back and forth until the image is focused clearly on the screen. Record the image distance and the characteristics of the image.
7. Repeat step 6 for the other object distances. Image distances for virtual images are not required.

Questions
1. What was the focal length of your converging lens?
2. In the investigation, focal lengths were measured for both sides of the lens. How do the two focal lengths compare?
3. As the object moves closer to the lens, what regular changes occur in the size of the image? The distance of the image? The attitude of the image?
4. At what distance was it difficult, if not impossible, to locate a clearly focused image?
5. Where would you place an object, in relation to the principal focus, to form a real image? To form a virtual image?

(Read Section 24.4 before answering questions 6 and 7.)

6. Using ray diagrams, locate the image for each object position in the investigation. To fit the diagram on your page, use a focal length of 3.0 cm. An object 1.0 cm high is suggested, and a scale of 1 cm = 10 cm.
7. Each of the diagrams in question 6 represents the ray diagram for an application of the converging lens. Beside each diagram, place an appropriate label chosen from the following: ''copy camera'' (image is the same size and real), ''hand magnifier'' (image is larger and virtual), ''slide projector'' (image is larger and real), ''35 mm camera'' (image is smaller and real), ''spot light'' (parallel light–there is no image).

If the image cannot be focused on a screen, it may be a virtual image. Look at the object through the lens to see whether a virtual image is present.

24.4 Ray Diagrams for Converging Lenses

The last investigation showed that converging lenses have two principal foci, which have the same focal length and thus are equidistant from the optical centre, on either side of the lens. These are usually designated F and F'.

An object gives off light rays in all directions (Section 22.3), but for the purpose of locating its image we are only interested in those that pass through the lens, and of them, as with curved mirrors

(Section 22.4), only three are used to find the tip of the image. These three rays are the ones mentioned in the following rules. Compare them with the rays used in a converging mirror (Section 22.3).

Rules for Rays in a Converging Lens

F represents the real principal focus, located on the side of the lens away from the object. The symbol *F'* represents the virtual principal focus, located on the same side of the lens as the object.

1. A ray that is parallel to the principal axis is refracted through the principal focus (*F*).
2. A ray that passes through the principal focus (*F'*) is refracted parallel to the principal axis.
3. A ray that passes through the optical centre goes straight through, without bending.

   Any two of these rays may be used to locate the tip of the image.

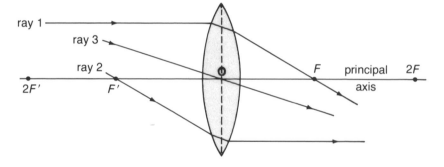

The non-refraction of the ray passing through the optical centre may seem strange, since most rays passing through the optical centre are laterally displaced (Section 22.7). The explanation is that, in the thin lenses we are using, the lateral displacement of the ray is so small that we may assume that the ray is not refracted.

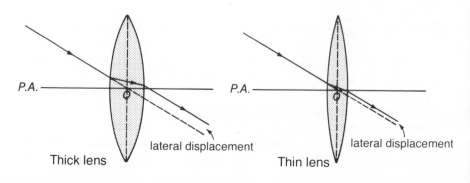

In the next diagrams, a construction line has been drawn through the optical centre perpendicular to the principal axis. The actual path of the light ray is indicated by a solid line. For simplicity, when drawing ray diagrams in lenses, we may represent all the refraction of light as occurring along the construction line. The result is almost the same.

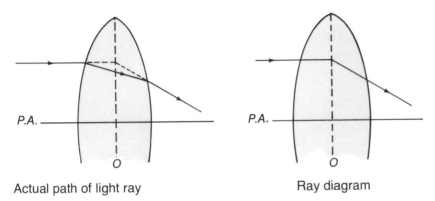

Actual path of light ray   Ray diagram

The rules for ray diagrams in converging lenses may be used as shown in the accompanying summary, to locate the images formed by a converging lens.

24.5 Images Formed by Diverging Lenses

In a diverging lens, parallel rays are refracted so that they radiate out from a virtual focus, as illustrated.

The rays we use to locate the position of the image in a diverging lens are similar to those we used with converging lenses. As a result, one set of rules is used for all lenses. The important difference is that the principal focus in the converging lens is real, whereas in the diverging lens it is virtual.

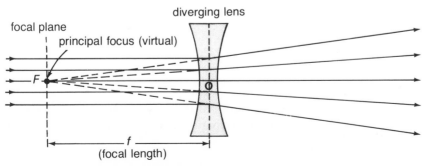

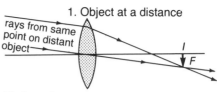

1. Object at a distance

The image is:
at F, real, inverted, smaller than the object.

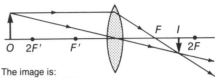

2. Object beyond $2F'$

The image is:
between F and $2F$, real, inverted, smaller than the object.

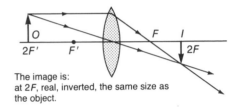

3. Object at $2F'$

The image is:
at $2F$, real, inverted, the same size as the object.

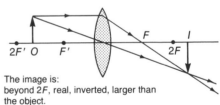

4. Object between F' and $2F'$

The image is:
beyond $2F$, real, inverted, larger than the object.

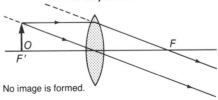

5. Object at F'

No image is formed.

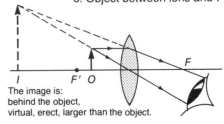

6. Object between lens and F'

The image is:
behind the object, virtual, erect, larger than the object.

Rules for Rays in Curved Lenses of Both Types

1. A ray that is parallel to the principal axis is refracted so that it passes through (or appears to pass through) the principal focus (F).
2. A ray that passes through (or appears to pass through) the principal focus (F') is refracted parallel to the principal axis.
3. A ray that passes through the optical centre goes straight through, without bending.

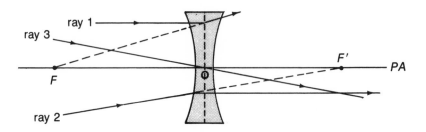

As with converging lenses, we assume, with ray diagrams in diverging lenses, that all refraction occurs at the construction line through the optical centre. This makes the ray diagrams easier to draw.

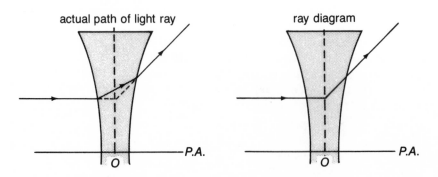

The next diagram illustrates the formation of an image by a diverging lens. For all positions of the object, the image is virtual, erect, and smaller. Also, it is always located between the principal focus and the optical centre.

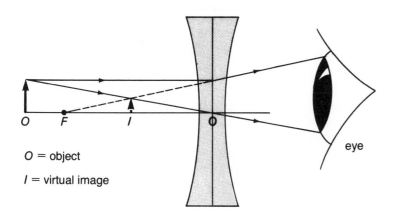

O = object

I = virtual image

The ray through the principal focus (F′) is not usually used to find the image formed by a diverging lens.

24.6 The Camera

A camera consists of a light-proof container using a lens or combination of lenses to form a real, inverted image on a light-sensitive **film**. The film provides a transparent base for a thin layer of silver bromide, which changes chemically when exposed to light. A sharp image of the scene being photographed is focused on the film by varying the distance between the film and the lens, usually by means of a screw mount carrying the lens. The amount of light striking the film is very important. A **shutter** of variable speed and a diaphragm with a variable **aperture** (opening) control the quantity of light admitted through the lens.

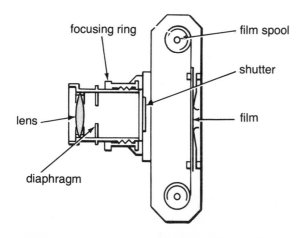

Interior view of a Polaroid camera

Normally, the shutter is closed. It opens for only a fraction of a second when the picture is being taken. The opening through which the light energy passes is calibrated in steps that progressively double the area of the opening. These steps are usually numbered $f/22$, $f/16$, $f/11$, $f/8$, $f/5.6$, $f/4$, etc. The smaller the **f-number** or **f-stop**, the greater the amount of light entering the lens. The smallest f-stop is the largest opening, and it is used to describe the ''speed'' of the lens. For example, a camera with a 1.9 lens has a lens with a maximum aperture of $f/1.9$.

Several combinations of shutter speed and f-stop allow the same amount of light to reach the film. For example, $f/16$ at $1/250$ s is equivalent to $f/11$ at $1/500$ s. A light meter calibrated in aperture/speed combinations is a necessary aid in determining the correct exposure of the film. Most light meters are electrically operated and incorporate a galvanometer connected to a needle.

24.7 The Human Eye

The human eye is in many respects similar to a camera. The **cornea** and **lens** combine to focus the image on a thin, curved layer of light-sensitive cells called **retina**. These cells respond to the various intensities and colours of light that fall upon them and send electric signals along the **optic nerve** to the brain. The image on the retina is inverted, but the brain straightens this out and you ''see'' the image the right way up.

The image is focused on the retina by the lens. The lens is flexible and its focal length can be altered by the pressure of the ring-shaped **ciliary muscles** surrounding it. The lens is thin at the middle when the ciliary muscles are relaxed and thick when they are contracted.

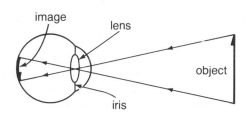

Main features of the human eye

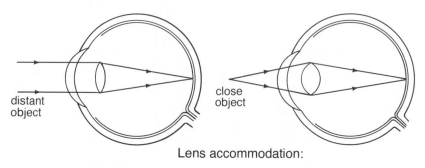

Lens accommodation:

Distant vision   Close vision

The process of changing the shape of the lens to make it possible to see nearby and faraway objects clearly is called **accommodation**. Accommodation occurs almost instantaneously, but the human eye can only focus on one object at a time. For example, when your eyes are focused on the print in a book, objects across the room are out of focus.

In front of the lens is a doughnut-shaped ring called the **iris diaphragm**, or, simply, the iris. The hole (aperture) in the centre is known as the **pupil**. The size of the pupil is controlled by the iris, governing the amount of light entering the eye.

The eyeball itself is made up of a tough white wall called the **sclerotic**. Its front portion is transparent and forms the cornea. The shape of the eye is maintained by the pressure of colourless, transparent fluids in the eye. The liquid between the cornea and the lens is a water-like substance, the **aqueous humour**. The remainder of the eye is filled with a clear, jelly-like substance, the **vitreous humour**.

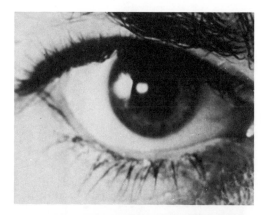

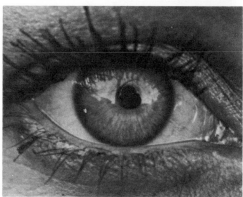

The iris diaphragm changes the size of the pupil.

24.8 Defects in Vision and Their Correction

Farsightedness

Farsightedness, or **hypermetropia**, is a defect in the eye resulting in the inability to see nearby objects clearly. It usually occurs because the distance between the lens and the retina is too small, but it can occur if the cornea-lens combination is too weak to focus the image on the retina. This defect can be corrected by glasses or contact lenses that converge the rays of light so that the lens can focus the image clearly.

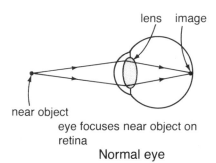

near object
eye focuses near object on retina
Normal eye

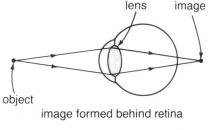

object
image formed behind retina
Farsighted eye

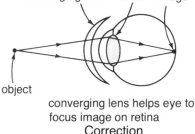

object
converging lens helps eye to focus image on retina
Correction

As a person grows older, the eye lenses lose some of their elasticity, resulting in a **loss in accommodation**. This kind of farsightedness is known as **presbyopia**. It, too, can be corrected by glasses with converging lenses. Distant vision is usually unaffected, so **bifocals** are used. These have converging lenses in the lower portion of each frame, convenient for reading and other close work for which the eyes are lowered.

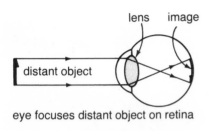

eye focuses distant object on retina

Normal eye

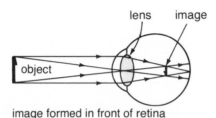

image formed in front of retina

Nearsighted eye

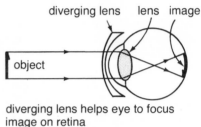

diverging lens helps eye to focus image on retina

Correction

Nearsightedness

In nearsightedness, or **myopia**, the distance between the lens and retina is too great or the cornea-lens combination is too strong. As a result, parallel light rays from distant objects are focused in front of the retina. Correction is accomplished by means of glasses or contact lenses with diverging lenses. These diverge the light rays so that the eye lens can focus the image clearly on the retina.

If the cornea, or eye lens, is curved more in one direction than another, the image is distorted in a condition called **astigmatism**. This is corrected by glasses with lenses that have more curvature where the eye has less, and vice versa.

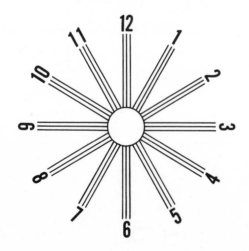

One test for astigmatism uses a wheel with numbered spokes. By noting which lines appear blurred to the patient, the oculist can determine what kind of astigmatism exists.

To "see" your blind spot, hold the book at arm's length, cover your left eye, and focus your right eye on the apple. By changing the distance between your eye and the book you can make the orange disappear as its image falls on the point of the retina where the optic nerve begins. The blind spot is outside the area of normal vision and is usually not noticed.

24.9 Some Applications of Lenses

1. Projector

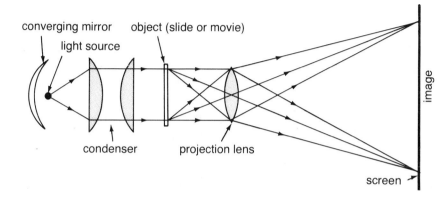

The diagram shows the arrangement of lenses and mirrors in a typical slide or movie projector. The source of light is usually a tungsten filament lamp, a carbon arc, or a quartz iodide lamp that produces the bright light necessary to illuminate a slide or movie. Two converging lenses refract the light so that the object to be projected is uniformly illuminated. The object is placed a distance of between one and two focal lengths in front of the projection lens so that a large real image is produced on the screen.

The image is inverted, so the slide or film must be inverted vertically and horizontally when placed in the projector. The projection lens is mounted in a sliding tube or geared mount so that it may be moved back and forth to focus the image on the screen.

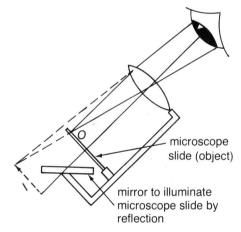

Simple microscope

2. Microscope

A simple microscope or magnifying glass consists of a single converging lens. The object to be magnified is placed inside the focal length. This produces a virtual, larger, and erect image.

A compound microscope uses two converging lenses of short focal length, arranged as illustrated. The **objective lens** produces, from the small object, an inverted, enlarged, real image I_1, which acts as the object for the second lens, called the **eyepiece**. Since the new object is located inside the focal length of the eyepiece, the eyepiece acts as a magnifying glass, producing a virtual, enlarged

The magnification of a compound microscope may be determined by multiplying the magnifying power of the eyepiece by that of the objective lens.

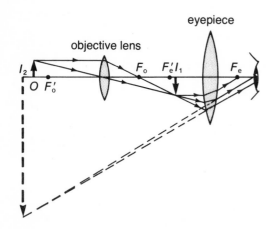

Compound microscope

image (I_2) of the real image (I_1). The focusing of the final image is achieved by mounting the eyepiece in a tube that can be adjusted up and down by means of a geared wheel.

In most compound microscopes, two or more objective lenses of different focal lengths are mounted on a rotating disc, called the nosepiece. Each has a different power of magnification. The limit of clear magnification for the compound microscope is about 900X.

3. Telescopes

The **astronomical telescope** is constructed from two converging lenses. The objective lens has a long focal length and the eyepiece has a short focal length. Since the telescope is used to view distant objects, the rays of light are nearly parallel when they enter the objective lens. The objective lens forms a real image (I) just inside the principal focus (F) of the eyepiece. The eyepiece acts as a magnifying glass, producing a virtual image of great magnification. The image is inverted, but for astronomical purposes this does not matter.

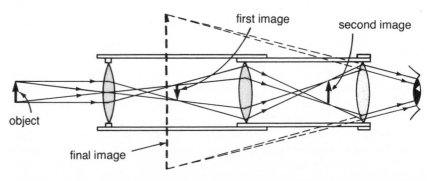

Terrestrial telescope

The **terrestrial telescope** is similar in construction to the astronomical telescope, except for an additional converging lens located between the objective lens and the eyepiece. The purpose of this extra lens is to invert the image so that it has the same attitude as the object.

Prism binoculars consist simply of two refracting telescopes mounted side by side, one for each eye. Between each pair of lenses is a pair of prisms. These invert the image to make it erect and to reduce the distance between the two lenses. Binoculars are much shorter than a telescope and thus easier to handle. Note that the

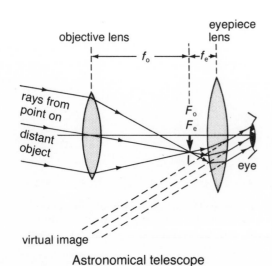

Astronomical telescope

distance the light travels between the two lenses in a telescope and between the two lenses on each side of a pair of binoculars is the same, although the telescope is longer.

24.10 Summary

1. The terms used with curved lenses are: optical centre, principal axis, principal focus, focal length, and focal plane.
2. The focal length of a lens is the distance between the optical centre and the principal focus, measured along the principal axis.
3. The rules for rays in curved lenses are:
   - A ray parallel to the principal axis is refracted so that it passes through (or appears to pass through) the principal focus (F).
   - A ray passing through (or appearing to pass through) the principal focus (F') is refracted parallel to the principal axis.
   - A ray passing through the optical centre goes straight through, without bending.
4. To locate the image formed by a lens, using a ray diagram, at least two of the rays listed in the rules, or their extensions, must intersect on one side of the lens or the other.
5. For an object located beyond the focal length of a converging lens, the image is inverted and real. For an object located inside the focal plane, the image is erect, virtual, and larger than the object.
6. The images formed in diverging lenses are always erect, smaller than the object, and virtual, and they are located between the principal focus and the optical centre.
7. The amount of light striking the film in a camera is controlled by the shutter and diaphragm. The smaller the f-stop setting, the larger the opening for light to enter the camera.
8. The primary parts of the human eye are: cornea, lens, retina, ciliary muscles, iris diaphragm, pupil, aqueous and vitreous humours, optic nerve, and sclerotic.
9. Farsightedness is a defect in the eye in which the images of nearby objects cannot be focused on the retina. It is corrected by using a converging lens.
10. Nearsightedness is a defect in the eye preventing the images of distant objects from being focused on the retina. The correction is to use a diverging lens.
11. Converging lenses and combinations of converging lenses are used in such applications as magnifying glasses, spotlights,

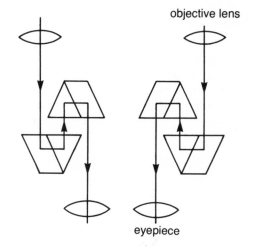

objective lens

eyepiece

projectors, cameras, telescopes, binoculars, and micro-scopes.

24.11 Review

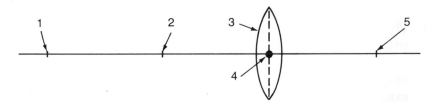

1. In your notebook, write the names of each of the numbered parts.
2. A lens can be formed by a bubble of air in water. Is such a lens a converging one or a diverging one? Use a diagram in your answer.
3. Two converging lenses of the same shape are constructed, one from diamond ($n_d = 2.42$) and one from glass ($n_g = 1.50$). Which lens has the smaller focal length? Explain your answer.
4. Each of the two diagrams shows an object and the image formed by a converging lens. Copy the diagrams into your notebook and by means of ray diagrams locate the principal focus of each lens.
5. An object 8.0 cm high is placed 80 cm in front of a converging lens of focal length 25 cm. By means of a scale ray diagram locate the image and determine its height.
6. Use accurate scale drawings to locate the images in each of the following situations and state whether the image is real or virtual, erect or inverted, and smaller, larger, or the same size.
   (a) A converging lens has a focal length of 20 cm. A 5.0 cm object is placed (i) 10 cm from the lens, (ii) 30 cm from the lens, and (iii) 40 cm from the lens.
   (b) A diverging lens has a focal length of 20 cm. A 5.0 cm object is placed at (i) 10 cm from the lens, and (ii) 30 cm from the lens.
7. A converging lens in a photocopy machine makes images the same size as the object. If the items to be copied are placed at a fixed distance of 30 cm from the lens, what is the focal length of the lens?
8. Using a scale ray diagram, locate the position of the image of a candle 10 cm high, placed 20 cm in front of a converging lens of focal length 25 cm.

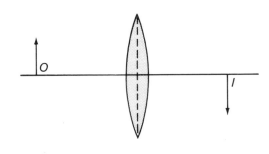

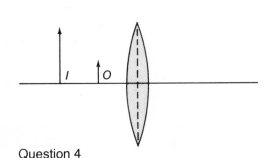

Question 4

9. Using a scale ray diagram, locate the image of an object 5.0 cm high that is 15 cm in front of a diverging lens of focal length 25 cm.
10. A lamp 10 cm high is placed 60 cm in front of a diverging lens of focal length 20 cm. By means of a scale ray diagram, locate the image and determine its height.
11. A picture is taken at 1/250 s with an f-stop of $f/11$. If the speed of the shutter is decreased to 1/125 s, what f-stop is required to obtain an equal exposure?
12. A cataract is a condition in the eye causing the normally transparent lens to become cloudy. The condition is corrected by removing the clouded lens. How do people who have undergone this operation regain the use of the affected eye?
13. To direct parallel light rays through the slide, the light source of a projector is located at the centre of curvature of the converging mirror and at the principal focus of the converging lens in the condenser, as illustrated. Why?

24.12 Learning Objectives

1. Given a diagram of a lens, to locate the following parts: principal axis, optical centre, principal focus, focal plane, and focal length.
2. To describe a method for finding the focal length of a converging lens, using a distant object.
3. Given the position of the object and the focal length of a lens, to locate on a ray diagram the position of the image, and to state the characteristics of the image.
4. Given the position of an object relative to a converging lens and focal length of the lens, to state an application for the lens.
5. To locate the principal parts of a camera on a diagram, and to describe their functions.
6. To locate the principal parts of the human eye on a diagram, and to describe their functions.
7. To describe, using a diagram, the eye defects commonly known as farsightedness and nearsightedness, and to state the type of lens that is used to correct each condition.
8. Given the location of the lenses and their focal lengths on a diagram, to illustrate how an image is formed in: a magnifying glass, a spotlight, a projector, a refracting telescope, and a microscope.

Numerical Answers to Review Questions

5. 36 cm, 3.6 cm
7. 15 cm
8. 100 cm
9. 9.4 cm
10. 15 cm, 2.5 cm
11. f 16

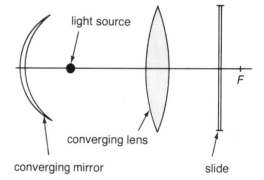

light source

converging lens

converging mirror   slide

F

25 Light and Colour

25.1 Dispersion and Recomposition

Robert Hooke (1635-1703), an English physicist, invented (or perfected) the air pump, the balance spring for watches, the first efficient compound microscope, the wheel barometer, the hygrometer, a wind gauge, a spiral gear, the iris diaphragm, the refractometer, and the universal joint. He also made the first microscopic study of insect anatomy, was the first to use the word "cell" in biology, proposed zero as the freezing point of water, was the first to study crystal structure, gave the first true explanation of fossils, explained the nature of colour in thin films, formulated the law of elasticity (See Section 5.7), surveyed London after the Great Fire, was the architect of Bedlam Hospital, and discovered (but was unable to prove) the inverse square law for gravitation. He is remembered today because he quarrelled with Newton!

It has been known at least since the days of the ancient Egyptians that fragments of clear, colourless glass and precious stones emit the colours of the rainbow when placed in the path of a beam of white light. It was not until 1666, however, that this phenomenon, called **dispersion**, was systematically investigated. The refracting telescope had recently been invented by a Dutch eyeglass maker named Lippershey, and Isaac Newton—then 23 years old—was starting to search for a technique for removing colouration from the images seen through telescopes.

In 1672, Newton described his experiments to the Royal Society in London. His theory, that white light was made up of many colours, was revolutionary and it was greeted with scepticism. Indeed Newton and another English physicist, Robert Hooke, became involved in a bitter debate, and Newton refused to publish his conclusions until after Hooke's death, 32 years later!

In the next investigation we will duplicate part of Newton's historic experiment.

Investigation: Dispersion in a Prism

Problems:
1. How is a ray of white light refracted by a prism?
2. What results when the colours of the spectrum are combined?

Materials:
ray box
triangular glass prism
white screen

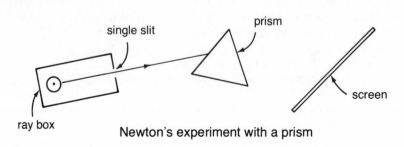

Newton's experiment with a prism

Procedure

1. Set up the apparatus illustrated, putting the screen at least 50 cm away from the prism.
2. Rotate the prism until it produces maximum bending of the incident light. Adjust the screen so that the refracted light strikes it. Observe the pattern on the screen and record in a small diagram both the pattern of the colours and the manner in which the pattern was formed by the prism.
3. Place a converging lens in the path of the beam of refracted light. Adjust the position of the lens in relation to the screen until the light rays converge at a single point on the screen. In a diagram, record the path taken by the light from the ray box to the screen.

Questions

1. List the colours on the screen, in order, beginning with the colour that was refracted the least. What is this band of many colours called? What is the name of the process of breaking down white light into its components?
2. What effect did the converging lens have on the band of coloured rays?
3. What is white light composed of?

Newton used, as a source of light, a small round hole in one of his window shutters at Cambridge. A prism placed in a beam of sunlight coming through the hole produced an elongated patch of coloured light on the opposite wall. Newton called this a **spectrum** and noted the colours—red, orange, yellow, green, blue, indigo, and violet.

The notion of seven basic colours comes from ancient times, but today we refer to only six basic colours because most people are unable to see indigo as a distinct colour. Actually, there is an infinite number of different colours, for each basic colour of the spectrum merges gradually with the next.

The colours of the spectrum may be recombined, by means of a lens, to form white light, as noted in the investigation. This process, called **recomposition**, may also be achieved with a series of mirrors, as illustrated. Newton also demonstrated recomposition by painting the spectral colours on a disc and rotating the disc at a high speed. The rotating disc appeared white.

The demonstration of recomposition with **Newton's Disc** is only possible because of the **persistence of vision**. The image of a colour produced on the retina of the eye is retained for a fraction of a second. If the disc is rotated fast enough, the image of one colour

Had Newton never worked in optics, astronomy, dynamics, or celestial mechanics, he would still be considered one of the greatest scientists on the basis of his contribution to mathematics. Best known for his fundamental breakthrough in calculus, including the concepts and methods of differentiation and integration, he did significant work in other aspects of analysis, algebra, classical and analytical geometry, methods of finite difference, the classification of curves, and interpolation.

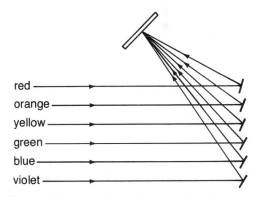

Recombination of spectrum colours by mirrors

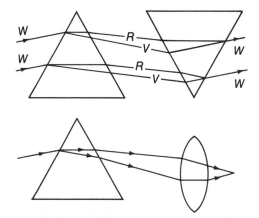

Recomposition using a second prism and a lens.

Recomposition using a Newton disc

The Newton disc demonstration of recomposition usually appears off-white because of the difficulty of reproducing pure colours with paint or ink.

is still present on the retina when the image of the next colour is formed. The brain sums up and blends together the rapidly changing coloured images on the retina, producing the effect of a white image.

25.2 Colour by Subtraction

Another way to disperse the colours of the spectrum is to use a **diffraction grating**. The diffraction grating consists of a series of fine lines very close together, printed or etched on a flat surface. Without going into the question of how a diffraction grating produces a spectrum, we will use one in the next investigation to determine what colours are present in a beam of light.

Investigation: Colour by Subtraction

Problem:
What colours are present after white light has passed through various coloured filters and filter combinations?

Materials:
clear showcase bulb
replica diffraction grating
set of coloured filters

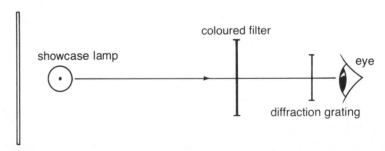

If the lamp is mounted in front of a black background, the spectral colours will be seen more easily. The spectrum will be repeated on either side of the lamp. The spectra closest to the lamp are the brightest and the easiest to see.

Procedure
1. Set up the showcase lamp in a darkened room so that the filament is vertical.
2. View the white light through the diffraction grating, adjusting the axis of the grating so that spectra are formed to the right and left of the filament. List the colours you see.
3. Place a red filter between the lamp and the diffraction grating. List the colours you see.

4. Repeat step 3, using a blue, a green, and a yellow filter, in turn.
5. Place a red and a yellow filter together so that light passes through both before reaching the grating. What colour(s) still pass through the two filters?
6. Repeat step 5, using filter combinations of yellow and blue, and red and green.

Questions

1. "None of the filters used was pure, that is, allowed only one colour to pass through it." Explain this statement, drawing on your observations.
2. Explain your observations for red-yellow, yellow-blue, and red-green, when each of these combinations was used to filter white light.
3. This method of producing a specific colour from white light uses a concept called the Subtractive Theory of Colour. Explain why this is an appropriate name for it.

If light energy is directed towards an object, some of the light is reflected and some is absorbed. And, when light energy is absorbed, it is usually converted into heat, causing the object to warm up. When white light falls on an object, and all of it is reflected, the object appears white. If some colours are reflected while others are absorbed, the object appears to be coloured, since the eye only receives the reflected colour or colours. Thus, a leaf appears green under white light because it absorbs all the colours except green, which is reflected. Similarly, a rose appears red under white light because all the colours, except red, are absorbed. Although black is usually considered to be a colour, in reality it is not. Black cannot be a colour of light since it is the absence of any light at all. For example, in a dark room, all objects appear black since they do not radiate or reflect any light.

When white light shines on red glass, the glass looks red whether you see it by reflected light or by transmitted light, since the glass absorbs all colours except red. Red is both transmitted and reflected. Most transparent substances appear the same by transmitted light as they do by reflected light, but there are some exceptions. The oil used to lubricate automobile engines appears reddish by transmitted light and greenish by reflected light.

The dyes and pigments used in transparent filters and in paints are not pure. For instance, yellow colouring should, in theory, absorb all the colours of the spectrum except yellow. In fact, most colourings are not that selective, and the colours adjacent to yellow in the spectrum, that is, orange and green, are only partially

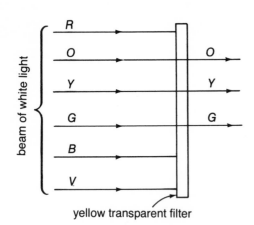

yellow transparent filter

The subtractive primary colours are blue, yellow, and red.

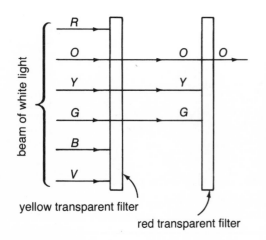

yellow transparent filter

red transparent filter

absorbed. The transmitted yellow is not pure and is referred to as **compound yellow**. Most objects which appear yellow by reflected or transmitted light are compound yellow.

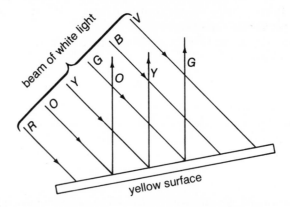

yellow surface

When several colour filters are combined, various parts of white light are absorbed, depending on the filters used. When a red transparent filter followed by a yellow transparent filter is placed in front of a beam of white light, the red filter absorbs all colours except red and orange, and the yellow filter absorbs all colours except orange, yellow, and green. Thus, orange is the only colour that is transmitted through the two-filter combination. Similarly, a combination of blue and yellow filters absorbs all colours except green. This technique of beginning with white light and absorbing or subtracting colours until the colour left is the one desired is called colour by subtraction, or the **Subtractive Theory of Colour**.

In the mixing of paints, a similar process occurs. When blue paint and yellow paint are mixed, the result is green paint. This would not be possible if pure blue was mixed with pure yellow. In fact, the process depends on the fact that the paint pigments in common use are compound colours. Compound yellow contains pigments that reflect orange, yellow, and green light and absorb blue light. **Compound blue**, being impure, reflects green, blue, and violet light but absorbs red and yellow light. When the two paints are combined, the only colour that is not absorbed by the blue and yellow pigment is green, which is reflected. The mixing of pigments or dyes and the use of transparent filters to obtain desired colours is a fairly complicated matter, and the explanations given here are simplified.

The colour of the light illuminating an object will affect the colour of the object. A red object will appear red under white light or red light, but it will appear black under blue light. The explanation is that the red object reflects only red light. Blue light contains no red light, so none of it is reflected. Objects coloured compound yellow appear black only under blue or violet light. For example, a yellow daffodil appears yellow in yellow light, red in red light, green in green light, but black in blue light.

Artificial lights do not emit all the colours of the spectrum. For example, mercury vapour street lamps emit little red light. White skin, normally pinkish in colour, will appear pale and greenish under such lamps because it is receiving no reds and few oranges and therefore cannot reflect them.

Most colour printing is done by a four-colour process. The colours used are blue, yellow, red, and black.

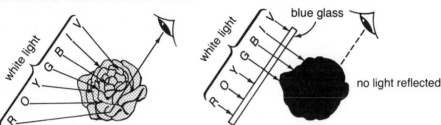

In white light, the rose appears red (left). In blue light (right), the same rose appears black.

25.3 Colour by Addition

If you examine the picture on a colour television tube, you will find thousands of tiny dots or bars of colour, each less than 1.0 mm in width. When the set is turned on, small dots of red, blue, and green light appear. No other colours are present. How is it possible for these small areas of colour to combine to produce all the colours of the spectrum, as well as white light?

Red, blue, and green are called the **additive primary colours**. If three spotlights with red, blue, and green filters are directed on a screen so that they overlap, yellow is produced by the red and green lights, cyan by the green and blue, and magenta by the red and blue. Yellow, cyan, and magenta are called secondary colours. In the central region, where red, blue, and green overlap, white is produced. By varying the intensities of the coloured lights, most of the colours of the spectrum can be produced. Creating a colour by combining the additive primaries is called using the **Additive Theory of Colour**. This technique is used in theatres and television studios. Banks of red, blue, and green lights are hung above the stage and any colour can be produced by varying the intensities of the banks. As mentioned above, the technique is also used in colour television (see Section 25.5).

Magenta is a colour similar to purple. Cyan is a blue-green colour similar to turquoise.

The Additive Theory of Colour is illustrated on the colour plate in this chapter.

Infrared paint-drying oven

An infrared colour photograph of Niagara Falls appears on the colour plate in this chapter.

Ultraviolet light is commonly called "black light". Most ultraviolet light sources emit some visible violet light as well.

Suntan lotion is supposed to filter out some of the ultraviolet light that causes burning.

25.4 Infrared and Ultraviolet Light

If the light from the sun is directed through a prism, it can be shown that invisible radiation is produced beyond either end of the visible spectrum.

Just beyond the red end of the spectrum is a region occupied by a radiation called **infrared**. This was discovered in 1800 by the English astronomer William Herschel (1738-1822). He used a blackened thermometer bulb on the various regions of the spectrum and found a heating effect beyond the visible red in the spectrum.

It has since been found that more than half of the energy coming from the sun is infrared radiation and that infrared radiation provides most of the heat energy requirement of the Earth. Infrared radiation can penetrate clouds, smoke, and haze. It is useful for photography at high altitudes, military reconnaissance, photography in the dark, "heat" photography of the human body to assist in the detection of cancer, and the locating of heat losses in a building. Infrared light also has a therapeutic effect when used on damaged muscles. Infrared heat lamps or radiators are also used to keep food warm in restaurants, dry paint in car body shops, and keep spectators warm in outdoor arenas.

The year after Herschel's discovery, Johann Ritter (1776-1810) placed certain salts in the region beyond the visible violet and found that they glowed, or were fluorescent, in the dark. Quinine sulphate, vaseline on paper, most white shirts, and natural white teeth are examples of other substances that are fluorescent under **ultraviolet** light.

Ultraviolet radiation is easily absorbed by clouds, smoke, and haze, but it has the ability to burn the outer layer of the skin, causing sunburn. It also has the beneficial effect of accelerating the manufacture of vitamin D in the skin. Ultraviolet light from sun lamps must be treated with respect. Excessive exposure may produce a bad sunburn or cause destruction of areas in the retina, resulting in blind spots. Carbon arc lamps and mercury vapour lamps also emit ultraviolet light, as well as visible light, and thus should be used with care. Most of the ultraviolet light received by the Earth, from the sun, is absorbed by our atmosphere.

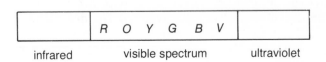

	R O Y G B V	
infrared	visible spectrum	ultraviolet

25.5 Rainbows and Other Colour Effects

1. The Rainbow

For a photograph of a rainbow, see the colour plate in this chapter.

A rainbow is the sun's spectrum produced by water droplets in the atmosphere. Light enters the spherical rain droplets where it is refracted, dispersed, and reflected internally. The violet and red rays intersect internally, as illustrated, emerging with the violet at the top, the red at the bottom, and the other colours of the spectrum in between. Looking at millions of drops, the observer sees the spectrum in an arc of a semi-circle with red on the outside and violet on the inside.

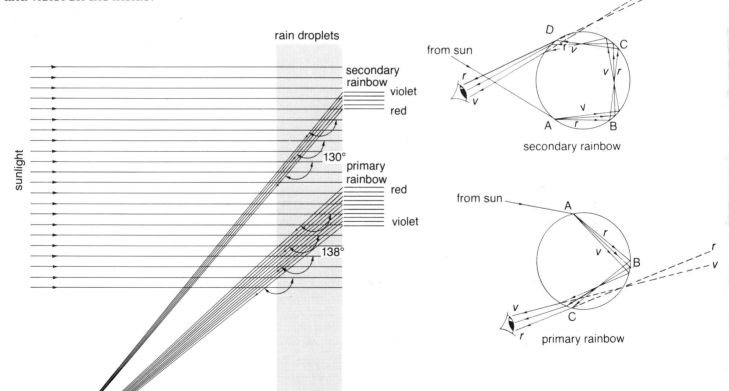

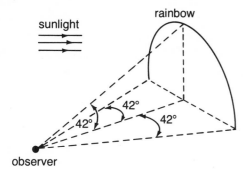

The rainbow arc appears at specific points in the sky because only droplets of water that are located along that arc will reflect the spectrum at the correct angle into the eye of the observer. The angle is approximately 42° to the Earth's surface. Note that the sun must be shining over the shoulder of the observer. Rainbows can only occur when sunlight shines directly on a large region of water droplets, not water vapour.

2. Chromatic Aberration

When white light passes through a lens, the lens disperses it into its components, forming the colours of the spectrum. This creates coloured fringes around objects viewed through the lens, which can be annoying in optical instruments such as cameras and telescopes. (This was the problem that prompted Newton to investigate light and colour.)

The defect, called **chromatic aberration**, is usually corrected by means of combinations of converging and diverging lenses made of glass with differing optical densities. The dispersion of one lens is corrected by that of the other. Cameras of good quality usually use two or more components to correct for the effects of dispersion. These combinations are called **achromatic lenses.**

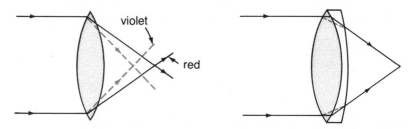

Chromatic aberration is due to the inability of a single lens to focus all colours at a single point. It is minimized by combining a converging lens with a weak diverging lens, constructed of a different type of glass.

3. The Spectrometer

A better way to produce a pure spectrum is to use a parallel beam of light in an instrument called a **spectrometer.** The source of light is placed at the principal focus of the first lens (in the **collimator**), which refracts the light so that its rays are nearly parallel when it is dispersed in the prism. This light then enters a **telescope** made up of two converging lenses, and the resulting spectrum is magnified by the eyepiece. In some instruments the eyepiece is replaced by photographic film on which the spectrum is recorded. Such a spectrometer is called a **spectrograph.**

The spectrum produced by a substance when it is heated to incandescence is called an **emission spectrum.** The emission spectra of solids and of liquids are continuous, one colour merging into the next. An example is the spectrum produced by the hot filament of an incandescent lamp. The emission spectra of gases, usually heated by an electric spark, appear as a series of bright coloured lines. Each element or compound has its own unique spectrum. Because of this property spectra can be used to identify the presence of an element or compound, even in a small sample of the substance.

The spectra of all known elements and compounds have been accurately recorded by scientists. These spectral "fingerprints" are used to identify elements, for example hydrogen, in distant stars. This is accomplished by directing light from the star into a spectrograph, which records the star's spectrum, and then comparing the star's spectrum with the known spectra of various substances.

Police scientists use a similar technique, for example, to identify a car that has been involved in a hit-and-run accident. The spectral analysis of a small chip of car paint, heated to incandescence, can be used to identify the make, colour, and year of the car.

Emission and line spectra are illustrated on the colour plate in this chapter.

The terms "continuous" and "line" are used to distinguish between the two main types of emission spectra. See Section 15.5 for the origin of line spectra.

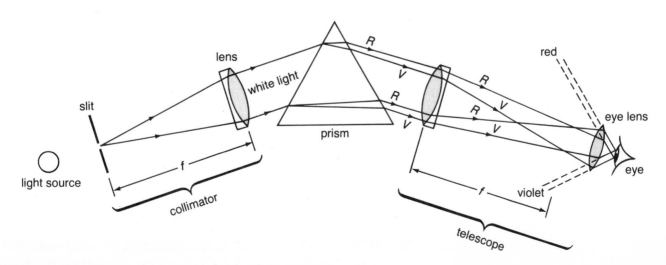

Spectrometer

4. Colour Television

For an illustration of the arrangement of coloured phosphors in a colour picture tube, see the colour plate in this chapter.

A colour television receiver produces all the colours of the spectrum, using the Additive Theory of Colour (see Section 25.3). On the back of the picture-tube screen is a thin coating of phosphor material. Phosphors are a group of chemicals that give off light when hit by fast-moving electrons (see Section 14.3). In black-and-white television, they give off white light and thus are called white phosphors. In colour television there are over 600 000 small dots or bars of three types of phosphor — red green and blue. These are arranged in groups of three, each group having the three additive primaries. Three separate electron beams are directed at these groups, one for each colour. When the red phosphors are hit, red light is given off. When the red and green phosphors are hit, yellow light appears. If all three are hit equally, white light results, and so on. Since the phosphor dots or bars are small and close together, only the resultant colours are seen, not the individual coloured light producing them. The intensity and colour of the picture is controlled by varying the energy of the three electron beams.

25.6 Summary

1. Dispersion is the separation of white light into its component colours by a prism.
2. The colours of the spectrum, when recombined, form white light.
3. White objects tend to reflect light. Black objects tend to absorb light.
4. In the Subtractive Theory of Colour, the colours of the spectrum, contained in white light, are subtracted by filters or dyes until the desired colour remains.
5. The additive primary colours are red, blue, and green. Using the Additive Theory of Colour, any other colour of the spectrum can be produced by adding additive primary colours together in the proper proportions.
6. Infrared light and ultraviolet light are radiations beyond the red and violet areas of the spectrum, respectively. Neither is visible to the human eye but both are important to life on Earth.
7. Rainbows are formed by the dispersion and internal reflection of the white light from the sun by water droplets in the atmosphere.

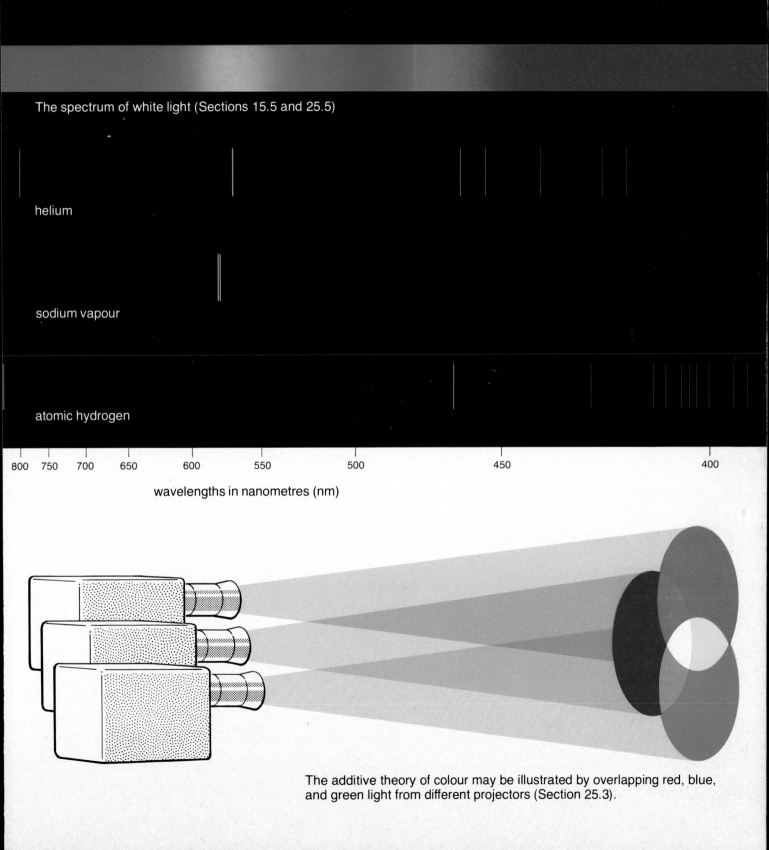

The spectrum of white light (Sections 15.5 and 25.5)

helium

sodium vapour

atomic hydrogen

800   750   700   650   600   550   500   450   400

wavelengths in nanometres (nm)

The additive theory of colour may be illustrated by overlapping red, blue, and green light from different projectors (Section 25.3).

The additive theory is used in colour television (Section 25.5).

A rainbow showing a primary and secondary bow (Section 25.5).

An infrared photograph of Niagara Falls. Such photographs are used to study Earth resources. Note that green plants, such as trees, are red. (Section 25.4).

The interference of white, red, and blue light produced using the same apparatus (Section 26.7).

8. Dispersion causes chromatic aberration in lenses. This defect can be partially corrected by using two or more lenses of glasses with different optical densities.
9. Each element and compound emits a characteristic spectrum when heated to incandescence. The spectrometer and the spectrograph are devices used to analyse such spectra.
10. Colour television makes use of the Additive Theory of Colour.

25.7 Review

1. When white light passes through a prism, the colours of the spectrum are produced on a screen. If a student views the spectral colours through a converging lens, he may see an image with the colours reversed. Explain why.
2. Why are nights brighter when there is snow on the ground?
3. A yellow filter is placed in front of a beam of red light. What colour of light emerges from the filter? Explain your answers.
4. Blue sky viewed through a yellow filter looks green. What conclusion can you draw about the sky and the filter that was used?
5. A British flag is illuminated by a blue light. What colours will its red, blue, and white parts appear to be? Explain your answer.
6. As the director of a school variety concert, how could you "dress" the students in black if all of them wore blue costumes?
7. Why is it against the law for a supermarket to put red lights over its meat display or to package bacon in red cellophane?
8. Yellow sodium vapour lamps are commonly used for street illumination. Skin and lips look different under these lights. Why?
9. A girl buys a dress in a store with fluorescent lighting, and finds when she gets home that the dress is a slightly different colour than she thought it was. Can you suggest a possible explanation?
10. You can get very hot when sunbathing under glass, but you will not get a sunburn. Why?
11. Why must the eyes be covered or shielded when a person is getting a tan under a sun lamp?
12. The sun gives off ultraviolet radiation and infrared radiation as well as visible light. During a solar eclipse, the moon blocks out most of the visible light coming from the sun, creating a dark shadow at certain points on the Earth. An observer is standing in the eclipse shadow.
   (a) What radiations will still be received by the observer?

(**b**) Since it is dark in the shadow, will the pupils of the observer's eyes be enlarged or contracted?

(**c**) Why is it dangerous to view the eclipse with the naked eye?

13. (**a**) In what direction will you see a rainbow when the sun is in the western sky?

(**b**) Can a rainbow be formed if the raindrops are located between you and the sun. Explain your answer.

14. Why is there chromatic aberration in lenses but none in plane mirrors or curved mirrors?

15. How might spectrographic analysis provide evidence that a specific industry has disposed of chemicals in the city's sewer system?

25.8 Learning Objectives

1. To describe, using a diagram, the dispersion of white light by a prism.
2. To describe two methods for recomposing the colours of the spectrum to form white light.
3. Given the colour of the incident light and the colour of a transparent filter or surface, to predict the colour that will be received by an observer.
4. To describe how the Additive Theory of Colour might be applied in colour television and on a stage or in a film studio.
5. To distinguish between infrared light, ultraviolet light, and visible light.
6. To describe, using a diagram, how dispersion and internal reflection occur in a single raindrop.
7. To illustrate how chromatic aberration is produced by converging lenses.
8. To describe how a spectrometer is used to identify an unknown compound.

26 The Nature of Light

26.1 Models in Science

Models made for fun are usually scale replicas of actual devices. Scientists and engineers use models to help them understand phenomena or devise better devices. It was while he was repairing a working model of a steam engine designed by Thomas Newcomen that James Watt devised a more efficient technique for delivering steam to a piston. From that working model, Watt developed the steam engine that had a profound effect on our civilization.

Model in this situation implies a working device, smaller than the original, that allows observation and experimentation with a view to improving the larger device. We have used the ripple tank as a working model to study waves. Unfortunately, many natural phenomena cannot be examined in this way because we cannot see them directly. Two examples are the structure of the atom and the transmission of light.

We often use analogies to help us describe and explain reality. For example, we may say, ''The car took off like a jack rabbit'', or ''He was as skinny as a rail.'' We know that the analogies are not the real thing, but they help us to understand. Scientists' models are like analogies. They do not portray reality exactly, but they sharpen our perception of it.

Scientists also use analogies in the form of models or **theories**, to assist them in understanding the world, especially parts of it that they cannot observe directly. The kinetic molecular theory, the theory of evolution, the theory of continental drift, the ''big bang'' theory, Bohr's model of the atom, the model of the nucleus, and the wave theory of light are all examples of the kind of model scientists use – the **theoretical model**.

Theoretical models, or theories (these two terms are used interchangeably), are used:

- to explain the known qualities or properties of a phenomenon;
- to predict behaviour and properties that may not be directly observable; and
- to help devise new applications for a known scientific phenomenon.

A good theoretical model, or theory, links observed behaviour with other facts. The greater the number of links, the happier the scientist is with his model. The theoretical model is not as a rule an

Sometimes the term "hypothesis" is used in reference to a model, theory, or statement that requires testing.

exact picture of reality. It is an approximation that works. By "work" we mean that it is able to combine and explain all related data without too much alteration. Good theoretical models are simple, and they are easy to use.

Once a scientist has what he believes to be a good model, he devises an experiment with which to test it. The experiment may support the theory or it may suggest that the theory is in need of modification, or is even incorrect. Theoretical models are never rigid, but are modified gradually in the light of new knowledge obtained from the experiments designed to test them. If a theoretical model is rejected, this is usually because several new pieces of contrary evidence have come to light, or because it has proved itself unable to explain one property of a phenomenon. Scientists tend to cling to old theories, or theoretical models, and do not, as popular writers tend to imply, blithely throw a theory away when discoveries are made that conflict with it.

Thus scientists, technologists, and students have two types of models to help them understand the world around them. Working models are used if the phenomenon can be observed directly, and theoretical models, or theories, are used if the phenomenon cannot be observed directly. Keep in mind that the scientific use of models is to help us understand the world and that the models must prove themselves able to stand the test of new evidence that becomes available. If they cannot do that, they are either discarded or revised.

26.2 The Wave Model of Light

We have been investigating the properties of light. Earlier, we investigated the properties of waves. Is there a connection between the two?

In the 17th century, there was a division of opinion between scientists about the nature of light. Some, like Newton, favoured a model based on a theory that light was a stream of fast-moving particles. This was known as the Corpuscular Theory, or **Particle Model of Light.** According to this theory, a source of light acted as a gun, shooting out in all directions a stream of small, fast-moving "bullets" of light. These "bullets" travelled in straight lines, and this explained some of the properties of light, such as shadow formation and reflection.

Christiaan Huygens

Christiaan Huygens (1629-95), a Dutch physicist and astronomer with early training in mathematics, devised a new way to grind lenses and made the best telescopes of his time, perfected the pendulum clock, originated the wave theory of light and explained the velocity change of light in different media, and discovered the moons of Saturn.

Newton's particle theory owed its popularity for a century to Newton's immense prestige, not to the strength of the theory!

Other scientists supported what was called the **Wave Model of Light**, first proposed by Christiaan Huygens in 1678. Huygens believed that the behaviour of light could be explained by studying the characteristics of waves. By the late 19th century, an overwhelming body of evidence appeared to support the Wave Model of Light.

It is fair to say that, if the Wave Model of Light is a good theoretical model, it should explain all the known properties of light including reflection, refraction, and dispersion, and it should predict the diffraction, polarization, and interference of light. If it cannot explain these phenomena, it will have to be altered or modified.

In this chapter, we will test the Wave Model of Light, examine the evidence that supports it, and try to reach a conclusion as to its validity.

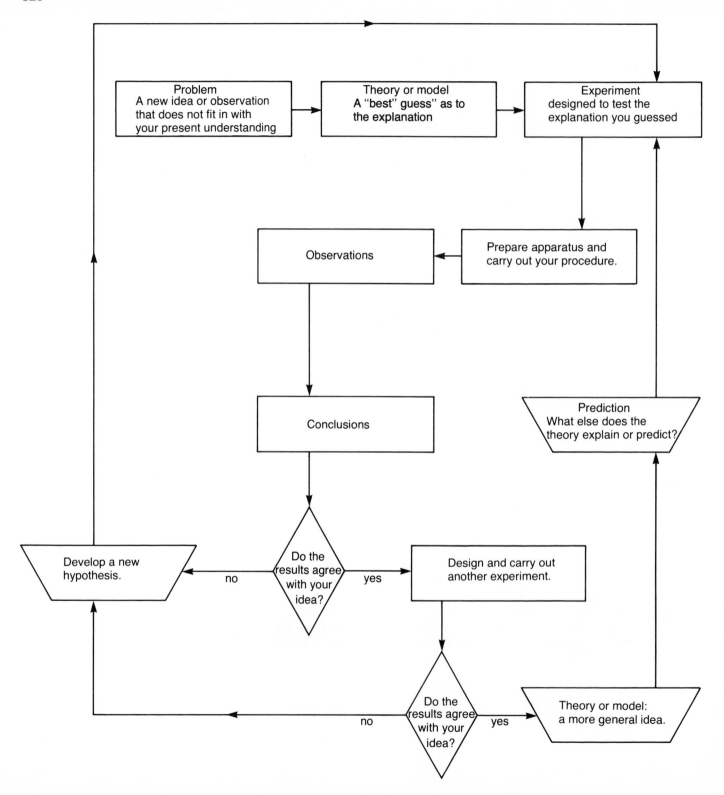

26.3 The Wave Model and Reflection

If the wave model for light is to be a good one for explaining the properties of light, both waves and light should exhibit the same behaviour when they are reflected by a solid obstacle. Note that both waves and light are reflected from a plane surface, according to the Laws of Reflection. In each case, the angle of incidence is equal to the angle of reflection.

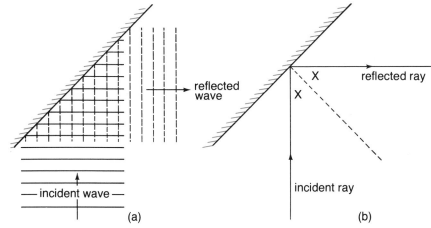

(a)   (b)

Reference: Sections 18.6 and 21.5.

Again, waves and light behave the same way when reflected from a curved reflector.

incident straight waves

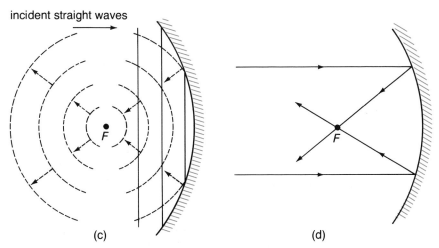

(c)   (d)

Reference: Sections 18.6 and 22.2.

The wave model seems to explain the reflection of light from both plane and curved surfaces, since waves and light both exhibit the same properties of reflection.

26.4 The Wave Model and Refraction

When straight waves pass from deep water to shallow water, their wavelength becomes smaller and their speed decreases. Also, when the angle of incidence is greater than zero, the change in wavelength and speed brings about a change in direction, towards the normal, as the waves cross the boundary between the two media. Light rays behave similarly when passing from one medium into another, for example, from air into glass.

Reference: Sections 18.8 and 23.3.

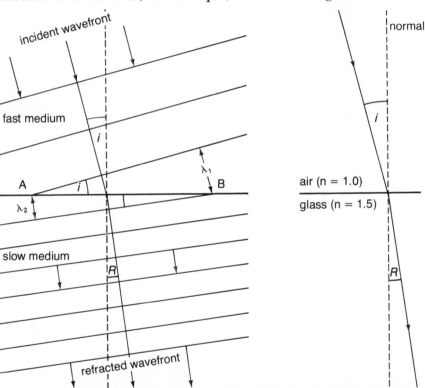

For light and for waves, the change in direction is predicted by Snell's Law and by the ratio of the velocities in the two media.

$$\frac{\sin i}{\sin R} = n \qquad\qquad\qquad n = \frac{v_1}{v_2}$$

When straight waves travel in the opposite direction, from shallow water to deep water, there is an increase in both wavelength and speed and a change in direction, away from the normal. As the angle of incidence increases, some waves are partially reflected as well as refracted. Light behaves in a similar way.

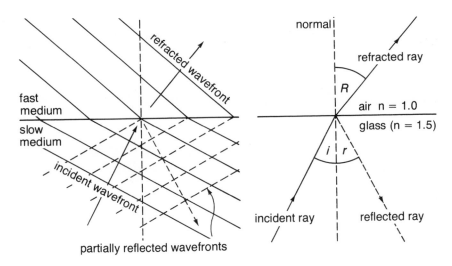

fast medium
slow medium
incident wavefront
refracted wavefront
partially reflected wavefronts

normal
refracted ray
R
air n = 1.0
glass (n = 1.5)
i | r
incident ray
reflected ray

Reference: Sections 18.8 and 23.4.

The wave model is quite successful in explaining the refraction of light. In fact, it can even be shown, using a ripple tank, that there is a critical angle for waves just as there is for light. For angles of incidence greater than the critical angle, all the waves are reflected and none is refracted.

26.5 The Wave Model Predicts Diffraction

Waves in a ripple tank are bent as they pass through a small opening or past a sharp edge (Section 18.7). This bending is called diffraction. The amount of diffraction depends on the wavelength and on the size of the opening. There is little diffraction when the wavelength is small compared with the opening. As the wavelength is increased, or the size of the opening decreased, the amount of diffraction increases.

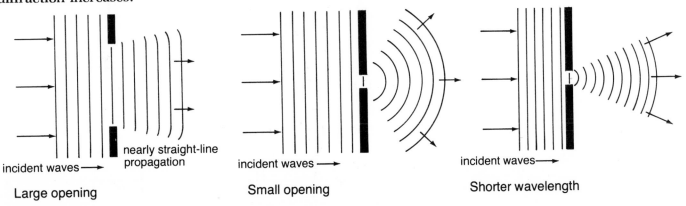

incident waves →
nearly straight-line propagation

Large opening

incident waves →

Small opening

incident waves →

Shorter wavelength

If light behaves like a wave, then light should be diffracted when it passes through a small slit.

Investigation: The Diffraction of Light

Problems:
1. What are the conditions for the diffraction of light?
2. Which is diffracted more, red light or blue light?

Materials:
long filament showcase lamp
red and blue celluloid filters
single-slit plate

Procedure
1. Set up the lamp so that the filament is vertical.
2. Press the pads of your two forefingers together, creating a small slit. The slit width is changed by adjusting the pressure you exert on your finger tips.
3. Carefully position the slit you have created so that it is in the same plane as the filament in the lamp (see illustration).

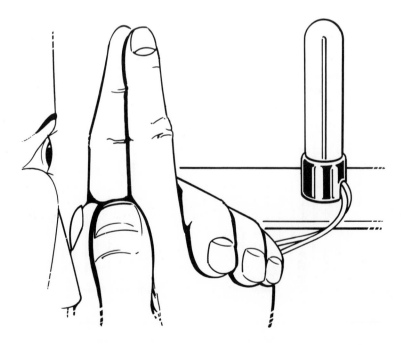

4. Vary the width of the slit, observing any changes in the light passing through the slit.
5. View the long filament again, this time using a prepared slit. Remember that the slit and the filament must be in the same plane. Record your observations in a simple sketch.
6. Attach both the red filter and the blue filter to the lamp with an elastic band so that very little white light is emitted in the direction of the single-slit plate.
7. Simultaneously, view the red light and the blue light through the single-slit plate. Which of the two colours is diffracted more?
8. Remove the coloured filters from the lamp so that only white light is emitted. View the white light through the single slit. What colours do you observe, in addition to the white light?

Questions
1. What size of slit is required to produce the diffraction of light? If light exhibits wave properties, what does this indicate to you about the size of the wavelength of light?
2. Comparing the diffraction of red light and blue light, which colour has the longer wavelength, red or blue? Explain your reasoning.
3. Why did you see colours in step 8? Were they in any special order? What does this indicate to you about the wavelengths of the colours of the spectrum?

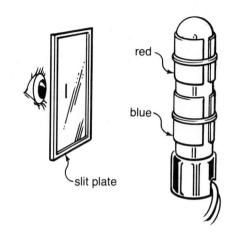

Reference: Section 18.7.

To observe the diffraction of light, a slit of very small width is required. Usually the width is less than 10^{-6} m. When water waves are diffracted, the opening is usually smaller than the size of the water wavelengths. Since light is diffracted as it passes through a small slit, the wavelength of light must be very small—approximately 10^{-6} m or less. The fact that red light is diffracted more than blue light indicates that red light has a greater wavelength than blue. When white light is viewed through a small slit, the colours of the spectrum, in addition to white light, are seen. The explanation for this might be that each colour of the spectrum has a different wavelength and thus is diffracted by a different amount by the same slit.

The diffraction of light indicates that light exhibits wave properties, that each colour in the spectrum may have a different wavelength, and that the wavelengths are longest in the red end of the spectrum and shortest in the blue end.

The refraction of straight waves. The black marker is placed parallel to the refracted wavefronts.

The refraction of straight waves with a smaller wavelength

Colour	Wavelength (nm)
violet	400-450
blue	450-500
green	500-570
yellow	570-590
orange	590-610
red	610-750

Note: 1 nm = 10^{-9} m

26.6 The Wave Model Examines Dispersion

White light, on passing through a prism, is broken up into its components to form a spectrum (Chapter 25). Each of the colours bends by a slightly different amount and emerges from the prism at a slightly different angle, which means that each colour has a slightly different index of refraction. This is called dispersion.

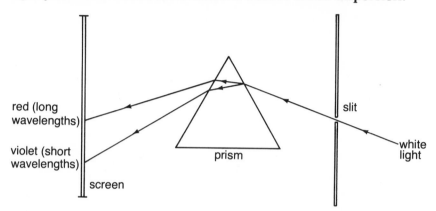

To explain dispersion, the wave model must show that waves of different wavelengths are bent by slightly different amounts on being refracted. Careful measurements in a ripple tank show that this is so, as the photographs verify. In the first photograph, a black marker indicates the position of the refracted waves, using a long wavelength. In the next photograph, with a short wavelength and the same angle of incidence, the refracted waves are not parallel to the marker. Each of these wavelengths has a slightly different index of refraction, since their directions of transmission in the same medium are different.

Dispersion and diffraction demonstrate that light behaves like a wave. If this is so, what are the wavelengths of the colours of the spectrum? These may be determined experimentally, using the wave properties of light. The wavelengths for visible light are listed in a table to give you some idea of their magnitude.

26.7 Interference of Light

When two point sources are attached to the wave generator in a ripple tank, two sets of circular waves are created. These waves interfere with each other to produce areas of constructive and destructive interference, as illustrated.

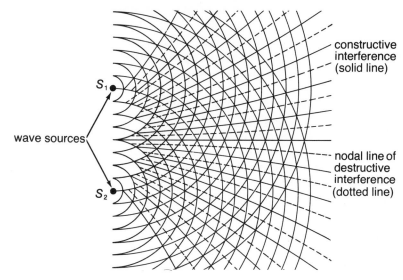

Interference of circular waves produced by two point sources in phase

If light has wave properties, two sources of light, emitting light waves, should produce a result similar to that just noted for waves in a ripple tank. In areas of constructive interference there should be increased brightness, and, in areas of destructive interference, there should be darkness.

At the end of the 18th century, scientists made many attempts to observe the interference of light. In most experiments, two sources of light were placed close together, side by side. The light falling on a nearby screen was carefully examined, but no interference was ever observed.

Those scientists did not realize that the wavelength of light is extremely small. In the ripple tank, at smaller wavelengths, the distance between nodal lines decreased. In the first experiments with light, this distance was so small that no nodal lines could be observed.

There was also a second, and more basic, problem. In the ripple tank, if the phase of the vibrating sources is changed – if they do not continue to vibrate together – then the interference pattern will

Reference: Section 18.11.

Thomas Young (1773-1829) was an English physician and scientist. His early medical research included basic studies of the eye and the functions of the heart and arteries. While studying the human voice he became interested in the physics of waves and was able to show that many of Newton's light experiments could be explained using waves. The fact that his conclusions implied that Newton might have been wrong resulted in severe criticism of his work by other English scientists.

shift and the nodal lines will move to one side or the other. When two incandescent light sources are used, light is emitted randomly by the atoms in each source, in short bursts, not necessarily in phase. When this light strikes a screen, a great many interference patterns are produced, with nodal lines in different places, and no single pattern is observed.

Early in the 19th century (1802), Thomas Young (1773-1829) performed the experiment, but instead of using two separate sources he used only one source, directing it through two pinholes placed very close together. The light was diffracted through the pinholes, so that they acted as two point sources of light. This spread the nodal lines far enough apart to be easily seen. Because the light from the two pinholes actually came from the same source, the two interfering beams of light were always in phase and a single pattern could be formed.

The two major problems in observing the interference of light were resolved, and Young obtained a series of light and dark bands, called **interference fringes**, on a screen placed in the path of the light. Later, he repeated the experiment, directing the light through two narrow parallel slits, with similar results. This experiment, now commonly called **Young's Experiment**, constituted very strong evidence supporting the wave theory of light.

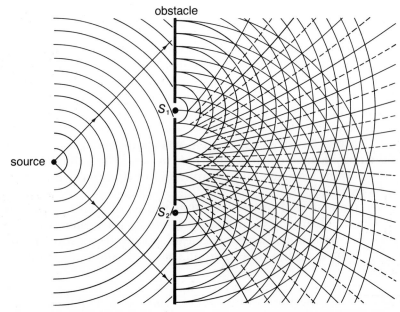

Young's experiment can be duplicated in the ripple tank, as illustrated.

Investigation: Young's Interference Experiment

Problem:
Do light waves interfere destructively and constructively?

Materials:
double-slit plate
showcase lamp
red and blue filters

Procedure
1. Set up the lamp so that the filament is vertical.
2. Attach the blue and red filters to the lamp with an elastic band so that very little white light is emitted in the direction of your position of observation.
3. View the red light and the blue light through the double slit. Draw a sketch of your observations for both colours of light.

Questions
1. How do your observations confirm that light waves have interfered constructively and destructively?
2. Why are the spaces between the nodal lines greater for red light than for blue light?

Double-slit interference pattern produced by red light

In the investigation, both red light and blue light interfere destructively and constructively to produce a series of equally spaced dark and bright lines. In the ripple tank, longer wavelengths produced nodal lines that were farther apart. Red light has a longer wavelength than blue. Thus, the bright and dark lines were farther apart for red light than for blue light.

The interference patterns for red, blue, and white light are illustrated on the colour plate in Chapter 25.

26.8 Why Is the Sky Blue?

When waves strike an obstacle smaller than the wavelength of the waves, a phenomenon occurs that is similar to diffraction through a small slit. The waves are **scattered** from the obstacle in all directions, as if the obstacle were acting as a point source for the waves. The amount of scattering depends on the wavelength of the incident waves, as illustrated. In fact, the shorter wavelengths are scattered much more than the longer ones.

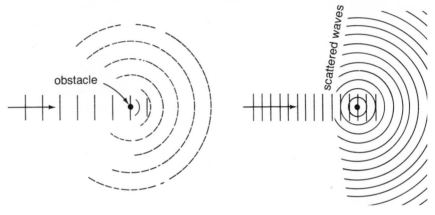

Long wavelength   Short wavelength

Each colour has a different wavelength (Section 26.6). Red light and orange light have longer wavelengths than blue light and violet light.

In the upper atmosphere there are many dust particles, and molecules of water and air that are smaller than the wavelengths of visible light. These act as obstacles to sunlight. Since blue light has a shorter wavelength, it is scattered much more than red light. If you look up at a clear sky, you see the blue light that has been scattered in all directions by the particles in the atmosphere. If the Earth had no atmosphere, there would be no scattered light and the sky would be black; stars would be visible in daylight, as they are on the moon. When the air is dry and clear of dust particles, the sky is a much deeper blue. The intense blue over the Rocky Mountains is the result of clear, dry air. The air on a hazy, humid day contains more particles, scattering more wavelengths than just those of blue, thus making the sky a much lighter shade of blue. At sunset or sunrise the light must travel through more air to reach an observer. On its way, most of the blue and green wavelengths are scattered out, leaving a predominance of wavelengths in the red end of the spectrum. **This is why the sun appears orange or reddish as it rises or sets.**

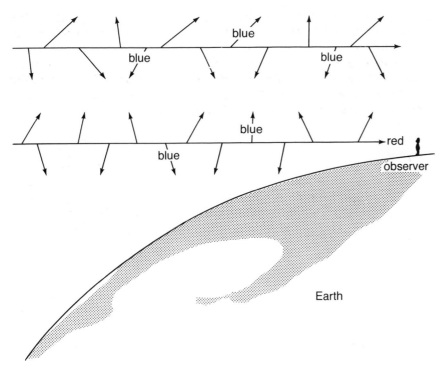

Scattering also affects the high-energy ultraviolet light that is emitted by the sun. This type of radiation can be produced on Earth, using a "black" light or "sun" lamp. It is particularly harmful to sensitive cells such as those in the retina of the eye. As ultraviolet wavelengths are very short, most of this radiation is scattered by the atmosphere, particularly by a type of oxygen molecule called **ozone.** If this did not happen, it is doubtful that life as we know it could exist on Earth, because most plant and animal life would not be able to survive the intense ultraviolet radiation from the sun. Fortunately, the Earth's atmosphere protects us.

Studies have indicated that certain hydrocarbons formerly used in aerosol cans as propellants and in refrigerators and air conditioners, and found in the exhausts of cars, trucks, and airplanes tend to accumulate in the upper atmosphere. These react chemically with ozone and may reduce the quantity of ozone in the upper atmosphere. Any large-scale depletion of the ozone in the upper atmosphere would reduce the degree of scattering and increase the amount of ultraviolet radiation received at the Earth's surface, possibly to harmful levels.

Reference: Section 25.4.

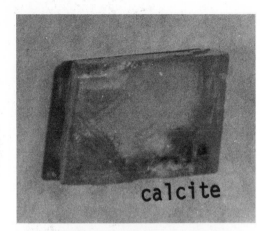

Calcite crystals polarize light.

26.9 The Wave Model Explains Polarization

While the phenomenon of interference is a crucial test that confirms the wavelike nature of light, it gives us no clue as to whether light waves are longitudinal or transverse. Interference between two point sources can be demonstrated with longitudinal sound waves, and with transverse water waves in the ripple tank. Evidence that light consists of transverse waves was first obtained when the wave theory was used to explain a phenomenon called **polarization**.

Polarization of light was first noted by a Danish scientist, Erasmus Bartholinus, in 1669. When he directed a ray of light through a crystal of Iceland spar, or calcite, the ray was split by unequal refraction into two rays. If the light from a typed word is directed through a calcite crystal, a double word is seen (see photograph). What causes the light to split into two components?

We may hypothesize that the vibrations in a light wave are transverse and that the vibrations go in all directions perpendicular to the direction in which the light is travelling.

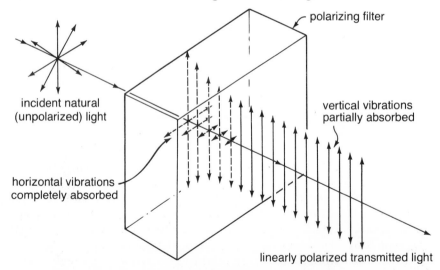

If such a wave encounters a filter that allows the transverse wave to vibrate only in one plane, then we have **polarized** the light wave. This can be demonstrated by generating transverse waves in a rope by moving it up and down and then sideways in rapid succession. If the rope passes through a vertical slit, the waves will vibrate only up and down in the vertical plane. If the vertically polarized waves encounter a second slit that is horizontal, the energy will be absorbed and the waves will be stopped completely.

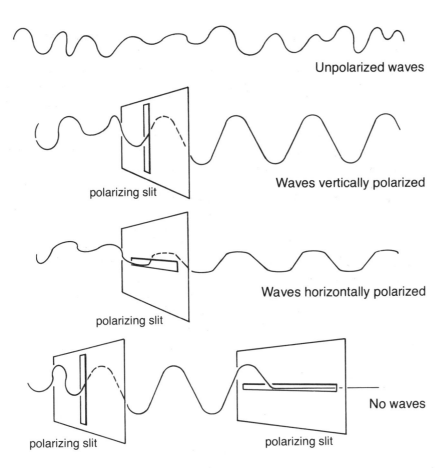

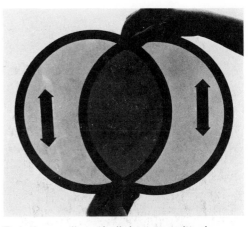

Polarizers aligned—light transmitted

Polarizers at right angles—no light transmitted

This resembles what happens when two polarizing filters are used. Each filter acts as one of the slits or sets of slits. When the light, vibrating transversely in all directions, goes through the first filter, it is polarized only in the direction permitted by that filter. When the axes of the two filters are parallel, the light polarized by the first filter passes through the second filter without further absorption. When the axes of the filters are at right angles, the polarized light from the first one is absorbed by the second. On the other hand, if the waves were longitudinal, they would vibrate in only one direction, namely that in which the waves were travelling. Thus, longitudinal waves cannot be polarized, and pass unaffected through the filters.

We may conclude that light, if it is wavelike, must behave like a transverse wave.

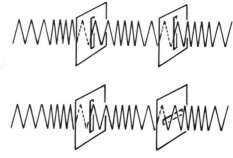

Longitudinal waves are unaffected by polarizing filters.

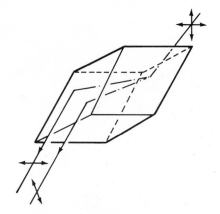

Polarization in a calcite crystal

Then why did the calcite crystal used by Bartholinus produce two light rays from one? When the unpolarized light wave strikes the calcite crystal, it is separated by the crystal structure into two beams polarized in different directions, as illustrated. Thus, calcite crystals may be used to create polarized light.

Calcite, tourmaline, and other naturally occurring polarizing crystals proved to be scarce and fragile, and polarization was a laboratory curiosity until 1928. Then Edwin H. Land, while still a student at university, invented a synthetic polarizing plastic sheet he called **Polaroid**. The original polarizer was made of microscopic, needle-like crystals of herapathite, which he later improved by using long crystals of iodine. With this polarizer many applications for everyday use became possible.

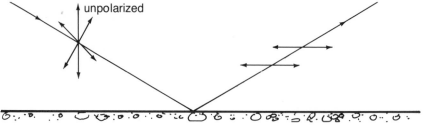

Reflected light is partially polarized in the horizontal plane.

Light is polarized naturally in many ways. One of the most common is by reflection. Light reflected from a flat surface, such as a body of water or a road, is partially polarized in the horizontal plane. The polarizing filters in Polaroid sunglasses are arranged in the vertical plane and therefore absorb the horizontally polarized light reflected from the flat surface. This reduces the glare coming from the reflecting surface.

The sun's light, when scattered in the atmosphere, becomes polarized. You can test this by rotating a Polaroid sheet while looking through it at the sky. The amount of polarization will depend on the direction in which you look and is greatest at 90° to the direction of the sun. Photographers use Polaroid filters to enhance photographs of sky and clouds. If the filters are aligned properly, the blue polarized light is absorbed while the white light from the clouds passes through. In the photograph, the sky appears darker against the white clouds.

Our eyes require a polarizing filter to detect polarized light. The eyes of some creatures, such as ants, horseshoe crabs, and honey bees, are sensitive to polarized light, and they can use the polarized light from the sky to help them navigate.

Photographs of the same boy taken by ordinary light (upper) and by polarized light (lower). The lower photograph is darker and clearer because much of the light reflected from the water has been blocked off by the polarizing filter on the camera's lens.

26.10 Status of the Wave Model for Light

How does the wave model for light hold up? Waves have been used successfully to explain reflection, refraction, diffraction, dispersion, interference, and polarization. The evidence seems to be overwhelming that light behaves like a series of regularly spaced transverse waves. Two questions, however, remain to be answered. First, what is the medium that transmits the vibrations caused by these waves? Second, what is the nature of the vibrations?

Water waves require water. Sound waves require air or some other substance having mass. In each case, a medium is required to transmit the waves. Light, however, travels in a vacuum, and in a vacuum there is no material medium to vibrate and to transmit the waves. Before 1900, scientists tried to explain this difficulty by proposing that there existed an undetected substance called **ether** filling all space, and that this medium transmitted the transverse vibrations of light. Many experiments were attempted to detect "ether" but none was successful.

We know now that light simply does not require a medium for transmission, even though it has wavelike properties. The failure of the wave model to explain this property of light may be disappointing. But remember the purpose of a good model. It is useful as long as it works in explaining and helping us to understand many of the properties of a phenomenon. The wave model has certainly done that for the phenomenon of light! Nevertheless, it will have to be modified to explain the transmission of light in a vacuum. The modification utilizes some of the concepts originally expressed in Newton's Particle Theory of Light, supplemented by the work of Planck and Einstein.

The answer to the second question, concerning the nature of the vibrations transmitted by light, was given by a Scottish physicist, James Maxwell (1831-79). He predicted that, when electric charges vibrate, they should generate transverse waves that travel through a vacuum at the speed of light. He called them **electromagnetic waves**.

James Clerk Maxwell

Ether is derived from "ethereal", meaning heavenly, not from the chemical of the same name.

Heinrich Hertz

26.11 Electromagnetic Waves

Twenty years after the publication of Maxwell's Theory, a German scientist, Heinrich Hertz (1857-94) showed that electromagnetic waves could indeed be produced by an oscillating electric spark. In further experiments, he showed that electromagnetic waves undergo reflection, refraction, diffraction, and interference. In short, they behave exactly like light except that their wavelengths are much greater. The work of Hertz, and of others such as Guglielmo Marconi (1874-1937), laid the foundations for the use of electromagnetic waves in radio communication.

The illustration shows the whole range of electromagnetic waves, in order of increasing frequency or decreasing wavelength. Each range of wavelengths is referred to as a **band**. A small group of wavelengths within a band is called a **channel**. Note that the visible-light wavelengths occupy a very small band in the electromagnetic spectrum.

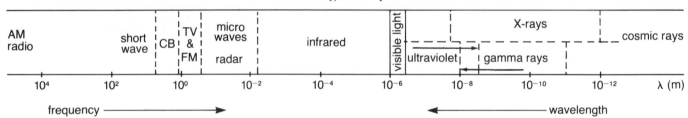

When electromagnetic waves travel out in all directions from a source, their energy is distributed over a larger and larger area, as illustrated.

For example, the energy emitted from a point source (see diagram) is distributed over 1 m² at the first distance. If the distance is doubled, the energy is distributed over 4 m², and the energy per square metre is one-quarter of what it was at x. If the distance is tripled, the energy per square metre will be one-ninth of what it was at x. Therefore, the intensity of an electromagnetic wave emitted from a point source varies inversely as the square of the distance from the source. This is called the **Inverse Square Law for Electromagnetic Waves**. It is a fundamental law of physics.

Sample problem

A detector of radio waves is moved from a point 2.0 m from a microwave transmitter to a point 6.0 m away.

(**a**) How will the reading on the meter change?
(**b**) If the reading at 2.0 m is 72 units, what will it be at 6.0 m?

(**a**) The distance increases, so the reading will decrease.
(**b**) Since the distance increases from 2.0 m to 6.0 m, or 3×, the

reading on the meter will decrease by $\dfrac{1}{3^2} = \dfrac{1}{9}$

Therefore the new reading will be: $72 \times \dfrac{1}{9} = 8$ units.

Practice
1. A light meter reads 5.0 lx when located 3.0 m from a bright
   light. What will it read at 15 m?   (0.2 lx)
2. Lamp A and lamp B both provide the same illuminance when
   measured with a meter, even though lamp A is twice as far away
   from the meter. Compare the powers of the two lamps.
                 (Lamp A has four times the power of lamp B.)

> The unit used to measure illumination (or illuminance) is the lux (lx).

Electromagnetic waves, such as light waves, originate from oscillating electric charges and are transmitted as changing electric and
magnetic fields at right angles to each other. That, at any rate, is
what those would say who believe that the wave theory provides a
complete explanation of the phenomenon of light. In this century,
the theories and experiments of Max Planck, Robert Millikan,
Albert Einstein, and others have shown that the wave theory is not
the final answer to the question, "What exactly is the nature of
light?"–which remains unanswered.

26.12 Summary

1. Two types of models used by scientists are working, or scale,
   models and theoretical models, or theories.
2. The theoretical model is used to explain known properties, to
   predict new properties, and to suggest applications of
   phenomena.
3. The wave model for light explains reflection from both plane
   and curved surfaces and refraction, including partial reflection and refraction, and total internal reflection.
4. Light is diffracted through a small slit, as predicted by the wave
   theory.
5. Red light is diffracted more than blue light, indicating that
   different colours of light have different wavelengths.

6. The wave theory of light provides a probable explanation for the dispersion of white light into the spectral colours, since each colour has its own unique wavelength.

7. The wavelength of visible light is less than 10^{-6} m.

8. The crucial test for the wave theory of light is interference. Areas of destructive and constructive interference are produced as predicted by the wave model.

9. The sky is blue because of the scattering, by small particles, at high altitudes, of the blue wavelengths from the sun.

10. Most of the ultraviolet light from the sun is "scattered" out at high altitudes, by the ozone molecules in the upper atmosphere.

11. The polarization of light indicates that light is a transverse wave.

12. The wave model of light is a good model because it works in explaining and predicting most of the properties of light, and in passing crucial experimental tests.

13. The wave model does not explain the transmission of light through a vacuum and thus requires alteration.

14. Electromagnetic waves include radio waves, television waves, microwaves, infrared light, visible light, ultraviolet light, X-rays, gamma rays, and cosmic rays.

15. The intensity of electromagnetic radiation decreases as the distance increases. This relationship is called the Inverse Square Law for Electromagnetic Waves and is one of the fundamental relationships in physics.

26.13 Review

1. The investigations in this chapter lead us to believe that:
   (a) Light has wave properties.
   (b) The wavelength of light is much smaller than that of water waves in a ripple tank.
   (c) The wavelength of blue light is smaller than the wavelength of red light.
   List the observations that lead us to the above conclusions.

2. When a specific colour of light passes from air into a denser medium, its frequency remains constant. What happens to its wavelength? Why?

3. White light incident on a thin layer of oil on top of a pool of water produces a complex pattern of the spectral colours. Why is this evidence for the wave theory of light? What change would occur if red light were incident on the water?

4. Young's double-slit interference pattern could not be produced if light were not diffracted. Why not?

5. It has been suggested that polarizing sheets could be placed in front of headlights and on windshields of cars to prevent drivers from being blinded at night.

   (a) For this system to work, the sheets would have to be mounted in the same way on every vehicle and with the polarizing plane at 45° to the horizontal. Explain why.

   (b) When tested, this system worked as predicted but was deemed to be unsatisfactory for reasons that had nothing to do with polarization. Can you think of a reason?

6. How do Polaroid sunglasses reduce glare?

7. Polarizing sheets could be used on facing windows in apartment buildings to ensure privacy. Explain how the polarizing sheets would have to be oriented, for maximum privacy.

8. Green light has a wavelength of 5.0×10^{-7} m. What is the frequency of green light? How does this frequency compare with the frequency of your favourite A.M. radio station?

9. The frequency of violet light is 7.3×10^{14} Hz. How many waves of this light would it take to form a train of waves 1.0 cm long?

10. Why are radio waves more easily diffracted around a mountain obstacle than microwaves?

11. Radio amateurs are licensed to broadcast on the "10-metre band". What frequency of radio waves corresponds to a wavelength of 10 m?

12. Name one type of wave examined in this book that does not travel at the speed of light.

13. In the diagram on page 542, what surface area will be covered by the electromagnetic radiation at a distance of 5x from S?

14. The illumination on the Earth's surface from two identical stars is found to be in the ratio 4:1. What is the ratio of their distances from the Earth?

15. The reading on a light meter is 12 lx when the meter is 4 m from a point source of light. What will the reading be when the meter is 8 m away? 2 m away?

Numerical Answers to Review Questions

8. 6.0×10^{14} Hz
9. 2.4×10^{4} waves
11. 3.0×10^{7} Hz
13. 25 m²
14. 16:1
15. 3 lx, 48 lx

26.14 Learning Objectives

1. To distinguish between the two types of models used by scientists.
2. To describe the three basic properties of a good scientific theory, or theoretical model.
3. To illustrate, using a diagram, how the wave theory explains the reflection, refraction, partial reflection and refraction, and total internal reflection of light.
4. To describe an experimental way of demonstrating the diffraction of light.
5. To explain why light of different colours must have different wavelengths, using the properties of diffraction or dispersion.
6. To compare, in detail, the properties of water-wave interference with those of light-wave interference, explaining the destructive interference of light.
7. To explain, using the wave properties of light, why the sky is blue.
8. To explain why most of the ultraviolet radiation from the sun is "filtered" by our atmosphere.
9. To explain the phenomenon of polarization, referring to the transverse properties of light waves.
10. To explain one application of the polarization of light.
11. To summarize the properties of light that are explained by the wave model, and to point out any deficiencies of that model.
12. To locate, in ascending order of frequency, the positions of the following electromagnetic radiations: X-rays, visible light, radio waves, gamma rays, ultraviolet light, cosmic rays, infrared light, microwaves, and television waves.
13. Given either the change in distance or the fractional change in the intensity of an electromagnetic radiation, to predict the other.

Ground stations receive electromagnetic waves that have been received and retransmitted by the Anak communications satellite 35 000 km above the equator. The satellite gives the people of the Canadian Arctic reliable telephone and television services.

Appendix A
System International (SI)
Summary

SI Base Units

Length: metre (m)
The metre is the length of 1 650 763.73 wavelengths (in a vacuum) of the orange-red light emitted by krypton-86.

Mass: kilogram (kg)
The kilogram is equal to the mass of the international prototype kilogram kept at the International Bureau of Weights and Measures, Sevres, France.

Time: second (s)
The second is the duration of 9 192 631 770 periods of the radiation corresponding to the transition between the two hyperfine levels in the ground state of cesium-133.

Electric current: ampere (A)
The ampere is the current that, if maintained in two straight, parallel conductors of infinite length and negligible cross-sectional area, and placed 1 m apart in a vacuum, would produce a force of 0.2 μN between these conductors for each metre of their length.

Temperature: kelvin (K)
The kelvin is the fraction $1/_{273 \cdot 16}$ of the thermodynamic temperature of the triple point of water.

Amount of substance: mole (mol)
The mole is the amount of substance of a system that contains as many individual entities as there are in 0.012 kg of carbon-12.

Luminous intensity: candela (cd)
The candela is the luminous intensity in a perpendicular direction of a surface of a black body with an area of $1/_{600\ 000}$ m^2 at the temperature of freezing platinum under a pressure of 101.325 kPa.

Metric Prefixes

Any unit in SI may be prefixed to form multiples and sub-multiples of the standard unit.

The following is a list of prefixes commonly used in SI:

Prefix	Abbreviation	Multiplier
exa	E	$\times\ 10^{18}$
peta	P	$\times\ 10^{15}$
tera	T	$\times\ 10^{12}$
giga	G	$\times\ 10^{9}$
mega	M	$\times\ 10^{6}$
kilo	k	$\times\ 10^{3}$
hecto	h	$\times\ 10^{2}$
deca	da	$\times\ 10$
deci	d	$\times\ 10^{-1}$
centi	c	$\times\ 10^{-2}$
milli	m	$\times\ 10^{-3}$
micro	μ	$\times\ 10^{-6}$
nano	n	$\times\ 10^{-9}$
pico	p	$\times\ 10^{-12}$
femto	f	$\times\ 10^{-15}$
atto	a	$\times\ 10^{-18}$

Quantities, Symbols, and Standard SI Units

Quantity	Symbol	Standard SI unit	Equivalent expression	Other acceptable units
acceleration	a, $\vec{a}$	metres per second per second (m/s^2)		
distance, displacement	d, $\vec{d}$	metre (m)		
electric charge	Q	coulomb (C)	$1\ C = 1\ A \cdot s$	
electric current	I	ampere (A)		
electric potential	V	volt (V)	$1\ V = 1\ J/C$	
electric resistance	R	ohm (Ω)	$1\ \Omega = 1\ V/A$	
energy	E	joule (J)	$1\ J = 1\ N \cdot m$	kilowatt hour $1\ kW \cdot h = 3.6 \times 10^6\ J$ electronvolt $1\ eV = 1.6 \times 10^{-19}\ J$
force	$\vec{F}$	newton (N)	$1\ N = 1\ kg \cdot m/s^2$	
frequency	f	hertz (Hz)	$1\ Hz = 1\ s^{-1}$	
mass	m	kilogram (kg)		tonne $1\ t = 1000\ kg$
period	T	second (s)		
power	P	watt (W)	$1\ W = 1\ J/s$	
specific heat capacity	c	joules per kilogram, degrees Celsius (J/(kg $\cdot$ °C))		
speed, velocity	v, $\vec{v}$	metres per second		
temperature	T	kelvin (K)		degree Celsius $1\text{°C} = 1\ K$
time	t	second (s)		minute $1\ min = 60\ s$ hour $1\ h = 60\ min$ day $1\ d = 24\ h$
work	W	joule (J)	$1\ J = 1\ N \cdot m$	

Appendix B
Scientific Notation—
Accuracy of Measured
Quantities

Expressing the Accuracy of Measurements—
Significant Digits

In this book, we measure many different physical quantities. No measured quantity is ever exact. There is always some error. The magnitude of the error is determined by the measuring device used and by the skill of the person using it. For example, if two students are measuring the frequency of a pendulum, one with an electronic stopwatch accurate to $^1/_{1000}$ s, and the other with his wristwatch accurate to the nearest $^1/_2$ s, their margins of error will differ because one measuring device is more accurate than the other. On the other hand, if both students are using the same electronic stopwatch, their measurements will probably again be different, because their reaction times will be different and one is more skilful or takes more care than the other.

The form in which a measured quantity is written down indicates not just the quantity but also its degree of accuracy. For example, if we measure the length of a desk and state it to be 1.754 m, we are indicating by the three measured digits to the right of the decimal point that we used a ruler that is accurate to the nearest $^1/_{1000}$ of a metre. Digits that are obviously the result of careful measurement are called **significant digits**, or significant figures. The degree of accuracy of a measurement depends on the number of significant digits it has. All non-zero digits are considered to be significant.

When zeros occur in a measurement, it is not always easy to determine the number of significant digits. For example, the distance from the Earth to the moon is commonly stated as 382 000 km. This number, as stated, is *probably* accurate only to the nearest 1000 km and thus has three significant digits (i.e., the 3, the 8, and the 2). The zeros merely indicate the position of the decimal point. Similarly, 0.000 482 cm contains only three significant digits.

However, zeros are sometimes significant. In each of the following cases there are four significant digits: 10.53 cm and 56.30 cm. In the second case, the zero indicates that the measurement is more accurate than 56.3 cm. Zeros cannot be added indiscriminately to a measured quantity, since each additional zero indicates a greater degree of accuracy.

A person with a wristwatch might reasonably be expected to measure time intervals to the nearest second.

$$1 \text{ s} = 0.017 \text{ min}$$
$$= 0.000 \, 28 \text{ h}$$

Therefore, a person can usually measure such time intervals as:

$$10 \text{ s}$$
$$500 \text{ s}$$
$$2.00 \text{ min}$$
$$157.32 \text{ min}$$
$$6.0005 \text{ h}$$

A person with an ordinary stopwatch ($^1/_{10}$ s) can do better, and the new electronic stopwatches measure to $^1/_{100}$ s.

$$0.01 \text{ s} = 0.000 \, 17 \text{ min}$$
$$= 0.000 \, 002 \, 8 \text{ h}$$

This means that he can measure time intervals such as:

$$10.13 \text{ s}$$
$$2.0003 \text{ min}$$
$$5.000 \, 007 \text{ h}$$

When we count objects, the number is exact. The degree of accuracy and the number of significant digits are not involved. For example, if we count the students in a class and get 35, we know that 35.2 or 34.9 are not possible answers. Only a whole-number answer is possible. Other examples of exact numbers are days in a month, swings of a pendulum, ticks from a recording timer, protons in a nucleus, and dimes in a dollar.

Practice
How many significant digits are there in each of the following measured quantities?

(a)	37.2 m	(3)
(b)	0.000 076 s	(2)
(c)	301.5 kg	(4)
(d)	56.02 m	(4)
(e)	5.00 cm	(3)
(f)	0.000 000 000 97 m	(2)
(g)	0.05 m	(1)

Scientific Notation, or Standard Form

Confusion often occurs over trailing zeros in whole numbers. For example, we said that 382 000 km was *probably* accurate only to three significant digits, because when we give the number of kilometres as "382 000" we imply that we cannot be any more precise than that—presumably because we have no knowledge of the accuracy of the instruments and techniques that were used in making this measurement of the distance to the moon. In fact, the reading may be correct to the nearest 10 km rather than just the nearest 1000 km, but we cannot record that information by means of common notation. Unless we know differently, all trailing zeroes in a whole number must be considered significant.

To resolve this problem, we use what is called **scientific notation**, which enables us to express very large and very small quantities in a form that is easily understood and conveys the necessary number of significant digits. In scientific notation, the number is expressed by writing the correct number of significant digits with one non-zero digit to the left of the decimal point, and then multiplying the number by the appropriate power of 10 (positive or negative). Thus, if 382 000 km is accurate to the nearest 10 km, there are five significant digits, and the measurement should be expressed as 3.8200×10^5 km.

The number of electrons in a coulomb of charge is 6 242 000 000 000 000 000. This measurement is accurate only to four significant figures, but the degree of accuracy is not evident in the form in which it is recorded. In scientific notation it would be expressed as 6.242×10^{18}, which makes the number of significant digits quite clear. The mass of a proton is 0.000 000 000 000 000 000 000 000 001 672 kg. This measurement is known to be accurate to four significant digits, which is evident from the way it is written. But the form of the number is very inconvenient, and it is expressed in scientific notation as 1.672×10^{-27} kg.

Sample problem

Express each of the following numbers in scientific notation with the correct number of significant digits.

*(a) 56 (5.6×10^1)
 (b) 0.80 (8.0×10^{-1})
*(c) 789 (7.89×10^2)
 (d) 4240 (four significant digits) (4.240×10^3)
 (e) 2 999 900 (five significant digits) (2.9999×10^6)
 (f) 0.000 15 (1.5×10^{-4})
 (g) 0.000 000 000 67 (6.7×10^{-10})
*(h) 560 (two significant figures) (5.6×10^2)

*Scientific notation is optional for numbers between 1 and 1000, except where the zeros preceding the decimal point create some uncertainty.

Calculations Involving Measured Quantities

Frequently, in physics, we are required to take a measured quantity and combine it mathematically with another measured quantity, or quantities, using the operations of addition, subtraction, multiplication, division, or square root. It is important that the mathematical operations do not themselves appear to express accuracy that is not based on direct measurement. As a general rule, the results of the mathematical operations can be no more accurate than the *least* accurate direct measurement used in the calculation.

Addition and Subtraction

Suppose we have three measurements of length that are to be added together, e.g., 5.6 m, 17.74 m, and 0.576 m. Since the least precise measurement is 5.6 m (it is accurate to only the nearest 0.1 m), the sum cannot be expressed any more accurately than to the nearest 0.1 m. Thus the sum of 23.910 m has to be rounded off to 23.9 m. A similar procedure is followed in subtraction.

In rounding off to the correct number of significant digits, if the digit to be dropped is greater than 5, the next digit to the left is increased by 1. If the digit is less than 5, the preceding digit remains the same. If the digit is 5, the preceding digit is increased if it is odd and left the same if it is even. For example, 0.565 becomes 0.56, whereas 0.575 becomes 0.58 when rounded off to two significant digits.

Rounding off is of particular importance when electronic calculators are being used. Even the simplest calculation may generate eight digits. It is important to understand when and how to round off, and to know the correct number of significant digits to use when rounding off.

Sample problems

1. Add 14.65 g, 256.5 g, and 0.645 g.
   14.65 g + 256.5 g + 0.645 g = 271.795 g, or 271.8 g
   (to the same accuracy as 256.5 g, the least accurate of the measurements being added)
2. Subtract 56.7 m from 76 m.
   76 m − 56.7 m = 19.3 m, or 19 m
   (to the same accuracy as 76 m)
3. Subtract 1.56 m from 5.65×10^2 m.
   5.65×10^2 m − 1.56 m
   = 565 m − 1.56 m
   = 563.44 m
   = 563 m (to the same accuracy as 5.65×10^2 m)
   = 5.63×10^2 m)

Multiplication and Division

The area of a rectangle whose dimensions are given as 16.24 cm and 5.62 cm is (by multiplication) 91.2688 cm². The product appears to be much more accurate than the two measurements, though this obviously could not be so. In any measured quantity, the last digit is the least reliable, and any calculation that involves this least reliable digit will itself be unreliable.

If we examine the multiplication of these two numbers, we note that the digits 2688 in the product were obtained by calculations involving the last digit in each number. The degree of unreliability increases from left to right, so that the 2 is not as unreliable as the 6, and so on. Since for all measured quantities the last digit involves some degree of unreliability, the product may reasonably be rounded off and expressed as 91.3 cm². (The least reliable digits are printed in red.)

$$
\begin{array}{r}
16.24 \\
\times \quad 5.62 \\
\hline
32.48 \\
974.4 \\
8120. \\
\hline
91.2688
\end{array}
$$

In general, the product of two or more measured quantities is only as accurate as the factor that has the fewest significant digits, regardless of the decimal point. This rule also holds for division, squaring, and square root.

In this case, 16.24 (four significant digits) times 5.62 (three significant digits) gives a product of 91.3 (three significant digits).

Sample problem

State the correct number of significant digits in the answer to each of the following calculations, involving measured quantities.

(a) (8.56 cm) (2.3 cm)   (2)

(b) $\dfrac{8.83 \text{ m}}{0.002 \text{ m}}$ (1)

(c) $(3.66 \times 10^{-2} \text{ km}) (1.6 \times 10^2 \text{ km})$ (2)

(d) $\dfrac{8.44 \times 10^4 \text{ m}}{1.35 \times 10^{-3}}$ (3)

(e) $\sqrt{5.6 \times 10^{-4} \text{ m}^2}$ (2)

Sometimes a calculation is easier to perform if scientific notation is used. In the answer to the expression $5650 \times \dfrac{0.000\ 65}{0.052}$, for example, there may be some difficulty in placing the decimal point correctly. If the numbers are expressed in scientific notation and the powers of 10 are moved to the right, the mathematical operations will be easier to perform and there will be no difficulty in determining the proper position of the decimal point.

$$
\begin{aligned}
\frac{5650 \times 0.000\ 65}{0.052} &= \frac{(5.65 \times 10^3)(6.5 \times 10^{-4})}{5.2 \times 10^{-2}} \\
&= \frac{(5.65)(6.5)}{5.2} \times \frac{(10^3)(10^{-4})}{10^{-2}} \\
&= 7.0625 \times 10^1 \\
&= 71 \text{ (correct to two significant digits)}
\end{aligned}
$$

Note: See Appendix G (page 558) for an investigation employing significant digits.

Summary

1. All measured quantities have some degree of error.
2. All counted quantities are exact.
3. All non-zero digits are significant; e.g., 189.57 has five significant digits.
4. All zeros between non-zero digits and trailing zeros to the right of a decimal point are significant; e.g., 505 and 6.00 both have three significant digits.
5. In whole numbers, all trailing zeros (those to the right of the last non-zero digit) are considered significant unless we are told otherwise; e.g., 46 000 is considered to have five significant digits.
6. In decimal fractions less than 1, leading zeros (to the left of the first non-zero digit) are not significant; e.g., 0.002 48 has only three significant digits.
7. When adding or subtracting measured quantities, the answer should be expressed to the same number of decimal places as the *least* accurate quantity used in the calculation.
8. When multiplying, dividing, or finding the square root of measured quantities, the answer should be expressed to the same number of significant digits as were present in the least accurate quantity used in the calculation.

Review

1. State the number of significant digits in each of the following.
   (a) 809   (b) 5.60   (c) 0.0060   (d) 0.010   (e) 560
   (f) 0.000 000 000 95   (g) 5.743
2. Express each of the following in scientific notation.
   (a) 5808   (b) 0.000 063   (c) 5300 (two significant digits)   (d) 29 979 280 000 (seven significant digits)
   (e) 0.000 000 000 913   (f) 0.060 30
   (g) 30 000 000 000 (one significant digit)   (h) 0.70
   (i) 58
3. Express each of the following in common notation.
   (a) 6×10^1 (b) 6.2×10^3 (c) 7.4×10^9
   (d) 9.1×10^{-2} (e) 4.3678×10^5 (f) 3.076×10^{-3}
   (g) 4.3×10^2
4. Perform each of the following mathematical operations, expressing the answers to the correct number of significant digits.
   (a) 37.2 + 0.12 + 363.55   (b) 362.66 − 29.2
   (c) 4005.34 − 325.2600   (d) 0.000 76 − 0.000 600 0
   (e) (2.4)(6.0)   (f) (0.23)(0.35)(4.0)   (g) (55)(0.54)(326)
   (h) (0.0060)(55.1)(26)   (i) $\dfrac{750}{3.0}$ (j) $\dfrac{635}{8.2}$ (k) $\dfrac{0.452}{0.014}$
   (l) $\dfrac{(6.21)(0.45)}{5.0}$ (m) $\dfrac{(0.094)(720)}{4.4}$ (n) 2.5^2 (o) $\sqrt{4.9}$

5. Simplify each of the following, using scientific notation where appropriate.
   (a) $10^1 \times 10^1$ (b) $10^3 \times 10^2$ (c) $10^{-1} \times 10^5$
   (d) $10^{-5} \times 10^2$ (e) $10^2 \div 10^4$ (f) $10^3 \div 10^7$
   (g) $10^{-5} \div 10^2$ (h) $10^{-5} \div 10^{-6}$ (i) $(1.3 \times 10^2)(3 \times 10^1)$
   (j) $(2.5 \times 10^3)(2.0 \times 10^{-2})$ (k) $(6.0 \times 10^{-4})(3.00 \times 10^{-2})$
   (l) $\dfrac{4.0 \times 10^6}{2.0 \times 10^3}$ (m) $\dfrac{6.33 \times 10^{-2}}{3.0 \times 10^{-4}}$
   (n) $\dfrac{(4.0 \times 10^5)(6.0 \times 10^{-3})}{2.00 \times 10^{-4}}$ (o) $\dfrac{(3.6 \times 10^{-4})(8.0 \times 10^{-5})}{4.0 \times 10^{-10}}$
   (p) $\dfrac{(0.634)(6.2 \times 10^{-2})}{2.0 \times 10}$ (q) $\dfrac{(460)(6.0 \times 10^{-4})}{0.000\ 20}$

6. The speed of light is 3.00×10^8 m/s. How many metres are there in a light-year? (To simplify your calculations, round off the numbers you use to two significant digits and express your answer to one significant digit.)

7. One estimate of the volume of water contained as ice in the Earth's polar icecaps and glaciers is 1.8×10^{16} m^3. If the area of the Earth's oceans is 1.4×10^{13} m^2, by how much would the ocean level increase if all the ice melted and was added to the oceans? What effect would this have on most of the coastal cities in the world?

8. The mass of the Earth is 6.0×10^{24} kg. If 1 kg of matter contains 10^{26} atoms, how many atoms are there in the Earth?

9. If the volume of a ping pong ball is approximately 1.0×10^{-4} m^3, how many ping pong balls could you put in an empty science laboratory whose dimensions are 15.2 m, 8.2 m, and 3.1 m?

Answers to Review Questions

1. (a) 3 (b) 3 (c) 2 (d) 2 (e) 3 (f) 2 (g) 4
2. (a) 5.808×10^3 (b) 6.3×10^{-5} (c) 5.3×10^3
   (d) $2.997\ 928 \times 10^{10}$ (e) 9.13×10^{-10} (f) 6.030×10^{-2} (g) 3×10^{10} (h) 7.0×10^{-1} (i) 5.8×10
3. (a) 60 (b) 6200 (c) 7 400 000 000 (d) 0.091
   (e) 436 780 (f) 0.003 076 (g) 430
4. (a) 400.9 (b) 333.5 (c) 3680.08 (d) 0.00016
   (e) 14 (f) 0.32 (g) 9.7×10^3 (h) 8.6 (i) 2.5×10^2
   (j) 77 (k) 32 (l) 0.56 (m) 15 (n) 6.2 (o) 2.2
5. (a) 10^2 (b) 10^5 (c) 10^4 (d) 10^{-3} (e) 10^{-2} (f) 10^{-4}
   (g) 10^{-7} (h) 10^1 (i) 4×10^3 (j) 5.0×10^1 (k) 1.8×10^{-5} (l) 2.0×10^3 (m) 2.1×10^2 (n) 1.2×10^7
   (o) 7.2×10 (p) 2.0×10^{-3} (q) 1.4×10^3
6. 9×10^{15} m
7. 1.3×10^3 m
8. 6.0×10^{50}
9. 3.9×10^6

Appendix C
Expressing Experimental Error

No matter how small a scale's divisions may be, there is a limit to the accuracy of every measurement made with it. Every measurement on every scale has some unavoidable error, usually one-half of the smallest division marked on the scale. This error is usually expressed as a **percentage error**, using the following equation:

$$\text{percentage error} = \frac{\text{measured value} - \text{accepted value}}{\text{accepted value}} \times 100\%$$

The **accepted value** is the value considered by experts to be the best measurement obtainable. Fundamental constants such as the speed of light and the elementary charge are examples of accepted values. If, when you measured the speed of sound in Chapter 19, you found it to be 342 m/s, when the accepted value at the same temperature is 352 m/s, you could calculate your percentage error as follows:

$$\text{percentage error} = \frac{342 \text{ m/s} - 352 \text{ m/s}}{352 \text{ m/s}} \times 100\%$$
$$= -2.84\%$$

The negative sign indicates that your measured value was less than the accepted value.

Many common measurements, such as the width of your desk, have no accepted value. When measuring with a metre stick marked in millimetres, the maximum possible error in any measurement is probably 0.5 mm. If you are measuring an object approximately 1 m long, you can calculate your percentage error as follows:

$$\text{percentage error} = \frac{\text{maximum error}}{\text{measured value}} \times 100\%$$
$$= \frac{0.5 \text{ mm}}{1000 \text{ mm}} \times 100\%$$
$$= 0.05\%$$

On the other hand, if the object being measured is only 1 cm long, the percentage error is:

$$\text{percentage error} = \frac{0.5 \text{ mm}}{10 \text{ mm}} \times 100\%$$
$$= 5\%$$

Two measured values of the same quantity may also be compared by calculating the percentage difference between them, as follows:

$$\text{percentage difference} = \frac{\text{difference in measurements}}{\text{average measurement}} \times 100\%$$

For example, if two measurements of the speed of sound are 342 m/s and 348 m/s, their percentage difference is:

$$\text{percentage difference} = \frac{6 \text{ m/s}}{345 \text{ m/s}} \times 100\%$$

$$= 2\%$$

Practice

1. A student measures the acceleration due to gravity and finds it to be 9.72 m/s². What is his percentage error, if the accepted value is 9.81 m/s²?   (−0.9%)
2. You estimate that the maximum possible error of an equal arm balance is 0.01 g. What is the possible percentage error when you use this balance to measure each of the following masses?
    (a) 700 g   (b) 20 g   (c) 3 kg   (d) 1.0 g
                    (0.001%, 0.05%, 0.0003%, 1%)

Appendix D
Graphing Scientific Data

You may have drawn X-Y graphs in your mathematics class. Most of the graphs used in this book are different in that they involve experimental data. The following guidelines are to assist you in drawing a graph based on experimental data.

Step 1 – Choosing the Axes

Determine which of the physical quantities is the **dependent variable** and which is the **independent variable**. The independent variable is the one whose values the experimenter chooses. In the graph illustrated, time is the independent variable since the experimenter chooses at which times he is going to measure the speed of the ball. The independent variable is plotted on the horizontal axis and the dependent variable on the vertical axis.

Step 2 – Scaling the Axes

When choosing scales, spread the measured values across the graph paper as widely as possible. The scales chosen must be easy to read and must have equal divisions. Each division must represent a small whole number of units of the variable being plotted, such as 1, 2, 5, 10, or some simple multiple of these. For example, the maximum measured reading for speed in the accompanying graph is 1.40 m/s.

The graph paper has 17 divisions that could be used to plot speed. If we divided the number of divisions (17) into the maximum value to be plotted (1.40 m/s) we would obtain $\frac{1.40}{17}$ or 0.0823 m/s per division. The plotted values of speed would then take up the entire axis, but the numbers on the divisions would be very awkward. To simplify, we round up 0.0823 m/s to 0.1 m/s, thereby using only 14 divisions and having three left over.

Similarly, if the number of divisions in the horizontal scale (12) is divided into the maximum value to be plotted (10 s), we get $\frac{10}{12}$ or 0.83 s per division. We round 0.83 s up to 1.0 s, thereby using 10 divisions and having two left over. To summarize, choose the correct scale for an axis by dividing the maximum number of divisions on the axis into the maximum value to be plotted, and round the result up to the nearest 1, 2, 5, 10, or some simple multiple of these values.

All the graphs used in this book have an origin of (0,0). It is not necessary to label every line on each axis, any more than it is necessary to label every division on a ruler. Each axis is labelled with the symbol for what is being plotted and the unit.

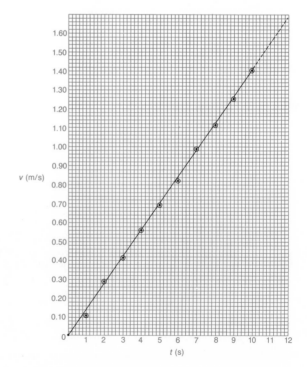

Speed-time graph for a ball rolling down a slope

Step 3 – Plotting the Data

Find each data point and mark it with a small dot *in pencil*. Around each dot draw a small circle not exceeding two small scale divisions in diameter. With a well-sharpened pencil, lightly draw in the smooth curve that best joins the small circles. Do not try to force your line to go through all dots, since experimental error will cause some points to be slightly off the smooth curve. If the points seem to lie on a straight line, use a ruler, preferably a transparent one, so that you can see all the points while selecting the best line. You have used pencil to mark your points, and draw your smooth curve, so that you could easily make changes, if necessary. Once you are satisfied with the curve you have chosen, draw it in, in ink.

Sometimes a point obviously has no experimental error, so the line must go through it. In the example we have used, (0,0) is such a point because the speed will be zero when $t = 0$.

Step 4 – Choosing a Title

Every graph should be given a title. In this case, "Speed-time graph for a ball rolling down a slope" is the title. The title may be placed at the top of the page, or in a box in a clear area on the graph.

Step 5 – Using the Graph

The graphing of data serves at least four functions:
1. It permits easy **interpolation** (finding values between measured points) and **extrapolation** (finding values beyond measured points). If a graph is extended, a dotted line is used.
2. The scatter of the points off the smooth curve gives an indication of the errors in the measured data.
3. Where a point falls far off the smooth curve, this suggests that a serious error may have been made and that the data for that point should be remeasured. Alternatively, it may indicate that there is another variable that has not been taken into consideration in the investigation.
4. We can deduce from the slope of the graph the mathematical relationship between the variables. For example, if the graph is a straight line through the origin, the relationship is of the form y = mx: y is directly proportional to x. In some cases, the experimental values will not result in a straight line.

Appendix E
Table of Natural Trigonometric Functions

Angle	Sine	Cosine	Tangent	Angle	Sine	Cosine	Tangent
1°	.0175	.9998	.0175	46°	.7193	.6947	1.0355
2°	.0349	.9994	.0349	47°	.7314	.6820	1.0724
3°	.0523	.9986	.0524	48°	.7431	.6691	1.1106
4°	.0698	.9976	.0699	49°	.7547	.6561	1.1504
5°	.0872	.9962	.0875	50°	.7660	.6428	1.1918
6°	.1045	.9945	.1051	51°	.7771	.6293	1.2349
7°	.1219	.9925	.1228	52°	.7880	.6157	1.2799
8°	.1392	.9903	.1405	53°	.7986	.6018	1.3270
9°	.1564	.9877	.1584	54°	.8090	.5878	1.3764
10°	.1736	.9848	.1763	55°	.8192	.5736	1.4281
11°	.1908	.9816	.1944	56°	.8290	.5592	1.4826
12°	.2079	.9781	.2126	57°	.8387	.5446	1.5399
13°	.2250	.9744	.2309	58°	.8480	.5299	1.6003
14°	.2419	.9703	.2493	59°	.8572	.5150	1.6643
15°	.2588	.9659	.2679	60°	.8660	.5000	1.7321
16°	.2756	.9613	.2867	61°	.8746	.4848	1.8040
17°	.2924	.9563	.3057	62°	.8829	.4695	1.8807
18°	.3090	.9511	3249	63°	.8910	.4540	1.9626
19°	.3256	.9455	.3443	64°	.8988	.4384	2.0503
20°	.3420	.9397	.3640	65°	.9063	.4226	2.1445
21°	.3584	.9336	.3839	66°	.9135	.4067	2.2460
22°	.3746	.9272	.4040	67°	.9205	.3907	2.3559
23°	.3907	.9205	.4245	68°	.9272	.3746	2.4751
24°	.4067	.9135	.4452	69°	.9336	.3584	2.6051
25°	.4226	.9063	.4663	70°	.9397	.3420	2.7475
26°	.4384	.8988	.4877	71°	.9455	.3256	2.9042
27°	.4540	.8910	.5095	72°	.9511	.3090	3.0777
28°	.4695	.8829	.5317	73°	.9563	.2924	3.2709
29°	.4848	.8746	.5543	74°	.9613	.2756	3.4874
30°	.5000	.8660	.5774	75°	.9659	.2588	3.7321
31°	.5150	.8572	.6009	76°	.9703	.2419	4.0108
32°	.5299	.8480	.6249	77°	.9744	.2250	4.3315
33°	.5446	.8387	.6494	78°	.9781	.2079	4.7046
34°	.5592	.8290	.6745	79°	.9816	.1908	5.1446
35°	.5736	.8192	.7002	80°	.9848	.1736	5.6713
36°	.5878	.8090	.7265	81°	.9877	.1564	6.3138
37°	.6018	.7986	.7536	82°	.9903	.1392	7.1154
38°	.6157	.7880	.7813	83°	.9925	.1219	8.1443
39°	.6293	.7771	.8098	84°	.9945	.1045	9.5144
40°	.6428	.7660	.8391	85°	.9962	.0872	11.4301
41°	.6561	.7547	.8693	86°	.9976	.0698	14.3007
42°	.6691	.7431	.9004	87°	.9986	.0523	19.0811
43°	.6820	.7314	.9325	88°	.9994	.0349	28.6363
44°	.6947	.7193	.9657	89°	.9998	.0175	57.2900
45°	.7071	.7071	1.0000	90°	1.0000	.0000	

Appendix F
Periodic Table of the Elements

1 H 1.0079																1 H 1.0079	2 He 4.00260
3 Li 6.941	4 Be 9.01218											5 B 10.81	6 C 12.011	7 N 14.0067	8 O 15.9994	9 F 18.99840	10 Ne 20.179
11 Na 22.98977	12 Mg 24.305											13 Al 26.98154	14 Si 28.086	15 P 30.97376	16 S 32.06	17 Cl 35.453	18 Ar 39.948
19 K 39.098	20 Ca 40.08	21 Sc 44.9559	22 Ti 47.90	23 V 50.9414	24 Cr 51.996	25 Mn 54.9380	26 Fe 55.847	27 Co 58.9332	28 Ni 58.70	29 Cu 63.546	30 Zn 65.38	31 Ga 69.72	32 Ge 72.59	33 As 74.9216	34 Se 78.96	35 Br 79.904	36 Kr 83.80
37 Rb 85.4678	38 Sr 87.62	39 Y 88.9059	40 Zr 91.22	41 Nb 92.9064	42 Mo 95.94	43 Tc 98.9062	44 Ru 101.07	45 Rh 102.9055	46 Pd 106.4	47 Ag 107.868	48 Cd 112.40	49 In 114.82	50 Sn 118.69	51 Sb 121.75	52 Te 127.60	53 I 126.9045	54 Xe 131.30
55 Cs 132.9054	56 Ba 137.34	57 *La 138.9055	72 Hf 178.49	73 Ta 180.9479	74 W 183.85	75 Re 186.207	76 Os 190.2	77 Ir 192.22	78 Pt 195.09	79 Au 196.9665	80 Hg 200.59	81 Tl 204.37	82 Pb 207.2	83 Bi 208.9804	84 Po (210)	85 At (210)	86 Rn (222)
87 Fr (223)	88 Ra 226.0254	89 †Ac (227)	104 (260)	105 (260)													

*Lanthanoid Series

58 Ce 140.12	59 Pr 140.9077	60 Nd 144.24	61 Pm (147)	62 Sm 150.4	63 Eu 151.96	64 Gd 157.25	65 Tb 158.9254	66 Dy 162.50	67 Ho 164.9304	68 Er 167.26	69 Tm 168.9342	70 Yb 173.04	71 Lu 174.97

†Actinoid Series

90 Th 232.0381	91 Pa 231.0359	92 U 238.029	93 Np 237.0482	94 Pu (244)	95 Am (243)	96 Cm (247)	97 Bk (247)	98 Cf (251)	99 Es (254)	100 Fm (257)	101 Md (258)	102 No (255)	103 Lr (256)

Atomic masses corrected to conform to
the 1973 values of the Commission on
Atomic Weights.

14	Atomic number
Si	Atomic symbol
28.086	Average atomic mass

Table of Isotopes

Element	Symbol	Atomic number	Mass numbers of naturally occurring isotopes
Actinium	Ac	89	**227***, 228*
Aluminum	Al	13	**27**
Americium	Am	95	(**243**)
Antimony	Sb	51	**121**, 123
Argon	Ar	18	36, 38, **40**
Arsenic	As	33	**75**
Astatine	At	85	**210***, 215*, 216*, 218*
Barium	Ba	56	130, 132, 134, 135, 136, 137, **138**
Berkelium	Bk	97	(247)
Beryllium	Be	4	9
Bismuth	Bi	83	**209**, 210*, 211*, 212*, 214*
Boron	B	5	10, **11**
Bromine	Br	35	**79**, 81
Cadmium	Cd	48	106, 108, 110, 111, 112, 113, **114**, 116
Calcium	Ca	20	**40**, 42, 43, 44, 46, 48
Californium	Cf	98	(249)
Carbon	C	6	**12**, 13, 14
Cerium	Ce	58	136, 138, **140**, 142
Cesium	Cs	55	133
Chlorine	Cl	17	**35**, 37
Chromium	Cr	24	50, **52**, 53, 54
Cobalt	Co	27	59
Copper	Cu	29	**63**, 65
Curium	Cm	96	(248)
Dysprosium	Dy	66	156, 158, 160, 161, 162, 163, **164**
Einsteinium	Es	99	(254)
Erbium	Er	68	162, 164, **166**, 167, 168, 170
Europium	Eu	63	151, **153**
Fermium	Fm	100	(253)
Fluorine	F	9	19
Francium	Fr	87	223*
Gadolinium	Gd	64	152, 154, 155, 156, 157, **158**, 160
Gallium	Ga	31	**69**, 71
Germanium	Ge	32	70, 72, 73, **74**, 76
Gold	Au	79	197
Hafnium	Hf	72	174, 176, 177, 178, 179, **180**
Helium	He	2	3, **4**
Holmium	Ho	67	165
Hydrogen	H	1	**1**, 2
Indium	In	49	113, **115**
Iodine	I	53	127
Iridium	Ir	77	191, **193**
Iron	Fe	26	54, **56**, 57, 58
Krypton	Kr	36	78, 80, 82, 83, **84**, 86
Lanthanum	La	57	138*, **139**
Lawrencium	Lw	103	(257)
Lead	Pb	82	204, 206, 207, **208**, 210*, 211*, 212*, 214*
Lithium	Li	3	6, **7**
Lutetium	Lu	71	**175**, 176*
Magnesium	Mg	12	**24**, 25, 26
Manganese	Mn	25	55
Mendelevium	Md	101	(256)
Mercury	Hg	80	196, 198, 199, **200**, 201, 202, 204
Molybdenum	Mo	42	92, 94, 95, 96, 97, **98**, 100
Neodymium	Nd	60	**142**, 143, 144*, 145, 146, 148, 150

Element	Symbol	Atomic number	Mass numbers of naturally occurring isotopes
Neon	Ne	10	**20**, 21, 22
Neptunium	Np	93	(237)
Nickel	Ni	28	**58**, 60, 61, 62, 64
Niobium	Nb	41	93
Nitrogen	N	7	**14**, 15
Nobelium	No	102	(253)
Osmium	Os	76	184, 186, 187, 188, 189, 190, **192**
Oxygen	O	8	**16**, 17, 18
Palladium	Pd	46	102, 104, 105, **106**, 108, 110
Phosphorus	P	15	31
Platinum	Pt	78	190*, 192, 194, **195**, 196, 198
Plutonium	Pu	94	(242)
Polonium	Po	84	**210***, 211*, 212*, 214*, 215*, 216*, 218*
Potassium	K	19	**39**, 40*, 41
Praseodymium	Pr	59	141
Promethium	Pm	61	(147)
Protactinium	Pa	91	**231***, 234*
Radium	Ra	88	223*, 224*, **226***, 228*
Radon	Rn	86	219*, 220*, **222**
Rhenium	Re	75	185, **187***
Rhodium	Rh	45	103
Rubidium	Rb	37	**85**, 87*
Ruthenium	Ru	44	96, 98, 99, 100, 101, **102**, 104
Samarium	Sm	62	144, 147*, 148, 149, 150, **152**, 154
Scandium	Sc	21	45
Selenium	Se	34	74, 76, 77, 78, **80**, 82
Silicon	Si	14	**28**, 29, 30
Silver	Ag	47	**107**, 109
Sodium	Na	11	23
Strontium	Sr	38	84, 86, 87, **88**
Sulphur	S	16	**32**, 33, 34, 36
Tantalum	Ta	73	180, **181**
Technetium	Tc	43	(99)
Tellurium	Te	52	120, 122, 123, 124, 125, 126, 128, **130**
Terbium	Tb	65	159
Thallium	Tl	81	203, **205**, 206*, 207*, 208*, 210*
Thorium	Th	90	227*, 228*, 230*, 231*, **232***, 234*
Thulium	Tm	69	169
Tin	Sn	50	112, 114, 115, 116, 117, 118, 119, **120**, 122, 124
Titanium	Ti	22	46, 47, **48**, 49, 50
Tungsten	W	74	180*, 182, 183, **184**, 186
Uranium	U	92	234*, 235*, **238***
Vanadium	V	23	50, **51**
Xenon	Xe	54	124, 126, 128, 129, 130, 131, **132**, 134, 136
Ytterbium	Yb	70	168, 170, 171, 172, 173, **174**, 176
Yttrium	Y	39	89
Zinc	Zn	30	**64**, 66, 67, 68, 70
Zirconium	Ar	40	**90**, 91, 92, 94, 96

NOTES: Isotopes marked with an asterisk are naturally occurring radioactive isotopes. Most are members of one of the natural radioactive decay series, and some are present only in extremely small amounts. For elements with no naturally occurring isotope, the atomic mass number of the longest half-life artificial isotope is given in parentheses. For elements with more than one naturally occurring isotope, the most abundant one is indicated in bold type.

Appendix G
Investigation: The Density of a Solid Object

Problem:
How is the density of a solid object calculated?

Materials:
solid block of aluminum
triple-beam balance
metric ruler

Procedure
1. Measure the mass of the object, using the balance.
2. Measure the appropriate dimensions of the object, using the ruler.

Observations
1. Record the mass and dimensions of the object. Be sure to identify the possible error in each measurement.
2. Calculate the minimum volume of the solid object by using the smallest possible value of each dimension.
3. Calculate the maximum volume of the object by using the largest possible value of each dimension.
4. Calculate the minimum density of the object.
5. Calculate the maximum density of the object.

Questions
1. How many significant figures are there in each of your measurements?
2. When calculating the minimum density, which two of the following four quantities do you use: minimum mass, maximum mass, minimum volume, maximum volume?
3. Which of the four above-mentioned quantities do you use to find the maximum density?
4. What is the percentage difference between the maximum density and the minimum density?
5. How would you obtain the average density of the object?
6. How many significant figures are there in your calculated average density?
7. Repeat your measurements using a vernier caliper. Calculate the average density. How many significant figures are there in this number?
8. Compare your average density with the known density of aluminum. What is your percentage error? Give as many reasons as you can to explain this error.

Index

Page numbers printed in **bold type** refer to explanations of important terms.